Student Study Guide

for

Calculus, Second Edition

by Faires and Faires

<u>Student Study Guide</u> for

CALCULUS

Second Edition

J. Douglas Faires and Barbara T. Faires

prepared by

Phillip Schmidt and David Ruppel

The University of Akron, Akron, Ohio

Random House New York

Second Edition

987654321

ISBN: 394-37411-8

Preface

This Study Guide contains exercise statements and solutions for approximately one-seventh of the exercises in the second edition of <u>Calculus</u> by J. Douglas Faires and Barbara T. Faires. These solutions are complete and consistent with the notation and terminology of the text. High quality illustrations supplement the solutions.

The Study Guide also contains several other features which are helpful to students. Each chapter begins with a short section entitled <u>Sharpening your skills</u> indicating which skills from previous chapters or earlier mathematics study will be encountered in the upcoming chapter. The section is immediately followed by a short set of <u>Practice Problems</u> with answers given in an Appendix. <u>Comments</u> and problem solving <u>strategies</u> are placed throughout the book. <u>Computer generated graphs</u> enhance the student's understanding of both two- and three-dimensional analytic geometry.

When used in conjunction with the Faires and Faires Calculus text, the Student Study Guide will provide example solutions and problem solving insight which will help to make the study of Calculus more rewarding.

Acknowledgments

The authors wish to thank Todd Feil of Dennison University for introducing us to and training us in the use of TeX, with which this manual was typeset. We are also deeply indebted to our local TeXnician, Scott Dudek, who worked long hours to produce the text of this manual, and to Xiao Dong, who helped verify the accuracy of our solutions. Finally, we thank our families who encouraged us throughout this project.

Contents

Student Study Guide

for

Calculus, Second Edition

by Faires and Faires

1
Functions, Limits, and Continuity

Sharpening your skills

There are some concepts from your prior study of mathematics that will be of help in this chapter. You may wish to review these by referring to the APPENDIX of your text or by referring to a pre-calculus text. Some practice problems are presented here. The answers are in the back of this manual in APPENDIX B.

Practice Problems

1. For each of the following points in the cartesian (xy) plane, state the coordinates of the points which are
   i) symmetric with respect to the x-axis,
   ii) symmetric with respect to the y-axis,
   iii) symmetric with respect to the origin.
   a) $(-4, 8)$, b) $(0, -7)$, c) $(3/2, 0)$, d) $(0, \pi - e)$, e) $(\sqrt{3}, \sqrt{3})$.

2. Factor each of the following expressions completely.
   a) $3x^4 - 6x^3 - 45x^2$ b) $5\sin^2 x - 9\sin x + 4$
   c) $27x^3 - 64y^6$ d) $16x^4 - 1$.

3. Simplify each of the following expressions.

   a) $\dfrac{4}{\sqrt{x} - 2}$ b) $\dfrac{\dfrac{1}{x} - \dfrac{1}{x+2}}{14x}$

   c) $\dfrac{1}{\sqrt[3]{x} - 1}$ d) $\dfrac{\dfrac{3}{\sqrt{x}} - \dfrac{5}{\sqrt{x} - 1}}{\sqrt{x} + 1}$.

Definition of a Function

1.1

5. Find the domain of $f(x) = \dfrac{x^2 - 1}{x^4 - x^2}$.

SOLUTION: $f(x)$ will be undefined only if $x^4 - x^2 = 0$. $x^4 - x^2 = 0 \implies x^2(x-1)(x+1) = 0 \implies x = 0, \pm 1$. Thus $f(x)$ will be undefined only if $x = 0, \pm 1$, and the domain of f is $\{x \in \mathbb{R} \mid x \neq 0, \pm 1\}$.

15. Determine whether $x^2 + 4x + y^2 = 12$ can be rewritten so that y is described as a function of x.

SOLUTION: Solve $x^2 + 4x + y^2 = 12$ for y.

$$y^2 = 12 - x^2 - 4x$$
$$y = \pm\sqrt{12 - x^2 - 4x}.$$

Clearly y is not a function of x since, if, for example, $x = 0$, $y = \pm 2\sqrt{3}$.

17. Given $f(x) = x^2 + 2$, describe the function given by $f(-x)$, $-f(x)$, $f(1/x)$, $1/f(x)$, $f(\sqrt{x})$, and $\sqrt{f(x)}$.

SOLUTION: First, note the domain of f is $\mathbb{R}$.

i) $f(-x) = (-x)^2 + 2 = x^2 + 2$, which has domain $\mathbb{R}$. Note that this proves f is an even function.

ii) $-f(x) = -(x^2 + 2)$, which also has domain $\mathbb{R}$.

iii) $f(1/x) = (1/x)^2 + 2 = 1/x^2 + 2 = \dfrac{1 + 2x^2}{x^2}$. Domain is $\{x \in \mathbb{R} \mid x \neq 0\}$.

iv) $1/f(x) = 1/(x^2 + 2)$. Domain is $\mathbb{R}$ since $x^2 + 2 \neq 0$.

v) $f(\sqrt{x}) = (\sqrt{x})^2 + 2 = x + 2$. The domain is $[0, \infty)$ since $\sqrt{x}$ is undefined if $x < 0$.

vi) $\sqrt{f(x)} = \sqrt{x^2 + 2}$. The domain is $\mathbb{R}$ since $x^2 + 2 > 0$. (In fact, $x^2 + 2 \geq 2$.)

23. Find a number in the domain of $f(x) = x^2 - 1$ such that $f(x) = 1/2$.

SOLUTION: Solve $x^2 - 1 = 1/2$. $x^2 - 1 = 1/2 \implies x^2 = 3/2 \implies x = \pm\sqrt{3/2} = \pm\sqrt{6}/2$. Either $\sqrt{6}/2$ or $-\sqrt{6}/2$ is the desired domain value since the domain of f is $\mathbb{R}$.

33. Find $f(x + h)$ and $\dfrac{f(x+h) - f(x)}{h}$, if $h \neq 0$, for $f(x) = 2x^2 - x$.

SOLUTION: i)

$$f(x + h) = 2(x + h)^2 - (x + h)$$
$$= 2\left(x^2 + 2xh + h^2\right) - (x + h)$$
$$= 2x^2 + 4xh + 2h^2 - x - h.$$

ii)

$$\frac{f(x+h) - f(x)}{h} = \frac{(2x^2 + 4xh + 2h^2 - x - h) - (2x^2 - x)}{h}$$

$$= \frac{4xh + 2h^2 - h}{h} = \frac{h(4x + 2h - 1)}{h}$$

$$= 4x + 2h - 1.$$

39. A rectangular plot of ground containing 432 square feet is to be fenced off within a large lot and a fence is to be constructed down the middle. Express the amount of fence required as a function of the length of the dividing fence. What is the domain of this function?

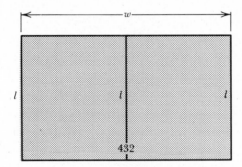

SOLUTION: Let F be the amount of fence. Then $F = 3l + 2w$. A relationship between l and w needs to be established to allow w to be expressed in terms of l. Since the area is 432 square feet, $lw = 432$ and $w = 432/l$. Thus $F = 3l + 2(432/l) = 3l + 864/l$. Clearly l cannot be zero, and from the physical constraints l cannot be negative. Thus the domain is $(0, \infty)$.

45. An open rectangular box is to be made from a sheet of metal 8 cm wide and 11 cm long by cutting a square from each corner, bending up the sides and welding the edges. Express the volume of the box as a function of the length of a side of the square cut from each corner and determine the domain of this function.

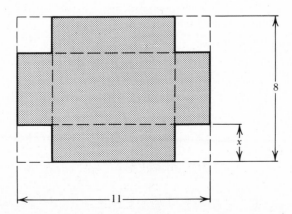

SOLUTION: Let x be the side of the square cut from each corner. The resulting box will have a length of $11 - 2x$, a width of $8 - 2x$, and a height of x. Since $V = lwh$, $V = (11 - 2x)(8 - 2x)x =$

$88x - 38x^2 + 4x^3$. Since all of the dimensions must be positive, $11 - 2x > 0 \implies 2x < 11 \implies x < 11/2, 8 - 2x > 0 \implies 2x < 8 \implies x < 4$ and $x > 0$. To satisfy $x < 11/2$ and $x < 4$, x must be less than 4, which yields $(0, 4)$ as the domain.

47. A house is built with a straight driveway 800 feet long, as shown in the figure. A utility pole on a line perpendicular to the driveway and 200 feet from the end of the driveway is the closest point from which electricity can be furnished. The utility company will furnish power with underground cable at $2 per foot and with overhead lines at no charge. However, for overhead lines the company requires that a strip 30 feet wide be cleared. The owner of the house estimates that to clear a strip this wide will cost $3 for each foot of overhead wire used. How much will it cost to run the lines if they are run overhead to a point on the driveway x feet from the end of the driveway $(0 \le x \le 800)$ and then run underground to the house?

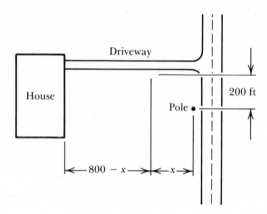

SOLUTION: If C is the cost, $C = 2(800 - x) + 3z$. To eliminate z, use the Pythagorean theorem to obtain $z^2 = x^2 + 200^2$ and $z = \pm\sqrt{x^2 + 200^2}$. Rejecting the negative value for z since a length must be positive, obtain $C = 2(800 - x) + 3\sqrt{x^2 + 200^2}$.

_____1.2
Linear and
Quadratic Functions

3. Find equations of the lines that pass through the point $(3, 2)$ and have slope   b) -1 c) 0.

SOLUTION: b) Applying the point-slope form, $y - y_1 = m(x - x_1)$, obtain $y - 2 = -1(x - 3)$ and $y = -x + 5$.

c) As in b), $y - 2 = 0(x - 3)$, and $y = 2$.

9. Find the slope-intercept form of the equation that passes through $(1,2)$ and is a) parallel to   b) perpendicular to $y = 3x - 2$.

SOLUTION: Note that $y = 3x - 2$ is in slope-intercept form, and the slope is 3. a) The slope of the parallel line is 3. Applying the point-slope form, obtain $y - 2 = 3(x - 1)$ and $y = 3x - 1$.

b) The slope of the perpendicular line is $-1/3$. Again apply point-slope to obtain $y - 2 = -(1/3)(x - 1)$ and $y = -x/3 + 7/3$.

13. Find the slope-intercept form of the equation that passes through $(0,0)$ and is   a) parallel to   b) perpendicular to $x + y + 1 = 0$.

SOLUTION: To obtain the slope, first place the equation in slope-intercept form, obtaining $y = -x - 1$. Thus the slope is -1.   a) The slope of the parallel line is -1. Applying point-slope form, obtain $y - 0 = -1(x - 0)$ and $y = -x$.

b) The slope of the perpendicular line is 1. Applying point-slope form, obtain $y - 0 = 1(x - 0)$ and $y = x$.

21. Sketch the graph of $y = x^2 - 4x + 3$ and find the range of the function.

SOLUTION: Completing the square, obtain

$$y = x^2 - 4x + \left(\frac{1}{2}(-4)\right)^2 - \left(\frac{1}{2}(-4)\right)^2 + 3$$

$$y = (x - 2)^2 - 1.$$

Thus, shift the graph of $y = x^2$ right 2 units and down 1.

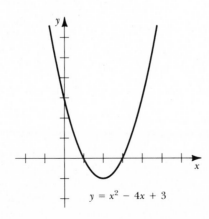

$y = x^2 - 4x + 3$

Since the range of $y = x^2$ is $[0, \infty)$, shifting down by 1 yields a range of $[-1, \infty)$.

27. Sketch the graph of $y = -x^2 - 1$ and find the range of the function.

SOLUTION: This graph is the graph of $y = -x^2$ shifted down by 1.

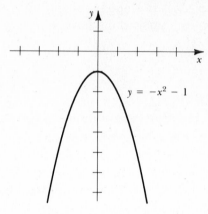

Since the range of $y = -x^2$ is $(-\infty, 0]$, shifting the graph down by 1 yields the range $(-\infty, -1]$.

37. Sketch the graph of $y = \frac{1}{2}x^2 - 2x + 2$ and find the range of the function.

SOLUTION: Factor out 1/2 to obtain $y = \frac{1}{2}(x^2 - 4x + 4) = \frac{1}{2}(x - 2)^2$. The graph is the graph of $y = \frac{1}{2}x^2$ shifted two units right.

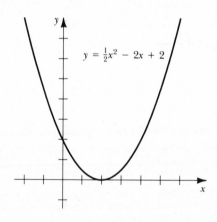

Since a right shift does not change the range and the range of $y = \frac{1}{2}x^2$ is $[0, \infty)$, the range of $y = \frac{1}{2}x^2 - 2x + 2$ is also $[0, \infty)$.

49. Determine the linear function that relates the temperature in degrees Celsius to the temperature in degrees Fahrenheit and use this function to determine the Fahrenheit temperature corresponding to 28° C.

SOLUTION: Let C and F be the temperatures in degrees Celsius and degrees Fahrenheit respectively. The hint provides the two ordered pairs, (C, F), of $(0, 32)$ and $(100, 212)$. Since the function is linear, determine the slope and then apply point-slope form:

$$m = \frac{212 - 32}{100 - 0} = 1.8.$$

So $F - 32 = 1.8(C - 0)$ and $F = 1.8C + 32$. If $C = 28$, $F = 1.8(28) + 32 = 82.4$. So $82.4°$ F is the same as $28°$ C.

53. When a solid rod is heated, its length increases by a certain amount depending on its coefficient of linear expansion. This coefficient, α, is assumed to be a constant, depending only on the material of the rod. The amount of increase in length is the product of the length, the change in temperature, and α. Suppose a steel rod has a length of 2 meters at $0°$ C and that the coefficient of linear expansion for this material is $\alpha = 11 \times 10^{-6}$.   a) Find a function that describes the length of the rod in terms of its temperature above $0°$ C. b) Determine its length when the temperature is $1000°$ C.

SOLUTION: a) Let L_2 be the new length, L_1 be the original length and ΔL be the change. Then in general, $L_2 = L_1 + \Delta L$. Also, if T_2 is the new temperature and T_1 is the original temperature, in general $\Delta L = \alpha L_1 (T_2 - T_1)$. So $L_2 = L_1 + \alpha L_1 (T_2 - T_1)$ and for the steel rod in question,

$$L_2 = 2 + (11 \times 10^{-6})(2)(T_2 - 0)$$
$$= 2 + 2.2 \times 10^{-5} T_2.$$

b) When $T_2 = 1000°$ C,

$$L_2 = 2 + 2.2 \times 10^{-5}(1 \times 10^3)$$
$$= 2 + 2.2 \times 10^{-2} = 2.022.$$

Thus the new length is 2.022 m.

—————————————————————————————————————1.3

Graphs of Some
Common Functions

7. Use the graphs of the sine and cosine functions to sketch the graph of $h(x) = 3 + 2\sin x$.

SOLUTION: Note that the amplitude has been doubled by multiplying $\sin x$ by 2, and the graph has been shifted up 3 by adding 3.

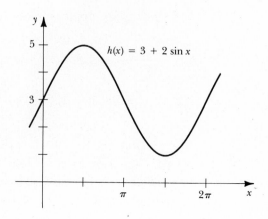

9. Use the graphs of the sine and cosine functions to sketch the graph of $g(x) = \cos 2x$.

SOLUTION: In this problem, the period has been halved due to multiplying x by 2.

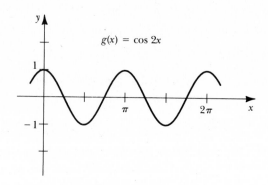

21. Use the graph of $y = |x|$ to sketch the graph of $f(x) = |2x + 5|$.

SOLUTION: First factor 2 from the expression $f(x) = |2x + 5| = |2(x + (5/2))|$. Now $f(x)$ can be analyzed, and one can see that the graph of f is the graph of $y = |2x|$ shifted left by 5/2 units.

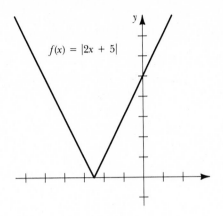

$f(x) = |2x + 5|$

29. a) Use the graph of $y = \sqrt{x}$ to sketch the graph of $g(x) = 2 - \sqrt{x+2}$.

b) Find the domain and range of $g(x)$.

SOLUTION: a) First reflect the graph of $y = \sqrt{x}$ through the x-axis to produce the graph of $y = -\sqrt{x}$. Second, shift the graph 2 units left to produce the graph of $y = -\sqrt{x+2}$. Finally, shift the graph 2 units up to produce the graph of $g(x) = 2 - \sqrt{x+2}$.

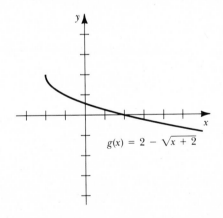

$g(x) = 2 - \sqrt{x + 2}$

b) To find the domain of $g(x) = 2 - \sqrt{x+2}$, set $x + 2 \geq 0$ since the radicand of a square root must be nonnegative. This yields $x \geq -2$, so the domain is $[-2, \infty)$. To find the range, set $\sqrt{x+2} \geq 0$ since the principal square root is nonnegative. Then $\sqrt{x+2} \geq 0 \implies -\sqrt{x+2} \leq 0 \implies 2 - \sqrt{x} = 2 \leq 2$ which yields the range, $(-\infty, 2]$. Note that the calculated domain and range agree with the appearance of the graph.

31. Using the graph of $f(x) = x^3$, sketch the graph of   c) $g(x) = x^3 - 1$ d) $g(x) = (x-1)^3$.

SOLUTION: c) The graph of $g(x) = x^3 - 1$ is generated by shifting the graph of $f(x) = x^3$ down by 1 unit.

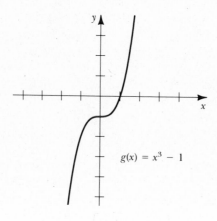

$g(x) = x^3 - 1$

d) The graph of $g(x) = (x - 1)^3$ is generated by shifting the graph of $f(x) = x^3$ right 1 unit.

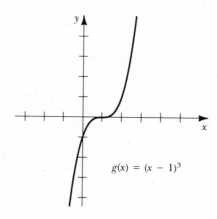

$g(x) = (x - 1)^3$

Note in these two problems the difference caused by subtracting 1 before and after the cubing operation.

33. Sketch the graphs of the following on the same set of coordinate axes.   a) $f_1(x) = \sin x$
b) $f_2(x) = \sin(x - (\pi/4))$ c) $f_3(x) = -\sin(x - (\pi/4))$ d) $f_4(x) = 1 - \sin(x - (\pi/4))$.

SOLUTION: The graph of $f_2(x) = \sin\left(x - \frac{\pi}{4}\right)$ is generated by shifting the graph of f_1 right $\pi/4$ units. The graph of $f_3(x) = -\sin\left(x - \frac{\pi}{4}\right)$ is generated from the graph of f_2 by reflecting the graph through the x-axis. Finally, the graph of $f_4(x) = 1 - \sin\left(x - \frac{\pi}{4}\right)$ is generated by shifting the graph of f_3 up 1 unit.

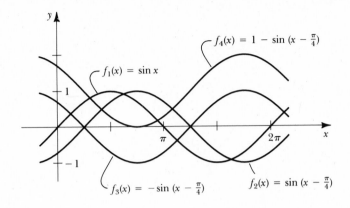

39. Use the graph of $y = [\![x]\!]$ to sketch the graph of $h(x) = [\![x + 2]\!] - 2$.

SOLUTION: First shift the graph of $y = [\![x]\!]$ left 2 units to produce the graph of $y = [\![x + 2]\!]$. Next shift the new graph 2 units down to produce the graph of $h(x) = [\![x + 2]\!] - 2$. Note that there is no apparent change in the graph.

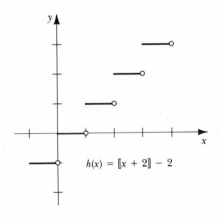

57. Find the center and radius of $x^2 + y^2 + 3x - 4y = 1$ and sketch the graph.

SOLUTION: First complete the square:

$$x^2 + y^2 + 3x - 4y = 1$$

$$x^2 + 3x + \left(\frac{1}{2}(3)\right)^2 + y^2 - 4y + \left(\frac{1}{2}(-4)\right)^2 = 1 + \left(\frac{1}{2}(3)\right)^2 + \left(\frac{1}{2}(-4)\right)^2$$

$$\left(x + \frac{3}{2}\right)^2 + (y - 2)^2 = \frac{29}{4}.$$

Thus the center is $(-3/2, 2)$ and the radius is $\sqrt{29}/2$.

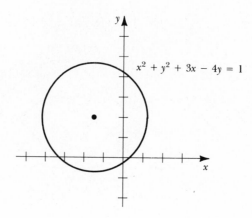

$$x^2 + y^2 + 3x - 4y = 1$$

63. Find an equation of the circle that passes through $(3,1)$, $(3,5)$, and $(5,3)$.

SOLUTION: The three points must satisfy the standard equation of the circle $(x - h)^2 + (y - k)^2 = r^2$. Substitute each point in turn into the equation and obtain

(1) $$(3 - h)^2 + (1 - k)^2 = r^2$$
(2) $$(3 - h)^2 + (5 - k)^2 = r^2$$
(3) $$(5 - h)^2 + (3 - k)^2 = r^2.$$

This produces three equations in three unknowns $(h, k$ and $r)$ which now must be solved simultaneously. Subtracting (1) from (2), obtain

$$(5 - k)^2 - (1 - k)^2 = 0$$
$$(25 - 10k + k^2) - (1 - 2k + k^2) = 0$$
$$24 - 8k = 0 \implies k = 3.$$

Substituting $k = 3$ into (2) and (3), obtain

(4) $$(3 - h)^2 + 4 = r^2$$
(5) $$(5 - h)^2 + 0 = r^2.$$

Subtracting (5) from (4), obtain

$$(3 - h)^2 + 4 - (5 - h)^2 = 0$$
$$(9 - 6h + h^2 + 4) - (25 - 10h + h^2) = 0$$
$$-12 + 4h = 0 \implies h = 3.$$

Substituting $h = 3$ into (5), obtain $4 = r^2$. Thus the equation of the circle is $(x-3)^2 + (y-3)^2 = 4$. To check this, substitute each of the points in turn and verify that each point does satisfy the equation.

67. Express the distance from the point $(0,1)$ to a point on the circle $x^2 + y^2 = 1$ as a function of the y-coordinate of the point on the curve.

SOLUTION: First sketch a graph.

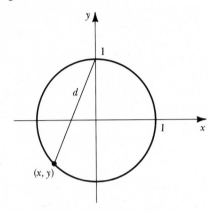

Using the distance formula to find an expression for d, obtain

$$d = \sqrt{(x-0)^2 + (y-1)^2} = \sqrt{x^2 + (y-1)^2}.$$

To express d as a function of y, x must be eliminated from the expression. This requires an equation relating x and y. Recall that (x, y) is a point on the circle $x^2 + y^2 = 1$. Thus $x^2 = 1 - y^2$ and $d = \sqrt{1 - y^2 + (y-1)^2} = \sqrt{2(1-y)}$.

_____**1.4**

Combining Functions

3. For $f(x) = 1/x$ and $g(x) = \sqrt{x-1}$ determine the equation and domain for each of the following:

   a) $f + g$ b) $f - g$ c) $f \cdot g$

   d) (f/g) e) $f \circ g$ f) $g \circ f$

SOLUTION: First note that the domain of f is $\{x \in \mathbb{R} \mid x \neq 0\}$, and the domain of g is $[1, \infty)$.

a) $(f + g)(x) = f(x) + g(x) = (1/x) + \sqrt{x-1}$.

b) $(f - g)(x) = f(x) - g(x) = (1/x) - \sqrt{x-1}$.

c) $(f \cdot g)(x) = f(x)g(x) = (1/x)\sqrt{x-1} = \dfrac{\sqrt{x-1}}{x}$.

For each of these three, the domain is the intersection of the domains of f and g: $\{x \in \mathbb{R} \mid x \neq 0\} \cap [1, \infty) = [1, \infty)$. Thus the domain of $f + g$, $f - g$ and $f \cdot g$ is $[1, \infty)$.

d)

$$\left(\frac{f}{g}\right)(x) = \frac{f(x)}{g(x)} = \frac{1/x}{\sqrt{x-1}} = \frac{1}{x\sqrt{x-1}} = \frac{\sqrt{x-1}}{x(x-1)}.$$

To find the domain of f/g, start with the intersection of the individual domains, $[1, \infty)$. Then remove any values from the domain for which $g(x) = 0$ since f/g is undefined when $g(x) = 0$. Set $g(x) = \sqrt{x-1} = 0$ and obtain $x = 1$. Remove 1 from $[1, \infty)$ and the domain of f/g becomes $(1, \infty)$.

e)

$$(f \circ g)(x) = f(g(x)) = f(\sqrt{x-1}) = \frac{1}{\sqrt{x-1}} = \frac{\sqrt{x-1}}{x-1}.$$

To find the domain of $f \circ g$, start with the domain of $g = [1, \infty)$. Then remove from the domain all values of x for which $g(x)$ is not in the domain of f. In this case, set $g(x) = \sqrt{x-1} = 0$ and obtain $x = 1$. This value must be removed, producing $(1, \infty)$ as the domain of $f \circ g$.

f)

$$(g \circ f)(x) = g(f(x)) = g\left(\frac{1}{x}\right) = \sqrt{\frac{1}{x} - 1} = \frac{\sqrt{x(1-x)}}{x}.$$

To find the domain, start with the domain of $f = \{x \in \mathbb{R} \mid x \neq 0\}$. Set $f(x) = (1/x) < 1$ since this is outside the domain of g. Obtain $x < 0$ or $x > 1$. These must be removed. Thus the domain of $g \circ f$ is $(0, 1]$.

7. For $f(x) = x^2 + x$ and $g(x) = \sin x$ determine the equation and domain for each of the following:

    a) $f + g$ b) $f - g$ c) $f \cdot g$

    d) (f/g) e) $f \circ g$ f) $g \circ f$

SOLUTION: Note that the domains of f and g are both $\mathbb{R}$.   a) $(f + g)(x) = f(x) + g(x) = x^2 + x + \sin x$.

b) $(f - g)(x) = f(x) - g(x) = x^2 + x - \sin x$.

c) $(f \cdot g)(x) = f(x)g(x) = (x^2 + x)\sin x$. The domain of each is the intersection of the individual domains, $\mathbb{R}$.

d)

$$\left(\frac{f}{g}\right)(x) = \frac{f(x)}{g(x)} = \frac{x^2 + x}{\sin x} = (x^2 + x)\csc x.$$

All x such that $\sin x = 0$ must be removed from the intersection. When x is an integral multiple of π, $\sin x = 0$. Thus the domain of f/g is $\{x \in \mathbb{R} \mid x \neq n\pi, \ n \text{ an integer}\}$.

e) $(f \circ g)(x) = f(g(x)) = f(\sin x) = \sin^2 x + \sin x$.

f) $(g \circ f)(x) = g(f(x)) = g(x^2 + x) = \sin(x^2 + x)$. In both $f \circ g$ and $g \circ f$, the domain is $\mathbb{R}$ since $f(x)$ and $g(x)$ are both defined for <u>all</u> values of x.

21. Sketch the graph of $f(x) = |x| - |x + 1|$.

SOLUTION: Start with the graphs of $g(x) = |x|$ and $h(x) = -|x + 1|$.

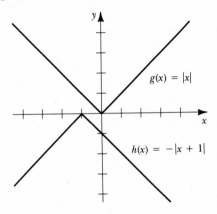

Then use addition of ordinates to produce the graph of $f(x) = g(x) + h(x)$.

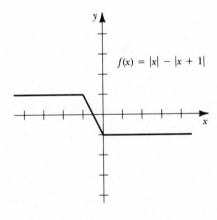

29. Sketch the graph of $f(x) = |\sin x|$.

SOLUTION: Start with the graph of $y = \sin x$.

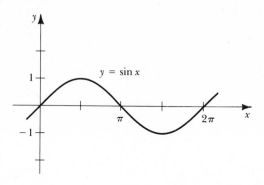

Since the absolute value leaves positive values alone and multiplies negative values by -1, reflect the portion of the graph below the x-axis through the x-axis and obtain

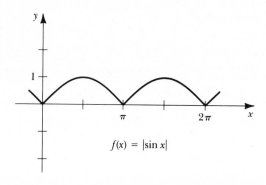

39. Express $f(x) = \sin(x-3)^2$ as the composition of two functions, one of which is a polynomial.

SOLUTION: Find functions g and h such that $f = g \circ h$. In evaluating $\sin(x-3)^2$ for some value of x, the <u>last</u> operation is evaluating a sine. Set $g(x) = \sin x$. The next to last operation is evaluating $(x-3)^2$. Set $h(x) = (x-3)^2$. Verifying $(g \circ h)(x) = g(h(x)) = g((x-3)^2) = \sin(x-3)^2$.

43. Express $f(x) = \left(\sqrt{x^2+1}+2\right)^4$ as a composition of three functions, two of which are polynomials.

SOLUTION: Find g, h and j, where $f = g \circ h \circ j$. Applying the technique of the previous problem, the last operation is raising a number to the 4th power so set $g(x) = x^4$. Before that, you would add 2 to the square root of a number, so set $h(x) = \sqrt{x} + 2$. The third function describes the remaining operations—adding 1 to the square of a number, so set $j(x) = x^2 + 1$. Verifying, $g\left(h\left(j(x)\right)\right) = g\left(h(x^2 + 1)\right) = g\left(\sqrt{x^2 + 1} + 2\right) = \left(\sqrt{x^2 + 1} + 2\right)^4$.

59. Show that the composition of two odd functions is an odd function.

SOLUTION: Let f and g be odd functions, that is, $f(-x) = -f(x)$ and $g(-x) = -g(x)$. Let $h = f \circ g$ and show h is odd. Show $h(-x) = -h(x)$.

$$h(-x) = (f \circ g)(-x) = f\left(g(-x)\right) = f\left(-g(x)\right) = -f\left(g(x)\right) = -h(x).$$

Thus the composition of two odd functions is an odd function.

——1.5

The Limit of a Function: The Intuitive Notion

7. Determine the limit of $f(x) = \dfrac{x^2 - 9}{x - 3}$ at $a = 3$, if it exists.

SOLUTION: $f(x) = \dfrac{x^2 - 9}{x - 3} = x + 3$ for $x \neq 3$. Thus, $\lim\limits_{x \to 3} f(x) = \lim\limits_{x \to 3} \dfrac{x^2 - 9}{x - 3} = \lim\limits_{x \to 3}(x + 3) = 6$.

13. Determine the limit of $f(x) = \dfrac{x^2 - 5x + 6}{x - 2}$ at $a = 2$, if it exists.

SOLUTION:

$$\lim\limits_{x \to 2} f(x) = \lim\limits_{x \to 2} \frac{x^2 - 5x + 6}{x - 2} = \lim\limits_{x \to 2} \frac{(x - 3)(x - 2)}{x - 2} = \lim\limits_{x \to 2}(x - 3) = -1.$$

19. Determine the limit of $f(x) = \dfrac{x^3 - 3x^2 - 4x + 12}{x - 3}$ at $a = 3$, if it exists.

SOLUTION: First determine if $x - 3$ is a factor of $x^3 - 3x^2 - 4x + 12$. By using polynomial long division or synthetic division, obtain $x^3 - 3x^2 - 4x + 12 = (x - 3)(x^2 - 4)$. Alternatively notice $x^3 - 3x^2 - 4x + 12 = x^2(x - 3) - 4(x - 3) = (x^2 - 4)(x - 3)$. In either case $\lim\limits_{x \to 3} \dfrac{x^3 - 3x^2 - 4x + 12}{x - 3} = \lim\limits_{x \to 3}(x^2 - 4) = 5$.

25. Determine the limit of $f(x) = \dfrac{|x|}{x}$ at $a = 0$, if it exists.

SOLUTION: For $x > 0$, $f(x) = |x|/x = x/x = 1$. For $x < 0$, $f(x) = |x|/x = -x/x = -1$. So, for values of x close to 0, $f(x)$ is 1 or -1 depending on whether x is positive or negative. Thus $\lim\limits_{x \to 0} \dfrac{|x|}{x}$ does not exist.

29. Determine the limit of $f(x) = \dfrac{x-4}{x-2}$ at $a = 2$, if it exists.

SOLUTION: For values of x close to 2, $x - 4$ is close to -2. If x is very slightly greater than 2, $x - 2$ is positive but close to 0. Dividing a number approaching -2 by a positive number approaching 0 yields numbers approaching $-\infty$. Similarly if x is very slightly less than 2, the result of the division approaches $+\infty$. Thus $\lim\limits_{x \to 2} \dfrac{x-4}{x-2}$ does not exist.

35. Determine the limit of $f(x) = \dfrac{\tan x}{\sec x}$ at $a = 0$, if it exists.

SOLUTION:

$$\lim_{x \to 0} \frac{\tan x}{\sec x} = \lim_{x \to 0} \frac{\sin x / \cos x}{1 / \cos x} = \lim_{x \to 0} \sin x = 0.$$

41. If $f(x) = \begin{cases} 2x, & \text{if } x < 2 \\ 0, & \text{if } x = 2 \\ x^2, & \text{if } x > 2 \end{cases}$, find   a) $f(2)$ b) $\lim\limits_{x \to 2} f(x)$ c) $\lim\limits_{x \to 1} f(x)$ d) $\lim\limits_{x \to 3} f(x)$.

SOLUTION: a) Since $f(x) = 0$ if $x = 2$, $f(2) = 0$.

b) For $x > 2$, $f(x) = x^2$. For x slightly larger than 2, $f(x)$ is close to $2^2 = 4$. For $x < 2$, $f(x) = 2x$. For x slightly smaller than 2, $f(x)$ is close to $2(2) = 4$. Thus $\lim\limits_{x \to 2} f(x) = 4$.

c) $\lim\limits_{x \to 1} f(x) = \lim\limits_{x \to 1} 2x = 2$ since as x approaches 1, x must become less than 2 and $f(x) = 2x$ for $x < 2$.

d) Similarly as x approaches 3, x becomes greater than 2 and $f(x) = x^2$ for $x > 2$. Thus $\lim\limits_{x \to 3} f(x) = \lim\limits_{x \to 3} x^2 = 9$.

47. a) For $f(x) = x^2$, find the slope of the secant line at the point $(2, 4)$ for $h \neq 0$. b) Find the limit of the slope as h approaches 0.

SOLUTION: a) Find the slope of the line between $(2, 4)$ and $\left(2 + h, (2 + h)^2\right)$.

$$m_{\text{sec}} = \frac{(2 + h)^2 - 4}{2 + h - 2} = \frac{4h + h^2}{h} = 4 + h.$$

b) $\lim\limits_{h \to 0} m_{\text{sec}} = \lim\limits_{h \to 0} (4 + h) = 4$.

53. a) For $f(x) = 1/x$, find the slope of the secant line at the point $(1, 1)$ for $h \neq 0$. b) Find the limit of the slope as h approaches 0.

SOLUTION: a) Find the slope of the line between $(1, 1)$ and $\left(1 + h, \dfrac{1}{1 + h}\right)$.

$$m_{\text{sec}} = \frac{\frac{1}{1+h} - 1}{1 + h - 1} = \frac{\frac{1 - (1+h)}{1+h}}{h} = \frac{-h}{h(1 + h)} = \frac{-1}{1 + h}.$$

b) $\lim\limits_{h \to 0} m_{\text{sec}} = \lim\limits_{h \to 0} \dfrac{-1}{1+h} = -1.$

_____1.6

The Limit of a Function: The Definition

5. Given $\epsilon = 0.1$, $L = 3$, $a = 1$, and $f(x) = 2x + 1$, find a number $\delta > 0$ with the property that $|f(x) - L| < \epsilon$ whenever $0 < |x - a| < \delta$.

SOLUTION: It is required that $|f(x) - L| < \epsilon$, or $|2x + 1 - 3| < 0.1$; equivalently, $|2(x - 1)| < 0.1$ or $|x - 1| < 0.05$. Choose $\delta = 0.05$ and require $0 < |x - 1| < 0.05$. Then $|x - 1| < 0.1/2 \implies 2|x - 1| < 0.1 \implies |2x - 2| < 0.1 \implies |f(x) - L| < \epsilon$.

Note that any positive number less than 0.05 would work as a choice for δ, and 0.05 is the largest value that could be used for δ.

COMMENT: In applying the definition of a limit you are required to determine a δ so that $|x - a| < \delta$ implies that $|f(x) - L| < \epsilon$. One way of doing this is to write equivalent inequalities to the inequality $|f(x) - L| < \epsilon$ with the last inequality in this chain involving only $|x - a|$.

9. Given $\epsilon = 0.01$, $L = 0$, $a = 2$, and $f(x) = \dfrac{x^2 - 4}{x + 2}$, find a number $\delta > 0$ with the property that $|f(x) - L| < \epsilon$ whenever $0 < |x - a| < \delta$.

SOLUTION: It is required that $|f(x) - L| < \epsilon$ or in this case, that

$$\left| \frac{x^2 - 4}{x + 2} - 0 \right| < 0.01, \qquad \text{or equivalently} \qquad |x - 2| < 0.01.$$

Choose $\delta = 0.01$ and require $0 < |x - 2| < 0.01$. Then

$$|x - 2| < 0.01 \implies \left| \frac{(x - 2)(x + 2)}{x + 2} - 0 \right| < 0.01 \implies \left| \frac{x^2 - 4}{x + 2} - 0 \right| < 0.01 \implies |f(x) - L| < \epsilon.$$

Again any positive number less than 0.01 will work as a value for δ.

17. Use the definition of the limit to prove $\lim\limits_{x \to -2}(-2x + 5) = 9$.

SOLUTION: Let $\epsilon > 0$ be given. Find $\delta > 0$ such that if $0 < |x - a| = |x + 2| < \delta$ then $|f(x) - L| = |-2x + 5 - 9| < \epsilon$. This is equivalent to $|-2x - 4| < \epsilon$ or $|-2(x + 2)| < \epsilon$ which may be written as $|x + 2| < \epsilon/2$.

Choose $\delta = \epsilon/2$ and require $0 < |x - a| < \delta$. Then $|x + 2| < \epsilon/2 \implies 2|x + 2| < \epsilon \implies$ $|-2| \, |x + 2| < \epsilon \implies |-2(x + 2)| < \epsilon \implies |-2x - 4| < \epsilon \implies |-2x + 5 - 9| = |f(x) - L| < \epsilon$. Thus $\lim_{x \to -2} (-2x + 5) = 9$.

23. Use the definition of the limit to prove $\lim_{x \to 2} \dfrac{1}{x} = \dfrac{1}{2}$.

SOLUTION: Let $\epsilon > 0$ be given. Find $\delta > 0$ such that if $0 < |x - a| = |x - 2| < \delta$ then $|f(x) - L| = \left| \dfrac{1}{x} - \dfrac{1}{2} \right| < \epsilon$. Requiring $\left| \dfrac{1}{x} - \dfrac{1}{2} \right| < \epsilon$ or $\left| \dfrac{2 - x}{2x} \right| < \epsilon$ is equivalent to requiring $\left| \dfrac{x - 2}{2x} \right| < \epsilon$ or $|x - 2| < \epsilon |2x|$. We cannot choose $\delta = \epsilon |2x|$ since δ cannot be dependent on x. Suppose we require $0 < |x - 2| < 1$. Then $-1 < x - 2 < 1 \implies 1 < x < 3 \implies 2 < 2x < 6 \implies 2 < |2x| \implies 2\epsilon < \epsilon |2x|$.

Choose $\delta = \min\{1, 2\epsilon\}$ and require $0 < |x - a| < \delta$. Then   (1) $|x - 2| < 1$ and (2) $|x - 2| < 2\epsilon$. Now, from (1), $|x - 2| < 1 \implies -1 < x - 2 < 1 \implies 1 < x < 3 \implies 2 < 2x < 6 \implies 2 < |2x| \implies 2\epsilon < \epsilon |2x|$. Thus, from (2),

$$|x - 2| < 2\epsilon < \epsilon |2x| \implies \frac{|x - 2|}{|2x|} < \epsilon \implies \left| \frac{2 - x}{2x} \right| < \epsilon \implies \left| \frac{1}{x} - \frac{1}{2} \right| < \epsilon \implies |f(x) - L| < \epsilon.$$

So, $\lim_{x \to 2} \dfrac{1}{x} = \dfrac{1}{2}$.

COMMENT: Requiring $|x - a|$ to be less than some arbitrary positive number, usually 1, is a technique that often leads to a choice for δ that is the minimum of the arbitrary number and some relationship involving ϵ.

25. Show that $\lim_{x \to a} f(x) = 0$ if and only if $\lim_{x \to a} |f(x)| = 0$.

SOLUTION: ($\implies$) Assume $\lim_{x \to a} f(x) = 0$ and $\epsilon > 0$. Then there exists $\delta_1 > 0$ such that if $0 < |x - a| < \delta_1$ then $|f(x) - 0| < \epsilon$.

To show $\lim_{x \to a} |f(x)| = 0$, find $\delta_2 > 0$ such that if $0 < |x - a| < \delta_2$, then $||f(x)| - 0| < \epsilon$. Now $||f(x)| - 0| = ||f(x)|| = |f(x)| = |f(x) - 0|$. $|f(x) - 0|$ will be less than ϵ if $0 < |x - a| < \delta_1$. Choose $\delta_2 = \delta_1$ and require $0 < |x - a| < \delta_2$. Then $0 < |x - a| < \delta_1$ and $|f(x) - 0| < \epsilon$. But then $||f(x)| - 0| < \epsilon$ and $\lim_{x \to a} |f(x)| = 0$.

($\impliedby$) Assume $\lim_{x \to a} |f(x)| = 0$ and $\epsilon > 0$. Then there exists $\delta_1 > 0$ such that if $0 < |x - a| < \delta_1$ then $||f(x)| - 0| < \epsilon$.

To show $\lim_{x \to a} f(x) = 0$, find $\delta_2 > 0$ such that if $0 < |x - a| < \delta_2$ then $|f(x) - 0| < \epsilon$. Now $|f(x) - 0| = |f(x)| = ||f(x)|| = ||f(x)| - 0|$. Choose $\delta_2 = \delta_1$ and require $0 < |x - a| < \delta_2$. Then $0 < |x - a| < \delta_1$ and $||f(x)| - 0| < \epsilon$. But then $|f(x) - 0| < \epsilon$ and $\lim_{x \to a} f(x) = 0$.

Note that to prove an if and only if proposition, two proofs must be constructed.

35. Show that if $\lim\limits_{x \to a} f(x) < 0$, then an interval containing a exists with $f(x) < 0$ for all $x \neq a$ in the interval.

SOLUTION: Let $\lim\limits_{x \to a} f(x) = L < 0$. Then for each $\epsilon > 0$, there exists $\delta > 0$ such that if $0 < |x - a| < \delta$, then $|f(x) - L| < \epsilon$. Let $\epsilon = |L/2| = -L/2$. Then there exists $\delta_1 > 0$ such that if $0 < |x - a| < \delta_1$, then $|f(x) - L| < \epsilon = -L/2$. Let $x \in (a - \delta_1, a + \delta_1)$ with $x \neq a$. Then $a - \delta_1 < x < a + \delta_2 \implies -\delta_1 < x - a < \delta_1 \implies 0 < |x - a| < \delta_1 \implies |f(x) - L| < -L/2 \implies -(-L/2) < f(x) - L < -L/2 \implies 3L/2 < f(x) < L/2 < 0$. Thus the required interval, $(a - \delta_1, a + \delta_1)$, has been found. Note that many such intervals exist.

———1.7

Limits and Continuity

7. Sketch the graph of $f(x) = \dfrac{x^2 - 4}{x - 2}$ and determine any numbers at which the function is discontinuous. For each discontinuity, give the criterion of DEFINITION 1.32 that is not met.

SOLUTION: $f(x) = \dfrac{x^2 - 4}{x - 2} = x + 2,\ x \neq 2.$

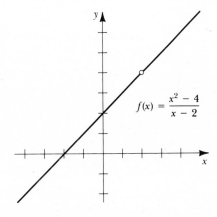

This function is discontinuous at $x = 2$ because $f(2)$ does not exist.

13. Sketch the graph of $f(x) = [\![x - 1]\!]$ and determine any numbers at which the function is discontinuous. For each discontinuity, give the criterion of DEFINITION 1.32 that is not met.

SOLUTION:

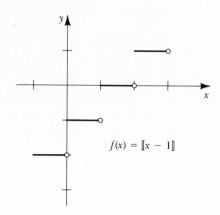

$$f(x) = [\![x - 1]\!]$$

This function is discontinuous at each integer value of x since $\lim_{x \to a} [\![x - 1]\!]$ does not exist for a an integer.

21. Sketch the graph of $f(x) = \begin{cases} x, & x \text{ is not an integer} \\ (-1)^x, & x \text{ is an integer} \end{cases}$ and determine any numbers at which the function is discontinuous. For each discontinuity, give the criterion of DEFINITION 1.32 that is not met.

SOLUTION:

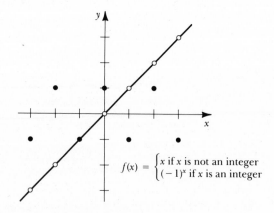

$$f(x) = \begin{cases} x \text{ if } x \text{ is not an integer} \\ (-1)^x \text{ if } x \text{ is an integer} \end{cases}$$

This function is discontinuous at each integer n except $n = -1$ since $\lim_{x \to n} f(x) = n$ and

$$f(n) = \begin{cases} 1, & n \text{ even} \\ -1, & n \text{ odd}. \end{cases}$$

25. Employ the limit theorems to determine $\lim_{x \to 4} (x^2 + 3)(x - 2)$. Determine whether

$f(x) = (x^2 + 3)(x - 2)$ is continuous at 4.

SOLUTION:

$$\lim_{x \to 4}(x^2 + 3)(x - 2) = \lim_{x \to 4}(x^2 + 3)\lim_{x \to 4}(x - 2)$$

$$= \left(\lim_{x \to 4} x^2 + \lim_{x \to 4} 3\right)(2) = \left(\left(\lim_{x \to 4} x\right)^2 + 3\right)(2) = (16 + 3)(2) = 38.$$

Also $f(4) = (16 + 3)(4 - 2) = 38$.

Since $\lim_{x \to 4} f(x) = f(4)$, f is continuous at 4.

31. Employ the limit theorems to determine $\lim_{x \to 6} \dfrac{3x - 7}{x^2 + 2}$. Determine whether $f(x) = \dfrac{3x - 7}{x^2 + 2}$ is continuous at 6.

SOLUTION: First,

$$\lim_{x \to 6} \frac{3x - 7}{x^2 + 2} = \frac{\lim_{x \to 6}(3x - 7)}{\lim_{x \to 6}(x^2 + 2)} = \frac{18 - 7}{\lim_{x \to 6} x^2 + \lim_{x \to 6} 2} = \frac{11}{\left(\lim_{x \to 6} x\right)^2 + 2} = \frac{11}{6^2 + 2} = \frac{11}{38}.$$

Now $f(6) = \dfrac{18 - 7}{36 + 2} = \dfrac{11}{38} = \lim_{x \to 6} \dfrac{3x - 7}{x^2 + 2}$ so the function is continuous at $x = 6$.

37. If $f(x) = x^2 - 5x + 6$ and $g(x) = \sqrt{x}$, find $f \circ g$ and $g \circ f$ and determine where the functions are continuous.

SOLUTION: $(f \circ g)(x) = f(\sqrt{x}) = (\sqrt{x})^2 - 5\sqrt{x} + 6 = x - 5\sqrt{x} + 6$. The domain of $f \circ g$ is $[0, \infty)$. $f \circ g$ is continuous at each point in the domain except at $x = 0$ since $\lim_{x \to 0}(f \circ g)(x) = \lim_{x \to 0}(x - 5\sqrt{x} + 6)$ does not exist.

$(g \circ f)(x) = g(f(x)) = g(x^2 - 5x + 6) = \sqrt{x^2 - 5x + 6}$. The domain of $g \circ f$ is $(-\infty, 2] \cup [3, \infty)$ and $g \circ f$ is continuous at each point in the domain except at $x = 2$ and $x = 3$ since the limits at those points do not exist.

43. Determine $\lim_{x \to -5/2} \dfrac{3x^2 - 2x + 1}{2x + 5}$ or explain why it does not exist.

SOLUTION: This limit does not exist since $2x + 5$ is not a factor of $3x^2 - 2x + 1$, and as $x \to -5/2$, $3x^2 - 2x + 1 \to 99/4$ and $2x + 5 \to 0$. The quotient approaches $\pm\infty$ depending on whether $x > -5/2$ or $x < -5/2$.

49. Determine $\lim_{x \to 2} \dfrac{\frac{1}{x} - \frac{1}{2}}{x - 2}$ or explain why it does not exist.

SOLUTION:

$$\lim_{x \to 2} \frac{\frac{1}{x} - \frac{1}{2}}{x - 2} = \lim_{x \to 2} \frac{\frac{2 - x}{2x}}{x - 2} = \lim_{x \to 2} \frac{-1}{2x} = -\frac{1}{4}.$$

53. Find the constant c that will make

$$f(x) = \begin{cases} \dfrac{x^2 - 1}{x - 1}, & \text{if } x \neq 1 \\ \\ c, & \text{if } x = 1 \end{cases}$$

continuous at $x = 1$.

SOLUTION: In order to satisfy the definition of continuity, $f(1)$ should be defined equal to $\lim\limits_{x \to 1} f(x)$ if that limit exists. So $\lim\limits_{x \to 1} \dfrac{x^2 - 1}{x - 1} = \lim\limits_{x \to 1} (x + 1) = 2$.
If $c = 2$ then $f(x)$ will be continuous at $x = 1$.

One Sided Limits and Continuity on Intervals
1.8

3. Evaluate $\lim\limits_{x \to 0^-} (2 - \sqrt{x})$ provided the limit exists.

SOLUTION: $\lim\limits_{x \to 0^-} (2 - \sqrt{x}) = \lim\limits_{x \to 0^-} 2 - \lim\limits_{x \to 0^-} \sqrt{x}$ does not exist since $\sqrt{x}$ does not exist for $x < 0$.

15. Evaluate $\lim\limits_{x \to 0^+} \left(\dfrac{1}{x} - \dfrac{1}{|x|} \right)$ provided the limit exists.

SOLUTION: Noting that $|x| = x$ for $x > 0$, $\lim\limits_{x \to 0^+} \left(\dfrac{1}{x} - \dfrac{1}{|x|} \right) = \lim\limits_{x \to 0^+} \left(\dfrac{1}{x} - \dfrac{1}{x} \right) = 0$.

19. Evaluate $\lim\limits_{x \to 2^+} \left(\dfrac{1}{x - 2} - \dfrac{4}{x^2 - 4} \right)$ provided the limit exists.

SOLUTION:

$$\lim\limits_{x \to 2^+} \left(\dfrac{1}{x - 2} - \dfrac{4}{x^2 - 4} \right) = \lim\limits_{x \to 2^+} \dfrac{x + 2 - 4}{x^2 - 4} = \lim\limits_{x \to 2^+} \dfrac{x - 2}{x^2 - 4}$$

$$= \lim\limits_{x \to 2^+} \dfrac{1}{x + 2} = \dfrac{1}{4}.$$

23. Evaluate $\lim\limits_{x \to 4} \dfrac{(x - 4)^2}{\sqrt{x + 12} - 4}$ provided the limit exists.

SOLUTION: Using the technique of "rationalizing the denominator,"

$$\lim\limits_{x \to 4} \dfrac{(x - 4)^2}{\sqrt{x + 12} - 4} \cdot \dfrac{\sqrt{x + 12} + 4}{\sqrt{x + 12} + 4} = \lim\limits_{x \to 4} \dfrac{(x - 4)^2 (\sqrt{x + 12} + 4)}{x + 12 - 16}$$

$$= \lim_{x \to 4} (x - 4)(\sqrt{x + 12} + 4) = 0(8) = 0.$$

27. Evalute $\lim_{x \to 3^+} (x - [\![x]\!])$ provided the limit exists.

SOLUTION: $\lim_{x \to 3^+} (x - [\![x]\!]) = \lim_{x \to 3^+} x - \lim_{x \to 3^+} [\![x]\!] = 3 - 3 = 0.$ As $x \to 3^+$, eventually $3 < x < 4$ and then $[\![x]\!] = 3.$

33. Evaluate $\lim_{x \to 1} f(x)$, if $f(x) = \begin{cases} x^2, & \text{when } x < 1 \\ -x, & \text{when } x \geq 1 \end{cases}$ provided the limit exists.

SOLUTION: $\lim_{x \to 1^+} f(x) = \lim_{x \to 1^+} (-x) = -1$ since $f(x) = -x$ when $x > 1.$

$\lim_{x \to 1^-} f(x) = \lim_{x \to 1^-} x^2 = 1$ since $f(x) = x^2$ when $x < 1.$

So $\lim_{x \to 1} f(x)$ does not exist since $\lim_{x \to 1^-} f(x) \neq \lim_{x \to 1^+} f(x).$

43. Determine the intervals on which $f(x) = \sqrt{x - 3}$ is continuous.

SOLUTION: The domain of f is $[3, \infty)$. Let $a > 3$. Then $\lim_{x \to a} f(x) = \lim_{x \to a} \sqrt{x - 3} = \sqrt{a - 3} = f(a)$. Thus f is continuous on $(3, \infty)$.

Also $\lim_{x \to 3^+} f(x) = \lim_{x \to 3^+} \sqrt{x - 3} = 0 = f(3)$. Thus $f(x) = \sqrt{x - 3}$ is continuous on $[3, \infty)$.

53. Find constants a and b that will make $g(x) = \begin{cases} x^2, & \text{if } x \leq 1 \\ ax + b, & \text{if } 1 < x < 2 \\ x^3, & \text{if } x \geq 2 \end{cases}$ continuous for all x.

SOLUTION: As defined, $g(x)$ is continuous at every real number except possibly at $x = 1$ and $x = 2$. $\lim_{x \to 1^-} g(x) = \lim_{x \to 1^-} x^2 = 1$ so we need $\lim_{x \to 1^+} g(x) = \lim_{x \to 1^+} (ax + b) = a + b = 1$. Similarly, $\lim_{x \to 2^+} g(x) = \lim_{x \to 2^+} x^3 = 8$ so we need $\lim_{x \to 2^-} g(x) = \lim_{x \to 2^-} (ax + b) = 2a + b = 8$. Solving $a + b = 1$ and $2a + b = 8$ simultaneously, obtain $a = 7$ and $b = -6.$

57. Given $f(x) = x^3 + 1$, $[-2, 3]$ and $k = 9$, find a number $c \in (-2, 3)$ with $f(c) = 9.$

SOLUTION: Set $f(c) = c^3 + 1 = 9$. Then $c^3 = 8 \implies c = 2$. Now $2 \in (-2, 3)$, which verifies the conclusion of the Intermediate Value Theorem.

61. For $f(x) = x^3 - 9x^2 + 12$ on $[-2, 0]$,

  a) use the Intermediate Value Theorem to show that $f(x) = 0$ has a solution on $[-2, 0].$

b) use the Bisection Technique on $[-2, 0]$ to determine the approximate solution that is accurate to within 10^{-1}.

SOLUTION: a) $f(-2) = -8 - 36 + 12 = -32$ and $f(0) = 12 > 0$. By the Intermediate Value Theorem for each number k between -32 and 12 there exists $c \in (-2, 0)$ such that $f(c) = k$. Since $-32 < 0 < 12$, a c exists such that $f(c) = 0$.

b)   The Bisection Technique continually halves the interval. $f(-1) = -1 - 9 + 12 = 2$. The solution to $f(x) = 0$ is between -2 and -1.

$f(-1.5) = -11.625$ so the solution is between -1.5 and -1.

$f(-1.25) \approx -4.016$ so the solution is between -1.25 and -1.

$f(-1.125) \approx -0.814$ so the solution is between -1.125 and -1. Thus the solution to $x^3 - 9x^2 + 12 = 0$ correct to within 10^{-1} is -1.1.

67. Find a function f with the property that $\lim_{x \to 1^+} f(x)$, $\lim_{x \to 1^-} f(x)$, and $\lim_{x \to 1} |f(x)|$ all exist, but $\lim_{x \to 1} f(x)$ does not exist.

SOLUTION: In order for $\lim_{x \to 1^+} f(x)$ and $\lim_{x \to 1^-} f(x)$ to exist but for $\lim_{x \to 1} f(x)$ to not exist, it is necessary that the two one-sided limits be different. Moreover, if $\lim_{x \to 1} |f(x)|$ exists, it is necessary that $\lim_{x \to 1^+} |f(x)| = \lim_{x \to 1^-} |f(x)|$. Thus $\lim_{x \to 1^+} f(x)$ must be $- \lim_{x \to 1^-} f(x)$. Any function satisfying $\lim_{x \to 1^+} f(x) = - \lim_{x \to 1^-} f(x)$ will suffice. One example is $f(x) = \dfrac{|x - 1|}{x - 1}$. Note that $\lim_{x \to 1^+} \dfrac{|x - 1|}{x - 1} = \lim_{x \to 1^+} \dfrac{x - 1}{x - 1} = 1$ and $\lim_{x \to 1^-} \dfrac{|x - 1|}{x - 1} = \lim_{x \to 1^-} \dfrac{1 - x}{x - 1} = -1$. Thus $\lim_{x \to 1} \dfrac{|x - 1|}{x - 1}$ does not exist. However,

$$\lim_{x \to 1} |f(x)| = \lim_{x \to 1} \left| \frac{|x - 1|}{x - 1} \right| = \lim_{x \to 1} \frac{||x - 1||}{|x - 1|} = \lim_{x \to 1} \frac{|x - 1|}{|x - 1|} = 1.$$

77. Suppose f, g, and h are functions with the property that $f(x) \le g(x) \le h(x)$ for each $x \ne a$ in the open interval $(a - \delta, a)$, for some constant $\delta > 0$. If $\lim_{x \to a^-} f(x) = L$ and $\lim_{x \to a^-} h(x) = L$, prove that $\lim_{x \to a^-} g(x) = L$. (This is the Squeeze Theorem for limits from the left.)

SOLUTION: Let $\lim_{x \to a^-} f(x) = \lim_{x \to a^-} h(x) = L$. Let $\epsilon > 0$ be given. Then there exists $\delta_1 > 0$ such that if $0 < a - x < \delta_1$, then $|f(x) - L| < \epsilon$. Also there exists $\delta_2 > 0$ such that if $0 < a - x < \delta_2$ then $|h(x) - L| < \epsilon$. Further, there exists $\delta_3 > 0$ such that if $x \in (a - \delta_3, a)$ then $f(x) \le g(x) \le h(x)$. To show $\lim_{x \to a^-} g(x) = L$, find $\delta > 0$ such that if $0 < a - x < \delta$ then $|g(x) - L| < \epsilon$.

Choose $\delta = \min\{\delta_1, \delta_2, \delta_3\}$ and require $0 < a - x < \delta$. Then $0 < a - x < \delta_1$ so $|f(x) - L| < \epsilon$ and $0 < a - x < \delta_2$ so $|h(x) - L| < \epsilon$. Also $0 < a - x < \delta_3 \implies -\delta_3 < x - a < 0 \implies a - \delta_3 < x < a \implies x \in (a - \delta_3, a)$ so $f(x) \le g(x) \le h(x)$. Now $|f(x) - L| < \epsilon \implies -\epsilon < f(x) - L < \epsilon \implies L - \epsilon \le f(x) \le L + \epsilon$. Similarly, $|h(x) - L| < \epsilon \implies L - \epsilon \le h(x) \le L + \epsilon$. Thus

$L - \epsilon \leq f(x) \leq g(x) \leq h(x) \leq L + \epsilon$ and $L - \epsilon \leq g(x) \leq L + \epsilon \implies |g(x) - L| < \epsilon$. Therefore $\lim_{x \to a^-} g(x) = L$.

_____1.9

Limits at Infinity:
Horizontal Asymptotes

_____

7. Find $\lim_{x \to \infty} \dfrac{x^2 + 3}{x^2 + 1}$, if it exists.

SOLUTION:

$$\lim_{x \to \infty} \frac{x^2 + 3}{x^2 + 1} = \lim_{x \to \infty} \frac{x^2 \left(1 + \dfrac{3}{x^2}\right)}{x^2 \left(1 + \dfrac{1}{x^2}\right)} = \frac{\lim_{x \to \infty} \left(1 + \dfrac{3}{x^2}\right)}{\lim_{x \to \infty} \left(1 + \dfrac{1}{x^2}\right)} = \frac{1}{1} = 1.$$

COMMENT: A <u>strategy</u> for evaluating limits at infinity is to factor the highest power of x present in the denominator (in this case, x^2) from both numerator and denominator. This generally yields an expression for which the limit can readily be determined.

11. Find $\lim_{x \to -\infty} \dfrac{50 - x^3}{-x^3}$, if it exists.

SOLUTION:

$$\lim_{x \to -\infty} \frac{50 - x^3}{-x^3} = \lim_{x \to -\infty} \frac{-x^3 \left(1 - \dfrac{50}{x^3}\right)}{-x^3} = \lim_{x \to -\infty} \left(1 - \frac{50}{x^3}\right) = 1.$$

15. Find $\lim_{x \to \infty} \dfrac{\cos x}{x + 2}$, if it exists.

SOLUTION:

$$\lim_{x \to \infty} \frac{\cos x}{x + 2} = \lim_{x \to \infty} \frac{x \left(\dfrac{\cos x}{x}\right)}{x \left(1 + \dfrac{2}{x}\right)} = \frac{\lim_{x \to \infty} \dfrac{\cos x}{x}}{\lim_{x \to \infty} \left(1 + \dfrac{2}{x}\right)} = \frac{\lim_{x \to \infty} \dfrac{\cos x}{x}}{1}.$$

To evaluate $\lim_{x \to \infty} \dfrac{\cos x}{x}$, note that $-1 \leq \cos x \leq 1 \implies -(1/x) \leq (\cos x / x) \leq 1/x$ for $x > 0$.

Now $\lim_{x \to \infty} \dfrac{1}{x} = 0$ and $\lim_{x \to \infty} (-1/x) = 0$. Thus $\lim_{x \to \infty} \dfrac{\cos x}{x} = 0$, so $\lim_{x \to \infty} \dfrac{\cos x}{x + 2} = 0$.

21. Find $\lim\limits_{x\to\infty} \dfrac{\sqrt{x^2-4}}{5x+2}$, if it exists.

$$\lim_{x\to\infty} \frac{\sqrt{x^2-4}}{5x+2} = \lim_{x\to\infty} \frac{\sqrt{x^2}\sqrt{1-\dfrac{4}{x^2}}}{x\left(5+\dfrac{2}{x}\right)} = \lim_{x\to\infty} \frac{|x|}{x}\cdot\frac{\sqrt{1-\dfrac{4}{x^2}}}{5+\dfrac{2}{x}} = \frac{\lim\limits_{x\to\infty}\sqrt{1-\dfrac{4}{x^2}}}{\lim\limits_{x\to\infty}\left(5+\dfrac{2}{x}\right)} = \frac{1}{5}.$$

Note that $\dfrac{|x|}{x} = \dfrac{x}{x} = 1$ for $x > 0$. As $x \to \infty$, x becomes positive and remains positive, so the above simplification is valid.

29. Find $\lim\limits_{x\to-\infty} \dfrac{(4-x^2)(\sqrt{x^2+2})}{3x^3-9x+\pi}$, if it exists.

SOLUTION: The highest power of x in the denominator is 3, so factor x^3 from numerator and denominator.

$$\lim_{x\to-\infty} \frac{(4-x)\sqrt{x^2+2}}{3x^3-9x+\pi} = \lim_{x\to-\infty} \frac{x^2\left(\dfrac{4}{x^2}-1\right)\sqrt{x^2}\sqrt{1+\dfrac{2}{x^2}}}{x^3\left(3-\dfrac{9}{x^2}+\dfrac{\pi}{x^3}\right)} = \lim_{x\to-\infty} \frac{|x|}{x}\cdot\frac{\left(\dfrac{4}{x^2}-1\right)\sqrt{1+\dfrac{2}{x^2}}}{3-\dfrac{9}{x^2}+\dfrac{\pi}{x^3}}.$$

Now as $x \to -\infty$, $\dfrac{|x|}{x} = \dfrac{-x}{x} = -1$, so the limit becomes

$$-\lim_{x\to\infty} \frac{\left(\dfrac{4}{x^2}-1\right)\sqrt{1+\dfrac{2}{x^2}}}{3-\dfrac{9}{x^2}+\dfrac{\pi}{x^3}} = -\frac{(-1)\sqrt{1}}{3} = \frac{1}{3}.$$

33. Find $\lim\limits_{x\to\infty} \left(\sqrt{x^2+x}-x\right)$, if it exists.

SOLUTION:

$$\lim_{x\to\infty} \frac{(\sqrt{x^2+x}-x)(\sqrt{x^2+x}+x)}{\sqrt{x^2+x}+x} = \lim_{x\to\infty} \frac{x^2+x-x^2}{\sqrt{x^2+x}+x} = \lim_{x\to\infty} \frac{x}{\sqrt{x^2+x}+x}$$

$$= \lim_{x\to\infty} \frac{x}{\sqrt{x^2}\left(\sqrt{1+\dfrac{1}{x}}+\dfrac{x}{\sqrt{x^2}}\right)} = \lim_{x\to\infty} \frac{x}{|x|\left(\sqrt{1+\dfrac{1}{x}}+\dfrac{x}{|x|}\right)}$$

$$= \lim_{x\to\infty} \frac{1}{\sqrt{1+\dfrac{1}{x}}+1} = \frac{1}{2}.$$

Note that multiplying by $\dfrac{\sqrt{x^2 + x} + x}{\sqrt{x^2 + x} + x}$ produces an expression which lends itself to the factoring technique.

41. Find the horizontal asymptotes of the graph of $f(x) = \dfrac{x}{\sqrt{x^2 + 1}}$ and sketch the graph.

SOLUTION: To find horizontal asymptotes, evaluate $\displaystyle\lim_{x \to \infty} f(x)$ and $\displaystyle\lim_{x \to -\infty} f(x)$.

$$\lim_{x \to \infty} \frac{x}{\sqrt{x^2 + 1}} = \lim_{x \to \infty} \frac{x}{\sqrt{x^2}\sqrt{1 + \dfrac{1}{x^2}}} = \lim_{x \to \infty} \frac{1}{\sqrt{1 + \dfrac{1}{x^2}}} = 1, \quad \text{and}$$

$$\lim_{x \to -\infty} \frac{x}{\sqrt{x^2 + 1}} = \lim_{x \to -\infty} \left(\frac{x}{|x|\sqrt{1 + \dfrac{1}{x^2}}} \right) = \lim_{x \to -\infty} \frac{-1}{\sqrt{1 + \dfrac{1}{x^2}}} = -1.$$

Thus, the horizontal asymptotes are $y = 1$ as $x \to \infty$ and $y = -1$ as $x \to -\infty$.

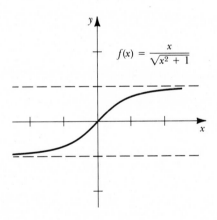

45. Use DEFINITION 1.51 to prove that $\displaystyle\lim_{x \to \infty} \frac{1}{x^2} = 0$.

SOLUTION: Let $\epsilon > 0$ be given. Find M such that if $x > M$ then $|f(x) - L| = \left| \dfrac{1}{x^2} \right| = \dfrac{1}{x^2} < \epsilon$.

Requiring $\dfrac{1}{x^2} < \epsilon$ is equivalent to requiring $x^2 > \dfrac{1}{\epsilon}$ or either $x > \dfrac{1}{\sqrt{\epsilon}}$ or $x < \dfrac{-1}{\sqrt{\epsilon}}$. Choose $M = \dfrac{1}{\sqrt{\epsilon}}$ and require $x > M$. Then $x > \dfrac{1}{\sqrt{\epsilon}} > 0 \implies x^2 > \dfrac{1}{\epsilon} > 0 \implies 0 < \dfrac{1}{x^2} < \epsilon \implies \left| \dfrac{1}{x^2} - 0 \right| = |f(x) - L| < \epsilon$. Thus $\displaystyle\lim_{x \to \infty} \frac{1}{x^2} = 0$.

_____1.10
Infinite Limits:
Vertical Asymptotes
_____

5. Find $\lim\limits_{x \to 2^+} \dfrac{x+2}{x-2}$ or state that the limit does not exist.

SOLUTION: $\lim\limits_{x \to 2^+} \dfrac{x+2}{x-2} = \lim\limits_{x \to 2^+} (x+2) \cdot \dfrac{1}{x-2}$. Now, $\lim\limits_{x \to 2^+}(x+2) = 4$ and $\lim\limits_{x \to 2^+} \dfrac{1}{x-2} = \infty$ since $x - 2$ approaches 0 from the right.

Thus $\lim\limits_{x \to 2^+} \dfrac{x+2}{x-2} = \infty$.

11. Find $\lim\limits_{x \to -3} \dfrac{x^2+2x-8}{x^2+x-6}$ or state that the limit does not exist.

SOLUTION:

$$\lim_{x \to -3} \frac{x^2+2x-8}{x^2+x-6} = \lim_{x \to -3} \frac{(x-2)(x+4)}{(x+3)(x-2)} = \lim_{x \to -3} \frac{x+4}{x+3} = \lim_{x \to -3}(x+4) \cdot \frac{1}{x+3}.$$

Now $\lim\limits_{x \to -3}(x+4) = 1$. However, $\lim\limits_{x \to -3^+} \dfrac{1}{x+3} = \infty$ and $\lim\limits_{x \to -3^-} \dfrac{1}{x+3} = -\infty$. Thus $\lim\limits_{x \to -3} \dfrac{1}{x+3}$ does not exist, and $\lim\limits_{x \to -3} \dfrac{x^2+2x-8}{x^2+x-6}$ does not exist.

17. Find $\lim\limits_{x \to (\pi/2)^-} \tan x$ or state that the limit does not exist.

SOLUTION: $\lim\limits_{x \to (\pi/2)^-} \tan x = \lim\limits_{x \to (\pi/2)^-} \sin x \cdot \dfrac{1}{\cos x}$. Now $\lim\limits_{x \to (\pi/2)^-} \sin x = 1$ and $\lim\limits_{x \to (\pi/2)^-} \dfrac{1}{\cos x} = \infty$ since $\cos x > 0$ as $x \to (\pi/2)^-$. Thus $\lim\limits_{x \to (\pi/2)^-} \tan x = \infty$.

23. Find $\lim\limits_{x \to 1^+} \sqrt{\dfrac{x}{x-1}}$ or state that the limit does not exist.

SOLUTION: $\lim\limits_{x \to 1^+} \sqrt{\dfrac{x}{x-1}} = \lim\limits_{x \to 1^+} \sqrt{x} \cdot \dfrac{1}{\sqrt{x-1}}$. Now $\lim\limits_{x \to 1^+} \sqrt{x} = 1$ and $\lim\limits_{x \to 1^+} \dfrac{1}{\sqrt{x-1}} = \infty$.

Thus, $\lim\limits_{x \to 1^+} \sqrt{\dfrac{x}{x-1}} = \infty$.

Note that $\lim\limits_{x \to 1^-} \dfrac{1}{\sqrt{x-1}}$ does not exist since $x - 1 < 0$ as $x \to 1^-$.

27. Find $\displaystyle\lim_{x\to-\infty}\frac{x^3+1}{x^2}$ or state that the limit does not exist.

SOLUTION:

$$\lim_{x\to-\infty}\frac{x^3+1}{x^2}=\lim_{x\to-\infty}\frac{x^2\left(x+\frac{1}{x^2}\right)}{x^2}=\lim_{x\to-\infty}\left(x+\frac{1}{x^2}\right)=-\infty.$$

Note the use of the technique of factoring the highest power of x in the denominator from both numerator and denominator. From this it can be seen that the graph of $f(x)=\dfrac{x^3+1}{x^2}$ has a slant asymptote of $y=x$ as $x\to-\infty$.

39. Determine the equations of any vertical and horizontal asymptotes to the graphs of $f(x)=\dfrac{x-1}{x+1}$ and sketch the graph.

SOLUTION: The domain of f is $\{x\in\mathbb{R}\mid x\neq-1\}$. To find any vertical asymptotes, examine $\displaystyle\lim_{x\to-1^-}\frac{x-1}{x+1}$ and $\displaystyle\lim_{x\to-1^+}\frac{x-1}{x+1}$. First, $\displaystyle\lim_{x\to-1^-}\frac{x-1}{x+1}=\infty$ since $x-1\to-2$ and $x+1<0$. Also $\displaystyle\lim_{x\to-1^+}\frac{x-1}{x+1}=-\infty$ since $x+1>0$. This indicates a vertical asymptote at $x=-1$.

To find any horizontal asymptotes, examine $\displaystyle\lim_{x\to+\infty}\frac{x-1}{x+1}$ and $\displaystyle\lim_{x\to-\infty}\frac{x-1}{x+1}$. Now $\displaystyle\lim_{x\to+\infty}\frac{x-1}{x+1}=1$ and $\displaystyle\lim_{x\to-\infty}\frac{x-1}{x+1}=1$. Thus the graph has a horizontal asymptote of $y=1$ at both $\pm\infty$.

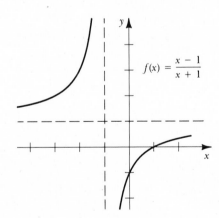

$$f(x)=\frac{x-1}{x+1}$$

49. Determine the equations of any vertical and horizontal asymptotes to the graphs of $f(x)=\dfrac{x^2-1}{x^2-2x+1}$ and sketch the graph.

SOLUTION: The domain of $f(x)=\dfrac{x^2-1}{x^2-2x+1}=\dfrac{x+1}{x-1}$ is $\{x\in\mathbb{R}\mid x\neq1\}$. $\displaystyle\lim_{x\to-1^-}\frac{x+1}{x-1}=-\infty$ and $\displaystyle\lim_{x\to-1^+}\frac{x+1}{x-1}=\infty$, which indicates a vertical asymptote at $x=1$.

$\displaystyle\lim_{x\to\infty}\frac{x+1}{x-1}=1$ and $\displaystyle\lim_{x\to-\infty}\frac{x+1}{x-1}=1$ indicate horizontal asymptotes of $y=1$ at both $\pm\infty$.

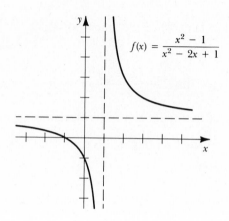

55. Determine the equations of any vertical and horizontal asymptotes to the graphs of $yx^2 + 4y - x = 0$ and sketch the graph.

SOLUTION: $yx^2 + 4y - x = 0 \implies y(x^2 + 4) = x \implies y = \dfrac{x}{x^2 + 4}$. The domain for this function is $\mathbb{R}$ so there are no vertical asymptotes.

$\lim\limits_{x \to \infty} \dfrac{x}{x^2 + 4} = 0$ and $\lim\limits_{x \to -\infty} \dfrac{x}{x^2 + 4} = 0$ which indicate $y = 0$ is a horizontal asymptote at both $\pm\infty$.

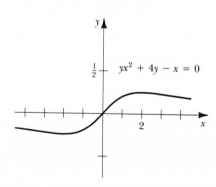

65. a) Use the fact that $|\sin x| \le 1$ to show that $\lim\limits_{x \to \infty} (x - \sin x) = \infty$.

    b) How large must x be to ensure that $x - \sin x$ is greater than 100?

SOLUTION: a) Since $|\sin x| \le 1$, $-1 \le \sin x \le 1 \implies -1 \le -\sin x \le 1 \implies x - 1 \le x - \sin x \le x + 1$. Now, $\lim\limits_{x \to \infty} (x - 1) = \infty$ and, since $x - \sin x \ge x - 1$ for all x, $\lim\limits_{x \to \infty} (x - \sin x) = \infty$. To prove this, let $M > 0$ be given. Find N so that if $x > N$, then $x - \sin x > M$. Since $\lim\limits_{x \to \infty} (x - 1) = \infty$ there exists N_1 so that if $x > N_1$, then $x - 1 > M$. Choose $N = N_1$ and require $x > N$. But then $x - 1 > M$ and since $x - \sin x \ge x - 1$, $x - \sin x > M$. Thus $\lim\limits_{x \to \infty} (x - \sin x) = \infty$.

b) For $x - \sin x > 100$, choose $x > 101$. Then $x - 1 > 100$ and by the above discussion $x - \sin x > x - 1 > 100$.

75. Construct functions g and h with $\lim\limits_{x \to \infty} g(x) = \infty$ and $\lim\limits_{x \to \infty} h(x) = -\infty$ so that $\lim\limits_{x \to \infty} \dfrac{g(x)}{h(x)} = -\infty$.

SOLUTION: Polynomial functions are the easiest to work with and do have infinite limits as $x \to \infty$. If the degree of g is greater than the degree of h, the desired quotient limit will be infinite. It remains to adjust the signs.

If $g(x) = x^2$ and $h(x) = -x$, then $\lim\limits_{x \to \infty} g(x) = \lim\limits_{x \to \infty} x^2 = \infty$ and $\lim\limits_{x \to \infty} h(x) = \lim\limits_{x \to \infty} (-x) = -\infty$ and $\lim\limits_{x \to \infty} \dfrac{g(x)}{h(x)} = \lim\limits_{x \to \infty} \dfrac{x^2}{-x} = \lim\limits_{x \to \infty} (-x) = -\infty$.

81. Show that the graph of $f(x) = \dfrac{x^2 + |x| + 1}{x}$ has a different slant asymptote at ∞ than it does at $-\infty$.

SOLUTION: Recall $|x| = x$ if $x \geq 0$ and $|x| = -x$ if $x < 0$. Thus,

$$\lim_{x \to \infty} \frac{x^2 + |x| + 1}{x} = \lim_{x \to \infty} \frac{x^2 + x + 1}{x} = \lim_{x \to \infty} \left(x + 1 + \frac{1}{x} \right) = \infty$$

and yields a slant asymptote of $y = x + 1$. However,

$$\lim_{x \to -\infty} \frac{x^2 + |x| + 1}{x} = \lim_{x \to -\infty} \frac{x^2 - x + 1}{x} = \lim_{x \to -\infty} \left(x - 1 + \frac{1}{x} \right) = \infty$$

but yields a slant asymptote of $y = x - 1$.

_____Chapter 1

Review Exercises

3. For $f(x) = x^2 - 7x + 10$, sketch the graph of f and find: a) $f(\sqrt{2})$ b) $f(\sqrt{2} + 1)$
   c) $f(\sqrt{2}) + f(1)$ d) $f(\sqrt{x})$ e) $\sqrt{f(x)}$ f) $\dfrac{f(x + h) - f(x)}{h}$.

SOLUTION: $f(x) = x^2 - 7x + 10 = x^2 - 7x + (7/2)^2 + 10 - (7/2)^2 = \left(x - \frac{7}{2} \right)^2 - \frac{9}{4}$. The graph of f is that of $y = x^2$ shifted right 7/2 and down 9/4 units.

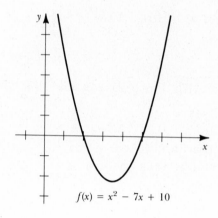

$f(x) = x^2 - 7x + 10$

a) $f(\sqrt{2}) = (\sqrt{2})^2 - 7\sqrt{2} + 10 = 12 - 7\sqrt{2}.$

b)

$$f(\sqrt{2} + 1) = (\sqrt{2} + 1)^2 - 7(\sqrt{2} + 1) + 10 = 2 + 2\sqrt{2} + 1 - 7\sqrt{2} - 7 + 10$$
$$= 6 - 5\sqrt{2}.$$

c) $f(\sqrt{2}) + f(1) = (12 - 7\sqrt{2}) + (1 - 7 + 10) = 16 - 7\sqrt{2}.$

d) $f(\sqrt{x}) = (\sqrt{x})^2 - 7\sqrt{x} + 10 = x - 7\sqrt{x} + 10.$

e) $\sqrt{f(x)} = \sqrt{x^2 - 7x + 10}.$

f)

$$\frac{f(x + h) - f(x)}{h} = \frac{((x + h)^2 - 7(x + h) + 10) - (x^2 - 7x + 10)}{h}$$
$$= \frac{x^2 + 2hx + h^2 - 7x - 7h + 10 - x^2 + 7x - 10}{h}$$
$$= \frac{2hx + h^2 - 7h}{h} = 2x + h - 7.$$

25. Use the graph of $f(x) = \dfrac{x^2}{x^2 + 1}$ to sketch the graph of $k(x) = \dfrac{-x^2}{x^2 + 1}$.

SOLUTION: Reflect the graph of f through the x-axis to obtain the graph of $k(x)$.

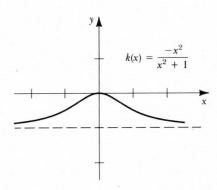

31. Use the graphs of the trigonometric functions to obtain the graph of $h(x) = 1 + \csc x$.

SOLUTION: The graph of $h(x)$ is the graph of $f(x) = \csc x$ shifted up 1 unit.

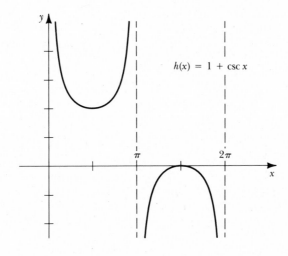

37. For $f(x) = \dfrac{1}{x^2 - 1}$ and $g(x) = x + 1$, find   a) $f \circ g$,   b) $g \circ f$, and   c) the domain of each.

SOLUTION: a) $(f \circ g)(x) = f\left(g(x)\right) = f(x + 1) = \dfrac{1}{(x + 1)^2 - 1} = \dfrac{1}{x^2 + 2x} = \dfrac{1}{x(x + 2)}$.

b) $(g \circ f)(x) = g\left(f(x)\right) = g\left(\dfrac{1}{x^2 - 1}\right) = \dfrac{1}{x^2 - 1} + 1 = \dfrac{1 + x^2 - 1}{x^2 - 1} = \dfrac{x^2}{x^2 - 1}$

c) To find the domain of $f \circ g$, start with the domain of g which is $\mathbb{R}$. Since the domain of f is $\{x \in \mathbb{R} \mid x \neq \pm 1\}$, remove all x such that $x + 1 = 1$ or $x + 1 = -1$. Thus the domain of $f \circ g$ is $\{x \in \mathbb{R} \mid x \neq -2, 0\}$.

To find the domain of $g \circ f$, start with the domain of f. Since the domain of g is $\mathbb{R}$, no additional values need to be removed from the domain. Thus the domain of $g \circ f$ is $\{x \in \mathbb{R} \mid x \neq \pm 1\}$.

47. Evaluate $\displaystyle\lim_{x \to 1^+} \frac{|x-1|}{x-1}$.

SOLUTION: $\displaystyle\lim_{x \to 1^+} \frac{|x-1|}{x-1} = \lim_{x \to 1^+} \frac{x-1}{x-1} = \lim_{x \to 1^+} 1 = 1$. Note that as $x \to 1^+$, $x - 1 > 0$, so $|x-1| = x - 1$.

51. Evaluate $\displaystyle\lim_{x \to \infty} \frac{x^5 - 3x^3 + x - 1}{x^2 + 3}$.

SOLUTION: Factor x^2 from numerator and denominator and obtain

$$\lim_{x \to \infty} \frac{x^5 - 3x^3 + x - 1}{x^2 + 3} = \lim_{x \to \infty} \frac{x^2}{x^2} \cdot \frac{x^3 - 3x + \dfrac{1}{x} - \dfrac{1}{x^2}}{1 + \dfrac{3}{x^2}}$$

$$= \lim_{x \to \infty} \frac{x^3 - 3x + \dfrac{1}{x} - \dfrac{1}{x^2}}{1 + \dfrac{3}{x^2}} = \infty.$$

55. Evaluate $\displaystyle\lim_{x \to 2} \frac{\sqrt{2+x} - 2}{x - 2}$.

SOLUTION: Recall the technique of "rationalizing the numerator" at times produces an expression where the limit can be evaluated directly.

$$\lim_{x \to 2} \frac{\sqrt{2+x} - 2}{x-2} \cdot \frac{\sqrt{2+x} + 2}{\sqrt{2+x} + 2} = \lim_{x \to 2} \frac{2 + x - 4}{(x-2)\sqrt{2+x} + 2} = \lim_{x \to 2} \frac{x - 2}{(x-2)(\sqrt{2+x} + 2)}$$

$$= \lim_{x \to 2} \frac{1}{\sqrt{2+x} + 2} = \frac{1}{\sqrt{2+2} + 2} = \frac{1}{4}.$$

61. Evaluate $\displaystyle\lim_{x \to 0} \frac{1}{|x|}$.

SOLUTION: Now $\displaystyle\lim_{x \to 0^+} \frac{1}{|x|} = \lim_{x \to 0^+} \frac{1}{x} = \infty$ and $\displaystyle\lim_{x \to 0^-} \frac{1}{|x|} = \lim_{x \to 0^-} \frac{1}{-x} = -\lim_{x \to 0^-} \frac{1}{x} = \infty$.

Thus $\displaystyle\lim_{x \to 0} \frac{1}{|x|} = \infty$ since $\displaystyle\lim_{x \to 0^+} \frac{1}{|x|} = \lim_{x \to 0^-} \frac{1}{|x|}$.

67. Evaluate $\lim\limits_{x\to\infty} (\sqrt{x^2 + x^{3/2}} - x)$.

SOLUTION:

$$\lim_{x\to\infty} (\sqrt{x^2 + x^{3/2}} - x) \cdot \frac{\sqrt{x^2 + x^{3/2}} + x}{\sqrt{x^2 + x^{3/2}} + x} = \lim_{x\to\infty} \frac{x^2 + x^{3/2} - x^2}{\sqrt{x^2 + x^{3/2}} + x}$$

$$= \lim_{x\to\infty} \frac{x^{3/2}}{\sqrt{x^2}\sqrt{1 + x^{-1/2}} + x} = \lim_{x\to\infty} \frac{x^{3/2}}{|x|\sqrt{1 + x^{-1/2}} + x}$$

$$= \lim_{x\to\infty} \frac{x^{3/2}}{x(\sqrt{1 + x^{-1/2}} + 1)} = \lim_{x\to\infty} \frac{x^{1/2}}{\sqrt{1 + x^{-1/2}} + 1} = \infty.$$

Note that as $x \to \infty$, $|x| = x$.

73. Determine any numbers at which $f(x) = \dfrac{x^2 - 5x + 6}{x^2 - 7x + 12}$ is discontinuous and give the reason for the discontinuity.

SOLUTION: $f(x)$ is undefined if $x^2 - 7x + 12 = 0$. $x^2 - 7x + 12 = 0 \implies (x - 4)(x - 3) = 0 \implies x = 4, 3$.

Thus f is discontinuous at $x = 3$ and $x = 4$ since neither $f(3)$ nor $f(4)$ exist. Note that even though $f(x) = \dfrac{(x - 2)(x - 3)}{(x - 3)(x - 4)} = \dfrac{x - 2}{x - 4}$, f is still undefined at $x = 3$. Note that, in addition, $\lim\limits_{x\to 4} f(x)$ does not exist.

81. Determine the interval on which $f(x) = \sec x$ is continuous.

SOLUTION: $f(x) = \sec x = \dfrac{1}{\cos x}$ is undefined when $\cos x = 0$. This occurs when x is an odd multiple of $\pi/2$, $x = (2n + 1)\frac{\pi}{2}$, where n is an integer. Thus f is continuous on the union of a series of open intervals

$$\cdots \cup \left(-\frac{3\pi}{2}, -\frac{\pi}{2}\right) \cup \left(-\frac{\pi}{2}, \frac{\pi}{2}\right) \cup \left(\frac{\pi}{2}, \frac{3\pi}{2}\right) \cup \cdots \cup \cdots \left((2n - 1)\frac{\pi}{2}, (2n + 1)\frac{\pi}{2}\right) \cup \cdots,$$

where n is an integer.

89. Find any horizontal, vertical, and slant asymptotes of $f(x) = \dfrac{x - 2}{x^2 - 2x}$ and sketch the graph.

SOLUTION: The domain of $f(x) = \dfrac{x - 2}{x^2 - 2x} = \dfrac{1}{x}$ is $\{x \in \mathbb{R} \mid x \neq 0, 2\}$.

Consider $\lim\limits_{x\to\infty} f(x)$. $\lim\limits_{x\to\infty} \dfrac{x - 2}{x^2 - 2x} = \lim\limits_{x\to\infty} \dfrac{1}{x} = 0$. Similarly $\lim\limits_{x\to-\infty} f(x) = 0$. Thus there are horizontal asymptotes $y = 0$ at both $\pm\infty$.

$$\lim_{x \to 0+} \frac{x-2}{x^2-2x} = \lim_{x \to 0+} \frac{1}{x} = \infty \text{ and } \lim_{x \to 0-} \frac{x-2}{x^2-2x} = -\infty, \text{ so there is a vertical asymptote at } x = 0.$$

$$\lim_{x \to 2} \frac{x-2}{x^2-2x} = \lim_{x \to 2} \frac{1}{x} = \frac{1}{2}, \text{ so there is no asymptote at } x = 2.$$

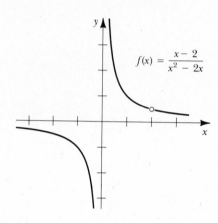

$$f(x) = \frac{x-2}{x^2-2x}$$

93. Use the definition of the limit to show that $\lim_{x \to 1}(3x + 5) = 8$.

SOLUTION: Let $\epsilon > 0$ be given. Find $\delta > 0$ so that if $|x - a| = |x - 1| < \delta$, then $|f(x) - L| = |3x + 5 - 8| = |3x - 3| < \epsilon$. Requiring $|3x - 3| < \epsilon$ is equivalent to $3|x - 1| < \epsilon$ or $|x - 1| < \epsilon/3$. Now let $\delta = \epsilon/3$ and require $|x - a| = |x - 1| < \delta$. Then $|x - 1| < \epsilon/3 \implies 3|x - 1| < \epsilon \implies |3x - 3| < \epsilon \implies |3x + 5 - 8| < \epsilon \implies |f(x) - L| < \epsilon$. Thus $\lim_{x \to 1}(3x + 5) = 8$.

95. If

$$f(x) = \begin{cases} x + 2, & \text{if } x < -2, \\ 2, & \text{if } -2 \le x \le 2, \\ 2 - x, & \text{if } x > 2, \end{cases}$$

find each of the following, if they exist.

a) $\lim_{x \to -2-} f(x)$ b) $\lim_{x \to -2+} f(x)$

c) $\lim_{x \to -2} f(x)$ d) $\lim_{x \to 2-} f(x)$

e) $\lim_{x \to 2+} f(x)$ f) $\lim_{x \to 2} f(x)$.

SOLUTION: a) $\lim_{x \to -2-} f(x) = \lim_{x \to -2-}(x + 2) = -2 + 2 = 0$ since $f(x) = x + 2$ for $x < -2$.

b) $\lim_{x \to -2+} f(x) = \lim_{x \to -2+} 2 = 2$ since $f(x) = 2$ for $-2 \le x \le 2$.

c) $\lim_{x \to -2} f(x)$ does not exist since $\lim_{x \to -2-} f(x) \ne \lim_{x \to -2+} f(x)$.

d) $\lim_{x \to 2-} f(x) = \lim_{x \to 2-} 2 = 2$ since $f(x) = 2$ for $-2 \le x \le 2$.

e) $\lim_{x \to 2+} f(x) = \lim_{x \to 2+}(2 - x) = 2 - 2 = 0$ since $f(x) = 2 - x$ for $x > 2$.

f) $\lim_{x \to 2} f(x)$ does not exist since $\lim_{x \to 2-} f(x) \ne \lim_{x \to 2+} f(x)$.

2

The Derivative

Sharpening your skills

In CHAPTER 2 you will need to evaluate limits. Reviewing SECTION 1.5 in the text along with some problems from numbers 3–40 from EXERCISE SET 1.5 will be helpful. You also will need to find the equation of a line given a point and information that will allow you to determine the slope of the line. This topic is presented in the text in SECTION 1.2 with problems 7–14 in the EXERCISE SET. You also will need to solve equations after they have been simplified. Some practice problems are included here. The answers are in APPENDIX B in this manual.

Practice Problems

1. Evaluate each of the following limits.

   a) $\lim_{h \to 0} \dfrac{(2(x+h)^2 - 7(x+h)) - (2x^2 - 7x)}{h}$,

   b) $\lim_{h \to 0} \dfrac{\dfrac{2}{(x+h)^2 - 4} - \dfrac{2}{x^2 - 4}}{h}$,

   c) $\lim_{h \to 0} \dfrac{\left((x+h)^3 - \dfrac{1}{x+h}\right) - \left(x^3 - \dfrac{1}{x}\right)}{h}$.

2. Find the equation of the line through $(2,3)$ which is   a) parallel to and   b) perpendicular to the line $4x - 3y = 1$.

3. Solve each of the following equations.

   a) $2x^3 - 10x^2 - 28x = 0$,   b) $-3x^2 + 5x + 10 = 0$,

   c) $\dfrac{x-3}{x^2} + \dfrac{2}{x} = 0$,   d) $\sqrt{x^2 - 6} - x + 2 = 0$.

2.1

The Slope
of a Curve

7. For $f(x) = x^3$,
   a) sketch the graph

b) find the slope of the tangent line to the graph at $(1,1)$

c) find an equation of the tangent line to the graph at $(1,1)$

d) find an equation of the normal line to the graph at $(1,1)$

SOLUTION: a)

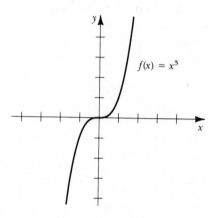

$f(x) = x^3$

b) The slope of the tangent line at $(a, f(a))$ is $\displaystyle\lim_{h \to 0} \frac{f(a+h) - f(a)}{h}$. Thus

$$\lim_{h \to 0} \frac{f(1+h) - f(1)}{h} = \lim_{h \to 0} \frac{(1+h)^3 - 1^3}{h} = \lim_{h \to 0} \frac{1 + 3h + 3h^2 + h^3 - 1}{h} = \lim_{h \to 0}(3 + 3h + h^2) = 3.$$

c) Since the slope of the tangent line is 3, use point-slope form to obtain $y - 1 = 3(x - 1)$. Thus $y = 3x - 2$ is an equation of the tangent line.

d) The slope of the normal line is $-1/3$ (the negative reciprocal of the slope of the tangent line). Thus $y - 1 = -\frac{1}{3}(x - 1)$, and $y = -\frac{1}{3}x + \frac{4}{3}$ is the equation of the normal line.

13. a) Find the slope of the tangent line to $f(x) = 2x^2 - 3x + 4$ at an arbitrary point $(a, f(a))$.

b) Determine any points on the graph of f at which the tangent line is horizontal.

SOLUTION: a) Evaluate $\displaystyle\lim_{h \to 0} \frac{f(a+h) - f(a)}{h}$.

$$\lim_{h \to 0} \frac{\left(2(a+h)^2 - 3(a+h) + 4\right) - (2a^2 - 3a + 4)}{h}$$

$$= \lim_{h \to 0} \frac{2a^2 + 4ah + 2h^2 - 3a - 3h + 4 - 2a^2 + 3a - 4}{h}$$

$$= \lim_{h \to 0} \frac{4ah + 2h^2 - 3h}{h} = \lim_{h \to 0}(4a + 2h - 3) = 4a - 3.$$

b) If the tangent line is horizontal, then its slope is 0. Set the slope of the tangent, $4a - 3$, equal to 0. $4a - 3 = 0 \implies a = 3/4$. Now $f(3/4) = 23/8$, so the desired point is $(3/4, 23/8)$.

19. For the function in EXERCISE 13 ($f(x) = 2x^2 - 3x + 4$), determine when the slope of the line tangent to the graph at $(a, f(a))$ is   a) positive   b) negative.

SOLUTION: From the SOLUTION to EXERCISE 13, the slope of the tangent line is $4a - 3$.

a) Set $4a - 3 > 0$. Then $a > 3/4$, so for $x > 3/4$, the slope of the tangent line to $f(x) = 2x^2 - 3x + 4$ is positive.

b) Set $4a - 3 < 0$. Then $a < 3/4$, so for $x < 3/4$, the slope of the tangent line to $f(x) = 2x^2 - 3x + 4$ is negative.

27. Find a point on the graph of $f(x) = 2x^2 + 3x$ where the tangent line is parallel to the line with equation $x + y = 4$.

SOLUTION: First find an equation for the slope of the tangent line at $(a, f(a))$.

$$\lim_{h \to 0} \frac{f(a + h) - f(a)}{h} = \lim_{h \to 0} \frac{\left(2(a + h)^2 + 3(a + h)\right) - (2a^2 + 3a)}{h}$$

$$= \lim_{h \to 0} \frac{2a^2 + 4ah + 2h^2 + 3a + 3h - 2a^2 - 3a}{h}$$

$$= \lim_{h \to 0} \frac{4ah + 2h^2 + 3h}{h} = \lim_{h \to 0} (4a + 2h + 3) = 4a + 3.$$

The slope of the line $x + y = 4$ is -1, since $y = -x + 4$.

To find the point on the graph, set $4a + 3 = -1$. Then $a = -1$ and $f(-1) = -1$. Thus the desired point is $(-1, -1)$.

31. Find two points on the graph of $f(x) = 1/x$ at which the tangent line is parallel to the line with equation $y = 3 - 4x$.

SOLUTION: Find the equation of the tangent line at $(a, f(a))$.

$$\lim_{h \to 0} \frac{f(a + h) - f(a)}{h} = \lim_{h \to 0} \frac{\frac{1}{a+h} - \frac{1}{a}}{h} = \lim_{h \to 0} \frac{\frac{a-(a+h)}{a(a+h)}}{h} = \lim_{h \to 0} \frac{\frac{-h}{a(a+h)}}{h}$$

$$= \lim_{h \to 0} \frac{-h}{ha(a + h)} = \lim_{h \to 0} \frac{-1}{a(a + h)} = \frac{-1}{a \cdot a} = -\frac{1}{a^2}.$$

COMMENT: Note that the approach in evaluating this limit is to simplify the original expression through standard algebraic techniques—simplify the numerator of the complex rational expression and then rewrite as a simple rational expression.

Now the slope of $y = 3 - 4x$ is -4. The coordinates of the desired points can be found by solving $-\frac{1}{a^2} = -4$. $-1/a^2 = -4 \implies a^2 = 1/4 \implies a = \pm 1/2$, and $f(1/2) = 2$, $f(-1/2) = -2$, so $(1/2, 2)$ and $(-1/2, -2)$ are the desired points.

35. On a walk over a gentle hill, we find that the altitude, in feet, t minutes after the walk has begun is given by $A(t) = 300 + 40t - 2t^2$, where $0 \le t \le 20$.

   a) Find the slope of the tangent line to the graph of A at an arbitrary point $(t, A(t))$.

   b) Use the result in a) to decide for which values of t the walk is uphill.

   c) Use the result in a) to decide for which values of t the walk is downhill.

   d) Determine the altitude at the summit.

SOLUTION: a) Evaluate $\lim\limits_{h \to 0} \dfrac{A(t+h) - A(t)}{h}$.

$$\lim_{h \to 0} \frac{(300 + 40(t+h) - 2(t+h)^2) - (300 + 40t - 2t^2)}{h}$$

$$= \lim_{h \to 0} \frac{300 + 40t + 40h - 2t^2 - 4th - 2h^2 - 300 - 40t + 2t^2}{h}$$

$$= \lim_{h \to 0} \frac{40h - 4th - 2h^2}{h} = \lim_{h \to 0} (40 - 4t - 2h) = 40 - 4t.$$

b) The walk is uphill while the altitude is increasing. This it true when the slope of the tangent line is positive. Set $40 - 4t > 0$. Then $40 > 4t \implies t < 10$. The walk is uphill for $0 \le t < 10$.

c) Similarly, the walk is downhill when the slope of the tangent line is negative. Set $40 - 4t < 0$. Then $t > 10$. Thus the walk is downhill for $10 < t \le 20$.

d) Since the walk at the instant the summit is reached is neither uphill nor downhill, that corresponds to a zero slope of the tangent line. This occurs when $t = 10$. The altitude is $A(10) = 300 + 40(10) - 2(10)^2 = 500$ feet.

_____2.2

The Derivative of a Function

11. Use the formula $f'(x) = \lim\limits_{h \to 0} \dfrac{f(x+h) - f(x)}{h}$ to find $f'(x)$ for $f(x) = \dfrac{1}{\sqrt{x}}$ at $x = 4$.

SOLUTION:

$$f'(x) = \lim_{h \to 0} \frac{\frac{1}{\sqrt{x+h}} - \frac{1}{\sqrt{x}}}{h} = \lim_{h \to 0} \frac{\frac{\sqrt{x} - \sqrt{x+h}}{\sqrt{x}\sqrt{x+h}}}{h}$$

$$= \lim_{h \to 0} \frac{\sqrt{x} - \sqrt{x+h}}{h\sqrt{x}\sqrt{x+h}} \cdot \frac{\sqrt{x} + \sqrt{x+h}}{\sqrt{x} + \sqrt{x+h}} = \lim_{h \to 0} \frac{x - (x+h)}{h\sqrt{x}\sqrt{x+h}(\sqrt{x} + \sqrt{x+h})}$$

$$= \lim_{h \to 0} \frac{-1}{\sqrt{x}\sqrt{x+h}(\sqrt{x} + \sqrt{x+h})} = \frac{-1}{\sqrt{x}\sqrt{x}(\sqrt{x} + \sqrt{x})} = -\frac{1}{2x\sqrt{x}}.$$

So $f'(4) = -\dfrac{1}{2(4)\sqrt{4}} = -\dfrac{1}{16}$.

COMMENT: The technique employed after simplifying the algebraic expression was to multiply numerator and denominator by the conjugate of the numerator—in effect, "rationalizing the numerator." Also the denominator was left in factored form until after the limit was evaluated. These techniques usually result in an efficient computation of the derivative.

15. Use the formula $f'(x) = \lim\limits_{h \to 0} \dfrac{f(x+h) - f(x)}{h}$ to find $f'(x)$ for $f(x) = x^2 + \dfrac{1}{x}$ at $x = 2$.

SOLUTION:

$$f'(x) = \lim_{h \to 0} \frac{f(x+h) - f(x)}{h} = \lim_{h \to 0} \frac{\left((x+h)^2 + \frac{1}{x+h}\right) - \left(x^2 + \frac{1}{x}\right)}{h}$$

$$= \lim_{h \to 0} \frac{(x+h)^2 - x^2}{h} + \lim_{h \to 0} \frac{\frac{1}{x+h} - \frac{1}{x}}{h} = \lim_{h \to 0} \frac{x^2 + 2xh + h^2 - x^2}{h} + \lim_{h \to 0} \frac{\frac{x - (x+h)}{x(x+h)}}{h}$$

$$= \lim_{h \to 0} \frac{2xh + h^2}{h} + \lim_{h \to 0} \frac{-h}{hx(x+h)}$$

$$= \lim_{h \to 0} (2x + h) + \lim_{h \to 0} \frac{-1}{x(x+h)} = 2x - \frac{1}{x^2}.$$

Thus $f'(2) = 4 - \frac{1}{4} = \frac{15}{4}$. The derivative was split into two limits in order to make the algebraic simplification easier.

19. Use the formula $f'(x) = \lim\limits_{z \to x} \dfrac{f(z) - f(x)}{z - x}$ to find $f'(x)$ for $f(x) = x^2 + 2x + 1$ at $x = -1$.

SOLUTION:

$$f'(x) = \lim_{z \to x} \frac{f(z) - f(x)}{z - x} = \lim_{z \to x} \frac{(z^2 + 2z + 1) - (x^2 + 2x + 1)}{z - x} = \lim_{z \to x} \frac{z^2 - x^2 + 2z - 2x}{z - x}$$

$$= \lim_{z \to x} \frac{(z - x)(z + x) + 2(z - x)}{z - x} = \lim_{z \to x} \frac{(z - x)\left((z + x) + 2\right)}{z - x} = \lim_{z \to x} (z + x + 2) = 2x + 2.$$

Thus $f'(-1) = 0$.

33. Find $f'(x)$ and its domain if $f(x) = x^{1/3}$. Sketch the graph of f and f'.

SOLUTION:

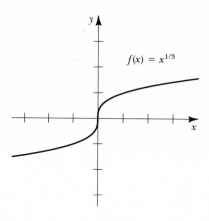

$f(x) = x^{1/3}$

$$f'(x) = \lim_{h \to 0} \frac{(x+h)^{1/3} - x^{1/3}}{h} \cdot \frac{(x+h)^{2/3} + x^{1/3}(x+h)^{1/3} + x^{2/3}}{(x+h)^{2/3} + x^{1/3}(x+h)^{1/3} + x^{2/3}}$$

$$= \lim_{h \to 0} \frac{x+h-x}{h\left((x+h)^{2/3} + x^{1/3}(x+h)^{1/3} + x^{2/3}\right)} = \lim_{h \to 0} \frac{1}{(x+h)^{2/3} + x^{1/3}(x+h)^{1/3} + x^{2/3}}$$

$$= \frac{1}{x^{2/3} + x^{1/3}x^{1/3} + x^{2/3}} = \frac{1}{3x^{2/3}}.$$

Again the technique of "rationalizing the numerator" is employed. The difference of two perfect cubes is used:

$$a - b = (a^{1/3})^3 - (b^{1/3})^3 = (a^{1/3} - b^{1/3})\left((a^{1/3})^2 + a^{1/3}b^{1/3} + (b^{1/3})^2\right),$$

with $a = x + h$ and $b = x$.

Since the domain of f is $\mathbb{R}$, the domain of f' is $\{x \in \mathbb{R} \mid x \neq 0\}$.

37. The area of a circle with radius r is given by $A(r) = \pi r^2$. Find the instantaneous rate of change of the area with respect to the radius.

SOLUTION: The instantaneous rate of change of the area with respect to the radius is

$$D_r[A(r)] = \lim_{h \to 0} \frac{A(r+h) - A(r)}{h} = \lim_{h \to 0} \frac{\pi(r+h)^2 - \pi r^2}{h}$$

$$= \lim_{h \to 0} \frac{\pi(r^2 + 2hr + h^2 - r^2)}{h} = \pi \lim_{h \to 0} \frac{2hr + h^2}{h} = \pi \lim_{h \to 0}(2r + h) = 2\pi r.$$

It is worth noting that the instantaneous rate of change of the area of a circle with respect to its radius is the circumference of the circle.

43. Find $f'_+(x)$ and $f'_-(x)$ for $f(x) = |x|$ at $x = 0$.

SOLUTION: Recall $f(x) = |x| = \begin{cases} x, & \text{if } x \geq 0 \\ -x, & \text{if } x < 0. \end{cases}$ Then

$$f'_+(0) = \lim_{h \to 0^+} \frac{f(0+h) - f(0)}{h} = \lim_{h \to 0^+} \frac{|h|}{h} = \lim_{h \to 0^+} \frac{h}{h} = 1, \quad \text{and}$$

$$f'_-(0) = \lim_{h \to 0^-} \frac{f(0+h) - f(0)}{h} = \lim_{h \to 0^-} \frac{|h|}{h} = \lim_{h \to 0^-} -\frac{h}{h} = -1.$$

49. Find the largest interval on which $f(x) = |x|$ is differentiable.

SOLUTION: From the SOLUTION to EXERCISE 43, recall $f'_-(0) = -1$ and $f'_+(0) = 1$. For $a > 0$,

$$f'(a) = \lim_{h \to 0} \frac{f(a+h) - f(a)}{h} = \lim_{h \to 0} \frac{|a+h| - |a|}{h} = \lim_{h \to 0} \frac{a+h-a}{h} = 1,$$

so $f(x) = |x|$ is differentiable on $[0, \infty)$, since $f'(x)$ exists for $x > 0$ and $f'_+(0)$ exists. For $a < 0$,

$$f'(a) = \lim_{h \to 0} \frac{|a+h| - |a|}{h} = \lim_{h \to 0} \frac{-(a+h) - (-a)}{h} = \lim_{h \to 0} \frac{-a - h + a}{h} = -1,$$

so $f(x) = |x|$ is differentiable on $(-\infty, 0]$, since $f'(x)$ exists for $x < 0$ and $f'_-(0)$ exists. Note that this is <u>not</u> the same as being differentiable on $\mathbb{R}$, since $f'(0)$ does not exist as $f'_-(0) \neq f'_+(0)$.

59. Suppose f is an even function and that f' is defined at every real number. Show that f' is an odd function and that $f'(0) = 0$.

SOLUTION: Let f be even and let f' be defined for each real number. Then $f(-x) = f(x)$. To show f' is odd, show $f'(-x) = -f'(x)$.

$$f'(x) = \lim_{h \to 0} \frac{f(x+h) - f(x)}{h}$$

$$f'(-x) = \lim_{h \to 0} \frac{f(-x+h) - f(-x)}{h} = \lim_{h \to 0} \frac{f(-(x-h)) - f(-x)}{h} = \lim_{h \to 0} \frac{f(x-h) - f(x)}{h}.$$

Let $k = -h$. As $h \to 0$, clearly $k \to 0$. Thus

$$\lim_{h \to 0} \frac{f(x-h) - f(x)}{h} = \lim_{k \to 0} \frac{f(x+k) - f(x)}{-k} = -\lim_{k \to 0} \frac{f(x+k) - f(x)}{k} = -f'(x),$$

and f' is odd.

Since $f'(-x) = -f'(x)$, $f'(-x) + f'(x) = 0$. So $f'(-0) + f'(0) = f'(0) + f'(0) = 2f'(0) = 0 \implies f'(0) = 0$.

Note that the proposition that if f is odd, then $f(0) = 0$ is true for **any** odd function. The fact that a derivative was used here is immaterial.

_____**2.3**

Formulas for
Differentiation

_____

7. Find the derivative of $f(t) = \pi t^2 + (3 + 4\sqrt{2})t + 9$.

SOLUTION:

$$D_t\left[\pi t^2 + (3 + 4\sqrt{2})t + 9\right] = D_t\left[\pi t^2\right] + D_t\left[(3 + 4\sqrt{2})t\right] + D_t\left[9\right]$$
$$= \pi D_t\left[t^2\right] + (3 + 4\sqrt{2})D_t\left[t\right] + 0$$
$$= \pi(2t) + (3 + 4\sqrt{2}) = 2\pi t + 3 + 4\sqrt{2}.$$

11. Find the derivative of $r(u) = (u^2 + u + 2)(u^4 + u^3)$.

SOLUTION: Applying the product rule,

$$D_u\left[(u^2 + u + 2)(u^4 + u^3)\right] = (u^2 + u + 2)D_u\left[u^4 + u^3\right] + (u^4 + u^3)D_u\left[u^2 + u + 2\right]$$
$$= (u^2 + u + 2)(4u^3 + 3u^2) + (u^4 + u^3)(2u + 1).$$

13. Find the derivative of $f(x) = \frac{1}{3}x^2 + \frac{3}{x^2}$.

SOLUTION:

$$D_x\left[\frac{1}{3}x^2 + \frac{3}{x^2}\right] = D_x\left[\frac{1}{3}x^2\right] + D_x\left[3x^{-2}\right] = \frac{1}{3}D_x\left[x^2\right] + 3D_x\left[x^{-2}\right]$$
$$= \frac{1}{3}(2x) + 3(-2x^{-3}) = \frac{2}{3}x - 6x^{-3}.$$

19. Find the derivative of $H(x) = \dfrac{3x + 4}{5x^2 + 1}$.

SOLUTION: Applying the quotient rule,

$$D_x\left[\frac{3x + 4}{5x^2 + 1}\right] = \frac{(5x^2 + 1)D_x\left[3x + 4\right] - (3x + 4)D_x\left[5x^2 + 1\right]}{(5x^2 + 1)^2} = \frac{(5x^2 + 1)(3) - (3x + 4)(10x)}{(5x^2 + 1)^2}$$

$$= \frac{15x^2 + 3 - 30x^2 - 40x}{(5x^2 + 1)^2} = \frac{-15x^2 - 40x + 3}{(5x^2 + 1)^2}.$$

23. Find the derivative of $F(s) = \left(\dfrac{s^2 + 1}{s^2 + 2}\right)(s^2 + 3)$.

SOLUTION: This problem can be attacked by applying the product rule followed by the quotient rule or by rewriting $F(s) = \dfrac{(s^2 + 1)(s^2 + 3)}{s^2 + 2}$ and applying the quotient rule followed by the product rule. Using the first approach,

$$D_s\left[\left(\frac{s^2 + 1}{s^2 + 2}\right)(s^2 + 3)\right] = \left(\frac{s^2 + 1}{s^2 + 2}\right)D_s\left[s^2 + 3\right] + (s^2 + 3)D_s\left[\frac{s^2 + 1}{s^2 + 2}\right]$$

$$= \left(\frac{s^2 + 1}{s^2 + 2}\right)(2s)$$

$$+ (s^2 + 3)\left(\frac{(s^2 + 2)D_s\left[s^2 + 1\right] - (s^2 + 1)D_s\left[s^2 + 2\right]}{(s^2 + 2)^2}\right)$$

$$= \frac{2s(s^2 + 1)}{s^2 + 2} + (s^2 + 3)\left(\frac{(s^2 + 2)(2s) - (s^2 + 1)(2s)}{(s^2 + 2)^2}\right)$$

$$= \frac{2s(s^2 + 1)}{s^2 + 2} + \frac{2s(s^2 + 3)\left((s^2 + 2) - (s^2 + 1)\right)}{(s^2 + 2)^2}$$

$$= \frac{2s(s^2 + 1)}{s^2 + 2} + \frac{2s(s^2 + 3)}{(s^2 + 2)^2}.$$

27. Find the derivative of $f(x) = (x + 1)(x + 2)(x + 3)$.

SOLUTION: Applying the product rule,

$$D_x\left[(x + 1)(x + 2)(x + 3)\right] = (x + 1)D_x\left[(x + 2)(x + 3)\right] + (x + 2)(x + 3)D_x\left[x + 1\right]$$
$$= (x + 1)\left((x + 2)D_x\left[x + 3\right] + (x + 3)D_x\left[x + 2\right]\right) + (x + 2)(x + 3)(1)$$
$$= (x + 1)\left((x + 2)(1) + (x + 3)(1)\right) + (x + 2)(x + 3)$$
$$= (x + 1)(x + 2) + (x + 1)(x + 3) + (x + 2)(x + 3).$$

37. Find the derivative of $g(t) = (2t + 1)^3$.

SOLUTION: At this point, to find the derivative the polynomial must be expanded. In SECTION 2.5, a method will be presented that allows the derivative to be calculated without expanding the polynomial. Recall $(a + b)^3 = a^3 + 3a^2b + 3ab^2 + b^3$. Thus,

$$D_t\left[(2t + 1)^3\right] = D_t\left[(2t)^3 + 3(2t)^2(1) + 3(2t)(1)^2 + (1)^3\right] = D_t\left[8t^3 + 12t^2 + 6t + 1\right]$$

$$= 24t^2 + 24t + 6 = 6(4t^2 + 4t + 1) = 6(2t + 1)^2.$$

41. Find an equation of the tangent line to the graph of $y = (x^2 - 1)/(x^2 + 1)$ at $(2, 3/5)$.

SOLUTION: Applying the quotient rule,

$$D_x y = D_x \left[\frac{x^2 - 1}{x^2 + 1} \right] = \frac{(x^2 + 1)D_x \left[x^2 - 1 \right] - (x^2 - 1)D_x \left[x^2 + 1 \right]}{(x^2 + 1)^2}$$

$$= \frac{(x^2 + 1)(2x) - (x^2 - 1)(2x)}{(x^2 + 1)^2} = \frac{2x\left((x^2 + 1) - (x^2 - 1)\right)}{(x^2 + 1)^2} = \frac{4x}{(x^2 + 1)^2}.$$

To find the slope of the tangent line at $(2, 3/5)$, evaluate the derivative at $x = 2$. $m_{\tan} = \frac{8}{(4 + 1)^2} = 8/25$. Applying point-slope,

$$y - \frac{3}{5} = \frac{8}{25}(x - 2) \implies y = \frac{8}{25}x - \frac{1}{25}.$$

47. For temperatures close to absolute zero ($-273°C$) the atomic heat of aluminum can be accurately described by Debye's equation

$$H = 464.6 \left(\frac{T}{375} \right)^3 \frac{\text{cal}}{\text{deg-mole}},$$

where T is the temperature in degrees Kelvin; $°K = °C + 273$. Find the instantaneous rate of change in the heat with respect to T when the temperature is $-250°C$.

SOLUTION: The instantaneous rate of change in the heat with respect to T is

$$D_T H = D_T \left[464.6 \left(\frac{T}{375} \right)^3 \frac{\text{cal}}{\text{deg-mole}} \right] = \frac{464.6}{(375)^3}(3T^2)\frac{\text{cal}}{\text{deg}^2\text{-mole}}.$$

Evaluating at $T = 23\,K$, $(-250 + 273)$,

$$D_T H \bigg|_{T=23} = \frac{3(464.6)}{(375)^3}(23)^2 = 0.01398 \frac{\text{cal}}{\text{deg}^2\text{-mole}}.$$

_____2.4

Differentiation of Trigonometric Functions

---

5. Find the derivative of $g(t) = t^3 \cos t$.

SOLUTION: Apply the product rule to the function and obtain

$$D_t \left[t^3 \cos t \right] = t^3 D_t \left[\cos t \right] + \cos t D_t \left[t^3 \right] = t^3(- \sin t) + \cos t (3t^2) = t^2(3 \cos t - t \sin t).$$

11. Find the derivative of $f(x) = \sin^2 x$.

SOLUTION: Rewrite $\sin^2 x$ as $\sin x \cdot \sin x$ and apply the product rule obtaining

$$D_x\left[\sin x \cdot \sin x\right] = (\sin x)D_x\left[\sin x\right] + (\sin x)D_x\left[\sin x\right] = 2\sin x\, D_x\left[\sin x\right]$$

$$= 2\sin x \cos x = \sin 2x.$$

15. Find the derivative of $f(x) = 2x \csc x$.

SOLUTION: Applying the product rule, obtain

$$D_x\left[2x \csc x\right] = 2x\, D_x\left[\csc x\right] + (\csc x)D_x\left[2x\right] = 2x(-\csc x \cot x) + (\csc x)(2)$$

$$= 2\csc x(1 - x \cot x).$$

21. Find the derivative of $h(\theta) = \dfrac{\sec \theta + 1}{\tan \theta}$.

SOLUTION: Apply the quotient rule to this function and obtain

$$D_\theta\left[\frac{\sec \theta + 1}{\tan \theta}\right] = \frac{(\tan \theta)D_\theta\left[\sec \theta + 1\right] - (\sec \theta + 1)D_\theta\left[\tan \theta\right]}{\tan^2 \theta}$$

$$= \frac{\tan \theta \sec \theta \tan \theta - (\sec \theta + 1)\sec^2 \theta}{\tan^2 \theta}$$

$$= \frac{\sec \theta\left(\tan^2 \theta - \sec \theta(\sec \theta + 1)\right)}{\tan^2 \theta} = \frac{\sec \theta\left(\tan^2 \theta - \sec^2 \theta - \sec \theta\right)}{\tan^2 \theta}$$

$$= \frac{\sec \theta(-1 - \sec \theta)}{\tan^2 \theta} = \frac{-\sec \theta(1 + \sec \theta)}{\sec^2 \theta - 1}$$

$$= \frac{\sec \theta}{1 - \sec \theta}.$$

Note that $\tan^2 \theta - \sec^2 \theta = -1$ from the Pythagorean identity $1 + \tan^2 \theta = \sec^2 \theta$.

29. Find the derivative of $r(t) = \dfrac{\csc t - \cot t}{t + 2}$.

SOLUTION: Apply the quotient rule to obtain

$$D_t\left[\frac{\csc t - \cot t}{t + 2}\right] = \frac{(t + 2)D_t\left[\csc t - \cot t\right] - (\csc t - \cot t)D_t\left[t + 2\right]}{(t + 2)^2}$$

$$= \frac{(t + 2)\left(-\csc t \cot t + \csc^2 t\right) - (\csc t - \cot t)(1)}{(t + 2)^2}$$

$$= \frac{(t+2)(\csc t)(\csc t - \cot t) - (\csc t - \cot t)}{(t+2)^2}$$

$$= \frac{(\csc t - \cot t)\left((t+2)\csc t - 1\right)}{(t+2)^2}.$$

33. Find $\lim\limits_{t \to 0} \dfrac{\sin^2 t}{t}$.

SOLUTION:

$$\lim_{t \to 0} \frac{\sin^2 t}{t} = \lim_{t \to 0} \frac{\sin t}{t} \lim_{t \to 0} \sin t = 1 \cdot 0 = 0.$$

37. Find $\lim\limits_{t \to 0} \dfrac{t}{\sin t}$.

SOLUTION:

$$\lim_{t \to 0} \frac{t}{\sin t} = \lim_{t \to 0} \frac{1}{(\sin t)/t} = \frac{1}{\lim\limits_{t \to 0} \dfrac{\sin t}{t}} = \frac{1}{1} = 1.$$

43. Find an equation of the tangent line to the graph of $y = \sin x$ when $x = \pi/3$.

SOLUTION: Evaluate the derivative of $y = \sin x$ at $x = \pi/3$. $D_x[\sin x] = \cos x$ and $\cos(\pi/3) = 1/2$. $\sin(\pi/3) = \sqrt{3}/2$ gives the point of tangency $(\pi/3, \sqrt{3}/2)$. Apply the point-slope form to obtain

$$y - \frac{\sqrt{3}}{2} = \frac{1}{2}\left(x - \frac{\pi}{3}\right) \qquad \text{or} \qquad y = \frac{1}{2}x - \frac{\pi}{6} + \frac{\sqrt{3}}{2},$$

which is the equation of the tangent line.

47. Show that the slope of the tangent line to the graph of $y = 2x + \sin x$ is never less than 1.

SOLUTION: The slope of the tangent line to the graph of $y = 2x + \sin x$ is
$D_x y = D_x[2x + \sin x] = 2 + \cos x$.
Since $-1 \le \cos x \le 1$, $1 \le 2 + \cos x \le 3$, and the slope of the tangent line is never less than 1.

———**2.5**

The Derivative of a Composite Function: the Chain Rule

3. Find the derivative of $f(x) = (x^2 - 3x + 4)^7$.

SOLUTION: If you set $u = x^2 - 3x + 4$, the interior function, then $y = (x^2 - 3x + 4)^7 = u^7$ and $f'(x) = dy/dx = dy/du \cdot du/dx$. Now $dy/du = 7u^6$ and $du/dx = 2x - 3$, so $dy/dx = 7u^6(2x - 3) = 7(2x - 3)(x^2 - 3x + 4)^6$.

11. Find the derivative of $f(x) = \dfrac{1}{(6x^2 - 2x)^2}$.

SOLUTION: First rewrite $y = f(x) = (6x^2 - 2x)^{-2}$. Set $u = 6x^2 - 2x$, so $y = (6x^2 - 2x)^{-2} = u^{-2}$.

Then $dy/du = -2u^{-3} = -2(6x^2 - 2x)^{-3}$ and $du/dx = 12x - 2 = 2(6x - 1)$. Thus,
$f'(x) = dy/dx = -4(6x - 1)(6x^2 - 2x)^{-3}$.

17. Find the derivative of $g(s) = \left(\dfrac{s-1}{s+1}\right)^3$.

SOLUTION: Set $u = \dfrac{s-1}{s+1}$ and $y = \left(\dfrac{s-1}{s+1}\right)^3 = u^3$. Use the quotient rule to find

$$\frac{du}{ds} = \frac{(s+1)(1) - (s-1)(1)}{(s+1)^2} = \frac{2}{(s+1)^2}.$$

Then $dy/du = 3u^2 = 3\left(\dfrac{s-1}{s+1}\right)^2$ and

$$g'(s) = \frac{dy}{du} \cdot \frac{du}{ds} = 3\left(\frac{s-1}{s+1}\right)^2 \cdot \frac{2}{(s+1)^2} = \frac{6(s-1)^2}{(s+1)^4}.$$

25. Find the derivative of $f(x) = \tan\left(\dfrac{x+1}{x-1}\right)$.

SOLUTION: Set $u = \dfrac{x+1}{x-1}$ and $y = \tan\left(\dfrac{x+1}{x-1}\right) = \tan u$. Then

$$\frac{du}{dx} = \frac{(x-1)(1) - (x+1)(1)}{(x-1)^2} = \frac{-2}{(x-1)^2} \quad \text{and}$$

$$\frac{dy}{du} = \sec^2 u = \sec^2\left(\frac{x+1}{x-1}\right). \quad \text{Thus,}$$

$$f'(x) = \frac{-2}{(x-1)^2} \sec^2\left(\frac{x+1}{x-1}\right).$$

31. Find the derivative of $h(x) = \tan^3 2x \sin(1 - x^2)$.

SOLUTION: Using the product rule, $h'(x) = \tan^3 2x\, D_x\left[\sin(1 - x^2)\right] + \sin(1 - x^2)D_x\left[\tan^3 2x\right]$.
i) To find $D_x\left[\sin(1 - x^2)\right]$, set $u = 1 - x^2$ and $y = \sin(1 - x^2) = \sin u$. Then $du/dx = -2x$ and $dy/du = \cos u = \cos(1 - x^2)$, so $D_x\left[\sin(1 - x^2)\right] = -2x \cos(1 - x^2)$.

ii) To find $D_x \left[\tan^3 2x\right]$, set $u = \tan 2x$ and $y = \tan^3 2x = u^3$. Then set $w = 2x$ and therefore $u = \tan 2x = \tan w$.

Now $D_x \left[\tan^3 2x\right] = \dfrac{dy}{dx} = \dfrac{dy}{du} \cdot \dfrac{du}{dw} \cdot \dfrac{dw}{dx}$.

$$\frac{dy}{du} = 3u^2 = 3\tan^2 2x, \qquad \frac{du}{dw} = \sec^2 w = \sec^2 2x, \qquad \text{and} \qquad \frac{dw}{dx} = 2.$$

Thus $D_x \left[\tan^3 2x\right] = 6\tan^2 2x \sec^2 2x$.

iii)

$$h'(x) = \tan^3 2x \left(-2x \cos(1 - x^2)\right) + \sin(1 - x^2) \left(6\tan^2 2x \sec^2 2x\right)$$

$$= 2\tan^2 2x \left(-x \tan 2x \cos(1 - x^2) + 3\sec^2 2x \sin(1 - x^2)\right).$$

35. Find the derivative of $r(t) = \left(\dfrac{\cos(2t - 1)}{\cot(t^2 + 1)}\right)^3$.

SOLUTION: Let $u = \dfrac{\cos(2t - 1)}{\cot(t^2 + 1)}$ and $y = u^3$. To find du/dt, use the quotient rule.

$$\frac{du}{dt} = \frac{\cot(t^2 + 1)D_t\left[\cos(2t - 1)\right] - \cos(2t - 1)D_t\left[\cot(t^2 + 1)\right]}{\cot^2(t^2 + 1)} \qquad \text{and}$$

$$\frac{dy}{du} = 3u^2 = 3\left(\frac{\cos(2t - 1)}{\cot(t^2 + 1)}\right)^2.$$

i) To find $D_t\left[\cos(2t - 1)\right]$, set $u = 2t - 1$ and $y = \cos(2t - 1) = \cos u$. Then $du/dt = 2$, $dy/du = -\sin u = -\sin(2t - 1)$, and $D_t\left[\cos(2t - 1)\right] = -2\sin(2t - 1)$.

ii) To find $D_t\left[\cot(t^2 + 1)\right]$, set $u = t^2 + 1$ and $y = \cot(t^2 + 1) = \cot u$. Then $du/dt = 2t$, $dy/du = -\csc^2 u = -\csc^2(t^2 + 1)$ and $D_t\left[\cot(t^2 + 1)\right] = -2t\csc^2(t^2 + 1)$.

iii) Back to the original problem,

$$r'(t) = 3\left(\frac{\cos(2t - 1)}{\cot(t^2 + 1)}\right)^2 \left(\frac{\cot(t^2 + 1)(-2\sin(2t - 1)) - \cos(2t - 1)(-2t(\csc^2(t^2 + 1)))}{\cot^2(t^2 + 1)}\right)$$

$$= \frac{-6\cos^2(2t - 1)\left(\cot(t^2 + 1)\sin(2t - 1) - t\csc^2(t^2 + 1)\cos(2t - 1)\right)}{\cot^4(t^2 + 1)}.$$

39. Find the derivative of each of the following functions.

    a) $f_1(x) = x^2 - x$

    b) $f_2(x) = \sin(x^2 - x)$

c) $f_3(x) = \left(x^3 + \sin(x^2 - x)\right)^2$

SOLUTION: a) $f_1(x) = x^2 - x \implies f_1'(x) = 2x - 1$.

b)

$$f_2(x) = \sin(x^2 - x) \implies f_2'(x) = \cos(x^2 - x) \cdot D_x \left[x^2 - x\right] = \left(\cos(x^2 - x)\right)(2x - 1)$$
$$= (2x - 1)\cos(x^2 - x).$$

c) $f_3(x) = \left(x^3 + \sin(x^2 - x)\right)^2 \implies$

$$f_3'(x) = 2\left(x^3 + \sin(x^2 - x)\right) \cdot D_x \left(x^3 + \sin(x^2 - x)\right)$$
$$= 2\left(x^3 + \sin(x^2 - x)\right)\left(D_x \left[x^3\right] + D_x \left[\sin(x^2 - x)\right]\right)$$
$$= 2\left(x^3 + \sin(x^2 - x)\right)\left(3x^2 + (2x - 1)\cos(x^2 - x)\right).$$

45. Find an equation of a line tangent to the graph of $f(x) = \left(\dfrac{x+1}{x-1}\right)^2$ and perpendicular to the line with equation $x = 1$.

SOLUTION: To find the slope of the tangent line, find $f'(x)$. $f(x) = \left(\dfrac{x+1}{x-1}\right)^2 \implies$

$$f'(x) = 2\left(\frac{x+1}{x-1}\right) \cdot D_x \left(\frac{x+1}{x-1}\right) = 2\left(\frac{x+1}{x-1}\right)\left(\frac{(x-1)(1) - (x+1)(1)}{(x-1)^2}\right)$$
$$= 2\left(\frac{x+1}{x-1}\right)\left(\frac{-2}{(x-1)^2}\right) = \frac{-4(x+1)}{(x-1)^3}.$$

Since the desired tangent line is perpendicular to $x = 1$, a vertical line, the slope of the tangent line must be 0. To find the point of tangency, determine the point(s) on the graph where the slope is 0. Setting $f'(x) = (-4(x+1))/(x-1)^3 = 0 \implies x = -1$. $f(-1) = 0$ so $(-1, 0)$ is the point of tangency.

Thus $y - 0 = 0(x + 1) \implies y = 0$ is the desired tangent line.

57. Use the chain rule to find $f'(x)$ for $f(x) = \left|1 - x^2\right|$.

SOLUTION: Set $u = 1 - x^2$ and $y = \left|1 - x^2\right| = |u|$. Now $du/dx = -2x$ and

$$\frac{dy}{du} = \begin{cases} 1, & \text{if } u > 0 \\ -1, & \text{if } u < 0. \end{cases} \quad \text{Thus,}$$

$$\frac{dy}{dx} = \begin{cases} -2x, & \text{for } 1 - x^2 > 0 \\ -(-2x), & \text{for } 1 - x^2 < 0 \end{cases} = \begin{cases} -2x, & \text{for } x^2 < 1 \\ 2x, & \text{for } x^2 > 1 \end{cases} = \begin{cases} -2x, & \text{for } -1 < x < 1 \\ 2x, & \text{for } x < -1 \text{ or } x > 1. \end{cases}$$

Implicit Differentiation

5. Use implicit differentiation to find $D_x y$ if $\sin y = x$.

SOLUTION: $\sin y = x \implies D_x(\sin y) = D_x(x) \implies (\cos y)D_x y = 1 \implies D_x y = \dfrac{1}{\cos y} =$ $\sec y$.

9. Use implicit differentiation to find $D_x y$ if $2x^2 - x^2 y^2 + y^{-3} = 4$.

SOLUTION:

$$2x^2 - x^2 y^2 + y^{-3} = 4$$
$$D_x\left[2x^2 - x^2 y^2 + y^{-3}\right] = D_x(4)$$
$$D_x\left[2x^2\right] - D_x\left[x^2 y^2\right] + D_x\left[y^{-3}\right] = 0$$
$$4x - \left((x^2)D_x\left[y^2\right] + (y^2)D_x\left[x^2\right]\right) - 3y^{-4}D_x y = 0$$
$$4x - x^2(2yD_x y) - y^2(2x) - 3y^{-4}D_x y = 0$$
$$4x - 2xy^2 - (2x^2 y + 3y^{-4})D_x y = 0$$
$$4x - 2xy^2 = (2x^2 y + 3y^{-4})D_x y$$
$$D_x y = \frac{2x(2 - y^2)}{2x^2 y + 3y^{-4}} = \frac{2xy^4(2 - y^2)}{2x^2 y^5 + 3}.$$

15. Use implicit differentiation to find $D_x y$ if $y = \tan(xy)$.

SOLUTION:

$$y = \tan(xy) \implies D_x y = D_x\left[\tan(xy)\right]$$
$$D_x y = \sec^2(xy)D_x\left[xy\right]$$
$$D_x y = \sec^2(xy)(xD_x y + yD_x x)$$
$$D_x y = \sec^2(xy)(xD_x y + y)$$
$$D_x y - x\sec^2(xy)D_x y = y\sec^2(xy)$$
$$\left(1 - x\sec^2(xy)\right)D_x y = y\sec^2(xy)$$
$$D_x y = \frac{y\sec^2(xy)}{1 - x\sec^2(xy)}.$$

21. Find $D_x y$ if $y = (x+1)^{2/3} + x$.

SOLUTION:

$$D_x y = D_x \left[(x+1)^{2/3} + x \right] = D_x \left[(x+1)^{2/3} \right] + D_x x$$
$$= \frac{2}{3}(x+1)^{-1/3} D_x [x+1] + 1 = \frac{2}{3}(x+1)^{-1/3} + 1.$$

27. Find $D_x y$ if $y = \sqrt[3]{(3x^2 + 4x)^2}$.

SOLUTION: First rewrite

$$y = \sqrt[3]{(3x^2 + 4x)^2} = \left((3x^2 + 4x)^2 \right)^{1/3} = (3x^2 + 4x)^{2/3}.$$

Then

$$D_x y = D_x \left[(3x^2 + 4x)^{2/3} \right] = \frac{2}{3}(3x^2 + 4x)^{-1/3} \cdot D_x \left[3x^2 + 4x \right]$$

$$= \frac{2}{3}(6x + 4)(3x^2 + 4x)^{-1/3} = \frac{4}{3}(3x + 2)(3x^2 + 4x)^{-1/3}.$$

35. Find $D_x y$ if $y = (x^2 + 2)^{1/3}(x^2 - 2)^{1/4}$.

SOLUTION:

$$D_x y = D_x \left[(x^2 + 2)^{1/3}(x^2 - 2)^{1/4} \right]$$
$$= (x^2 + 2)^{1/3} D_x \left[(x^2 - 2)^{1/4} \right] + (x^2 - 2)^{1/4} D_x \left[(x^2 + 2)^{1/3} \right]$$
$$= (x^2 + 2)^{1/3} \left(\frac{1}{4}(x^2 - 2)^{-3/4} D_x \left[x^2 - 2 \right] \right) + (x^2 - 2)^{1/4} \left(\frac{1}{3}(x^2 + 2)^{-2/3} D_x \left[x^2 + 2 \right] \right)$$
$$= \frac{1}{4}(x^2 + 2)^{1/3}(x^2 - 2)^{-3/4}(2x) + \frac{1}{3}(x^2 - 2)^{1/4}(x^2 + 2)^{-2/3}(2x)$$
$$= \frac{1}{6}x(x^2 + 2)^{-2/3}(x^2 - 2)^{-3/4} \left(3(x^2 + 2) + 4(x^2 - 2) \right)$$
$$= \frac{1}{6}x(x^2 + 2)^{-2/3}(x^2 - 2)^{-3/4}(7x^2 - 2).$$

45. Find $D_x y$ if $y^2 = \dfrac{x}{xy + 1}$.

SOLUTION:

$$D_x \left[y^2 \right] = D_x \left[\frac{x}{xy + 1} \right]$$

$$2yD_xy = \frac{(xy+1)D_xx - xD_x[xy+1]}{(xy+1)^2}$$

$$2y(xy+1)^2D_xy = xy+1 - x\left(D_x[xy] + D_x[1]\right)$$
$$2y(xy+1)^2D_xy = xy+1 - x\left(xD_xy + yD_xx + 0\right)$$
$$2y(xy+1)^2D_xy = xy+1 - x^2D_xy - xy$$
$$\left(2y(xy+1)^2 + x^2\right)D_xy = 1$$

$$D_xy = \frac{1}{2y(xy+1)^2 + x^2}.$$

55. Show that if $\sin y = x$ and $-\pi/2 < y < \pi/2$, then $\dfrac{dy}{dx} = \dfrac{1}{\sqrt{1-x^2}}$.

SOLUTION: $\sin y = x \implies D_x[\sin y] = D_x[x] \implies \cos y D_xy = 1 \implies dy/dx = D_xy = \frac{1}{\cos y}$.

Now $\sin^2 y + \cos^2 y = 1 \implies \cos^2 y = 1 - \sin^2 y \implies \cos y = \pm\sqrt{1 - \sin^2 y} = \pm\sqrt{1 - x^2}$. Since $-\pi/2 < y < \pi/2$ (quadrants IV and I), $\cos y > 0$ and therefore $\cos y = \sqrt{1 - x^2}$ and $\dfrac{dy}{dx} = \dfrac{1}{\sqrt{1-x^2}}$.

63. The graph of $x^3 + y^3 = 9xy$ is called a *folium of Descartes*. Find an equation of the tangent line to the folium of Descartes at $(4, 2)$.

SOLUTION:

$$x^3 + y^3 = 9xy$$
$$D_x\left[x^3 + y^3\right] = D_x[9xy]$$
$$D_x\left[x^3\right] + D_x\left[y^3\right] = 9xD_xy + 9yD_xx$$
$$3x^2 + 3y^2D_xy = 9xD_xy + 9y$$
$$(y^2 - 3x)D_xy = 3y - x^2$$
$$D_xy = \frac{3y - x^2}{y^2 - 3x}.$$

To determine the slope of the tangent line at $(4, 2)$,

$$D_xy\Big|_{(4,2)} = \frac{6 - 16}{4 - 12} = \frac{5}{4}.$$

So $y - 2 = \frac{5}{4}(x - 4) \implies y = \frac{5}{4}x - 3$ is the equation of the tangent line.

Maxima and Minima
of Functions

13. Find the critical points of $f(x) = \dfrac{x}{x-1}$.

SOLUTION: The domain of f is $\{x \in \mathbb{R} \mid x \neq 1\}$.

$$f'(x) = \frac{(x-1)(1) - x(1)}{(x-1)^2} = \frac{-1}{(x-1)^2}.$$

i) $f'(x) \neq 0$ since $\dfrac{-1}{(x-1)^2} < 0$. No critical points are produced.

ii) The domain of f' is the same as the domain of f so no critical points are produced.
Thus $f(x) = \dfrac{x}{x-1}$ has no critical points.

19. Find the critical points of $h(s) = \dfrac{s^2 - 3s + 2}{s^2 + s - 2}$.

SOLUTION: $h(s) = \dfrac{s^2 - 3s + 2}{s^2 + s - 2} = \dfrac{(s-2)(s-1)}{(s+2)(s-1)} = \dfrac{s-2}{s+2}$.
The domain of h is $\{x \in \mathbb{R} \mid x \neq -2, 1\}$. Now

$$h'(s) = \frac{(s+2)(1) - (s-2)(1)}{(s+2)^2} = \frac{4}{(s+2)^2}.$$

i) $h'(s) \neq 0$ since $\dfrac{4}{(s+2)^2} > 0$. No critical points are produced.

ii) The domain of h' is the same as that of h, so no critical points are produced.
Thus $h(s) = \dfrac{s^2 - 3s + 2}{s^2 + s - 2}$ has no critical points.

25. Find the critical points of $g(t) = \sqrt{t^2 - 3t + 2}$.

SOLUTION: $g(t) = \sqrt{t^2 - 3t + 2} = \sqrt{(t-2)(t-1)}$. The domain of g is $(-\infty, 1] \cup [2, \infty)$.
$g(t) = (t^2 - 3t + 2)^{1/2} \implies g'(t) = \frac{1}{2}(t^2 - 3t + 2)^{-1/2}(2t - 3)$.

i) $g'(t) = 0 \implies \dfrac{2t - 3}{2\sqrt{t^2 - 3t + 2}} = 0 \implies 2t - 3 = 0 \implies t = 3/2$. However, $3/2$ is not in the
domain of f, so it is not a critical point.

ii) The domain of $g'(t)$ is $(-\infty, 1) \cup (2, \infty)$. Thus $t = 1$ and $t = 2$ are critical points.
The critical points of $g(t) = \sqrt{t^2 - 3t + 2}$ are $t = 1$ and $t = 2$.

31. Find the critical points of $h(x) = \sin^2 x + \cos x$.

SOLUTION: The domain of h is $\mathbb{R}$.

$h'(x) = 2\sin x \cos x - \sin x$.

i) $h'(x) = 0 \implies 2\sin x \cos x - \sin x = 0 \implies \sin x(2\cos x - 1) = 0 \implies \sin x = 0$ or $\cos x = 1/2 \implies x = n\pi$ or $x = \pm\frac{\pi}{3} + 2n\pi$ for n an integer, so $x = n\pi$ or $x = \pm\frac{\pi}{3} + 2n\pi$ with n an integer are critical points.

ii) The domain of h' is $\mathbb{R}$ so no additional critical points are generated.

Thus $x = n\pi$ or $x = \pm\frac{\pi}{3} + 2n\pi$ for n an integer; that is,

$x = \ldots, -2\pi, -\frac{5\pi}{3}, -\pi, -\frac{\pi}{3}, 0, \frac{\pi}{3}, \pi, \frac{5\pi}{3}, 2\pi, \ldots$ are the critical points of $h(x) = \sin^2 x + \cos x$.

37. Find the critical points of $v(t) = t^4 - 6t^2 + 8t$ and sketch the graph. Where do relative and absolute extrema occur?

SOLUTION: First, $v'(t) = 4t^3 - 12t + 8$.

Then, $v'(t) = 0 \implies 4(t^3 - 3t + 2) = 0 \implies t^3 - 3t + 2 = 0 \implies (t-1)^2(t+2) = 0 \implies t = 1$ or $t = -2$.

Since the domain of f' is $\mathbb{R}$, $t = 1$ and $t = -2$ are the only critical points.

$v(1) = 1 - 6 + 8 = 3$ and $v(-2) = 16 - 24 - 16 = -24$. Now $\lim_{x\to\infty} v(t) = \infty$ and $\lim_{x\to-\infty} v(t) = \infty$ and $v(0) = 0$.

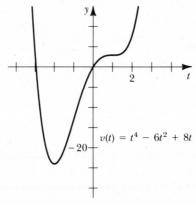

$v(t) = t^4 - 6t^2 + 8t$

An absolute minimum occurs at $(-2, -24)$. Note that even though $t = 1$ is a critical point, an extremum does not occur at $t = 1$.

43. Find the critical points of $f(x) = x^2 + \dfrac{1}{x^2}$ and sketch the graph. Where do relative and absolute extrema occur?

SOLUTION: $f(x) = x^2 + x^{-2} \implies f'(x) = 2x - 2x^{-3}$.

$f'(x) = 0 \implies 2\left(x - \dfrac{1}{x^3}\right) = 0 \implies \dfrac{x^4 - 1}{x^3} = 0 \implies x^4 - 1 = 0 \implies x = -1$ or $x = 1$.

The domain of f' is the same as that of f, so $x = \pm 1$ are the only critical points.

$f(-1) = 2$ and $f(1) = 2$.

Now $\lim\limits_{x\to\infty} f(x) = \infty$ and $\lim\limits_{x\to-\infty} f(x) = \infty$ with $y = x^2$ as a slant asymptote.

Also, $\lim\limits_{x\to 0} f(x) = \infty$, which gives $x = 0$ as a vertical asymptote.

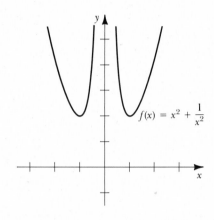

There is no absolute maximum, but $(-1, 2)$ and $(1, 2)$ are absolute minima.

47. Find the critical points of $f(s) = s - \cos s$ and sketch the graph. Where do relative and absolute extrema occur?

SOLUTION: $f'(s) = 1 + \sin s$. $f'(s) = 0 \implies 1 + \sin s = 0 \implies \sin s = -1 \implies s = \dfrac{3\pi}{2} + 2n\pi$ for n an integer.

$$f\left(\frac{3\pi}{2} + 2n\pi\right) = \frac{3\pi}{2} + 2n\pi - \cos\left(\frac{3\pi}{2} + 2n\pi\right) = \frac{3\pi}{2} + 2n\pi,\text{ for } n \text{ an integer.}$$

Now $\lim\limits_{s\to\infty} f(s) = \infty$ and $\lim\limits_{s\to-\infty} f(s) = -\infty$ so there are no absolute extrema.

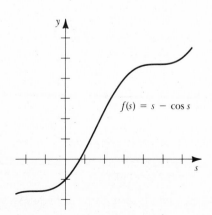

53. Find the critical points of $f(x) = |x^3 - x^2|$ and sketch the graph. Where do relative and absolute extrema occur?

SOLUTION: $f(x) = |x^3 - x^2| = |x^2(x - 1)| = x^2 |x - 1|$. Now

$$f'(x) = x^2 D_x(|x - 1|) + |x - 1| D_x[x^2] = \begin{cases} x^2 + 2x|x - 1|, & \text{for } x > 1 \\ -x^2 + 2x|x - 1|, & \text{for } x < 1 \end{cases}$$

$$= \begin{cases} x^2 + 2x(x - 1), & \text{for } x > 1 \\ -x^2 + 2x(1 - x), & \text{for } x < 1 \end{cases} = \begin{cases} 3x^2 - 2x, & \text{for } x > 1 \\ -3x^2 + 2x, & \text{for } x < 1 \end{cases}.$$

Assume $x > 1$. Then $f'(x) = 0 \implies 3x^2 - 2x = 0 \implies x(3x - 2) = 0 \implies x = 0$ or $x = 2/3$, which is impossible since $x > 1$.

Assume $x < 1$. Then $f'(x) = 0 \implies -3x^2 + 2x = 0 \implies x(-3x + 2) = 0 \implies x = 0$ or $x = 2/3$. Thus $x = 0$ and $x = 2/3$ are critical points.

Also $x = 1$ is a critical point since $f'(1)$ does not exist.

$f(0) = 0$, $f(1) = 0$, $f(2/3) = 4/27$.

Since $f(x) \geq 0$, $(0,0)$ and $(1,0)$ are absolute minima.

There are no absolute maxima since $\lim\limits_{x \to \infty} f(x) = \lim\limits_{x \to -\infty} f(x) = \infty$. There is a relative maximum at $\left(\frac{2}{3}, \frac{4}{27}\right)$.

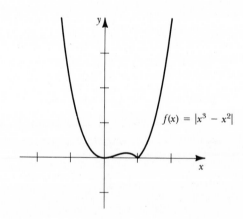

$f(x) = |x^3 - x^2|$

59. The domain of $f(x) = \dfrac{2}{x - 3}$ is restricted to $[4,5]$. Sketch the graph and determine the absolute extrema if they exist.

SOLUTION: $f(x) = 2(x - 3)^{-1} \implies f'(x) = -2(x - 3)^{-2}(1) = \dfrac{-2}{(x - 3)^2}$. $f'(x) \neq 0$ since $\dfrac{-2}{(x - 3)^2} < 0$. There are no critical points, so any extrema will occur at $x = 4$ or $x = 5$. $f(4) = 2$ and $f(5) = 1$ so $(4,2)$ is the absolute maximum and $(5,1)$ is the absolute minimum.

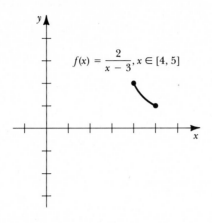

69. The domain of $f(x) = \begin{cases} 2x + 7, & \text{for } -2 \le x < -1 \\ 4 - x, & \text{for } -1 \le x \le 5 \end{cases}$ is restricted to the given domain. Sketch the graph and determine the absolute extrema if they exist.

SOLUTION:

$$f'(x) = \begin{cases} 2, & \text{for } -2 < x < -1 \\ -1, & \text{for } -1 < x < 5 \end{cases}.$$

The only critical point is $x = -1$ which has the function value $f(-1) = 5$. At the endpoints of the domain, $f(-2) = 3$ and $f(5) = -1$.

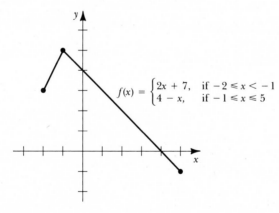

$(5, -1)$ is an absolute minimum. $(-1, 5)$ is an absolute maximum. $(-2, 3)$ is a relative minimum.

77. The power P of a steam turbine depends upon the peripheral speed of the wheel surrounding the turbine blades. If S_1 is the speed of the steam entering the turbine and S_2 is the peripheral speed of the wheel, then $P = kS_2(S_1 - S_2)$ for some constant k. Suppose that the turbine blades can be tilted to vary S_2 while S_1 remains constant. What value of S_2 produces the maximum power?

SOLUTION: In $P = kS_2(S_1 - S_2)$, k and S_1 are constant, while S_2 is variable. To find the maximum power, find $\dfrac{dP}{dS_2}$ and determine the critical points. Using the product rule,

$\dfrac{dP}{dS_2} = kS_2(0-1) + k(S_1 - S_2)$. $\dfrac{dP}{dS_2} = 0 \implies k(-S_2 + (S_1 - S_2)) = 0 \implies -2S_2 + S_1 = 0 \implies S_2 = \dfrac{S_1}{2}$. Thus $\dfrac{S_1}{2}$ is a critical point. The domain of the function is $[0, S_1]$, so $P(0) = 0$ and $P(S_1) = 0$ are the absolute minima.

$P(S_1/2) = k\dfrac{S_1}{2}\left(S_1 - \dfrac{S_1}{2}\right) = k\dfrac{S_1^2}{4}$ is the maximum power that could be produced, which occurs at $S_2 = \frac{1}{2}S_1$.

The Mean Value Theorem

2.8

5. Determine whether the hypotheses of Rolle's theorem are satisfied for $f(x) = \dfrac{x^2 - 1}{x}$ on $[-1, 1]$. If so, find a number $c \in (-1, 1)$ with $f'(c) = 0$.

SOLUTION: The domain of f is $\{x \in \mathbb{R} \mid x \neq 0\}$ so f is clearly not continuous at $x = 0$, and the hypotheses of Rolle's theorem are not satisfied.

9. Determine whether the hypotheses of Rolle's theorem are satisfied for $f(x) = \sin x - \cos x$ on $\left[\frac{\pi}{4}, \frac{5\pi}{4}\right]$. If so, find a number $c \in (\pi/4, 5\pi/4)$ with $f'(c) = 0$.

SOLUTION: The domain of $f(x) = \sin x - \cos x$ is $\mathbb{R}$ and the domain of $f'(x) = \cos x + \sin x$ is $\mathbb{R}$. Thus f is differentiable on $\left[\frac{\pi}{4}, \frac{5\pi}{4}\right]$ and, since differentiability at a implies continuity at a, f is continuous on $\left[\frac{\pi}{4}, \frac{5\pi}{4}\right]$. This satisfies the first two hypotheses of Rolle's theorem. Now $f(\pi/4) = \sin \pi/4 - \cos \pi/4 = \frac{\sqrt{2}}{2} - \frac{\sqrt{2}}{2} = 0$ and $f(5\pi/4) = \sin 5\pi/4 - \cos 5\pi/4 = -\frac{\sqrt{2}}{2} - \left(-\frac{\sqrt{2}}{2}\right) = 0$, which satisfies the final hypothesis of Rolle's theorem.
To find c such that $f'(c) = 0$, set $f'(x) = \cos x + \sin x = 0$.
Then $\sin x = -\cos x \implies \tan x = -1 \implies x = -\frac{\pi}{4} + n\pi$ for n an integer. If $n = 1$, then $x = -\frac{\pi}{4} + \pi = \frac{3\pi}{4} \in \left(\frac{\pi}{4}, \frac{5\pi}{4}\right)$, so the desired value of c is $\frac{3\pi}{4}$.

17. Determine whether the hypotheses of the mean value theorem are satisfied for $f(x) = \sqrt{1 - x^2}$ on $[-1, 1]$. If so, find a number $c \in (-1, 1)$ that is ensured by the conclusion of the mean value theorem.

SOLUTION: The domain of f is $[-1, 1]$.

$$f(x) = (1 - x^2)^{1/2} \implies f'(x) = \frac{1}{2}(1 - x^2)^{-1/2}(-2x) \implies f'(x) = \frac{-x}{\sqrt{1 - x^2}}.$$

The domain of f' is $(-1, 1)$ so f' is differentiable on $(-1, 1)$ and therefore continuous on $(-1, 1)$. Also f is continuous from the right at -1 and continuous from the left at 1, so f is continuous on $[a, b]$. Thus the hypotheses of the mean value theorem are satisfied.

To find $c \in (-1,1)$ set $f'(x) = \dfrac{-x}{\sqrt{1-x^2}} = \dfrac{f(1) - f(-1)}{1 - (-1)}$.

Then $\dfrac{-x}{\sqrt{1-x^2}} = \dfrac{0}{2} \implies x = 0$, which is in $(-1,1)$, so $c = 0$ is the point whose existence is guaranteed by the mean value theorem.

31. Find a function f that satisfies $f(-2) = 4$, $f'(x) = 3x^2 - 5$ for all x.

SOLUTION: $f(x) = x^3 - 5x + C$ describes all antiderivatives of $f'(x) = 3x^2 - 5$.
Since $4 = f(-2) = (-2)^3 - 5(-2) + C \implies 4 = 2 + C \implies 2 = C$, $f(x) = x^3 - 5x + 2$ is the desired function.

33. Find a function f that satisfies $f(0) = -1$, $f'(x) = 3\sin 3x$ for all x.

SOLUTION: $f(x) = -\cos 3x + C$ describes all antiderivatives of $f(x) = 3\sin 3x$.
Verifying this, $D_x\left[-\cos 3x + C\right] = -D_x\left[\cos 3x\right] + D_x\left[C\right] = -(-\sin 3x)(3) + - = 3\sin 3x$.
Since $-1 = f(0) = -\cos 3(0) + C \implies -1 = -\cos 0 + C \implies -1 = -1 + C \implies 0 = C$, $f(x) = -\cos 3x$ is the desired function.

41. Find a function f that satisfies $f(0) = 0$, $f'(0) = 0$, and $f''(x) = \sin x - \cos x$ for all x.

SOLUTION: $f'(x) = -\cos x - \sin x + C$ describes all antiderivatives of $f''(x) = \sin x - \cos x$.
Since $0 = f'(0) = -\cos 0 - \sin 0 + C \implies 0 = -1 - 0 + C \implies 1 = C$, $f'(x) = -\cos x - \sin x + 1$ is the derivative of the desired function.

$f(x) = -\sin x + \cos x + x + C$ describes all antiderivatives of $f'(x)$.
Now $0 = f(0) = -\sin 0 + \cos 0 + 0 + C \implies 0 = 0 + 1 + C \implies -1 = C$, so $f(x) = -\sin x + \cos x + x - 1$ is the desired funtion.

45. Use Rolle's theorem to show that the graph of $f(x) = x^3 + 2x + k$ crosses the x-axis exactly once, regardless of the value of the constant k.

SOLUTION: First, show $f(x) = x^3 + 2x + k$ crosses the x-axis at least once. Consider three cases: i) $k = 0$,   ii) $k > 0$, and   iii) $k < 0$.
i) $k = 0 \implies f(x) = x^3 + 2x$. Now $f(-1) = (-1)^3 + 2(-1) = -3$ and $f(1) = 1^3 + 2(1) = 3$. Since $-3 < 0 < 3$, and $f(x)$ is continuous on $\mathbb{R}$, the intermediate value theorem guarantees the existence of c such that $f(c) = 0$. Thus the graph crosses the x-axis at least once.
ii) If $k > 0$, then $f(k) = k^3 + 2k + k = k^3 + 3k > 0$ and $f(-k) + (-k)^3 + 2(-k) + k = -k^3 - k = -(k^3 + k) < 0$. Again the intermediate value theorem ensures that the graph crosses the x-axis at least once.
iii) If $k < 0$, then $f(k) = k^3 + 3k < 0$ and $f(-k) = -(k^3 + k) > 0$ and the graph crosses the x-axis at least once.
Now show that the graph does not cross more than once. Let $x = a$ be the point where the graph crosses the axis. A general approach to proving uniqueness once existence has been proved is to proceed by contradiction. Assume there exists $x = b \neq a$ where the graph crosses the

x-axis. Then $f(a) = f(b)$. Now, $f(x)$ is differentiable on $\mathbb{R}$ $(f'(x) = 3x^2 + 2)$ and thus is continuous on $\mathbb{R}$. This satisfies the hypotheses of Rolle's theorem for the interval $[a, b]$ or $[b, a]$ depending on whether $a < b$ or $b < a$. Thus there exists c between a and b with $f'(c) = 0$. But $f'(x) = 3x^2 + 2 > 0$ for all x, so c cannot exist. Thus the assumption that b exists must be wrong. This means that the graph crosses the x-axis <u>only</u> at $x = a$, exactly once.

51. Use the mean value theorem to show that $|\sin a - \sin b| \leq |a - b|$ and deduce from this result that $|\sin a + \sin b| \leq |a + b|$.

SOLUTION: Since $f(x) = \sin x$ is differentiable and continuous on $\mathbb{R}$, f is continuous on $[a, b]$ or $[b, a]$ and differentiable on (a, b) or (b, a) depending on whether $a < b$ or $b < a$. Without loss of generality, assume $a < b$. The hypotheses of the mean value theorem are satisfied. Thus there exists $c \in (a, b)$ so that $f'(c) = \dfrac{f(b) - f(a)}{b - a}$. Since $f'(x) = \cos x$, there exists $c \in (a, b)$ such that $\cos c = \dfrac{\sin b - \sin a}{b - a}$. But $|\cos c| \leq 1 \implies \left| \dfrac{\sin b - \sin a}{b - a} \right| \leq 1 \implies \dfrac{|\sin b - \sin a|}{|b - a|} \leq 1 \implies$ $|\sin b - \sin a| \leq |b - a| \implies |\sin a - \sin b| \leq |a - b|$, since $|x - y| = |y - x|$.
Since a and b are any reals,
$|\sin a - \sin(-b)| \leq |a - (-b)| \implies |\sin a - (-\sin b)| = |\sin a + \sin b| \leq |a + b|$.

2.9

Increasing and Decreasing Functions: The First Derivative Test

5. The graph of a function is given.

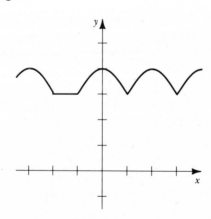

a) Use the graph to determine the intervals on which the function is increasing and those on which it is decreasing.

b) Where do relative and absolute extrema occur? What is the derivative at these points?

c) Find the absolute extrema when they exist.

SOLUTION: a) The function is increasing on $(-\infty, -3] \cup [-1, 0] \cup [1, 2] \cup [3, \infty)$ and is decreasing on $[-3, -2] \cup [0, 1] \cup [2, 3]$.

b) and c) Relative maxima occur at $(-3, 4)$, $(0, 4)$, and $(2, 4)$ while relative minima occur at $(x, 3)$ for $-2 \le x \le -1$, $(1, 3)$, and $(3, 3)$. There are no absolute extrema.

The derivative is 0 at $x = -3$, $x = 0$, $x = 2$ and on $(-2, -1)$. The derivative does not exist, however, at the remaining extrema, $x = -2$, $x = -1$, $x = 1$, and $x = 3$.

15. Determine the intervals on which $f(x) = x^4 - 2x^2$ is increasing and those on which f is decreasing. Find the relative extrema and sketch the graph of the function.

SOLUTION: Note that this function is even and thus will be symmetric with respect to the y-axis.

$$f'(x) = 4x^3 - 4x = 0 \implies 4x(x^2 - 1) = 0 \implies x = 0 \text{ or } x = \pm 1.$$

$f'(x)$	$-$	$+$	$-$	$+$
x	$-$	$-$	$+$	$+$
$x + 1$	$-$	$+$	$+$	$+$
$x - 1$	$-$	$-$	$-$	$+$
	-1	0	$+1$	

From the diagram above, f is increasing on $[-1, 0] \cup [1, \infty)$ and decreasing on $(-\infty, -1] \cup [0, 1]$. Thus yields a relative maximum at $(0, 0)$ and absolute minima at $(\pm 1, -1)$.

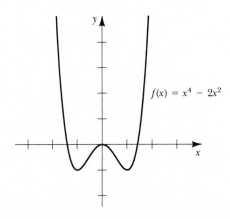

19. Determine the intervals on which $f(x) = x^3(1 - x)$ is increasing and those on which f is decreasing. Find the relative extrema and sketch the graph of the function.

SOLUTION:

$$f'(x) = 3x^2(1 - x) + x^3(-1) = 3x^2 - 3x^3 - x^3$$

$$= 3x^2 - 4x^3 = x^2(3 - 4x).$$

$f'(x) = 0 \implies x^2(3 - 4x) = 0 \implies x = 0$ or $x = 3/4$. So $x = 0$ and $x = 3/4$ are the critical points.

$f'(x)$	+	+	−
$3 - 4x$	+	+	−
x^2	+	+	+
	0	$\frac{3}{4}$	

From above, $f(x)$ is increasing on $(-\infty, 3/4]$ and decreasing on $[3/4, \infty)$. There is a relative maximum at $(3/4, 27/256)$. Note that while $x = 0$ is a critical point, it does not produce an extremum.

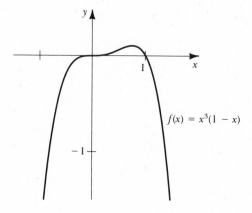

$$f(x) = x^3(1 - x)$$

25. Determine the intervals on which $f(x) = x^2 + \dfrac{1}{x^2}$ is increasing and those on which f is decreasing. Find the relative extrema and sketch the graph of the function.

SOLUTION: $f(x) = x^2 + x^{-2}$ so $f'(x) = 2x - 2x^{-3} = 0 \implies 2\left(x - \dfrac{1}{x^3}\right) = 0 \implies \dfrac{x^4 - 1}{x^3} = 0 \implies x^4 = 1 \implies x = \pm 1$.

Thus $x = \pm 1$ are the critical points. There is also a vertical asymptote $x = 0$ and the graph approaches $y = x^2$ as $x \to \infty$.

$f'(x)$	−	+	−	+
x^3	−	−	+	+
$x^4 - 1$	+	−	−	+
	−1	0	+1	

$f(x)$ is decreasing on $(-\infty, -1] \cup (0, 1]$ and increasing on $[-1, 0) \cup [1, \infty)$. There are absolute minima at $(\pm 1, 2)$ but no relative maxima.

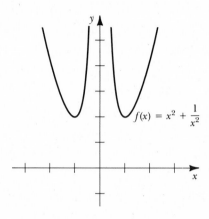

31. Determine the intervals on which $f(x) = x\sqrt{9 - x^2}$ is increasing and those on which f is decreasing. Find the relative extrema and sketch the graph of the function.

SOLUTION: $f(x) = x(9 - x^2)^{1/2} \implies$

$$f'(x) = (9 - x^2)^{1/2} + x\left(\frac{1}{2}(9 - x^2)^{-1/2}(-2x)\right) = (9 - x^2)^{1/2} - x^2(9 - x^2)^{-1/2}$$

$$= (9 - x^2)^{-1/2}(9 - x^2 - x^2) = \frac{9 - 2x^2}{\sqrt{9 - x^2}}.$$

$$f'(x) = 0 \implies 9 - 2x^2 = 0 \implies x^2 = \frac{9}{2} \implies x = \pm\frac{3}{\sqrt{2}}.$$

The domain of f is $[-3, 3]$, but $f'(3)$ and $f'(-3)$ are not defined; thus $x = \pm 3$ and $x = \pm 3/\sqrt{2}$ are critical points.

$f'(x)$	$-$		$+$		$-$
$\sqrt{9 - x^2}$	$+$		$+$		$+$
$9 - 2x^2$	$-$		$+$		$-$

$$-3 \qquad \frac{-3}{\sqrt{2}} \qquad \frac{3}{\sqrt{2}} \qquad +3$$

f is decreasing on $[-3, -3/\sqrt{2}] \cup [3/\sqrt{2}, 3]$ and increasing on $[-3/\sqrt{2}, 3/\sqrt{2}]$.

There are relative minima at $\left(\frac{-3}{\sqrt{2}}, \frac{-9}{2}\right)$ and $(3, 0)$ and relative maxima at $\left(\frac{3}{\sqrt{2}}, \frac{9}{2}\right)$ and $(-3, 0)$.

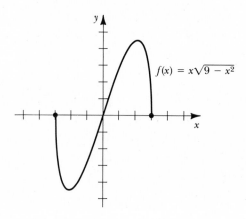

$f(x) = x\sqrt{9 - x^2}$

35. Determine the intervals on which $f(x) = (x-1)^2(x-2)^3(x-3)^4$ is increasing and those on which f is decreasing. Find the relative extrema and sketch the graph of the function.

SOLUTION:

$$f'(x) = 2(x-1)(1)(x-2)^3(x-3)^4$$
$$+ 3(x-2)^2(1)(x-1)^2(x-3)^4 + 4(x-3)^3(1)(x-1)^2(x-2)^3$$
$$= (x-1)(x-2)^2(x-3)^3 \left(2(x-2)(x-3) + 3(x-1)(x-3) + 4(x-1)(x-2)\right)$$
$$= (x-1)(x-2)^2(x-3)^3 \left(2x^2 - 10x + 12 + 3x^2 - 12x + 9 + 4x^2 - 12x + 8\right)$$
$$= (x-1)(x-2)^2(x-3)^3(9x^2 - 34x + 29).$$

$f'(x) = 0 \implies x = 1, x = 2, x = 3,$ or $9x^2 - 34x + 29 = 0$.
Applying the quadratic formula to $9x^2 - 34x + 29 = 0$,

$$x = \frac{34 \pm \sqrt{1156 - 1044}}{18} = \frac{34 \pm \sqrt{112}}{18} = \frac{34 \pm 4\sqrt{7}}{18} = \frac{1}{9}(17 \pm 2\sqrt{7}).$$

The critical points are $x = 1$, $x = 2$, $x = 3$, and $x = \frac{1}{9}(17 \pm 2\sqrt{7})$ ($x \approx 2.47$ and $x \approx 1.30$).

$f'(x)$	$+$	$-$	$+$	$+$	$-$	$+$
$(x-3)^3$	$-$	$-$	$-$	$-$	$-$	$+$
$x - \frac{1}{9}(17 - 2\sqrt{7})$	$-$	$-$	$-$	$-$	$+$	$+$
$(x-2)^2$	$+$	$+$	$+$	$+$	$+$	$+$
$x - \frac{1}{9}(17 - 2\sqrt{7})$	$-$	$-$	$+$	$+$	$+$	$+$
$x - 1$	$-$	$+$	$+$	$+$	$+$	$+$
	1	$\frac{1}{9}(17 - 2\sqrt{7})$	2	$\frac{1}{9}(17 + 2\sqrt{7})$	3	

Thus f is decreasing on

$$\left[1, \frac{1}{9}(17 - 2\sqrt{7})\right] \cup \left[\frac{1}{9}(17 + 2\sqrt{7}), 3\right]$$

and increasing on

$$(-\infty, 1] \cup \left[\frac{1}{9}(17 - 2\sqrt{7}), \frac{1}{9}(17 + 2\sqrt{7})\right] \cup [3, \infty).$$

There are relative maxima at $(1, 0)$ and at the point whose coordinates are approximately $(2.47, 0.018)$ and relative minima at the point whose coordinates are approximately $(1.30, -0.26)$ and $(3, 0)$.

Note that there is not an extremum at $x = 2$ even though it is a critical point.

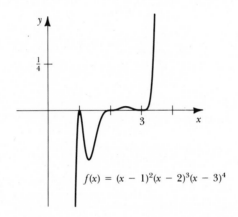

$$f(x) = (x - 1)^2(x - 2)^3(x - 3)^4$$

45. Determine the intervals on which $f(x) = \sin x - \dfrac{x}{2}$ is increasing and those on which f is decreasing. Find the relative extrema and sketch the graph of the function.

SOLUTION: $f'(x) = \cos x - \frac{1}{2}$.

$f'(x) = 0 \implies \cos x = \frac{1}{2} \implies x = \pm\dfrac{\pi}{3} + 2n\pi$ for n an integer.

$f'(x)$ $\quad -\quad|\quad +\quad|\quad -\quad|\quad +\quad|\quad -\quad|\quad +\quad|\quad -$

$\cdots \quad -\dfrac{7\pi}{3} \qquad -\dfrac{5\pi}{3} \qquad -\dfrac{\pi}{3} \qquad \dfrac{\pi}{3} \qquad \dfrac{5\pi}{3} \qquad \dfrac{7\pi}{3} \quad \cdots$

Thus $f(x)$ is increasing on $\cdots \cup \left[-\dfrac{7\pi}{3}, -\dfrac{5\pi}{3}\right] \cup \left[-\dfrac{\pi}{3}, \dfrac{\pi}{3}\right] \cup \left[\dfrac{5\pi}{3}, \dfrac{7\pi}{3}\right] \cup \cdots$ or the union of a set

of intervals characterized by $\left[2n\pi - \dfrac{\pi}{3}, 2n\pi + \dfrac{\pi}{3}\right]$ for n an integer.

$f(x)$ is decreasing on $\cdots \cup \left[-\dfrac{5\pi}{3}, -\dfrac{\pi}{3}\right] \cup \left[\dfrac{\pi}{3}, \dfrac{5\pi}{3}\right] \cup \cdots$ or the union of a set of intervals charac-

terized by $\left[2n\pi + \dfrac{\pi}{3}, 2(n + 1)\pi - \dfrac{\pi}{3}\right]$ for n an integer.

There are relative minima at

$$\left(2n\pi - \frac{\pi}{3}, -\frac{1}{2} - \left(2n\pi - \frac{\pi}{3}\right)\right)$$

and relative maxima

$$\left(2n\pi + \frac{\pi}{3}, \frac{1}{2} - \left(2n\pi - \frac{\pi}{3}\right)\right).$$

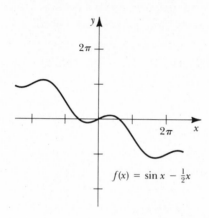

$$f(x) = \sin x - \tfrac{1}{2}x$$

51. A ball is thrown upward from the earth. Its distance above the ground is $s(t) = 88t - 16t^2 + 3$ (in feet). This equation is valid from time (in seconds) $t = 0$ until the ball returns to the ground.

a) Find the values of t for which the distance is increasing.

b) What is the maximum distance of the ball above the ground; that is, how high does the ball go?

SOLUTION: a) $s(t) = 88t - 16t^2 + 3 \implies s'(t) = 88 - 32t.$ $s'(t) = 0 \implies 88 - 32t = 0 \implies t = \frac{88}{32} = \frac{11}{4}.$

Since $t \geq 0$, the distance is increasing for $t \in [0, 11/4]$.

b) Since there is a relative maximum at $t = 11/4$, the maximum distance of the ball above the ground is attained at $t = 11/4$.

$s(11/4) = 88(11/4) - 16(11/4)^2 + 3 = 242 - 121 + 3 = 124 \, \text{ft}.$

59. Find values of a, b, and c that ensure that $f(x) = ax^3 + bx^2 + cx$ is increasing on $(-\infty, -1]$, decreasing on $[-1, 1]$ and increasing on $[1, \infty)$ or show that no such constants exist.

SOLUTION: For f to be increasing on $(-\infty, -1]$, $f'(x) > 0$ for $x < -1$. Similarly, $f'(x) > 0$ for $x > 1$. Since f is to be decreasing on $[-1, 1]$, $f'(x) < 0$ for $-1 < x < 1$. Also $f'(-1) = f'(1) = 0$.

Since $f'(x) = 3ax^2 + 2bx + c$, then $f'(1) = 3a + b + c = 0$ and $f'(-1) = 3a - 2b + c = 0$. The difference of these imply that $b = 0$ and thus that $c = -3a$. Thus $f'(x) = 3ax^2 - 3a = 3a(x^2 - 1)$.

For $x > 1$ or $x < -1$, $f'(x) = 3a(x^2 - 1)$ is positive if and only if $a > 0$. For $-1 \le x \le 1$, $f'(x) = 3a(x^2 - 1)$ is negative if and only if $a > 0$.

The choices of $a > 0$, $b = 0$, and $c = -3a$ give $f(x) = ax^3 - 3ax$.

_____**2.10**

Higher Derivatives: Concavity and the Second Derivative Test

7. Find $D_x y$ and $D_x^2 y$ for $y = \sin 2x$.

SOLUTION: Applying the chain rule, $D_x y = D_x[\sin 2x] = \cos 2x\, D_x[2x] = 2\cos 2x$.

Again applying the chain rule,

$$D_x^2 y = D_x[D_x y] = D_x[2\cos 2x] = 2D_x[\cos 2x] = 2(-\sin 2x)D_x[2x] = -4\sin 2x.$$

11. Find $f'(x)$ and $f''(x)$ if $f(x) = \sqrt{x} + \sqrt{x^3}$.

SOLUTION: $f(x) = \sqrt{x} + \sqrt{x^3} = x^{1/2} + x^{3/2}$. Thus, $f'(x) = \frac{1}{2}x^{-1/2} + \frac{3}{2}x^{1/2}$ and $f''(x) = -\frac{1}{4}x^{-3/2} + \frac{3}{4}x^{-1/2}$.

23. Use implicit differentiation to find $D_x^2 y$ if $x = \sin y$.

SOLUTION: $x = \sin y \implies D_x[x] = D_x[\sin y] \implies 1 = \cos y\, D_x y \implies D_x y = \dfrac{1}{\cos y} = \sec y$.

Thus $D_x[D_x y] = D_x[\sec y] \implies D_x^2 y = \sec y \tan y\, D_x y \implies = \sec y \tan y \sec y = \sec^2 y \tan y$.

25. Use implicit differentiation to find $D_x^2 y$ if $x^2 + xy = y$.

SOLUTION: $D_x[x^2 + xy] = D_x y \implies D_x[x^2] + D_x[xy] = D_x y \implies 2x + x\,D_x y + y \implies$
$2x + y = D_x y - x\,D_x y \implies 2x + y = (1 - x)D_x y \implies D_x y = \dfrac{2x + y}{1 - x}$.

Now $D_x[D_x y] = D_x\left[\dfrac{2x + y}{1 - x}\right] \implies$

$$D_x^2 y = \frac{(1 - x)D_x[2x + y] - (2x + y)D_x[1 - x]}{(1 - x)^2} = \frac{(1 - x)(2 + D_x y) - (2x + y)(-1)}{(1 - x)^2}$$

$$= \frac{(1 - x)\left(2 + \dfrac{2x + y}{1 - x}\right) + (2x + y)}{(1 - x)^2} = \frac{2(1 - x) + 2x + y + 2x + y}{(1 - x)^2}$$

$$= \frac{2(y + x + 1)}{(1 - x)^2}.$$

31. Use the second derivative test to determine relative extrema and sketch the graph for $f(x) = x^3 + 6x^2 + 2$.

SOLUTION: First, find the first derivative and determine the critical points. $f'(x) = 3x^2 + 12x$.
Now $f'(x) = 0 \implies 3x(x + 4) = 0 \implies x = 0$ or $x = -4$.
Next find $f''(x)$ and then evaluate $f''(0)$ and $f''(-4)$. $f''(x) = 6x + 12$.
Now, $f''(0) = 12 > 0$ which indicates that f is concave up at $x = 0$, and f has a relative minimum at $x = 0$. Also, $f''(-4) = -12 < 0$, which indicates that f is concave down at $x = -4$ and f has a relative maximum at $x = -4$.

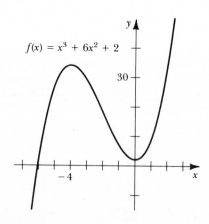

$f(x) = x^3 + 6x^2 + 2$

37. Use the second derivative test to determine relative extrema and sketch the graph for $f(x) = x^{3/2} - 3x^{1/2}$.

SOLUTION: First note that the domain of f is $[0, \infty)$.
Next $f'(x) = \frac{3}{2}x^{1/2} - \frac{3}{2}x^{-1/2}$ and $f'(x) = 0 \implies \frac{3}{2}x^{-1/2}(x - 1) = 0 \implies x = 1$.

Then $f''(x) = \frac{3}{4}x^{-1/2} + \frac{3}{4}x^{-3/2}$ and $f''(1) = \frac{3}{4} + \frac{3}{4} > 0$, which indicates that f is concave up at $x = 1$ and f has an absolute minimum at $x = 1$.

f also has a relative maximum at $x = 0$ by the first derivative test at this critical point.

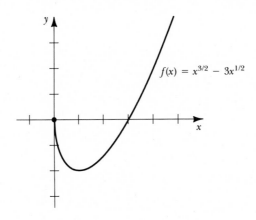

$f(x) = x^{3/2} - 3x^{1/2}$

45. Determine intervals on which the graph of $f(x) = \dfrac{x+1}{x-1}$ is concave upward, intervals on which the graph is concave downward and any points of inflection of the function. Sketch the graph.

SOLUTION: In sketching the graph, it is helpful to determine extrema as well as concavity and points of inflection. Now $f'(x) = \dfrac{(x-1)(1) - (x+1)(1)}{(x-1)^2} = \dfrac{-2}{(x-1)^2} = -2(x-1)^{-2}$, so $f'(x) \neq 0$ since $\dfrac{-2}{(x-1)^2} < 0$. Thus there are no extrema.

Furthermore, $f''(x) = 4(x-1)^{-3} = \dfrac{4}{(x-1)^3}$. Now $f''(x) \neq 0$ since $\dfrac{4}{(x-1)^3} \neq 0$, so there are no points of inflection. Since 1 is not in the domain of f, examine $f''(x)$ on either side of $x = 1$. $f''(x) > 0$ for $x > 1$, and $f''(x) < 0$ for $x < 1$, so f is concave up on $(1, \infty)$ and concave down on $(-\infty, 1)$.

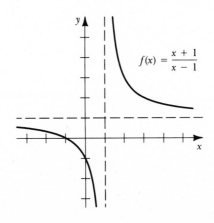

$f(x) = \dfrac{x+1}{x-1}$

49. Determine intervals on which the graph of $f(x) = x\sqrt{x^2 - 4}$ is concave upward, intervals on which the graph is concave downward and any points of inflection of the function. Sketch the graph.

SOLUTION: Note that the domain of f is $\{x : |x| \geq 2\}$.

$f(x) = x(x^2 - 4)^{1/2} \implies f'(x) = (x^2 - 4)^{1/2} + x^2(x^2 - 4)^{-1/2} \implies f'(x) = (x^2 - 4)^{-1/2}(2x^2 - 4).$

Thus $f'(x) = 0 \implies \dfrac{2x^2 - 4}{\sqrt{x^2 - 4}} = 0 \implies x^2 = 2 \implies x = \pm\sqrt{2}.$

These points are discarded since they are not in the domain of f, but $x = \pm 2$ are critical points since $f'(\pm 2)$ does not exist but $f(\pm 2)$ does exist. Now

$$f''(x) = -\frac{1}{2}(x^2 - 4)^{-3/2}(2x)(2x^2 - 4) + 4x(x^2 - 4)^{-1/2}$$

$$= -x(2x^2 - 4)(x^2 - 4)^{-3/2} + 4x(x^2 - 4)^{-1/2}$$

$$= x(x^2 - 4)^{-3/2}\left(-(2x^2 - 4) + 4(x^2 - 4)\right) = x(x^2 - 4)^{-3/2}(2x^2 - 12).$$

Then $f''(x) = 0 \implies \dfrac{2x(x^2 - 6)}{(x^2 - 4)^{3/2}} \implies x = 0$ or $x = \pm\sqrt{6}.$

The point $x = 0$ is discarded, but $x = \pm\sqrt{6}$ are candidates for points of inflection.

$f''(x)$	$-$		$+$		$-$		$+$
$(x^2 - 4)^{3/2}$	$+$		$+$		$+$		$+$
x	$-$		$-$		$+$		$+$
$x^2 - 6$	$+$		$-$		$-$		$+$

$$\qquad -\sqrt{6} \qquad -2 \qquad 2 \qquad \sqrt{6}$$

Thus there are points of inflection at $(-\sqrt{6}, -2\sqrt{3})$ and $(\sqrt{6}, 2\sqrt{3})$, and f is concave up on $(-\sqrt{6}, -2) \cup (\sqrt{6}, \infty)$ and concave down on $(-\infty, -\sqrt{6}) \cup (2, \sqrt{6})$.

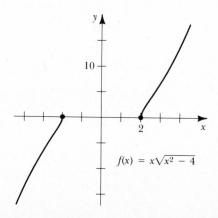

$$f(x) = x\sqrt{x^2 - 4}$$

53. Determine intervals on which the graph of $f(x) = (x-2)^2(x+1)^2$ is concave upward, intervals on which the graph is concave downward and any points of inflection of the function. Sketch the graph.

SOLUTION:

$$f'(x) = 2(x-2)(x+1)^2 + 2(x+1)(x-2)^2 = 2(x-2)(x+1)(2x-1).$$

Setting $f'(x) = 0$ to find critical points, obtain $f'(x) = 0 \implies 2(x-2)(x+1)(2x-1) = 0 \implies x = 2$, $x = -1$ or $x = \frac{1}{2}$.

Now

$$f''(x) = 2(x+1)(2x-1) + 2(x-2)(2x-1) + 4(x-2)(x+1)$$
$$= 2(2x^2 + x - 1 + 2x^2 - 5x + 2 + 2x^2 - 2x - 4) = 2(6x^2 - 6x - 3) = 6(2x^2 - 2x - 1).$$

Thus $f''(x) = 0 \implies 2x^2 - 2x - 1 = 0 \implies x = \dfrac{2 \pm \sqrt{4 - 4(2)(-1)}}{4} = \dfrac{2 \pm \sqrt{12}}{4} = \dfrac{1 \pm \sqrt{3}}{2}$.

Thus $x = \frac{1}{2}(1 + \sqrt{3})$ and $x = \frac{1}{2}(1 - \sqrt{3})$ are candidates for points of inflection.

$f''(x)$	$+$	$-$	$+$
$2x^2 - 2x - 1$	$+$	$-$	$+$
	$\frac{1}{2}(1 - \sqrt{3})$	$\frac{1}{2}(1 + \sqrt{3})$	

So f is concave up on $\left(-\infty, \frac{1}{2}(1 - \sqrt{3})\right) \cup \left(\frac{1}{2}(1 + \sqrt{3}), \infty\right)$ and concave down on $\left(\frac{1}{2}(1 - \sqrt{3}), \frac{1}{2}(1 + \sqrt{3})\right)$, and there are points of inflection at

$$\left(\frac{1}{2}(1 - \sqrt{3}), \frac{9}{4}\right) \quad \text{and} \quad \left(\frac{1}{2}(1 + \sqrt{3}), \frac{9}{4}\right).$$

Examining the critical points, $f''(2) > 0$, $f''(-1) > 0$ and $f''(1/2) < 0$ so there are relative minima at $x = 2$ and $x = -1$ and a relative maximum at $x = 1/2$.

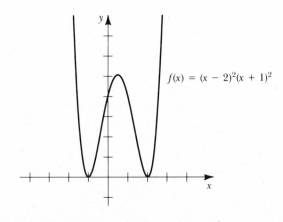

$f(x) = (x - 2)^2(x + 1)^2$

55. Determine intervals on which the graph of $f(x) = \sin 2x + 8 \sin x$ is concave upward, intervals on which the graph is concave downward and any points of inflection of the function. Sketch the graph.

SOLUTION: $f'(x) = 2\cos 2x + 8\cos x$ and $f''(x) = -4\sin 2x - 8\sin x$.
Now $f'(x) = 0 \implies 2(\cos 2x + 4\cos x) = 0 \implies 2\cos^2 x + 4\cos x - 1 = 0 \implies \cos x = \dfrac{-4 \pm \sqrt{16 - 4(2)(-1)}}{4} = \dfrac{-4 \pm \sqrt{24}}{4} = \dfrac{-4 \pm 2\sqrt{6}}{4} = -1 \pm \frac{1}{2}\sqrt{6}.$
However, $\cos x = -1 - \frac{1}{2}\sqrt{6}$ is impossible, so $x = \pm \cos^{-1}(-1 + \frac{1}{2}\sqrt{6}) + 2n\pi$, where n is an integer, are the critical points.

$f''(x) = 0 \implies -4(\sin 2x + 2\sin x) = 0 \implies 2\sin x \cos x + 2\sin x = 0 \implies 2\sin x(\cos x + 1) = 0 \implies \sin x = 0$ or $\cos x = -1 \implies x = n\pi$ where n is an integer are candidates for points of inflection.

$f''(x)$	$+$	$-$	$+$	$-$	$+$	$-$
$\cos x + 1$	$+$	$+$	$+$	$+$	$+$	$+$
$\sin x$	$-$	$+$	$-$	$+$	$-$	$+$

$\cdots \quad -2\pi \qquad -\pi \qquad 0 \qquad \pi \qquad 2\pi \quad \cdots$

The above diagram shows that there are points of inflection at $(n\pi, 0)$ where n is an integer and f is concave down on $(2n\pi, (2n+1)\pi)$ and concave up on $((2n-1)\pi, 2n\pi)$ where n is an integer.

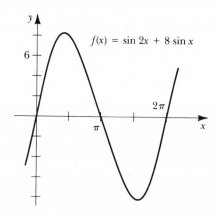

59. Find a general formula expressing $f^{(n)}(x)$ for any positive integer n for $f(x) = \dfrac{1}{x+1}$.

SOLUTION: First calculate the first few derivatives of f to detect a pattern:

$$f(x) = (x+1)^{-1}$$
$$f'(x) = f^{(1)}(x) = -(x+1)^{-2}$$
$$f''(x) = f^{(2)}(x) = 2(x+1)^{-3}$$

$$f'''(x) = f^{(3)}(x) = -(2)(3)(x+1)^{-4}$$
$$f^{(4)}(x) = (2)(3)(4)(x+1)^{-5}.$$

Note: i) The nth derivative is negative when n is odd and positive when n is even. This suggests the use of $(-1)^n$ in the formula.

ii) The exponent of $(x+1)$ is one less than the negative of n. This suggests using $-n-1 = -(n+1)$ for the exponent.

iii) The coefficients of $(x+1)$ appear to be forming n-factorial. This suggests $n!$.

Thus the formula appears to be

$$f^{(n)}(x) = (-1)^n n!(x+1)^{-(n+1)}.$$

It remains to prove by math induction that this formula is, in fact, correct.

i) Prove true for $n = 1$. From above $f^{(1)}(x) = -(x+1)^{-2}$. Applying the formula, $f^{(1)}(x) = (-1)^1 1!(x+1)^{-(1+1)} = -(x+1)^{-2}$. Thus the formula works for $n = 1$.

ii) Assume true for $n = k$; i.e., assume $f^{(k)}(x) = (-1)^k k!(x+1)^{-(k+1)}$. Prove true for $n = k+1$; i.e., show $f^{(k+1)}(x) = (-1)^{k+1}(k+1)!(x+1)^{-((k+1)+1)}$. Now

$$f^{(k+1)}(x) = D_x\left[f^{(k)}(x)\right] = D_x\left[(-1)^k k!(x+1)^{-(k+1)}\right]$$

$$= (-1)^k k!\, D_x\left[(x+1)^{-(k+1)}\right] = (-1)^k k!\left(-(k+1)(x+1)^{-(k+1)-1}\right)$$

$$= (-1)^k(-1)k!(k+1)(x+1)^{-((k+1)+1)} = (-1)^{k+1}(k+1)!(x+1)^{-((k+1)+1)}.$$

Thus, by the Principle of Mathematical Induction, $f^{(n)}(x) = (-1)^n n!(x+1)^{-(n+1)}$.

_____2.11

Comprehensive Graphing

3. Sketch the graph of $f(x) = x^4 - 2x^2$ as completely as possible. When appropriate, describe symmetry, intercepts, asymptotes, relative extrema, points of inflection, concavity and so on.

SOLUTION: Since $f(x) = f(-x)$, this function is even, and the graph is symmetric with respect to the y-axis. $f(0) = 0$ is the y-intercept. Set $f(x) = 0$ to determine x-intercepts. This yields $x^2(x^2 - 2) = 0 \implies x = 0$ or $x = \pm\sqrt{2}$. There are no asymptotes since this is a polynomial function. $f'(x) = 4x^3 - 4x$ and $f''(x) = 12x^2 - 4$. To determine extrema, solve $f'(x) = 0$. $4x(x^2 - 1) = 0 \implies x = 0$ or $x = \pm 1$. $f''(-1) > 0$, $f''(0) < 0$ and $f''(1) > 0$ so there are relative minima at $x = \pm 1$ and a relative maximum at $x = 0$. Since $f'(x) < 0$ on $(-\infty, -1) \cup (0, 1)$, $f(x)$ is decreasing for $x < -1$ and $0 < x < 1$. Also $f'(x) > 0$ on $(-1, 0) \cup (1, \infty)$ indicates $f(x)$ is increasing for $-1 < x < 0$ and $x > 1$. To determine points of inflection, solve

$f''(x) = 0$. $4(3x^2 - 1) = 0 \implies x = \pm 1/\sqrt{3}$. Since $f''(x) < 0$ on $(-1/\sqrt{3}, 1/\sqrt{3})$ and $f''(x) > 0$ on $(-\infty, -1/\sqrt{3}) \cup (1/\sqrt{3}, \infty)$, $x = \pm 1/\sqrt{3}$ are points of inflection, and $f(x)$ is concave up for $|x| > 1/\sqrt{3}$ and concave down for $|x| < 1/\sqrt{3}$.

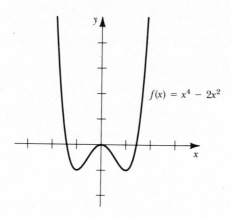

$f(x) = x^4 - 2x^2$

15. Sketch the graph of $f(x) = x^{2/3} + x^{5/3}$ as completely as possible. When appropriate, describe symmetry, intercepts, asymptotes, relative extrema, points of inflection, concavity and so on.

SOLUTION: Note that the domain of f is $\mathbb{R}$. Since the function is neither even nor odd, the graph does not exhibit symmetry.

Intercepts: x : $f(0) = 0$, y : $x^{2/3}(1 + x) = 0 \implies x = 0$ or $x = -1$. $f'(x) = \frac{2}{3}x^{-1/3} + \frac{5}{3}x^{2/3}$ and $f''(x) = -\frac{2}{9}x^{-4/3} + \frac{10}{9}x^{-1/3}$. Since $f'(0)$ and $f''(0)$ do not exist, $x = 0$ is a candidate for an extremum or point of inflection. $f'(x) = 0 \implies \frac{1}{3}x^{-1/3}(2 + 5x) = 0 \implies x = -\frac{2}{5}$. $f''(-2/5) < 0$, so $x = -\frac{2}{5}$ is a relative maximum. $f'(x) > 0$ on $(-\infty, -2/5) \cup (0, \infty)$ and $f'(x) < 0$ on $(-2/5, 0)$, so $x = 0$ is a relative minimum, and f is decreasing for $-2/5 < x < 0$ and increasing for $x < -2/5$ or $x > 0$.

$f''(x) = 0 \implies \frac{2}{9}x^{-4/3}(-1 + 5x) \implies x = 1/5$. Since $f''(x) < 0$ on $(-\infty, 0) \cup (0, 1/5)$ and $f''(x) > 0$ on $(1/5, \infty)$, f is concave up and concave down on the respective intervals, and there is a point of inflection at $x = 1/5$, though this is difficult to see in the graph.

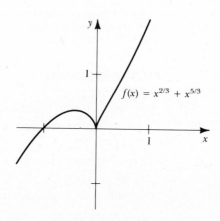

$f(x) = x^{2/3} + x^{5/3}$

23. Sketch the graph of $f(x) = \dfrac{3 - 2x - 5x^2}{x^2}$ as completely as possible. When appropriate, describe symmetry, intercepts, asymptotes, relative extrema, points of inflection, concavity and so on.

SOLUTION: The domain is $\{x : x \neq 0\}$, which makes $x = 0$ a candidate for a vertical asymptote. Since $\lim\limits_{x \to 0} f(x) = \infty$, $x = 0$ is a vertical asymptote. $y = -5$ is a horizontal asymptote since $\lim\limits_{x \to \infty} \dfrac{3 - 2x - 5x^2}{x^2} = \lim\limits_{x \to -\infty} \dfrac{3 - 2x - 5x^2}{x^2} = -5$. There is no y-intercept since $x \neq 0$.
$f(x) = 0 \implies 3 - 2x - 5x^2 = 0 \implies (-5x + 3)(x + 1) = 0 \implies x = 3/5$ and $x = -1$ are x-intercepts.

$$f'(x) = \frac{x^2(-2 - 10x) - (3 - 2x - 5x^2)(2x)}{x^4} = \frac{-2x - 10x^2 - 6 + 4x + 10x^2}{x^3}$$

$$= \frac{2x - 6}{x^3} = \frac{2(x - 3)}{x^3}, \qquad \text{and}$$

$$f''(x) = \frac{x^3(2) - (2x - 6)(3x^2)}{x^6} = \frac{2x - (2x - 6)(3)}{x^4}$$

$$= \frac{-4x + 18}{x^4} = \frac{-2(2x - 9)}{x^4}.$$

Now $f'(x) = 0 \implies x = 3$ and $f''(3) > 0$, so f attains a relative minimum at $x = 3$. f is increasing on $(-\infty, 0) \cup (3, \infty)$ and decreasing on $(0, 3)$.
$f''(x) = 0 \implies x = 9/2$ and $f''(x) > 0$ on $(-\infty, 0) \cup (0, 9/2)$ and $f''(x) < 0$ on $(9/2, \infty)$, so there is a point of inflection at $x = 9/2$.

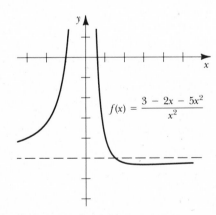

$$f(x) = \frac{3 - 2x - 5x^2}{x^2}$$

31. Sketch the graph of $f(x) = \cos^2 x + 2$ as completely as possible. When appropriate, describe symmetry, intercepts, asymptotes, relative extrema, points of inflection, concavity and so on.

SOLUTION: The graph is symmetric with respect to the y-axis since $f(x) = f(-x)$.
There are no x-intercepts since $f(x) \geq 2$ for all x and 3 is the y-intercept ($\cos 0 = 1$).

$f'(x) = 2\cos x(-\sin x) = -\sin 2x$, and $f''(x) = -2\cos 2x$. $f'(x) = 0 \implies \sin 2x = 0 \implies 2x = n\pi \implies x = n\pi/2$ for n an integer. Also $f'(x) > 0$ for $x \in \left((2n+1)\dfrac{\pi}{2},(2n+2)\dfrac{\pi}{2}\right)$ so there are relative maxima at odd multiples of $\pi/2$ and relative minima at even multiples of $\pi/2$.

$f''(x) = 0 \implies \cos 2x = 0 \implies 2x = (2n+1)\dfrac{\pi}{2} \implies x = (2n+1)\dfrac{\pi}{4}$ for n an integer. Also, $f''(x) > 0$ on $\left((2n-3)\dfrac{\pi}{4},(2n+1)\dfrac{\pi}{4}\right)$ and $f''(x) < 0$ on $\left((2n+1)\dfrac{\pi}{4},(2n-3)\dfrac{\pi}{4}\right)$, so there are points of inflection at odd multiples of $\pi/4$.

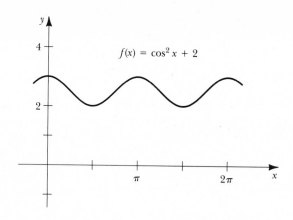

33. Sketch the graph of $x^2y^2 - x^2 - y^2 = 1$ as completely as possible. When appropriate, describe symmetry, intercepts, asymptotes, relative extrema, points of inflection, concavity and so on.

SOLUTION: Note that this relation is not a function in x since $y^2(x^2-1) = 1 + x^2 \implies y = \pm\sqrt{\dfrac{1+x^2}{x^2-1}}$. However, it can be seen that $|x| > 1$. Similarly, $x^2(y^2-1) = 1 + y^2 \implies x = \pm\sqrt{\dfrac{1+y^2}{y^2-1}}$, so $|y| > 1$. Also there are vertical asymptotes at $x = \pm1$. Since $(x,-y)$ and $(-x,y)$ each satisfy the relation, the graph is symmetric with respect to the x-axis and y-axis respectively and is therefore symmetric with respect to the origin.

Differentiating implicitly, obtain $2xy^2 + x^2(2y\,D_xy) - 2x - 2y\,D_xy = 0 \implies 2xy^2 - 2x = (2y - 2x^2y)D_xy \implies D_xy = \dfrac{xy^2 - x}{y - x^2y}$. To determine extrema, solve $D_xy = 0$. $\dfrac{xy^2 - x}{y - x^2y} = 0 \implies x(y^2 - 1) = 0 \implies x = 0$ or $y = \pm1$. These points must all be discarded so there are no extrema. Examining $D_xy = \dfrac{x(y^2-1)}{y(1-x^2)}$, the curve is decreasing in Quadrant I ($x > 1$, $y > 1$), increasing in Quadrant II ($x < -1$, $y > 1$), decreasing in Quadrant III ($x < -1$, $y < -1$), and increasing in Quadrant IV ($x > 1$, $y < -1$).

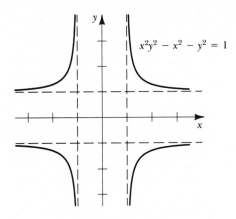

$$x^2y^2 - x^2 - y^2 = 1$$

39. Sketch the graph of $x^2 - xy + 1 = 0$ as completely as possible. When appropriate, describe symmetry, intercepts, asymptotes, relative extrema, points of inflection, concavity and so on.

SOLUTION: This is a function since $x^2 - xy + 1 = 0 \implies y = \dfrac{x^2 + 1}{x}$ and the domain is $\{x : x \neq 0\}$. There is a vertical asymptote at $x = 0$ and a slant asymptote at $y = x$. Since $(-x, -y)$ satisfies the equation, the graph is symmetric with respect to the origin.

Differentiating, $2x - y - x\,D_x y = 0 \implies D_x y = \dfrac{2x - y}{x}$. Solving $D_x y = 0 \implies y = 2x \implies x^2 - x(2x) + 1 = 0 \implies -x^2 + 1 = 0 \implies x = \pm 1$.

$$D_x^2 y = \frac{x(2 - D_x y) - (2x - y)}{x^2} = \frac{2x - x\,D_x y - 2x + y}{x^2}$$

$$= \frac{-(2x - y) + y}{x^2} = \frac{2(y - x)}{x^2},$$

and $D_x^2 y = 0 \implies x = y \implies x^2 - x(x) + 1 = 0$, which is impossible, so there are no points of inflection.

To evaluate $D_x^2 y$ at $x = \pm 1$, find y. $x = 1 \implies 1 - y + 1 = 0 \implies y = 2$ and $x = -1 \implies 1 + y + 1 = 0 \implies y = -2$.

$$D_x^2 y \bigg|_{(1,2)} = \frac{2(2 - 1)}{1} = 2 > 0,$$

so there is a relative minimum at $x = 1$.

$$D_x^2 y \bigg|_{(-1,-2)} = \frac{2(-2 + 1)}{1} = -2 < 0,$$

so there is a relative maximum at $x = -1$.

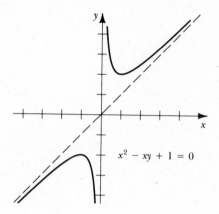

$$x^2 - xy + 1 = 0$$

_____Chapter 2

Review Exercises

5. Find the derivative of $g(t) = \dfrac{16t^2 - 32}{t}$.

SOLUTION: Applying the quotient rule,

$$g'(t) = \frac{tD_t[16t^2 - 32] - (16t^2 - 32)D_t t}{t^2} = \frac{t(32t) - (16t^2 - 32)(1)}{t^2}$$

$$= \frac{32t^2 - 16t^2 + 32}{t^2} = \frac{16(t^2 + 2)}{t^2}.$$

11. Find the derivative of $f(x) = (x^2 - 7)^3(x^4 + 1)$.

SOLUTION: Applying the product rule, obtain

$$f'(x) = (x^2 - 7)^3 D_x[x^4 + 1] + (x^4 + 1)D_x\left[(x^2 - 7)^3\right].$$

To find $D_x\left[(x^2 - 7)^3\right]$, apply the chain rule. Let $u = x^2 - 7$ and $y = u^3 = (x^2 - 7)^3$. Then $du/dx = 2x$ and $dy/du = 3u^2 = 3(x^2 - 7)^2$. So $D_x\left[(x^2 - 7)^3\right] = \frac{dy}{du} \cdot \frac{du}{dx} = 3(x^2 - 7)^2(2x) = 6x(x^2 - 7)^2$. Then

$$f'(x) = (x^2 - 7)^3(4x^3) + (x^4 + 1)\left(6x(x^2 - 7)^2\right) = 2x(x^2 - 7)^2\left(2x^2(x^2 - 7) + 3(x^4 + 1)\right)$$

$$= 2x(x^2 - 7)^2(5x^4 - 14x^2 + 3).$$

17. Find the derivative of $g(s) = \left((2s+1)^3 + s^{1/3}\right)^4$.

SOLUTION: Apply the chain rule with $u = (2s+1)^3 + s^{1/3}$ and $y = u^4 = \left((2s+1)^3 + s^{1/3}\right)^4$. Then

$$\frac{du}{ds} = D_s\left[(2s+1)^3 + s^{1/3}\right] = D_s\left[(2s+1)^3\right] + D_s\left[s^{1/3}\right].$$

To find $D_s\left[(2s+1)^3\right]$, let $w = 2s+1$ and $v = w^3 = (2s+1)^3$. Then

$$D_s\left[(2s+1)^3\right] = \frac{dv}{ds} = \frac{dv}{dw} \cdot \frac{dw}{ds} = 3w^2(2) = 6w^2 = 6(2s+1)^2.$$

So $\dfrac{du}{ds} = 6(2s+1)^2 + \dfrac{1}{3}s^{-2/3}$ and $\dfrac{dy}{du} = 4u^3$. Thus

$$g'(s) = \frac{dy}{du} \cdot \frac{du}{ds} = 4u^3\left(6(2s+1)^2 + \frac{1}{3}s^{-2/3}\right) = \frac{4}{3}\left((2s+1)^3 + s^{1/3}\right)^3\left(18(2s+1)^2 + s^{-2/3}\right).$$

23. Find the derivative of $f(x) = \left(\dfrac{x}{x^3+1}\right)^{-4}$.

SOLUTION: Apply the chain rule with $u = \dfrac{x}{x^3+1}$ and $y = u^{-4} = \left(\dfrac{x}{x^3+1}\right)^{-4}$. Then $f'(x) = \frac{dy}{du} \cdot \frac{du}{dx} = -4u^{-5}\frac{du}{dx}$. To find $\frac{du}{dx}$, apply the quotient rule and obtain

$$\frac{du}{dx} = \frac{(x^3+1)D_x x - x D_x[x^3+1]}{(x^3+1)^2} = \frac{x^3+1-x(3x^2)}{(x^3+1)^2} = \frac{1-2x^3}{(x^3+1)^2}.$$

Thus

$$f'(x) = -4\left(\frac{x}{x^3+1}\right)^{-5}\left(\frac{1-2x^3}{(x^3+1)^2}\right) = \frac{-4(x^3+1)^3(1-2x^3)}{x^5}.$$

27. Find the derivative of $h(x) = \sin^2(2x+1)$.

SOLUTION: Applying the chain rule with $w = 2x+1$, $u = \sin(2x+1) = \sin w$ and $y = u^2 = \sin^2(2x+1)$, obtain

$$h'(x) = \frac{dy}{du} \cdot \frac{du}{dw} \cdot \frac{dw}{dx} = 2u \cdot \cos w \cdot 2 = 4\sin(2x+1)\cos(2x+1)$$

$$= 2\sin 2(2x+1) = 2\sin(4x+2)$$

since $2\sin A \cos A = \sin 2A$.

31. Find the derivative of $h(t) = \sqrt{\sec(t^2 + 1)}$.

SOLUTION: Apply the chain rule with $w = t^2 + 1$, $u = \sec w = \sec(t^2 + 1)$ and $y = \sqrt{u} = (\sec(t^2 + 1))^{1/2}$. Then

$$h'(t) = \frac{dy}{du} \cdot \frac{du}{dw} \cdot \frac{dw}{dx} = \frac{1}{2}u^{-1/2}(\sec w \tan w)(2t)$$

$$= t\left(\sec(t^2 + 1)\right)^{-1/2}\left(\sec(t^2 + 1)\tan(t^2 + 1)\right) = t\tan(t^2 + 1)\sqrt{\sec(t^2 + 1)}.$$

49. Find dy/dx if $2xy - xy^2 + x = 0$.

SOLUTION: Differentiating implicitly,

$$D_x\left[2xy - xy^2 + x\right] = D_x[0]$$

$$D_x[2xy] - D_x[xy^2] + D_x[x] = 0$$

$$2\left(yD_xx + xD_xy\right) - \left(xD_x[y^2] + y^2 D_xx\right) + 1 = 0$$

$$2\left(y + x\frac{dy}{dx}\right) - x\left(2y\frac{dy}{dx}\right) - y^2 + 1 = 0$$

$$2y + 2x\frac{dy}{dx} - 2xy\frac{dy}{dx} - y^2 + 1 = 0$$

$$(2x - 2xy)\frac{dy}{dx} = y^2 - 1 - 2y$$

$$\frac{dy}{dx} = \frac{y^2 - 2y - 1}{2x(1 - y)}.$$

57. Find dy/dx if $\tan(xy) + y\tan x = x$.

SOLUTION:

$$D_x[\tan(xy) + y\tan x] = D_x[x]$$

$$D_x[\tan(xy)] + D_x[y\tan x] = 1$$

$$(\sec^2(xy))D_x[xy] + yD_x[\tan x] + (\tan x)D_xy = 1$$

$$(\sec^2(xy))\left(yD_xx + xD_xy\right) + y\sec^2 x + \tan x\frac{dy}{dx} = 1$$

$$(\sec^2(xy))\left(y + x\frac{dy}{dx}\right) + y\sec^2 x + \tan x\frac{dy}{dx} = 1$$

$$y \sec^2 xy + x \sec^2 xy \frac{dy}{dx} + y \sec^2 x + \tan x \frac{dy}{dx} = 1$$

$$(x \sec^2 xy + \tan x)\frac{dy}{dx} = 1 - (y \sec^2 xy + y \sec^2 x)$$

$$\frac{dy}{dx} = \frac{1 - y(\sec^2 xy + \sec^2 x)}{x \sec^2 xy + \tan x}.$$

61. Find   a) dy/dx and   b) d^2y/dx^2 if $\sin y + xy = 0$.

SOLUTION: a)

$$D_x[\sin y + xy] = D_x[0]$$

$$D_x[\sin y] + D_x[xy] = 0$$

$$\cos y \frac{dy}{dx} + yD_x x + xD_x y = 0$$

$$\cos y \frac{dy}{dx} + y + x\frac{dy}{dx} = 0$$

$$(\cos y + x)\frac{dy}{dx} = -y$$

$$\frac{dy}{dx} = \frac{-y}{x + \cos y}.$$

b)

$$\frac{d^2 y}{dx^2} = D_x\left[\frac{dy}{dx}\right] = D_x\left[\frac{-y}{x + \cos y}\right] = -D_x\left[\frac{y}{x + \cos y}\right]$$

$$= -\frac{(x + \cos y)D_x y - yD_x[x + \cos y]}{(x + \cos y)^2} = -\frac{(x + \cos y)\frac{dy}{dx} - y\left(1 - \sin y \frac{dy}{dx}\right)}{(x + \cos y)^2}$$

$$= -\frac{(x + \cos y)\left(\frac{-y}{x + \cos y}\right) - y + y \sin y\left(\frac{-y}{x + \cos y}\right)}{(x + \cos y)^2} = -\frac{-y - y - \dfrac{y^2 \sin y}{(x + \cos y)}}{(x + \cos y)^2}$$

$$= \frac{-2y(x + \cos y) - y^2 \sin y}{(x + \cos y)^3} = \frac{y\left(2(x + \cos y) + y \sin y\right)}{(x + \cos y)^3}.$$

67. For $f(x) = x^{3/2} - 3x^{1/2}$, find the critical points, intervals on which the function is decreasing and increasing, relative extrema, intervals on which the function is concave upward or downward, and points of inflection. Find any horizontal or vertical asymptotes to the graph and sketch the graph of the function.

SOLUTION: Note that the domain of f is $[0, \infty)$. Now $f'(x) = \frac{3}{2}x^{1/2} - \frac{3}{2}x^{-1/2}$ and $f''(x) = \frac{3}{4}x^{-1/2} + \frac{3}{4}x^{-3/2}$.

First solve $f'(x) = 0$. $f'(x) = \frac{3}{2}x^{-1/2}(x - 1) = 0 \implies x - 1 = 0 \implies x = 1$.

$f'(x)$	$-$	$+$
$x^{-1/2}$	$+$	$+$
$x - 1$	$-$	$+$

$$0 \qquad 1$$

From the above diagram, f is increasing on $[1, \infty)$ and decreasing on $[0, 1]$. Thus there is an absolute minimum at $x = 1$. There is a relative maximum at the critical point $x = 0$.

Next solve $f''(x) = 0$. Now $f''(x) = \frac{3}{4}x^{-3/2}(x + 1) = 0 \implies x + 1 = 0 \implies x = -1$. However, $x = -1$ is not in the domain of f, so there are no points of inflection. Also $f''(x) > 0$, so the curve is concave upward on its entire domain.

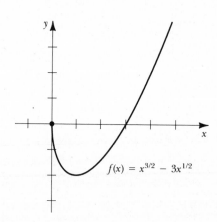

$$f(x) = x^{3/2} - 3x^{1/2}$$

71. For $f(x) = 3\sin 2x$, find the critical points, intervals on which the function is decreasing and increasing, relative extrema, intervals on which the function is concave upward or downward and points of inflection. Find any horizontal or vertical asymptotes to the graph and sketch the graph of the function.

SOLUTION: The domain of f is $\mathbb{R}$; $f'(x) = 6\cos 2x$ and $f''(x) = -12\sin 2x$.

First, solve $f'(x) = 0$. $f'(x) = 0 \implies 6\cos 2x = 0 \implies \cos 2x = 0 \implies 2x = (2n + 1)\frac{\pi}{2}$ for n an integer $\implies x = (2n + 1)\frac{\pi}{4}$ for n an integer.

$$f'(x)$$
$$\cos 2x$$

	$-$	$+$	$-$	$+$	
	$-$	$+$	$-$	$+$	

$$\cdots \qquad -\frac{3\pi}{4} \qquad -\frac{\pi}{4} \qquad \frac{\pi}{4} \qquad \frac{3\pi}{4} \qquad \frac{5\pi}{4} \qquad \cdots$$

From the above diagram, f is increasing on $\left[(4n-1)\frac{\pi}{4},(4n+1)\frac{\pi}{4}\right]$ and decreasing on $\left[(4n+1)\frac{\pi}{4},(4n+3)\frac{\pi}{4}\right]$, where n is an integer. There are absolute maxima at $x=(4n+1)\frac{\pi}{4}$ and absolute minima at $x=(4n+3)\frac{\pi}{4}$.

Next solve $f''(x)=0$. $f''(x)=0 \implies -12\sin 2x = 0 \implies \sin 2x = 0 \implies 2x = n\pi$ for n an integer $\implies x = n\frac{\pi}{2}$ for n an integer.

$$f''(x)$$
$$\sin 2x$$

	$-$	$+$	$-$	$+$	
	$+$	$-$	$+$	$-$	

$$\cdots \qquad -\pi \qquad -\frac{\pi}{2} \qquad 0 \qquad \frac{\pi}{2} \qquad \pi \qquad \cdots$$

From the above diagram, f is concave downward on $\left((2n)\frac{\pi}{2},(2n+1)\frac{\pi}{2}\right)$ and concave upward on $\left((2n-1)\frac{\pi}{2},(2n)\frac{\pi}{2}\right)$ for n an integer. There are points of inflection at $x=n\frac{\pi}{2}$ for n an integer.

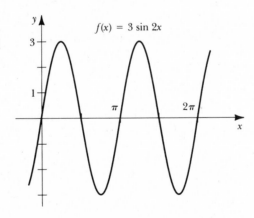

75. For $f(x) = \dfrac{x+1}{\sqrt{x-1}}$, find the critical points, intervals on which the function is decreasing and increasing, relative extrema, intervals on which the function is concave upward or downward and points of inflection. Find any horizontal or vertical asymptotes to the graph and sketch the graph of the function.

SOLUTION: The domain of f is $(1,\infty)$.

$$f'(x) = \frac{(x-1)^{1/2}(1)-(x+1)\left(\frac{1}{2}(x-1)^{-1/2}\right)}{\left((x-1)^{1/2}\right)^2} = \frac{(x-1)^{-1/2}\left((x-1)-\frac{1}{2}(x+1)\right)}{(x-1)}$$

$$= \frac{\frac{1}{2}x - \frac{3}{2}}{(x-1)^{3/2}} = \frac{\frac{1}{2}(x-3)}{(x-1)^{3/2}} = \frac{(x-3)}{2(x-1)^{3/2}},$$

and

$$f''(x) = \frac{2(x-1)^{3/2}(1) - (x-3)\left(2(3/2)(x-1)^{1/2}\right)}{\left(2(x-1)^{3/2}\right)^2}$$

$$= \frac{2(x-1)^{3/2} - 3(x-3)(x-1)^{1/2}}{4(x-1)^3}$$

$$= \frac{2(x-1) - 3(x-3)}{4(x-1)^{5/2}} = \frac{-x+7}{4(x-1)^{5/2}}.$$

First solve $f'(x) = 0$. Now $f'(x) = 0 \implies x - 3 = 0 \implies x = 3$.

$f'(x)$		$-$	$+$
$(x-1)^{3/2}$		$+$	$+$
$x-3$		$-$	$+$
		1	3

From the above diagram there is a minimum at $x = 3$ and f is decreasing on $(1,3]$ and increasing on $[3,\infty)$.

Next solve $f''(x) = 0$. Now $f''(x) = 0 \implies -x + 7 = 0 \implies x = 7$.

$f''(x)$		$+$	$-$
$(x-1)^{5/2}$		$+$	$+$
$-x+7$		$+$	$-$
		1	7

From the above diagram, there is a point of inflection at $x = 7$ and f is concave upward on $(0,7)$ and concave downward on $(7,\infty)$.

Furthermore,

$$\lim_{x\to\infty} \frac{x+1}{\sqrt{x-1}} = \lim_{x\to\infty} \frac{\sqrt{x}}{\sqrt{x}} \cdot \frac{\sqrt{x} + \frac{1}{\sqrt{x}}}{\sqrt{1 - \frac{1}{x}}} = \lim_{x\to\infty} \frac{\sqrt{x} + \frac{1}{\sqrt{x}}}{\sqrt{1 - \frac{1}{x}}} = \infty$$

so there is no horizontal asymptote; but $y = \sqrt{x}$ is a slant asymptote.

$\displaystyle\lim_{x\to 1^+} \frac{x+1}{\sqrt{x-1}} = \infty$, so there is a vertical asymptote at $x = 1$.

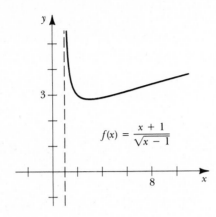

$$f(x) = \frac{x + 1}{\sqrt{x} - 1}$$

79. Use the definition of the derivative to verify $D_x \left[\dfrac{2}{x} + x - 1 \right] = -\dfrac{2}{x^2} + 1.$

SOLUTION: $f'(x) = \lim\limits_{h \to 0} \dfrac{f(x + h) - f(x)}{h}$ so

$$D_x \left[\frac{2}{x} + x - 1 \right] = \lim\limits_{h \to 0} \frac{\left(\dfrac{2}{x + h} + x + h - 1 \right) - \left(\dfrac{2}{x} + x - 1 \right)}{h}$$

$$= \lim\limits_{h \to 0} \frac{\dfrac{2}{x + h} + x + h - 1 - \dfrac{2}{x} - x + 1}{h}$$

$$= \lim\limits_{h \to 0} \frac{\dfrac{2}{x + h} - \dfrac{2}{x}}{h} + \lim\limits_{h \to 0} \frac{h}{h} = \lim\limits_{h \to 0} \frac{\dfrac{2x - 2(x + h)}{x(x + h)}}{h} + 1$$

$$= \lim\limits_{h \to 0} \frac{-2h}{hx(x + h)} + 1 = \lim\limits_{h \to 0} \frac{-2}{x(x + h)} + 1$$

$$= \frac{-2}{x(x)} + 1 = \frac{-2}{x^2} + 1.$$

83. Find an equation of the tangent line to the graph of $f(x) = x(4 - x^2)^{1/2}$ at $(0,0)$.

SOLUTION: Find $f'(0)$. $f(x) = x(4 - x^2)^{1/2} \implies$

$$f'(x) = x \left(\frac{1}{2}(4 - x^2)^{-1/2}(-2x) \right) + (4 - x^2)^{1/2}(1) = -x^2(4 - x^2)^{-1/2} + (4 - x^2)^{1/2}$$

$$= (4 - x^2)^{-1/2} \left(-x^2 + (4 - x^2) \right) = 2(4 - x^2)^{-1/2}(2 - x^2),$$

so $f'(0) = 2(4)^{-1/2}(2) = 4/\sqrt{4} = 2$.

Applying the point-slope form, $y - 0 = 2(x - 0)$ and $y = 2x$ is the equation of the desired tangent line.

87. Find an equation of the tangent line to the graph of $f(x) = x^3 - 3x + 2$ that passes through $(0, 0)$.

SOLUTION: Determine $f'(x)$. $f(x) = x^3 - 3x + 2 \implies f'(x) = 3x^2 - 3 = 3(x^2 - 1)$. Let (x_0, y_0) be the point on $f(x) = x^3 - 3x + 2$ that is the point of tangency for the line through $(0, 0)$.

Then $3(x_0 - 1)^2$ is the slope of the tangent line and $y - 0 = 3(x_0 - 1)^2(x - 0)$ is the equation of the tangent line. Evaluating $y = 3(x_0 - 1)^2 x$ at (x_0, y_0) produces $y_0 = 3(x_0 - 1)^2 x_0$. But (x_0, y_0) is also a point on $f(x) = x^3 - 3x + 2$, so $y_0 = x_0^3 - 3x_0 + 2$. Thus

$$3(x_0 - 1)^2 x_0 = x_0^3 - 3x_0 + 2 \implies$$
$$3(x_0^2 - 2x_0 + 1)x_0 = x_0^3 - 3x_0 + 2 \implies$$
$$3x_0^3 - 6x_0^2 + 3x_0 = x_0^3 - 3x_0 + 2 \implies$$
$$2x_0^3 - 6x_0^2 + 6x_0 - 2 = 0 \implies$$
$$2(x_0^3 - 3x_0^2 + 3x_0 - 1) = 0 \implies$$
$$2(x_0 - 1)^3 = 0 \implies x_0 = 1$$

and $y = 3(1 - 1)^2 x$ or $y = 0$ is the equation of the desired tangent line.

97. Let f be such that $f(0) = 1$ and $f'(x) = 3x^2$ for all x. What is $f(x)$?

SOLUTION: Since $f'(x) = 3x^2$, $f(x) = x^3 + C$ characterizes all antiderivatives of $f'(x)$. Since $f(0) = 1$, $f(0) = 0^3 + C = 1 \implies C = 1$ and $f(x) = x^3 + 1$ is the desired function.

3.
Applications of the Derivative

Sharpening your skills

In preparation for CHAPTER 3, you should review calculating derivatives as this will be a part of most of the problems in this chapter. In particular, review SECTIONS 2.3–2.6 which present formulas and techniques for differentiation. Some additional practice problems are presented here. The answers are found in APPENDIX B in this manual.

Practice Problems

1. Find $D_x y$ for each of the following.
   a) $y = (4x^3 - 3x)^4 (2x + 7)^2$,
   b) $y = \dfrac{(x - 8)^3}{2x + 5}$,
   c) $x^2 y + xy^3 = 9$,
   d) $y = \sin 4x + \tan^2(2x + 3)$,
   e) $\sin(x + y) - \sin(x - y) = \tan y$,
   f) $y = \dfrac{1}{\sqrt{2x}} + \dfrac{4}{\sqrt[3]{(2x - 7)^2}}$.

3.1
Rectilinear Motion

5. $s(t) = \sqrt[3]{t^2 + 2t + 1}$ describes the distance of an object from a specified point at the end of time t. Find the instantaneous velocity and acceleration at the time $t = 0$.

SOLUTION: $s(t) = (t^2 + 2t + 1)^{1/3} = (t+1)^{2/3}$. $v(t) = s'(t) = \frac{2}{3}(t+1)^{-1/3}$ so the initial velocity is $v(0) = \frac{2}{3}(0 + 1)^{-1/3} = \frac{2}{3}$. $a(t) = v'(t) = s''(t) = -\frac{2}{9}(t + 1)^{-4/3}$ so $a(0) = -\frac{2}{9}(0 + 1)^{-4/3} = -\frac{2}{9}$. From the above, it can be seen that at $t = 0$, the object was moving in the positive direction (velocity > 0) but slowing down (acceleration < 0).

13. $s(t) = t^4 - 4t^3 + 4t^2 + 1$ describes the distance of an object from a specified point at the end of time $t \geq 0$. Sketch a figure of the motion of the object. Determine if the object is ever momentarily stopped.

SOLUTION: $v(t) = 4t^3 - 12t^2 + 8t = 4t(t^2 - 3t + 2) = 4t(t-2)(t-1)$, so $v(t) = 0 \implies t = 0$, $t = 1$ or $t = 2$. The object is stopped at those times. For $0 < t < 1$, $v(t) > 0$, so the object is moving in a positive direction from $s(0) = 1$ to $s(1) = 2$. For $1 < t < 2$, $v(t) < 0$, so the object is moving in a negative direction from $s(1) = 2$ to $s(2) = 1$. Finally for $t > 2$, $v(t) > 0$, so the object is moving in a positive direction from that time on.

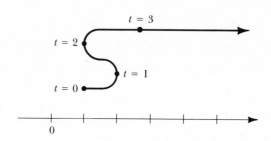

17. A ball thrown upward at 24 ft/sec from a platform 16 feet above the ground is $s(t) = 16 + 24t - 16t^2$ feet above the ground t seconds after it is thrown. Find:

a)   the velocity and acceleration of the ball at any time t,

b)   how many seconds it takes the ball to reach its highest point,

c)   how high the ball will go,

d)   how many seconds it takes the ball to reach the ground, and

e)   the velocity of the ball when it hits the ground.

SOLUTION: Note that the domain is $[0, \infty)$. a) $v(t) = s'(t) = 24 - 32t$ and $a(t) = v'(t) = s''(t) = -32$.

b) At the highest point the velocity is 0, so solve $v(t) = 0$. $24 - 32t = 0 \implies t = 24/32 = 3/4$. The ball reaches its highest point at 0.75 seconds.

c) To find how high the ball will go, evaluate $s(0.75)$. $s(0.75) = 16 + 24(0.75) - 16(0.75)^2 = 25$ ft.

d) When the ball reaches the ground, $s(t) = 0$. $0 = 16 + 24t - 16t^2 \implies 2t^2 - 3t - 2 = 0 \implies (2t+1)(t-2) = 0 \implies t = -1/2$ or $t = 2$. Since $t \geq 0$, discard $t = -1/2$. Thus the ball reaches the ground at 2 seconds.

e) $v(2) = 24 - 32(2) = -40$, so the ball will strike the ground at 40 ft/sec (in this context, the negative sign indicates the ball is moving downward).

21. A student with a water balloon is at the top of a 42 ft building. A mathematics professor who is 6 ft tall is walking below. How long before the professor arrives should the student release the missile if the object is to score a direct hit on the top of the professor's head?

SOLUTION: First draw a picture of the situation.

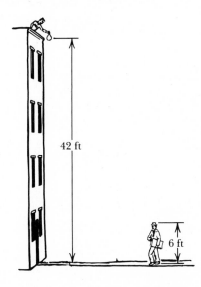

Assume that $a(t) = -32\,\text{ft/sec}^2$. Now $a(t) = v'(t)$, so $v(t) = -32t + C$, the family of all antiderivatives of $a(t)$. Since the student is going to drop (not throw) the balloon, the initial velocity, $v(0)$, is 0. Thus $v(0) = -32(0) + C = 0 \implies C = 0$, and $v(t) = -32t$. But $v(t) = s'(t)$, so $s(t) = -16t^2 + C$, the family of all antiderivatives of $v(t)$. Defining $s(t)$ as the distance from the ground at time t, obtain $s(0) = -16(0)^2 + C = 42 \implies C = 42$. This yields the equation $s(t) = -16t^2 + 42$, which yields the distance of the balloon above the ground at $t \geq 0$. What is desired is the time for the balloon to travel from the top of the building ($s = 42$, $t = 0$) to the top of the professor's head ($s = 6$). So $s(t) = -16t^2 + 42 = 6 \implies -16t^2 = -36 \implies t^2 = 36/16 \implies t = \pm 6/4 = \pm 3/2$. Since $t \geq 0$, discard $t = -3/2$. The desired time is 1.5 sec.

33. A track star figures that he starts with zero initial velocity and accelerates for the first 16 yd at a constant rate. He then runs the remainder of a 100-yd dash with a constant velocity. He knows he can run the 100 yd in 10 sec.   a) What is his acceleration for the first 16 yd.   b) How long does it take to run the first 16 yards?

SOLUTION: Examining the first part of the problem, set $a_1(t) = a$. Then $v_1(t) = at + C$ and since the initial velocity is 0, $v(0) = a(0) + C \implies C = 0$ and $v_1(t) = at$. Now $s_1(t) = \frac{1}{2}at^2 + C$ and, since the initial position is 0, $s_1(t) = \frac{1}{2}at^2$. Let t_1 be the time at which the runner reaches the 16 yard mark. Then $s_1(t_1) = \frac{1}{2}at_1^2 = 48 \implies t_1 = \pm\sqrt{96/a}$. Discarding $-\sqrt{96/a}$ since $t_1 > 0$, $t_1 = \sqrt{96/a}$.

Considering the second part of the problem, $v_2(t)$ is constant. In fact, $v_2(t) = v_1(t_1) = at_1$ since $v_1(t_1)$ is the velocity at the 16 yard mark. Now $s_2(t) = (at_1)t + C$. Defining $s_2(t)$ as the distance from the 16 yard mark yields $s_2(0) = (at_1)(0) + C = 0 \implies C = 0$, so $s_2(t) = at_1t$. Let t_2 be the time at which the runner reaches the 100 yard mark.

Then $s_2(t_2) = at_1t_2 = 252 \implies t_2 = (252/at_1)$.

In addition, $t_1 + t_2 = \sqrt{96/a} + (252/at_1) = \sqrt{96/a} + \dfrac{252}{a\sqrt{96/a}} = 10 \implies \dfrac{96}{a} + \dfrac{252}{a} =$

$10\sqrt{96/a} \implies \dfrac{348}{a} = 10\sqrt{96/a} \implies \dfrac{121104}{a^2} = 100(96/a) \implies 121104 = 9600a \implies a =$

$\dfrac{121104}{9600} = 12.615$.

Thus the runner's acceleration for the first 16 yards is $12.615\,\text{ft/sec}^2$ and the length of time he takes to cover that distance is $\sqrt{\dfrac{96}{12.615}} \approx 2.76\,\text{sec}$.

37. A building consists of 140 stories, each story being the same height. An object is dropped from the roof of the building and is observed to take two seconds to pass from the 105th story to the 70th story. What is the height of the building?

SOLUTION: Let x be the height of one story of the building in feet. Then the building is $140x$ feet high. Assume that $a(t) = -32$. Then $v(t) = -32t + C$, and since the object was dropped rather than thrown, $v(0) = 0$. Thus $C = 0$ and $v(t) = -32t$. So $s(t) = -16t^2 + C$. Defining $s(t)$ as the position above the ground, $s(0) = 140x$, so $C = 140x$ and $s(t) = -16t^2 + 140x$. Remember that x is a constant. Let t_1 be the time when the object passes the 105th story and t_2 be the time it passes the 70th story. Then $t_2 - t_1 = 2$, $s(t_1) = -16t_1^2 + 140x = 105x$, and $s(t_2) = -16t_2^2 + 140x = -16(t_1 + 2)^2 + 140x = 70x$.

So $16t_1^2 = 35x$ and $16(t_1 + 2)^2 = 70x$. Thus $32t_1^2 = 16(t_1 + 2)^2 \implies 2t_1^2 = (t_1 + 2)^2 \implies 2t_1^2 = t_1^2 + 4t + 4 \implies t_1^2 - 4t - 4 = 0 \implies t_1 = \dfrac{4 \pm \sqrt{16 + 16}}{2} = \dfrac{4 \pm 4\sqrt{2}}{2} = 2 \pm 2\sqrt{2}$. Discard $t_1 = 2 - 2\sqrt{2} < 0$ since $t_1 > 0$. Thus $t_1 = 2 + 2\sqrt{2} \approx 4.83\,\text{sec}$.

So $16(2 + 2\sqrt{2})^2 = 35x \implies x \approx 10.66$, and the height of the building is approximately $1492.08\,\text{ft}$.

_____**3.2**

Applications Involving
Maxima and Minima

COMMENT: Review the general strategy for solving max-min problems given in the text at (3.4).

7. A rectangular box with no top is to contain $2250\,\text{in}^3$. Find the dimensions to minimize the amount of material used to construct the box if the length of the base is three times the width.

SOLUTION:

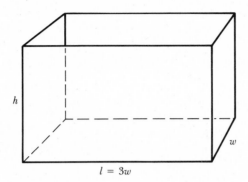

The amount of material needed is $A = lw + 2wh + 2lh$. In order to minimize this function, two of the three variables must be eliminated. It is given that $l = 3w$ and $V = lwh = 2250$. Thus $3w^2 h = 2250$ and $h = \dfrac{750}{w^2}$. Substitute into A and obtain

$$A = 3w^2 + 2w \left(\frac{750}{w^2} \right) + 6w \left(\frac{750}{w}^2 \right) = 3w^2 + 6000w^{-1},$$

a function in w with domain $(0, \infty)$.

$\dfrac{dA}{dw} = 6w - 6000w^{-2}$. To minimize A, solve $\dfrac{dA}{dw} = 0$. So $6w - \dfrac{6000}{w^2} = 0 \implies 6w^3 = 6000 \implies w^3 = 1000 \implies w = 10$. To show this is a minimum, evaluate $\dfrac{d^2 A}{dw^2}$ at $w = 10$.

$\dfrac{d^2 A}{dw^2} = 6 + 12000w^{-3}$ which is positive on $(0, \infty)$ so $w = 10$ is a minimum. The desired dimensions are: length $= 30$ in, width $= 10$ in, and height $= \dfrac{750}{10^2} = 7.5$ in.

11. The turning effect of a ship's rudder is known to be $T = k \cos \theta \sin^2 \theta$, where k is a positive constant and θ is the angle that the direction of the rudder makes with the keel line of the ship $(0 \leq \theta \leq \pi/2)$. For what value of θ is the rudder most effective?

SOLUTION: To maximize T, find $\dfrac{dT}{d\theta}$ and solve $\dfrac{dT}{d\theta} = 0$.

$\dfrac{dT}{d\theta} = k(-\sin \theta) \sin^2 \theta + k \cos \theta (2 \sin \theta \cos \theta) = 0 \implies -k \sin^3 \theta + 2k \sin \theta \cos^2 \theta = 0 \implies$
$-\sin^3 \theta + 2 \sin \theta (1 - \sin^2 \theta) = 0 \implies -\sin^3 \theta + 2 \sin \theta - 2 \sin^3 \theta = 0 \implies$
$\sin \theta (-3 \sin^2 \theta + 2) = 0 \implies \sin \theta = 0$ or $\sin \theta = \pm \sqrt{2/3}$.
Since $0 \leq \theta \leq \pi/2$, reject $\sin \theta = -\sqrt{2/3}$.

Thus $\theta = 0$ or $\theta = \arcsin \sqrt{2/3}$. To determine which, if either, is a maximum evaluate $\dfrac{d^2 T}{d\theta^2}$.

$$\frac{d^2 T}{d\theta^2} = -3k \sin^2 \theta \cos \theta + 2k \cos \theta \cos^2 \theta + 2k \sin \theta (2 \cos \theta)(-\sin \theta)$$

$$= k \left(-7 \sin^2 \theta \cos \theta + 2 \cos^3 \theta \right).$$

Now $\left.\dfrac{d^2 T}{d\theta^2}\right|_{\theta=0} = 2k > 0$ and $\left.\dfrac{d^2 T}{d\theta^2}\right|_{\theta=\arcsin \sqrt{2/3}} \approx -2.31 < 0$. Thus there is a maximum at $\theta = \arcsin \sqrt{2/3} \approx 54.7°$ and this is the angle which makes the rudder most effective.

15. An open rectangular box is to be made from a piece of cardboard 8 inches wide and 8 inches long by cutting a square from each corner and bending up the sides. Find the dimensions of the box with the largest volume.

SOLUTION:

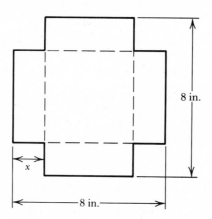

The volume of the resulting box is $V(x) = x(8 - 2x)(8 - 2x) = 4x(4 - x)^2$. The domain of the function is $(0,4)$ since both quantities x and $8 - 2x$ must be positive as they represent sides of the box. To maximize the volume, solve $V'(x) = 0$.

$$V'(x) = 4(4 - x)^2 + 8x(4 - x)(-1) = 4(4 - x)\left((4 - x) - 2x\right) = 4(4 - x)(4 - 3x).$$

$V'(x) = 0 \implies 4(4 - x)(4 - 3x) = 0 \implies x = 4$ or $x = 4/3$. Discard $x = 4$ since it is not in the domain. To determine that $x = 4/3$ is a maximum, evaluate $V''(4/3)$.

$$V''(x) = 4(-1)(4 - 3x) + 4(4 - x)(-3) = 4(3x - 4 + 3x - 12) = 4(6x - 16) = 8(3x - 8).$$

$V''(4/3) = 8(4 - 8) < 0$, so V does achieve a maximum at $x = 4/3$. Thus the desired dimensions are: length = width = $8 - \frac{8}{3} = \frac{16}{3}$ in and height = $\frac{4}{3}$ in.

27. Find the volume of the largest right circular cylinder that can be placed inside a sphere of radius 1.

SOLUTION: Examine a cross section through the center of the sphere and perpendicular to the base, imposing a set of coordinate axes with origin at the center of the sphere.

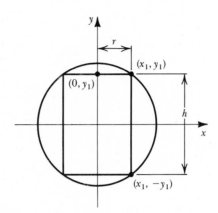

The volume to be maximized is $V = \pi r^2 h$. Since chords of equal length are equidistant from the center of a circle, the x-axis does bisect the length h. Thus (x_1, y_1) and $(x_1, -y_1)$ are valid ordered pairs for the two points above. So $r = x_1 - 0 = x_1$, $h = y_1 - (-y_1) = 2y_1$ and $V = \pi x_1^2 (2y_1)$. Since $x_1^2 + y_1^2 = 1$, $V = 2\pi(1 - y_1^2)y_1 = 2\pi(y_1 - y_1^3)$. Now $\dfrac{dV}{dy_1} = 2\pi(1 - 3y_1^2)$ and $\dfrac{dV}{dy_1} = 0 \implies y_1 = \pm\sqrt{1/3}$. Since $y_1 > 0$, discard $y_1 = -\sqrt{1/3}$. $\dfrac{d^2V}{dy_1^2} = 2\pi(-6y_1)$ which is negative at $y_1 = \sqrt{1/3}$. Thus $y_1 = \sqrt{1/3}$ does yield a maximum. $y_1 = \sqrt{1/3} \implies V = 2\pi\left(1 - (\sqrt{1/3})^2\right)\sqrt{1/3} = 2\pi(2/3)\sqrt{1/3} = \dfrac{4\pi}{3\sqrt{3}} = \dfrac{4\pi\sqrt{3}}{9}$.

41. Boondockia Inc. has decided that the tent described in EXERCISE 40 using the minimal amount of material is not marketable because it does not have enough floor space. They have decided instead to design the tent so that it is 6 ft wide at the bottom and has a cross section in the form of a rectangle topped by a triangle. The minimal height of the rectangle is to be one foot and the total height to the center of the tent at least 30 in. Assuming all other specifications are the same as those in EXERCISE 40, how should the tent be designed to minimize the amount of material required?

SOLUTION: Since $d \geq 1$, let $d = 1 + x$ with $x \geq 0$. Since $d + h \geq 2.5$ let $d + h = 2.5 + y$ with $y \geq 0$. Then $h = 2.5 + y - d = 2.5 + y - (1 + x) = 1.5 + y - x$.

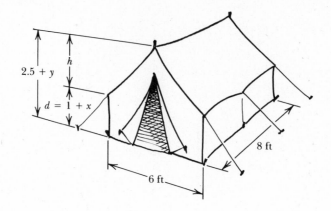

Then the surface area to be minimized is

$$S = 6(8) + 2(6d) + 2(8d) + 2\left(\frac{1}{2}(6h)\right) + 2\left(8\sqrt{h^2 + 3^2}\right) = 48 + 28d + 6h + 16\sqrt{h^2 + 9}$$

$$= 48 + 28(1 + x) + 6(1.5 + y - x) + 16\sqrt{(1.5 + y - x)^2 + 9}$$

$$= 85 + 22x + 6y + 16\sqrt{(1.5 + y - x)^2 + 9}.$$

The volume of the tent will be $8A$ where A is the cross-sectional area of the tent.

$$A = 6d + \frac{1}{2}(6h) = 6(1 + x) + 3(1.5 + y - x) = 10.5 + 3x + 3y,$$

and thus $V = 8(10.5 + 3x + 3y) = 12(7 + 2x + 2y)$.

So $V = 100 \implies 12(7 + 2x + 2y) = 100 \implies 7 + 2x + 2y = \dfrac{25}{3} \implies y = \dfrac{2}{3} - x$. Recall that $y \geq 0$ so $x \leq 2/3$.

So minimize $S(x)$ for $0 \leq x \leq \frac{2}{3}$ where

$$S(x) = 85 + 22x + 6\left(\frac{2}{3} - x\right) + 16\sqrt{\left(\frac{3}{2} + \frac{2}{3} - x - x\right)^2 + 9}$$

$$= 89 + 16x + 16\sqrt{\left(\frac{13}{6} - 2x\right)^2 + 9}, \qquad \text{and}$$

$$\frac{dS}{dx} = 16 + 16\left(\frac{1}{2}\left(\left(\frac{13}{6} - 2x\right)^2 + 9\right)^{-1/2}\left(2\left(\frac{13}{6} - 2x\right)(-2)\right)\right)$$

$$= 16\left(1 - \frac{2\left(\dfrac{13}{6} - 2x\right)}{\left(\left(\dfrac{13}{6} - 2x\right)^2 + 9\right)^{1/2}}\right).$$

Now $\dfrac{dS}{dx} = 0 \implies \left(\left(\dfrac{13}{6} - 2x\right)^2 + 9\right)^{1/2} - 2\left(\dfrac{13}{6} - 2x\right) = 0 \implies \left(\dfrac{13}{6} - 2x\right)^2 + 9 =$

$4\left(\dfrac{13}{6} - 2x\right)^2 \implies 9 = 3\left(\dfrac{13}{6} - 2x\right)^2 \implies \dfrac{13}{6} - 2x = \pm\sqrt{3} \implies x = \dfrac{13}{12} \pm \dfrac{\sqrt{3}}{2}.$

$x = \dfrac{13}{12} - \dfrac{\sqrt{3}}{2}$ yields $d = 1 + \dfrac{13}{12} - \dfrac{\sqrt{3}}{2} = \dfrac{25}{12} - \dfrac{\sqrt{3}}{2}$ and $h = \dfrac{3}{2} + \dfrac{2}{3} - \left(\dfrac{13}{12} - \dfrac{\sqrt{3}}{2}\right) - \left(\dfrac{13}{12} - \dfrac{\sqrt{3}}{2}\right) =$

$\dfrac{13}{6} - \dfrac{13}{6} + \sqrt{3} = \sqrt{3}.$

So $d \approx 1.22\,\text{ft}$ and $h \approx 1.73\,\text{ft}$ produces the desired minimum.

Related Rates ———3.3

11. Gas is being pumped into a spherical balloon at the rate of $1\,\text{ft}^3/\text{min}$. How fast is the diameter of the balloon increasing when the balloon contains $36\,\text{ft}^3$ of gas?

SOLUTION: The volume of the sphere is $V = \frac{4}{3}\pi r^3 = \frac{4}{3}\pi\left(\frac{d}{2}\right)^3 = \frac{1}{6}\pi d^3$. Find $\left.\dfrac{dd}{dt}\right|_{V=36}$ if

$\dfrac{dV}{dt} = 1$. By the chain rule, $\dfrac{dV}{dt} = \dfrac{dV}{dd} \cdot \dfrac{dd}{dt} = \dfrac{1}{2}\pi d^2 \dfrac{dd}{dt}$ and $\dfrac{dd}{dt} = \dfrac{2dV/dt}{\pi d^2}$. When $V = 36$,

$\dfrac{1}{6}\pi d^3 = 36 \implies d^3 = \dfrac{216}{\pi} \implies d = \dfrac{6}{\sqrt[3]{\pi}}$. So $\left.\dfrac{dd}{dt}\right|_{V=36} = \dfrac{2(1)}{\pi\left(6/\sqrt[3]{\pi}\right)^2} = \dfrac{2}{36\sqrt[3]{\pi}} = \dfrac{1}{18\sqrt[3]{\pi}}$. Thus

the radius is increasing at $\dfrac{1}{18\sqrt[3]{\pi}}\,\text{ft}/\text{min}$.

19. A rectangular swimming pool 50 feet long and 30 feet wide is being filled with water to a depth of 8 feet at the rate of $3\,\text{ft}^3/\text{min}$. a) How long does it take to fill the pool? b) At what rate is the depth of water in the pool increasing when the pool is half full of water?

SOLUTION: a) The volume of the pool is $(50)(30)(8) = 12{,}000\,\text{ft}^3$. Since the pool is being filled at the constant rate of $3\,\text{ft}^3/\text{min}$, it will take $\dfrac{12{,}000\,\text{ft}^3}{3\,\text{ft}^3/\text{min}} = 4000\,\text{min} = 66\frac{2}{3}\,\text{hr}$ to fill the pool.

b) During filling, the volume of water is $V = (30)(50)(x) = 1500x$ and $\dfrac{dV}{dt} = \dfrac{dV}{dx} \cdot \dfrac{dx}{dt} = 1500\dfrac{dx}{dt}$ so $\dfrac{dx}{dt} = \dfrac{dV/dt}{1500} = \dfrac{3}{1500} = \dfrac{1}{500}\,\text{ft}/\text{min}$ at all times.

23. A kite is carried horizontally at 1.5 m/sec and is rising at 2.0 m/sec. How fast is the string released to maintain this flight when 100 m of string have been released and the kite is at an altitude of 80 m?

SOLUTION:

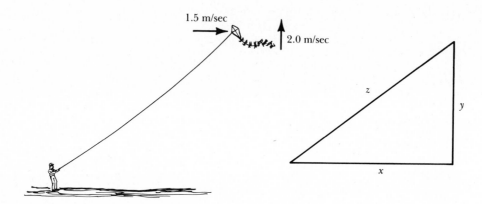

Let x be the vertical distance and y the horizontal distance of the kite at time t. We know $\dfrac{dx}{dt} = 2.0$ and $\dfrac{dy}{dt} = 1.5$. Also, from the Pythagorean Theorem, $z^2 = x^2 + y^2$. Find $\dfrac{dz}{dt}\Big|_{z=100, x=80}$. Differentiating implicitly with the chain rule,

$$2z\frac{dz}{dt} = 2x\frac{dx}{dt} + 2y\frac{dy}{dt} \quad \text{and} \quad \frac{dz}{dt} = \frac{x\dfrac{dx}{dt} + y\dfrac{dy}{dt}}{z}.$$

Find y when $x = 80$ and $z = 100$. Now $y^2 = 100^2 - 80^2 = 3600 \implies y = \pm 60$, so $y = 60$ since $y > 0$.

Thus $\dfrac{dz}{dt}\Big|_{z=100, x=80} = \dfrac{80(2) + 60(1.5)}{100} = 2.5$, and the string must be released at 2.5 m/sec.

29. A revolving beacon located 1 mi from a straight shoreline turns at 1 revolution per minute. Find the speed of the spot of light along the shore when it is 2 mi away from the point on the shore nearest the light.

SOLUTION: Let θ be the angle formed by the rays from the beacon to the nearest spot on the shore and any other spot on the shore, and let x be the length between those two rays along the shore.

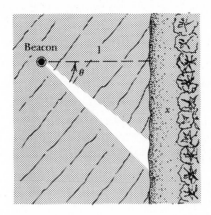

We know $\dfrac{d\theta}{dt} = 2\pi$, i.e., one revolution per minute, and $\tan\theta = \dfrac{x}{1}$. Find $\dfrac{dx}{dt}\Big|_{x=2}$.

Thus $\sec^2\theta\,\dfrac{d\theta}{dt} = \dfrac{dx}{dt}$ and when $x = 2$, $z = \sqrt{5}$ and $\sec\theta = \dfrac{\sqrt{5}}{1}$. So $\dfrac{dx}{dt}\Big|_{x=2} = (\sqrt{5})^2 2\pi = 10\pi$ mi/min.

33. A horse trough 10 ft long has a cross section in the shape of an inverted equilateral triangle with an altitude of 2 ft. When filled with water it is found that the trough leaks water through a crack in the bottom at the rate of $1\,\text{ft}^3$/hour.   a) At what rate is the height of the water in the trough decreasing when the depth of water is 1 foot?   b) At what rate is the height of water in the trough decreasing when the trough contains $10\,\text{ft}^3$ of water?

SOLUTION:

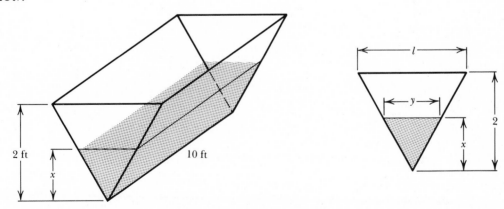

Let y be the length of a side of the equilateral triangle describing the water in the trough. The volume of water when the depth is x ft is $V = 10(\frac{1}{2}yx) = 5yx$. Also $\dfrac{dV}{dt} = -1$. Find   a) $\dfrac{dx}{dt}\Big|_{x=1}$

and   b) $\dfrac{dx}{dt}\Big|_{V=10}$.

a) Let l be the length of a side of the triangle describing the trough. Then $l^2 = \left(\frac{1}{2}l\right)^2 + 2^2 \implies$ $\frac{3}{4}l^2 = 4 \implies l^2 = 16/3 \implies l = \pm 4/\sqrt{3}$. Since $l > 0$, reject $l = -4/\sqrt{3}$.

Since the triangles are similar, $\dfrac{y}{l} = \dfrac{x}{2} \implies y = \dfrac{lx}{2} = \dfrac{4x/\sqrt{3}}{2} = \dfrac{2x}{\sqrt{3}}$ and $V = 5xy = 5x\left(\dfrac{2x}{\sqrt{3}}\right) =$ $\dfrac{10}{\sqrt{3}}x^2$. Thus $\dfrac{dV}{dt} = \dfrac{20}{\sqrt{3}}x \cdot \dfrac{dx}{dt}$ and $\dfrac{dx}{dt} = \dfrac{\sqrt{3}\,dV/dt}{20x}$; so $\dfrac{dx}{dt}\bigg|_{x=1} = \dfrac{\sqrt{3}(-1)}{20}$.

Thus the depth is decreasing at $\dfrac{\sqrt{3}}{20}$ ft/hr (the negative sign indicates that the depth is decreasing).

b) To find $\dfrac{dx}{dt}\bigg|_{V=10}$, find x. From a), $V = \dfrac{10}{\sqrt{3}}x^2$, so $10 = \dfrac{10}{\sqrt{3}}x^2 \implies x^2 = \sqrt{3} \implies x = \pm\sqrt[4]{3}$

and, since $x \geq 0$, reject $x = -\sqrt[4]{3}$. Thus $\dfrac{dx}{dt}\bigg|_{V=10} = -\dfrac{\sqrt[4]{3}}{20}$, and the depth is decreasing at $-\dfrac{\sqrt[4]{3}}{20}$ ft/hr.

Differentials _____3.4

11. Find dy and Δy in terms of x and Δx if $y = \tan x$.

SOLUTION: $\dfrac{dy}{dx} = \sec^2 x$ so $dy = \sec^2 x\,\Delta x$. Also, $\Delta y = f(x+\Delta x) - f(x) = \tan(x+\Delta x) - \tan x$.

15. Find dy and Δy if $y = f(x) = x^3 - 2x$ and   a) $x = 2, \Delta x = 0.1$,   b) $x = -1, \Delta x = -0.2$.

SOLUTION: $f'(x) = 3x^2 - 2$ so $dy = (3x^2 - 2)\,\Delta x$.

$$\Delta y = f(x + \Delta x) - f(x) = \left((x + \Delta x)^3 - 2(x + \Delta x)\right) - (x^3 - 2x)$$
$$= x^3 + 3x^2\Delta x + 3x(\Delta x)^2 + (\Delta x)^3 - 2x - 2\Delta x - x^3 + 2x$$
$$= \Delta x\left(3x^2 + 3x\,\Delta x + (\Delta x)^2 - 2\right).$$

a) $dy = \left(3(2)^2 - 2\right)(0.1) = 1.$
$\Delta y = 0.1\left(3(2)^2 + 3(2)(0.1) + (0.1)^2 - 2\right) = 0.1\,(12 + 0.6 + 0.01 - 2) = 1.061.$
b) $dy = \left(3(-1)^2 - 2\right)(-0.2) = -0.2.$
$\Delta y = -0.2\left(3(-1)^2 + 3(-1)(-0.2) + (-0.2)^2 - 2\right) = -0.2\,(3 + 0.6 + 0.04 - 2) = -0.328.$

21. Find   a) dy,   b) Δy, and   c) approximate $f(x + \Delta x)$ for $y = f(x) = \sqrt{x} = x^{1/2}$ with $x = 9$ and $\Delta x = 0.03$.

SOLUTION: $dy = \frac{1}{2}x^{-1/2}\,\Delta x$. $\Delta y = \sqrt{x + \Delta x} - \sqrt{x}$.
Using $x = 9$ and $\Delta x = 0.03$, $dy = \frac{1}{2}(9)^{-1/2}(0.03) = \frac{1}{2} \cdot \frac{1}{3} \cdot \frac{3}{100} = \frac{1}{200} = 0.005.$

Using $x = 9$ and $\Delta x = 0.03$,

$$\Delta y = \sqrt{9 + 0.03} - \sqrt{9} = \sqrt{9.03} - \sqrt{9} \approx 0.00499584.$$

Also $f(9) = 3$, so $f(9 + 0.03) \approx 3 + 0.05 = 3.005$.

23. Use differentials and an easily calculated value to approximate $\sin 31°$.

SOLUTION: Select $y = f(x) = \sin x$ with $x = 30° = \dfrac{\pi}{6}$ and $\Delta x = 1° = \dfrac{2\pi}{360}$. Then $dy = \cos x\, dx$ and at $x = \pi/6$ and $\Delta x = \pi/180$, $dy = \left(\cos \frac{\pi}{6}\right)\left(\frac{\pi}{180}\right) = \dfrac{\pi\sqrt{3}}{360}$.

Thus, $\sin 31° \approx \dfrac{1}{2} + \dfrac{\pi\sqrt{3}}{360} = \dfrac{180 + \pi\sqrt{3}}{360} \approx 0.5151$.

33. A hole 1/4 inch in diameter has been drilled through a wooden 4×4. The hole is to be enlarged to 5/16 inch in diameter. Use differentials to approximate how much additional wood has to be removed. (The dimensions of a wooden 4×4 are 3.5 inches by 3.5 inches.)

SOLUTION: The hole is a cylinder with radius 1/8 inch and height 3.5 inch whose radius is to be expanded to 5/32 inch. The volume of a cylinder is $V = \pi r^2 h$. In this case, $V = \frac{7}{2}\pi r^2$ with $r = 1/8$ and $\Delta r = 1/32$. Then $dV = 7\pi r\, \Delta r$, so $dV = 7\pi(1/8)(1/32) = 7\pi/256$.

Thus approximately $0.0859\, \text{in}^3$ of wood must be removed.

37. A metal spherical ball with a volume of $36\, \text{cm}^3$ is given a chrome plating 0.2 cm thick. Use differentials to approximate the volume of the chromium required to plate the ball.

SOLUTION: The volume of a sphere is $V = \frac{4}{3}\pi r^3$, so $dV = 4\pi r^2\, \Delta r$. $V = 36 = \frac{4}{3}\pi r^3 \implies r^3 = \dfrac{27}{\pi} \implies r = \dfrac{3}{\sqrt[3]{\pi}}$. Thus $dV = 4\pi \left(\dfrac{3}{\sqrt[3]{\pi}}\right)^2 (0.2) = \dfrac{36\sqrt[3]{\pi}}{5}$ and approximately $10.54\, \text{cm}^3$ of chromium are needed.

41. Temperature on weather forecasts is generally given to the nearest degree. Suppose you are told that the present temperature is $20°C$, which means that it is somewhere between $19.5°C$ and $20.5°C$. Use differentials to approximate the maximum error in degrees Fahrenheit that can be produced if the $20°C$ figure is converted to $68°F$.

SOLUTION: Since $0°C = 32°F$ and $100°C = 212°F$ and the function is linear, $m = \dfrac{212 - 32}{100 - 0} = 9/5$ and $F = \frac{9}{5}C + 32$.

Thus $dF = \frac{9}{5}\Delta C$. Since $dC = \pm 0.5$, $dF = \frac{9}{5}\left(\pm\frac{1}{2}\right) = \pm 0.9$. This is true regardless of the Celsius temperature, so the temperature will be between $67.1°F$ and $68.9°F$.

Indeterminate Forms: L'Hôpital's Rule

5. Determine $\lim\limits_{x \to -2} \dfrac{2 + 9x - 2x^2 - 3x^3}{2x^4 + 7x^3 + 10x^2 + 7x - 2}$.

SOLUTION: First determine that the hypotheses of L'Hôpital's rule are satisfied. $\lim\limits_{x \to -2}(2 + 9x - 2x^2 - 3x^3) = 0$ and $\lim\limits_{x \to -2}(2x^4 + 7x^3 + 10x^2 + 7x - 2) = 0$ which does yield the indeterminate form $\dfrac{0}{0}$. Thus

$$\lim_{x \to -2} \frac{2 + 9x - 2x^2 - 3x^3}{2x^4 + 7x^3 + 10x^2 + 7x - 2} = \lim_{x \to -2} \frac{9 - 4x - 9x^2}{8x^3 + 21x^2 + 20x + 7}$$

$$= \frac{\lim\limits_{x \to -2}(9 - 4x - 9x^2)}{\lim\limits_{x \to -2}(3x^3 + 21x^2 + 20x + 7)} = \frac{9 + 8 - 36}{-64 + 84 - 40 + 7} = \frac{19}{13}.$$

9. Determine $\lim\limits_{x \to 0} \dfrac{\sin 2x}{3x}$.

SOLUTION: $\lim\limits_{x \to 0} \sin 2x = 0$ and $\lim\limits_{x \to 0} 3x = 0$ which yields the indeterminate form $\dfrac{0}{0}$. So $\lim\limits_{x \to 0} \dfrac{\sin 2x}{3x} = \lim\limits_{x \to 0} \dfrac{(\cos 2x)(2)}{3} = \dfrac{2}{3}$.

15. Determine $\lim\limits_{x \to 2} \dfrac{\sqrt{4x + 1} - \sqrt[3]{13x + 1}}{x + 2}$.

SOLUTION: L'Hôpital's rule <u>cannot</u> be used here since $\lim\limits_{x \to 2}(x + 2) = 4$. $\lim\limits_{x \to 2} \dfrac{\sqrt{4x + 1} - \sqrt[3]{13x + 1}}{x + 2} = \dfrac{\sqrt{9} - \sqrt[3]{27}}{4} = 0$.

21. Determine $\lim\limits_{x \to -\infty} \dfrac{5 - 2x^3 - 3x^4}{3 + 2x + 7x^4}$.

SOLUTION: $\lim\limits_{x \to -\infty}(5 - 2x^3 - 3x^4) = -\infty$ and $\lim\limits_{x \to -\infty}(3 + 2x + 7x^4) = \infty$ which yields the indeterminate form $-\infty/\infty$. Thus $\lim\limits_{x \to -\infty} \dfrac{5 - 2x^3 - 3x^4}{3 + 2x + 7x^4} = \lim\limits_{x \to -\infty} \dfrac{-6x^2 - 12x^3}{2 + 28x^3}$.

But $\lim\limits_{x\to-\infty}(-6x^2-12x^3)=\infty$ and $\lim\limits_{x\to-\infty}(2+28x^3)=-\infty$ which is the indeterminate form $\infty/-\infty$. Thus

$$\lim_{x\to-\infty}\frac{-6x^2-12x^3}{2+28x^3}=\lim_{x\to-\infty}\frac{-12x-36x^2}{84x^2}=\lim_{x\to-\infty}\frac{-1-3x}{7x}.$$

Again $\lim\limits_{x\to-\infty}(-1-3x)=-\infty$ and $\lim\limits_{x\to-\infty}(7x)=\infty$ which yields the indeterminate form $-\infty/\infty$.
So $\lim\limits_{x\to-\infty}\dfrac{-1-3x}{7x}=\lim\limits_{x\to-\infty}\dfrac{-3}{7}=\dfrac{-3}{7}$. Thus $\lim\limits_{x\to-\infty}\dfrac{5-2x^3-3x^4}{3+2x+7x^4}=-\dfrac{3}{7}$.
Note that this limit can be evaluated without L'Hôpital's rule by factoring x^4 from numerator and denominator.

29. Determine $\lim\limits_{x\to0}\dfrac{4x^2\cos3x}{\sin^2 3x}$.

SOLUTION: $\lim\limits_{x\to0}(4x^2\cos3x)=0$ and $\lim\limits_{x\to0}\sin^2 3x=0$ which yields the indeterminate form $\dfrac{0}{0}$.
Thus

$$\lim_{x\to0}\frac{4x^2\cos3x}{\sin^2 3x}=\lim_{x\to0}\frac{8x\cos3x+4x^2(-\sin3x)(3)}{2\sin3x(\cos3x)(3)}$$

$$=\lim_{x\to0}\frac{8x\cos3x-12x^2\sin3x}{6\sin3x\cos3x}=\lim_{x\to0}\frac{8x\cos3x-12x^2\sin3x}{3\sin6x}.$$

Now $\lim\limits_{x\to0}(8x\cos3x-12x^2\sin3x)=0$ and $\lim\limits_{x\to0}(3\sin6x)=0$ which yields the indeterminate form $\dfrac{0}{0}$. So

$$\lim_{x\to0}\frac{8x\cos3x-12x^2\sin3x}{3\sin6x}=\lim_{x\to0}\frac{8\cos3x-(8x\sin3x)(3)-24x\sin3x-(12x^2\cos3x)(3)}{(3\cos6x)(6)}$$

$$=\lim_{x\to0}\frac{8\cos3x-24x\sin3x-24x\sin3x-36x^2\cos3x}{18\cos6x}$$

$$=\lim_{x\to0}\frac{4(2-9x^2)\cos3x-48x\sin3x}{18\cos6x}=\frac{4(1)(2-0)-0}{18(1)}=\frac{4}{9}.$$

Thus $\lim\limits_{x\to0}\dfrac{4x^2\cos3x}{(\sin3x)^2}=\dfrac{4}{9}$.

33. Determine $\lim\limits_{x\to\infty}\left(\dfrac{1}{x^2+2}-\dfrac{1}{x}\right)$.

SOLUTION: L'Hôpital's rule cannot be used on this form of the limit. However,

$$\lim_{x\to\infty}\left(\frac{1}{x^2+2}-\frac{1}{x}\right)=\lim_{x\to\infty}\frac{x-(x^2+2)}{(x^2+2)x}=\lim_{x\to\infty}\frac{-x^2+x-2}{x^3+2x},$$

which does yield the indeterminate form $-\infty/\infty$.

Thus $\lim\limits_{x\to\infty} \dfrac{-x^2 + x - 2}{x^3 + 2x} = \lim\limits_{x\to\infty} \dfrac{-2x + 1}{3x^2 + 2}$. This again yields the indeterminate form $-\infty/\infty$.

Thus $\lim\limits_{x\to\infty} \dfrac{-2x + 1}{3x^2 + 2} = \lim\limits_{x\to\infty} \dfrac{-2}{6x} = 0$. Therefore, $\lim\limits_{x\to\infty} \left(\dfrac{1}{x^2 + 2} - \dfrac{1}{x} \right) = \lim\limits_{x\to\infty} \dfrac{-2}{6x} = 0$.

39. Determine $\lim\limits_{x\to\frac{\pi}{2}^-} \left(x - \dfrac{\pi}{2} \right) \sec x$.

SOLUTION: This limit is not in the proper form to use L'Hôpital's rule. However,

$$\lim\limits_{x\to\frac{\pi}{2}^-} \left(x - \dfrac{\pi}{2} \right) \sec x = \lim\limits_{x\to\frac{\pi}{2}^-} \dfrac{x - (\pi/2)}{\cos x},$$

which does yield the indeterminate form $\dfrac{0}{0}$. Thus $\lim\limits_{x\to\frac{\pi}{2}^-} \dfrac{x - (\pi/2)}{\cos x} = \lim\limits_{x\to\frac{\pi}{2}^-} \dfrac{1}{-\sin x} = -1$, so

$\lim\limits_{x\to\frac{\pi}{2}^-} \left(x - \dfrac{\pi}{2} \right) \sec x = -1$.

45. Find all values of c that satisfy the conclusions of the Cauchy mean value theorem, if the hypotheses of the theorem hold for $f(x) = x^2 - 3x$, $g(x) = x^2 - 1$, on $[0, 2]$.

SOLUTION: $f'(x) = 2x - 3$ and $g'(x) = 2x$, so f and g are differentiable on $(0, 2)$ and continuous on $[0, 2]$. Also, $g'(x) = 2x \neq 0$ on $(0, 2)$. Thus the hypotheses of the Cauchy mean value theorem are satisfied and there exists c such that $\dfrac{f(2) - f(0)}{g(2) - g(0)} = \dfrac{f'(c)}{g'(c)} \implies \dfrac{(4 - 3(2)) - (0 - 0)}{(4 - 1) - (0 - 1)} = $

$\dfrac{2c - 3}{2c} \implies \dfrac{-2}{4} = \dfrac{2c - 3}{2c} \implies -4c = 8c - 12 \implies -12c = -12 \implies c = 1$.

53. Suppose $f'(a)$ and $\lim\limits_{x\to a} f'(x)$ exist. Show that f' must be continuous at a.

SOLUTION: Since $f'(a)$ exists and $\lim\limits_{x\to a} f'(x)$ exists, it remains to show that $\lim\limits_{x\to a} f'(x) = f'(a)$.

Since $f'(a)$ exists, $\lim\limits_{x\to a} \dfrac{f(x) - f(a)}{x - a}$ exists. Let $F(x) = f(x) - f(a)$ and $G(x) = x - a$.

Now $\lim\limits_{x\to a} F(x) = f(a) - f(a) = 0$ and $\lim\limits_{x\to a} G(x) = a - a = 0$, which yields the indeterminate form $\dfrac{0}{0}$. Applying L'Hôpital's rule, $\lim\limits_{x\to a} \dfrac{F(x)}{G(x)} = \lim\limits_{x\to a} \dfrac{F'(x)}{G'(x)} = \lim\limits_{x\to a} \dfrac{f'(x) - 0}{1 - 0} = f'(a)$.

Thus f' is continuous at a.

Newton's Method

3. Approximate to four decimal places the value of x lying in $[-2, 0]$ for which $f(x) = x^3 - 9x^2 + 12 = 0$.

SOLUTION: $f'(x) = 3x^2 - 18x$. Let $x_0 = -1$. Then

$$x_1 = x_0 - \frac{f(x_0)}{f'(x_0)} = -1 - \frac{f(-1)}{f'(-1)} = -1 - \frac{-1 - 9 + 12}{3 + 18} = -1 - \frac{2}{21} \approx -1.095238$$

$$x_2 = -1.095238 - \frac{f(-1.095238)}{f'(-1.095238)} = -1.095238 - (-0.004705) = -1.090532$$

$$x_3 = -1.090532 - \frac{f(-1.090532)}{f'(-1.090532)} = -1.090532 - (-0.000011),$$

so the solution correct to four decimal places is -1.0905.

13. Consider the equation $0 = \dfrac{1}{x} - a$, where a is a nonzero constant. The only solution to this equation is $\dfrac{1}{a}$, the reciprocal of a. Show that Newton's method applied to $f(x) = \dfrac{1}{x} - a$ produces the approximations $x_{n+1} = 2x_n - ax_n^2$.

SOLUTION: Let $f(x) = \dfrac{1}{x} - a$. Then $f'(x) = \dfrac{-1}{x^2}$, and

$$x_{n+1} = x_n - \frac{f(x_n)}{f'(x_n)} = x_n - \frac{\dfrac{1}{x_n} - a}{-\dfrac{1}{x_n^2}}$$

$$= x_n + \frac{x_n^2}{x_n} - ax_n^2 = 2x_n - ax_n^2.$$

17. Find an approximation, accurate to within six decimal places, to the nonzero intercept of the graph of $y = x^2$ and $y = \sin x$.

SOLUTION: The intercept of the graphs of $y = x^2$ and $y = \sin x$ can be found by solving $f(x) = x^2 - \sin x = 0$. Let $x_0 = 1$. $f'(x) = 2x - \cos x$. Then

$$x_1 = 1 - \frac{1 - \sin 1}{2 - \cos 1} \approx 0.89139599$$

$$x_2 = 0.89139599 - \frac{(0.89139599)^2 - \sin(0.89139599)}{2(0.89139599) - \cos(0.89139599)} \approx 0.87698484$$

$$x_3 = 0.87698484 - \frac{(0.87698484)^2 - \sin(0.87698484)}{2(0.87698484) - \cos(0.87698484)} \approx 0.87672629$$

$$x_4 = 0.87672629 - \frac{(0.87672629)^2 - \sin(0.87672629)}{2(0.87672629) - \cos(0.87672629)} \approx 0.87672621.$$

The intercept is $(0.876726, 0.768649)$ correct to six decimal places.

23. Use Newton's method to find an approximation, accurate to three decimal places, to the point on the graph of $y = \dfrac{1}{x}$ that is closest to the point $(1, 0)$.

SOLUTION: Let $\left(x, \dfrac{1}{x}\right)$ be a point on the graph of $y = \dfrac{1}{x}$. Then the distance between $\left(x, \dfrac{1}{x}\right)$ and $(1, 0)$ is $d = \sqrt{(x - 1)^2 + \left(\dfrac{1}{x} - 0\right)^2}$. To minimize the distance, solve $\dfrac{dd}{dx} = 0$.

$$\frac{dd}{dx} = \frac{1}{2}\left((x - 1)^2 + \left(\frac{1}{x}\right)^2\right)^{-1/2}\left(2(x - 1) + 2\left(\frac{1}{x}\right)\left(\frac{-1}{x^2}\right)\right)$$

$$= \frac{(x - 1) - \dfrac{1}{x^3}}{\sqrt{(x - 1)^2 + (1/x)^2}} = \frac{x^4 - x^3 - 1}{x^3\sqrt{(x - 1)^2 + (1/x)^2}}.$$

$\dfrac{dd}{dx} = 0 \implies x^4 - x^3 - 1 = 0.$

Let $f(x) = x^4 - x^3 - 1$. Then $f'(x) = 4x^3 - 3x^2$. Let $x_0 = 1$.

$$x_1 = 1 - \frac{1 - 1 - 1}{4 - 3} = 2$$

$$x_2 = 2 - \frac{2^4 - 2^3 - 1}{4(2)^3 - 3(2)^2} = 1.65$$

$$x_3 = 1.65 - \frac{(1.65)^4 - (1.65)^3 - 1}{4(1.65)^3 - 3(1.65)^2} \approx 1.454113$$

$$x_4 = 1.454113 - \frac{(1.454113)^4 - (1.454113)^3 - 1}{4(1.454113)^3 - 3(1.454113)^2} \approx 1.387577$$

$$x_5 = 1.387577 - \frac{(1.387577)^4 - (1.387577)^3 - 1}{4(1.387577)^3 - 3(1.387577)^2} \approx 1.380357$$

$$x_6 = 1.380357 - \frac{(1.380357)^4 - (1.380357)^3 - 1}{4(1.380357)^3 - 3(1.380357)^2} \approx 1.380312.$$

Thus the point is $\left(1.380, \dfrac{1}{1.380}\right) = (1.380, 0.725)$ accurate to three decimal places.

29. Use the secant method to approximate the solution of $f(x) = x^3 - 9x^2 + 12 = 0$ on $[-2, 0]$.

SOLUTION: Let $x_0 = -1$ and $x_1 = -1.5$.
Then

$$x_2 = -1.5 - \frac{\left((-1.5)^3 - 9(-1.5)^2 + 12\right)(-1.5 + 1)}{\left((-1.5)^3 - 9(-1.5)^2 + 12\right) - (-1 - 9 + 12)} \approx -1.073394$$

$$x_3 = -1.073394 - \frac{\left((-1.073394)^3 - 9(-1.073394)^2 + 12\right)(-1.073394 + 1.5)}{\left((-1.073394)^3 - 9(-1.073394)^2 + 12\right) - \left((-1.5)^3 - 9(-1.5)^2 + 12\right)}$$

$$\approx -1.087368$$

$$x_4 = -1.087368 - \frac{\left((-1.087368)^3 - 9(-1.087368)^2 + 12\right)(-1.087368 + 1.073394)}{\left((-1.087368)^3 - 9(-1.087368)^2 + 12\right) - \left((-1.073394)^3 - 9(-1.073394)^2 + 12\right)}$$

$$\approx -1.090549$$

$$x_5 = -1.090549 - \frac{\left((-1.090549)^3 - 9(-1.090549)^2 + 12\right)(-1.090549 + 1.087368)}{\left((-1.090549)^3 - 9(-1.090549)^2 + 12\right) - \left((-1.087368)^3 - 9(-1.087368)^2 + 12\right)}$$

$$\approx -1.090520.$$

Thus the solution is -1.0905 accurate to four decimal places.

_____**3.7**

Applications to Business and Economics

1. For the cost function, $C(x) = 1500 + 2x - 0.0003x^2$, find   a) the average cost function,   b) the marginal cost function,   c) the marginal average cost function,   d) the average cost per unit if 1000 units of an item are produced, and   e) the cost of the one-thousand-and-first unit produced.

SOLUTION: a) $c(x) = \dfrac{C(x)}{x} = \dfrac{1500}{x} + 2 - 0.0003x$ is the average cost function.

b) $C'(x) = 2 - 0.0006x$ is the marginal cost function.

c) $c'(x) = \dfrac{-1500}{x^2} - 0.0003$ is the marginal average cost function.

d) $c(1000) = \dfrac{1500}{1000} + 2 - 0.0003(1000) = 1.5 + 2 - 0.3 = 3.2$ is the average cost per unit if 1000 units are produced.

e) This is approximated by $C'(x) \approx C(x+1) - C(x)$. Thus the cost of the 1001st unit is

$$C(1001) - C(1000) \approx C'(1000) = 2 - 0.0006(1000) = 1.4.$$

7. $x^2 R(x) - 500x + 300R(x) - 1900 = 0$ denotes the revenue realized from the sale of x units of an item. Find the marginal revenue function.

SOLUTION: Differentiating implicitly, $2x R(x) + x^2 R'(x) - 500 + 300R'(x) = 0$, so $R'(x)(x^2 + 300) = 500 - 2x R(x)$ and $R'(x) = \dfrac{500 - 2x R(x)}{x^2 + 300}$ is the marginal revenue function.

15. Given a cost function of $C(x) = 2400 + 0.76x + 0.0001x^2$ dollars and a revenue function of $R(x) = 2.85x - 0.00008x^2$ dollars, what is the maximum profit that can now be realized and how many wastebaskets should be produced?

SOLUTION: The profit function to be maximized is

$$P(x) = R(x) - C(x) = (2.85x - 0.00008x^2) - (2400 + 0.76x + 0.0001x^2)$$
$$= 2.09x - 0.00018x^2 - 2400.$$

To maximize profit, solve $P'(x) = 0$. $P'(x) = 2.09 - 0.00036x = 0 \implies x = \dfrac{2.09}{0.00036} = 5805.\bar{5}$. $P''(x) = -0.00036$ is negative everywhere, so there is a maximum at $x = 5805.\bar{5}$. Thus, $5805.\bar{5}$ baskets should be produced. But this is impossible, so consider the profit from producing 5805 baskets against the profit from producing 5806 baskets.

$$P(5805) = 2.09(5805) - 0.00018(5805)^2 - 2400 = 3666.8055$$
$$P(5806) = 2.09(5806) - 0.00018(5806)^2 - 2400 = 3666.8055.$$

The same profit is realized whether 5805 of 5806 baskets are produced, so 5805 baskets should be produced, which will realize a profit of $3666.80.

21. The demand function for a certain item is $p(x) = 80 - 0.01x$ dollars per unit. Find the number of units at which a price change will not influence total revenue.

SOLUTION: To determine the number of units at which a price change will not affect total revenue, find x so that the elasticity, $E(x) = \dfrac{-p(x)}{x p'(x)} = 1$.

$E(x) = \dfrac{-p(x)}{xp'(x)}$, so $1 = \dfrac{-(80 - 0.01x)}{x(-0.01)} \implies -0.01x = -80 + 0.01x \implies -0.02x = -80 \implies$
$x = \dfrac{80}{0.02} = 4000.$

Thus if 4000 units are produced, unit elasticity will result, and a price change will not affect total revenue.

_____**Chapter 3**

Review Exercises

7. For $y = \tan x$, $x = \pi/4$ and $\Delta x = 0.01$ find: a) dy b) Δy c) approximate $f(x + \Delta x)$, assuming $y = f(x)$.

SOLUTION: a) $y = \tan x \implies \dfrac{dy}{dx} = \sec^2 x \implies dy = \sec^2 x \, \Delta x = \left(\sec^2 \frac{\pi}{4}\right)(0.01) = 0.02.$

b) $\Delta y = (y + \Delta y) - (y) = \tan(x + \Delta x) - \tan x = \tan\left(\frac{\pi}{4} + 0.01\right) - \tan \frac{\pi}{4} \approx 1.0202027 - 1 = 0.0202027.$

c) To approximate $f\left(\frac{\pi}{4} + 0.001\right)$, use $f(x + \Delta x) \approx f(x) + dy$. Thus, from a) and b) above,

$$f(x + \Delta x) = \tan(x + \Delta x) = \tan\left(\frac{\pi}{4} + 0.01\right) \approx \tan\frac{\pi}{4} + dy = 1 + 0.02 = 1.02.$$

11. Use L'Hôpital's rule, if applicable, to determine $\lim\limits_{x \to 3} \dfrac{\sqrt{x + 1} - 2}{x^2 - 9}$.

SOLUTION: $\lim\limits_{x \to 3} \dfrac{\sqrt{x + 1} - 2}{x^2 - 9} \to \dfrac{\sqrt{4} - 2}{3^2 - 9} = \dfrac{0}{0}$ so L'Hôpital's rule can be used.

$$\lim\limits_{x \to 3} \dfrac{(x + 1)^{1/2} - 2}{x^2 - 9} = \lim\limits_{x \to 3} \dfrac{\frac{1}{2}(x + 1)^{-1/2}}{2x} = \lim\limits_{x \to 3} \dfrac{1}{4x\sqrt{x + 1}} = \dfrac{1}{4(3)\sqrt{3 + 1}} = \dfrac{1}{24}.$$

17. Use L'Hôpital's rule, if applicable, to determine $\lim\limits_{x \to 0^+} \left(\dfrac{1}{x} - \dfrac{1}{\tan x}\right)$.

SOLUTION: This limit is the indeterminate form $\infty - \infty$. The expression can be written as $\dfrac{1}{x} - \dfrac{1}{\tan x} = \dfrac{\tan x - x}{x \tan x}$ and $\lim\limits_{x \to 0^+} \dfrac{\tan x - x}{x \tan x}$ does yield $0/0$, so L'Hôpital's rule can be used.

$$\lim\limits_{x \to 0^+} \dfrac{\tan x - x}{x \tan x} = \lim\limits_{x \to 0^+} \dfrac{\sec^2 x - 1}{\tan x + x \sec^2 x} = \lim\limits_{x \to 0^+} \dfrac{\tan^2 x}{\tan x + x \sec^2 x}$$

which also yields 0/0. Apply L'Hôpital's rule and obtain

$$\lim_{x \to 0^+} \frac{2 \tan x \sec^2 x}{\sec^2 x + (\sec^2 x + 2x \sec x \sec x \tan x)} = \lim_{x \to 0^+} \frac{2 \tan x \sec^2 x}{2 \sec^2 x + 2x \sec^2 x \tan x}$$

$$= \lim_{x \to 0^+} \frac{2 \sec^2 x \tan x}{2 \sec^2 x (1 + x \tan x)} = \lim_{x \to 0^+} \frac{\tan x}{1 + x \tan x} = \frac{0}{1} = 0.$$

Thus $\displaystyle \lim_{x \to 0^+} \left(\frac{1}{x} - \frac{1}{\tan x} \right) = 0.$

21. Find an approximation, accurate to 10^{-3}, to a value of x in the interval $[0, 2]$ for which $f(x) = x^4 - x^3 - 1 = 0$ by using   a) Newton's Method.

SOLUTION: a) $f'(x) = 4x^3 - 3x^2$. Let $x_0 = 1$. Then

$$x_1 = x_0 - \frac{f(x_0)}{f'(x_0)} = 1 - \frac{f(1)}{f'(1)} = 1 - \frac{1 - 1 - 1}{4 - 3} = 1 - \frac{-1}{1} = 2$$

$$x_2 = 2 - \frac{f(2)}{f'(2)} = 2 - \frac{7}{20} = 1.65$$

$$x_3 = 1.65 - \frac{f(1.65)}{f'(1.65)} \approx 1.65 - 0.195887 = 1.454114$$

$$x_4 = 1.454114 - \frac{f(1.454114)}{f'(1.454114)} \approx 1.454114 - 0.066536 = 1.387578$$

$$x_5 = 1.387578 - \frac{f(1.387578)}{f'(1.387578)} \approx 1.387578 - 0.007221 = 1.380357$$

$$x_6 = 1.380357 - \frac{f(1.380357)}{f'(1.380357)} \approx 1.380357 - 0.000080 = 1.380278.$$

Thus the desired solution is 1.380.

29. A ball is thrown upward from a point 3 ft above the ground with an initial velocity of 88 ft/sec. How long will the ball remain in the air?

SOLUTION: We know that $s(0) = 3$, $v(0) = 88$ and $a(t) = -32$. Thus $s(t) = -16t^2 + 88t + 3$ describes the distance above the ground at time t. To find the time the ball is in the air assuming the ball lands on the ground, solve $s(t) = 0$. Now $s(t) = 0 \implies -16t^2 + 88t + 3 = 0 \implies$
$t = \frac{-88 \pm \sqrt{7744 - 4(-16)(3)}}{-32} \approx \frac{-88 \pm 89.08}{-32}.$

Since $t \geq 0$, the ball is in the air approximately 5.53 sec.

35. Determine the point on the line with equation $2x + y = 3$ that is closest to the point $(2,1)$.

SOLUTION:

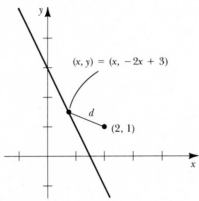

Let (x, y) be any point on the line $2x + y = 3$. Then $d = \sqrt{(x - 2)^2 + (y - 1)^2}$ is the distance to be minimized. Since $y = -2x + 3$,

$$d = \left((x - 2)^2 + (-2x + 2)^2\right)^{1/2} = \left(x^2 - 4x + 4 + 4x^2 - 8x + 4\right)^{1/2} = (5x^2 - 12x + 8)^{1/2}.$$

To minimize d, solve $dd/dx = 0$.

$$\frac{dd}{dx} = \frac{1}{2}(5x^2 - 12x + 8)^{-1/2}(10x - 12) = \frac{5x - 6}{\sqrt{5x^2 - 12x + 8}}$$

and $\frac{dd}{dx} = 0 \implies 5x - 6 = 0 \implies x = 6/5$. Since $\frac{dd}{dx} > 0$ for $x > 6/5$ and $\frac{dd}{dx} < 0$ for $x < 6/5$, there is a minimum at $x = 6/5$.

Thus the desired point is $\left(\dfrac{6}{5}, -2\left(\dfrac{6}{5}\right) + 3\right) = \left(\dfrac{6}{5}, \dfrac{3}{5}\right)$.

41. A closed rectangular box with a square base is constructed with a top costing twice as much as the sides and bottom. The box is to contain $96\,\text{in}^3$. What should be the dimensions of the box in order to minimize the building cost?

SOLUTION:

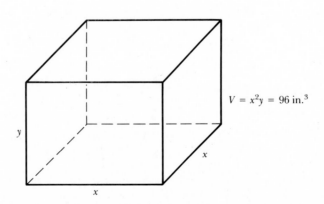

$V = x^2y = 96 \text{ in.}^3$

From the diagram, $V = x^2y = 96$. Let k be the cost/in^2 for the sides and bottom. Then $2k$ is the cost/in^2 for the top. The cost function for the box is

$$C = 2kx^2 + k(x^2 + 4xy) = 3kx^2 + 4kxy.$$

To eliminate y, use $y = 96x^{-2}$ and thus

$$C(x) = 3kx^2 + 4kx(96x^{-2}) = 3kx^2 + 384kx^{-1}.$$

To minimize the cost, solve $C'(x) = 0$. Now $C'(x) = 6kx - 384kx^{-2} = 6kx^{-2}(x^3 - 64) = \dfrac{6k(x^3 - 64)}{x^2}$ and $C'(x) = 0 \implies x^3 - 64 = 0 \implies x = 4$. Note that $k \neq 0$. Since $C''(x) = 6k + 768kx^{-3}$ and $C''(4) > 0$ for $k > 0$, there is a minimum at $x = 4$.

When $x = 4$, $y = 96/16 = 6$. Thus the dimensions of the box should be $4\,\text{in} \times 4\,\text{in} \times 6\,\text{in}$ in order to minimize the cost.

49. An angler has a fish at the end of a line. The line is reeled in at the rate of $2\,\text{ft/sec}$ from a bridge $30\,\text{ft}$ above the water. At what rate is the fish moving through the water when the length of the line is $50\,\text{ft}$?

SOLUTION:

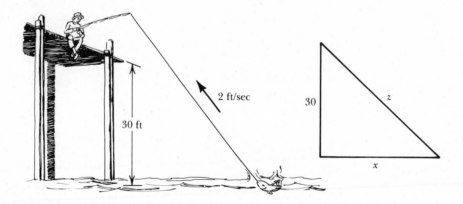

Let z be the length of the line and x be the horizontal distance of the fish from the bridge. Since the line is reeled in at $2\,\text{ft/s}$, $dz/dt = -2$. Also $z^2 = x^2 + 30^2$.

Find $\dfrac{dx}{dt}\bigg|_{z=50}$. Differentiating implicitly and using the chain rule, obtain $2z\dfrac{dz}{dt} = 2x\dfrac{dx}{dt} + 0$. Thus $\dfrac{dx}{dt} = \dfrac{z(dz/dt)}{x} = -\dfrac{2z}{x}$. Now $z = 50 \implies 50^2 = x^2 + 30^2 \implies x^2 = 40^2 \implies x = \pm 40$. Discarding $x = -40$,

$$\frac{dx}{dt}\bigg|_{z=50} = -\frac{2(50)}{40} = -2.5.$$

Thus the fish is moving through the water toward the bridge (negative rate) at $2.5\,\text{ft/sec}$ when the length of the line is $50\,\text{ft}$.

59. A spherical balloon is inflated with air. Use differentials to approximate the change in the volume and the surface area of the balloon as the radius increases from 5 to 5.5 in.

SOLUTION: The volume of the balloon is $V = \frac{4}{3}\pi r^3$ and $S = 4\pi r^2$, where r is the radius of the balloon. Use differentials to approximate ΔV and ΔS with $r = 5$ and $\Delta r = 0.5$. Now $dV = 4\pi r^2 \Delta r$, so $dV = 4\pi(5)^2(0.5) = 50\pi$. Also $dS = 8\pi r \Delta r$, so $dS = 8\pi(5)(0.5) = 20\pi$. Thus the change in the volume is 50π in$^3 \approx 157.1 \, textin^3$, and the change in the surface area is 20π in$^2 \approx 62.8$ in^2.

63. Let $p(x) = (400 - x)/15$ be the selling price when x units are sold.
   a)   Find the price elasticity of demand.
   b)   Find the value of x that gives unit elasticity.
   c)   Will a rise in price increase or decrease revenue if 150 units are sold? if 250 units are sold?

SOLUTION: a) $E(x) = -\dfrac{p(x)}{xp'(x)}$ is the elasticity and $p'(x) = -\dfrac{1}{15}$ since $p(x) = \dfrac{400}{15} - \dfrac{1}{15}x$.

Thus $E(x) = -\dfrac{(400 - x)/15}{x(-1/15)} = \dfrac{400 - x}{x}$.

b)   To determine the price which will produce unit elasticity, solve $E(x) = \dfrac{400 - x}{x} = 1$.

Thus $400 - x = x$ and $x = 200$. Hence production of 200 units produces unit elasticity.

c)   Calculate $E(150)$ and $E(250)$. $E(150) = \dfrac{400 - 150}{150} = 1.67 > 1$. Thus the demand function is elastic at this point, and a price increase will increase total revenue if 150 units are sold.

$$E(250) = \frac{400 - 250}{250} = 0.6 < 1.$$

Thus the demand function is inelastic at this point, and a price increase will decrease total revenue if 250 units are sold.

4
The Integral

Sharpening your skills

In preparation for your work in this chapter, you should review the process of finding antiderivatives. This is presented in the text in SECTION 2.8. Also review SECTIONS 2.3–2.5 on finding derivatives. Some practice problems are presented to help you review. The answers are in APPENDIX B in this manual.

Practice Problems

1. Find the function $f(x)$ which satisfies the requirements stated in each of the following.
   a) $f'(x) = 2x + 7$ and $f(1) = 0$,
   b) $f'(x) = 1 + 2\cos 2x$ and $f(\pi/4) = 1$,
   c) $f''(x) = 6x + 8$, $f'(0) = 1$ and $f(0) = -2$,
   d) $f''(x) = \sin x$, $f(0) = 2$ and $f(\pi) = 2$.

2. Find $D_y x$ in each of the following.
   a) $y = (x^3 + 4x^2 - 8)^{-4}$,
   b) $y = \sin^2(3x)$,
   c) $y = \sqrt{5x} + \dfrac{1}{\sqrt[4]{x^3}}$,
   d) $y = (x^2 - 7x)^9$.

--4.1
Area

11. Find $\displaystyle\sum_{j=2}^{4}(ij + kj^2)$.

SOLUTION: $\displaystyle\sum_{j=2}^{4}(ij + kj^2) = (2i + 4k) + (3i + 9k) + (4i + 16k) = 9i + 29k.$

17. Use formulas 4.3 to evaluate $\displaystyle\sum_{i=10}^{20}(i^3 - i^2)$.

SOLUTION: In order to use the formulas, the sum must be rewritten so that the lower limit is 1. The technique is to subtract the first nine terms $(i = 1, \dots, 9)$ from the first 20 $(i = 1, \dots, 20)$. This will leave the terms from $i = 10$ to $i = 20$.

$$\sum_{i=10}^{20}(i^3 - i^2) = \sum_{i=1}^{20}(i^3 - i^2) - \sum_{i=1}^{9}(i^3 - i^2) = \left(\sum_{i=1}^{20}i^3 - \sum_{i=1}^{20}i^2\right) - \left(\sum_{i=1}^{9}i^3 - \sum_{i=1}^{9}i^2\right)$$

$$= \left(\frac{20^2(21)^2}{4} - \frac{20(21)(41)}{6}\right) - \left(\frac{9^2(10)^2}{4} - \frac{9(10)(19)}{6}\right)$$

$$= (44100 - 2870) - (2025 - 285) = 39,490.$$

23. Express the sum $1 - \dfrac{1}{2} + \dfrac{1}{3} - \dfrac{1}{4} + \cdots + \dfrac{1}{11}$ in closed form by using the summation notation.

SOLUTION: Note that the even terms of the sum are negative while the odd terms are positive. A factor of $(-1)^{n+1}$ included in the nth term will be negative for even terms and positive for odd terms.

Thus $\dfrac{1}{1} - \dfrac{1}{2} + \dfrac{1}{3} - \dfrac{1}{4} + \cdots + \dfrac{1}{11} = \sum_{i=1}^{11}(-1)^{i+1}\dfrac{1}{i} = \sum_{i=1}^{11}\dfrac{(-1)^{i+1}}{i}.$

27. Find the area of the region bounded by the x-axis, the graph of $f(x) = x^2$, $x = 0$ and $x = 1$.

SOLUTION: First sketch the graph of the area.

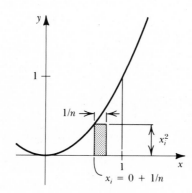

From 4.4 in the text, $A_n = \sum_{i=1}^{n} f\left(a + \dfrac{b-a}{n}i\right)\left(\dfrac{b-a}{n}\right)$. With $a = 0$ and $b = 1$,

$$A_n = \sum_{i=1}^{n} f\left(0 + \dfrac{1-0}{n}i\right)\left(\dfrac{1-0}{n}\right) = \sum_{i=1}^{n} f\left(\dfrac{i}{n}\right)\left(\dfrac{1}{n}\right)$$

$$= \sum_{i=1}^{n} \frac{i^2}{n^2} \cdot \frac{1}{n} = \frac{1}{n^3} \sum_{i=1}^{n} i^2 = \frac{1}{n^3} \cdot \frac{n(n+1)(2n+1)}{6} = \frac{(n+1)(2n+1)}{6n^2}.$$

Thus

$$A = \lim_{n \to \infty} A_n = \lim_{n \to \infty} \frac{(n+1)(2n+1)}{6n^2}$$

$$= \frac{1}{6} \lim_{n \to \infty} \frac{n+1}{n} \lim_{n \to \infty} \frac{2n+1}{n} = \frac{1}{6} \cdot 1 \cdot 2 = \frac{1}{3}.$$

33. Find the area of the region bounded by the x-axis, the graph of $f(x) = 4 - x^2$, $x = -2$ and $x = 0$.

SOLUTION:

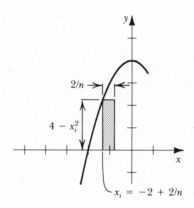

From 4.4 in the text, $A_n = \sum\limits_{i=1}^{n} f\left(a + \dfrac{b-a}{n} i\right)\left(\dfrac{b-a}{n}\right)$ with $a = -2$ and $b = 0$ yields

$$A_n = \sum_{i=1}^{n} f\left(-2 + \frac{0-(-2)}{n} i\right)\left(\frac{0-(-2)}{n}\right) = \sum_{i=1}^{n} f\left(-2 + \frac{2}{n} i\right)\left(\frac{2}{n}\right)$$

$$= \frac{2}{n} \sum_{i=1}^{n} f\left(-2 + \frac{2}{n} i\right) = \frac{2}{n} \sum_{i=1}^{n}\left(4 - \left(-2 + \frac{2}{n} i\right)^2\right) = \frac{2}{n} \sum_{i=1}^{n}\left(4 - \left(4 - \frac{8}{n} i + \frac{4}{n^2} i^2\right)\right)$$

$$= \frac{2}{n} \sum_{i=1}^{n}\left(\frac{8}{n} i - \frac{4}{n^2} i^2\right) = \frac{8}{n} \sum_{i=1}^{n}\left(\frac{2i}{n} - \frac{i^2}{n^2}\right) = \frac{8}{n}\left(\frac{2}{n} \sum_{i=1}^{n} i - \frac{1}{n^2} \sum_{i=1}^{n} i^2\right)$$

$$= \frac{8}{n}\left(\frac{2}{n} \cdot \frac{n(n+1)}{2} - \frac{1}{n^2} \cdot \frac{n(n+1)(2n+1)}{6}\right) = 8\left(\frac{n+1}{n} - \frac{(n+1)(2n+1)}{6n^2}\right).$$

Thus

$$A = \lim_{n \to \infty} A_n = \lim_{n \to \infty} 8\left(\frac{n+1}{n} - \frac{(n+1)(2n+1)}{6n^2}\right)$$

$$= 8 \left(\lim_{n \to \infty} \frac{n+1}{n} - \frac{1}{6} \lim_{n \to \infty} \frac{n+1}{n} \lim_{n \to \infty} \frac{2n+1}{n} \right) = 8 \left(1 - \frac{1}{6} \cdot 1 \cdot 2 \right) = \frac{16}{3}.$$

39. A grocer stacks oranges in pyramid form with 150 on the bottom level in 15 rows of 10 each. How many oranges are in this pyramid if they are stacked until only one row is on top?

SOLUTION: The pyramid will consist of ten levels of oranges. The bottom level will contain $10(15) = 10(10+5)$ oranges. The next level will contain $9(14) = 9(9+5)$ oranges and the top level will contain $1(6) = 1(1+5)$ oranges. The total number of oranges will be

$$10(10+5) + 9(9+5) + \cdots + 1(1+5) = \sum_{i=1}^{10} i(i+5)$$

$$= \sum_{i=1}^{10} i^2 + 5 \sum_{i=1}^{10} i = \frac{10(11)(21)}{6} + 5 \cdot \frac{10(11)}{2} = 385 + 275 = 660.$$

The Definite Integral 4.2

5. Find the value of the Riemann sum associated with $f(x) = x^2$, $\wp = \{0, 1/4, 1/2, 3/4, 1\}$ and the points $z_1 = 0$, $z_2 = 1/2$, $z_3 = 1/2$, and $z_4 = 1$.

SOLUTION: The Riemann sum S is described by

$$S = \sum_{i=1}^{4} f(z_i) \Delta x_i = f(z_1) \left(\frac{1}{4} - 0 \right) + f(z_2) \left(\frac{1}{2} - \frac{1}{4} \right) + f(z_3) \left(\frac{3}{4} - \frac{1}{2} \right) + f(z_4) \left(1 - \frac{3}{4} \right)$$

$$= \frac{1}{4} f(0) + \frac{1}{4} f \left(\frac{1}{2} \right) + \frac{1}{4} f \left(\frac{1}{2} \right) + \frac{1}{4} f(1)$$

$$= \frac{1}{4}(0) + \frac{1}{4} \left(\frac{1}{4} \right) + \frac{1}{4} \left(\frac{1}{4} \right) + \frac{1}{4}(1) = \frac{3}{8}.$$

11. Find the value of the Riemann sum associated with $f(x) = \sin x$, $\wp = \{0, \pi/4, 2\pi/3, \pi\}$ and the points $z_1 = \pi/4$, $z_2 = \pi/3$, $z_3 = 3\pi/4$.

SOLUTION: The Riemann sum is

$$S = \sum_{i=1}^{3} f(z_i) \Delta x_i = f(z_1) \left(\frac{\pi}{4} - 0 \right) + f(z_2) \left(\frac{2\pi}{3} - \frac{\pi}{4} \right) + f(z_3) \left(\pi - \frac{2\pi}{3} \right)$$

$$= \frac{\pi}{4} \sin \frac{\pi}{4} + \frac{5\pi}{12} \sin \frac{\pi}{3} + \frac{\pi}{3} \sin \frac{3\pi}{4} = \pi \left(\frac{7\sqrt{2} + 5\sqrt{3}}{24} \right).$$

15. Find the value of $\int_0^1 (2x + 1)\,dx$ by taking the limit of an appropriate Riemann sum.

SOLUTION: Let the interval $[0, 1]$ be partitioned into n subintervals of equal width, Δx. Then $\Delta x_i = \frac{1 - 0}{n} = \frac{1}{n}$ for $i = 1, 2, \ldots, n$. Let z_i be the right-hand endpoint of the ith subinterval. Then $z_1 = 0 + \frac{1}{n}$, $z_2 = 0 + \frac{2}{n}$ and $z_i = 0 + \frac{i}{n} = \frac{i}{n}$. Then

$$\int_0^1 (2x + 1)\,dx = \lim_{n \to \infty} \sum_{i=1}^n (2z_i + 1)\Delta x_i = \lim_{n \to \infty} \sum_{i=1}^n \left(\frac{2i}{n} + 1 \right) \frac{1}{n}$$

$$= \lim_{n \to \infty} \frac{1}{n} \sum_{i=1}^n \left(\frac{2i}{n} + 1 \right) = \lim_{n \to \infty} \frac{1}{n} \left(\frac{2}{n} \sum_{i=1}^n i + \sum_{i=1}^n 1 \right)$$

$$= \lim_{n \to \infty} \frac{1}{n} \left(\frac{2}{n} \cdot \frac{n(n + 1)}{2} + n \right) = \lim_{n \to \infty} \left(\frac{n + 1}{n} + 1 \right) = 1 + 1 = 2.$$

21. Find the value of $\int_{-1}^1 x^3\,dx$ by taking the limit of an appropriate Riemann sum.

SOLUTION: Let the interval $[-1, 1]$ be partitioned into n subintervals each of equal width, Δx. Then $\Delta x_i = \frac{1 - (-1)}{n} = \frac{2}{n}$ for $i = 1, 2, \ldots, n$. Let z_i be the right-hand endpoint of the ith subinterval. Then $z_1 = -1 + \frac{2}{n}$, $z_2 = -1 + \frac{4}{n}$ and $z_i = -1 + \frac{2i}{n}$. Thus

$$\int_{-1}^1 x^3\,dx = \lim_{n \to \infty} \sum_{i=1}^n f(z_i)\Delta x_i = \lim_{n \to \infty} \sum_{i=1}^n \left(-1 + \frac{2i}{n} \right)^3 \left(\frac{2}{n} \right)$$

$$= \lim_{n \to \infty} \frac{2}{n} \sum_{i=1}^n \left(-1 + \frac{6i}{n} - \frac{12i^2}{n^2} + \frac{8i^3}{n^3} \right)$$

$$= \lim_{n \to \infty} \frac{2}{n} \left(-\sum_{i=1}^n 1 + \frac{6}{n} \sum_{i=1}^n i - \frac{12}{n^2} \sum_{i=1}^n i^2 + \frac{8}{n^3} \sum_{i=1}^n i^3 \right)$$

$$= \lim_{n \to \infty} \frac{2}{n} \left(-n + \frac{6}{n} \cdot \frac{n(n + 1)}{2} - \frac{12}{n^2} \cdot \frac{n(n + 1)(2n + 1)}{6} + \frac{8}{n^3} \cdot \frac{n^2(n + 1)^2}{4} \right)$$

$$= \lim_{n \to \infty} \left(-2 + \frac{6(n+1)}{n} - \frac{4(n+1)(2n+1)}{n^2} + \frac{4(n+1)^2}{n^2} \right) = -2 + 6 - 8 + 4 = 0.$$

25. Use the application of the definite integral as an area to evaluate $\int_{-1}^{1} \sqrt{1 - x^2}\, dx.$

SOLUTION: Consider $y = \sqrt{1 - x^2}$. Note $y \geq 0$. Then $y^2 = 1 - x^2$ and $x^2 + y^2 = 1$, which is the equation of a circle with radius 1 and center at $(0,0)$. Thus $y = \sqrt{1 - x^2}$ for $-1 \leq x \leq 1$ is the semicircle in quadrants I and II.

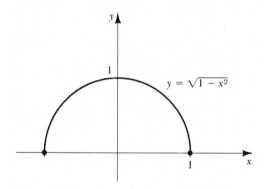

Since the area of the circle is $\pi r^2 = \pi$, the area of the semicircle is $\pi/2$ and thus

$$\int_{-1}^{1} \sqrt{1 - x^2}\, dx = \pi/2.$$

33. Determine upper and lower bounds for $\int_{1}^{3} \frac{2x}{x^2 + 5x + 4}\, dx$ by finding the extrema of the integrand and using COROLLARY 4.14.

SOLUTION: Consider $f(x) = \dfrac{2x}{x^2 + 5x + 4}$ on $[1,3]$.

$$f'(x) = \frac{(x^2 + 5x + 4)(2) - 2x(2x + 5)}{(x^2 + 5x + 4)^2} = \frac{-2x^2 + 8}{(x^2 + 5x + 4)^2} = \frac{-2(x-2)(x+2)}{((x+4)(x+1))^2}.$$

Now $f'(x) = 0 \implies -2(x - 2)(x + 2) = 0 \implies x = \pm 2$. Discard $x = -2$ since it is not in $[1,3]$. For $1 \leq x < 2$, $f'(x) > 0$ and for $2 < x \leq 3$, $f'(x) < 0$. Hence there is a relative maximum at $x = 2$ and $f(2) = 2/9$. Also $f(1) = 1/5$ and $f(3) = 3/14$. Thus the absolute minimum of $f(x)$ on $[1,3]$ is at $x = 1$ and the absolute maximum is at $x = 2$. Thus, by COROLLARY 4.14,

$$\frac{1}{5}(3 - 1) \leq \int_{1}^{3} \frac{2x}{x^2 + 5x + 4}\, dx \leq \frac{2}{9}(3 - 1) \implies \frac{2}{5} \leq \int_{1}^{3} \frac{2x}{x^2 + 5x + 4}\, dx \leq \frac{4}{9}.$$

The Fundamental Theorem
of Calculus

7. Use the fundamental theorem of calculus to evaluate $\int_1^3 (3x^2 - 2x)\,dx$.

SOLUTION: Since $F(x) = x^3 - x^2$ is an antiderivative of $f(x) = 3x^2 - 2x$, $\int_1^3 (3x^2 - 2x)\,dx = F(3) - F(1) = (3^3 - 3^2) - (1^3 - 1^2) = 18$.

11. Use the fundamental theorem of calculus to evaluate $\int_0^{\pi/2} \sin x\,dx$.

SOLUTION: Since $F(x) = -\cos x$ is an antiderivative of $f(x) = \sin x$,

$$\int_0^{\pi/2} \sin x\,dx = F(\pi/2) - F(0) = -\cos \frac{\pi}{2} - (-\cos 0) = 0 - (-1) = 1.$$

19. Use the fundamental theorem of calculus to evaluate $\int_1^2 t^{-3}\,dt$.

SOLUTION: Since $F(t) = -\frac{1}{2}t^{-2}$ is an antiderivative of $f(t) = t^{-3}$,

$$\int_1^2 t^{-3}\,dt = F(2) - F(1) = -\frac{1}{2}(2)^{-2} - \left(-\frac{1}{2}\right)(1)^{-2} = -\frac{1}{8} + \frac{1}{2} = \frac{3}{8}.$$

25. Use the fundamental theorem of calculus to evaluate $\int_1^2 (x^3 - x^{-2})\,dx$.

SOLUTION: Since $F(x) = \frac{1}{4}x^4 + x^{-1}$ is an antiderivative of $f(x) = x^3 - x^{-2}$,

$$\int_1^2 (x^3 - x^{-2})\,dx = F(2) - F(1) = \left(\frac{1}{4}(2)^4 + 2^{-1}\right) - \left(\frac{1}{4}(1)^4 + 1^{-1}\right) = 4 + \frac{1}{2} - \frac{1}{4} - 1 = \frac{13}{4}.$$

31. Use the fundamental theorem of calculus to find the area of the region bounded by the x-axis, the graph of $f(x) = 3x^2 + 1$ and the lines $x = -1$ and $x = 1$. Sketch the region.

SOLUTION:

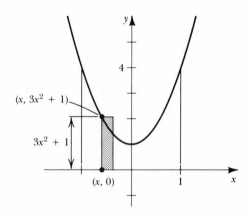

$A = \displaystyle\int_{-1}^{1} (3x^2 + 1)\, dx$ since $f(x) = 3x^2 + 1$ is nonnegative on $[-1, 1]$. Now $F(x) = x^3 + x$ is an antiderivative of $f(x)$. Thus $\displaystyle\int_{-1}^{1} (3x^2 + 1)\, dx = F(1) - F(-1) = (1^3 + 1) - ((-1)^3 + (-1)) = 2 - (-2) = 4$, and the desired area is 4.

35. Use the fundamental theorem of calculus to find the area of the region bounded by the x-axis, the graph of $f(x) = \cos x$ and the lines $x = -\pi/2$ and $x = \pi/2$. Sketch the region.

SOLUTION:

As $f(x) = \cos x$ is nonnegative on $[-\pi/2, \pi/2]$, the desired area A, is $\displaystyle\int_{-\pi/2}^{\pi/2} \cos x\, dx$.

Since $F(x) = \sin x$ is an antiderivative of $f(x)$, $A = \displaystyle\int_{-\pi/2}^{\pi/2} \cos x\, dx = F(\pi/2) - F(-\pi/2) = \sin\dfrac{\pi}{2} - \sin\left(-\dfrac{\pi}{2}\right) = 1 - (-1) = 2.$

41. Find the average value of $f(x) = 3x^2$ on $[-1, 1]$.

SOLUTION: The average value of $f(x)$ on $[-1, 1]$ is $\dfrac{1}{1-(-1)} \displaystyle\int_{-1}^{1} f(x)\,dx = \dfrac{1}{2} \displaystyle\int_{-1}^{1} 3x^2\,dx =$

$\dfrac{1}{2}\left([x^3]\Big|_{-1}^{1}\right) = \dfrac{1}{2}\left(1^3 - (-1)^3\right) = \dfrac{1}{2}(2) = 1.$

49. Use the fundamental lemma of calculus to find $D_x\left[x\displaystyle\int_{1}^{x}\sqrt{t^2+9}\,dt\right]$.

SOLUTION: By the product rule,

$$D_x\left[x\int_{1}^{x}\sqrt{t^2+9}\,dt\right] = x\,D_x\left[\int_{1}^{x}\sqrt{t^2+9}\,dt\right] + \int_{1}^{x}\sqrt{t^2+9}\,dt.$$

Now $f(t) = \sqrt{t^2+9}$ is continuous on $\mathbb{R}$ which satisfies the hypothesis of the fundamental lemma. Thus $D_x\left[\displaystyle\int_{1}^{x}\sqrt{t^2+9}\,dt\right] = \sqrt{x^2+9}$ and $D_x\left[x\displaystyle\int_{1}^{x}\sqrt{t^2+9}\,dt\right] = x\sqrt{x^2+9} + \displaystyle\int_{1}^{x}\sqrt{t^2+9}\,dt.$

57. Determine $D_x\left[\displaystyle\int_{x}^{\sqrt{x}} t\cos t^3\,dt\right]$.

SOLUTION: Note that $f(t) = t\cos t^3$ is continuous on $\mathbb{R}$ which satisfies the hypothesis of the fundamental lemma of calculus. Let $a \in \mathbb{R}$. Then

$$D_x\left[\int_{x}^{\sqrt{x}} t\cos t^3\,dt\right] = D_x\left[\int_{x}^{a} t\cos t^3\,dt + \int_{a}^{\sqrt{x}} t\cos t^3\,dt\right]$$

$$= D_x\left[\int_{x}^{a} t\cos t^3\,dt\right] + D_x\left[\int_{a}^{\sqrt{x}} t\cos t^3\,dt\right].$$

Now $D_x\left[\displaystyle\int_{x}^{a} t\cos t^3\,dt\right] = D_x\left[-\displaystyle\int_{a}^{x} t\cos t^3\,dt\right] = -D_x\left[\displaystyle\int_{a}^{x} t\cos t^3\,dt\right] = -x\cos x^3.$

To evaluate $D_x\left[\displaystyle\int_{a}^{\sqrt{x}} t\cos t^3\,dt\right]$, let $u = \sqrt{x}$ and use the chain rule. Then

$$D_x\left[\int_{a}^{u} t\cos t^3\,dt\right] = D_u\left[\int_{a}^{u} t\cos t^3\,dt\right]\cdot D_x(u) = (u\cos u^3)\left(\frac{1}{2}x^{-1/2}\right)$$

$$= \frac{1}{2\sqrt{x}}\cdot\sqrt{x}\,\cos(\sqrt{x})^3 = \frac{1}{2}\cos x^{3/2}.$$

Thus, $D_x \left[\int_x^{\sqrt{x}} t \cos t^3 \, dt \right] = -x \cos x^3 + \dfrac{1}{2} \cos x^{3/2}$.

61. Use the mean value theorem for integrals to show that if f is continuous and $\int_a^b f(x) \, dx = 0$, then $f(c) = 0$ for some number c in (a, b).

SOLUTION: Let f be continuous on $[a, b]$ and $\int_a^b f(x) \, dx = 0$. By the mean value theorem for integrals, there exists $z \in (a, b)$ such that

$$f(z) = \frac{1}{b-a} \int_a^b f(x) \, dx = \frac{1}{b-a} \cdot 0 = 0.$$

Pick $c = z$ and thus $f(c) = 0$ for some number $c \in (a, b)$.

63. Use L'Hôpital's rule and the fundamental lemma of calculus to find $\displaystyle \lim_{x \to 0} \dfrac{\displaystyle \int_0^x t\sqrt{3 + t^2} \, dt}{x^2}$.

SOLUTION: Since $\displaystyle \lim_{x \to 0} \int_0^x t\sqrt{3 + t^2} \, dt = \int_0^0 t\sqrt{3 + t^2} \, dt = 0$ and $\displaystyle \lim_{x \to 0} x^2 = 0$, the hypotheses of L'Hôpital's rule are satisfied. Thus

$$\lim_{x \to 0} \frac{\displaystyle \int_0^x t\sqrt{3 + t^2} \, dt}{x^2} = \lim_{x \to 0} \frac{D_x \left[\displaystyle \int_0^x t\sqrt{3 + t^2} \, dt \right]}{D_x x^2} = \lim_{x \to 0} \frac{x\sqrt{3 + x^2}}{2x} = \lim_{x \to 0} \frac{1}{2}\sqrt{3 + x^2} = \frac{\sqrt{3}}{2}.$$

Note that applying the fundamental lemma of calculus to the numerator is valid since $f(t) = t\sqrt{3 + t^2}$ is continuous on $\mathbb{R}$.

The Indefinite Integral
_____4.4

5. Find $\displaystyle \int (2y^3 + 3y^2) \, dy$. Check the answer by differentiating the result.

SOLUTION: $\displaystyle \int (2y^3 + 3y^2) \, dy = 2 \int y^3 \, dy + 3 \int y^2 \, dy = 2\left(\frac{1}{4}y^4\right) + 3\left(\frac{1}{3}y^3\right) + C = \frac{1}{2}y^4 + y^3 + C.$

Check: $D_y \left(\dfrac{1}{2}y^4 + y^3 + C\right) = \dfrac{1}{2} D_y(y^4) + D_y(y^3) + D_y(C) = \dfrac{1}{2}(4y^3) + 3y^2 + 0 = 2y^3 + 3y^2.$

9. Find $\int (x^{2/3} + 3x^{1/3} + 4x^2)dx$.

SOLUTION:

$$\int (x^{2/3} + 3x^{1/3} + 4x^2)dx = \int x^{2/3}dx + 3\int x^{1/3}dx + 4\int x^2 dx$$

$$= \frac{3}{5}x^{5/3} + 3\left(\frac{3}{4}x^{4/3}\right) + 4\left(\frac{1}{3}x^3\right) + C = \frac{3}{5}x^{5/3} + \frac{9}{4}x^{4/3} + \frac{4}{3}x^3 + C.$$

13. Find $\int \cot^2 u\, du$.

SOLUTION: Recall the Pythagorean identity $1 + \cot^2 x = \csc^2 x$. Thus

$$\int \cot^2 u\, du = \int (\csc^2 u - 1)\, du = \int \csc^2 u\, du - \int du = -\cot u - u + C.$$

21. Find $\int 3(3x + 1)^2\, dx$.

SOLUTION:

$$\int 3(3x + 1)^2\, dx = 3\int (9x^2 + 6x + 1)dx = 3\left(9\int x^2 dx + 6\int x\, dx + \int dx\right)$$

$$= 3\left(9\left(\frac{1}{3}x^3\right) + 6\left(\frac{1}{2}x^2\right) + x\right) + C = 3(3x^3 + 3x^2 + x) + C$$

$$= 9x^3 + 9x^2 + 3x + C.$$

27. Find $\int \frac{x^3 - 2x^2 + 4}{x^5}\, dx$.

SOLUTION:

$$\int \frac{x^3 - 2x^2 + 4}{x^5}\, dx = \int \left(\frac{x^3}{x^5} - \frac{2x^2}{x^5} + \frac{4}{x^5}\right)dx = \int \left(\frac{1}{x^2} - \frac{2}{x^3} + \frac{4}{x^5}\right)dx$$

$$= \int x^{-2}\, dx - 2\int x^{-3}\, dx + 4\int x^{-5}\, dx$$

$$= -x^{-1} - 2\left(-\frac{1}{2}x^{-2}\right) + 4\left(-\frac{1}{4}x^{-4}\right) + C = -x^{-1} + x^{-2} - x^{-4} + C.$$

35. Find $\displaystyle\int_1^4 \left(\sqrt{x} + \frac{1}{\sqrt{x}}\right) dx.$

SOLUTION:

$$\int_1^4 \left(\sqrt{x} + \frac{1}{\sqrt{x}}\right) dx = \int_1^4 (x^{1/2} + x^{-1/2})\, dx = \left[\frac{2}{3}x^{3/2} + 2x^{1/2}\right]\Big|_1^4$$

$$= \left(\frac{2}{3}(4)^{3/2} + 2(4)^{1/2}\right) - \left(\frac{2}{3}(1)^{3/2} + 2(1)^{1/2}\right)$$

$$= \frac{2}{3}(8) + 2(2) - \frac{2}{3} - 2 = \frac{20}{3}.$$

39. Find $\displaystyle\int_1^2 \left(z + \frac{1}{z}\right)^2 dz.$

SOLUTION:

$$\int_1^2 \left(z + \frac{1}{z}\right)^2 dz = \int_1^2 (z^2 + 2 + z^{-2})\, dz = \left[\frac{1}{3}z^3 + 2z - z^{-1}\right]\Big|_1^2$$

$$= \left(\frac{1}{3}(2)^3 + 2(2) - (2)^{-1}\right) - \left(\frac{1}{3}(1)^3 + 2(1) - (1)^{-1}\right)$$

$$= \frac{8}{3} + 4 - \frac{1}{2} - \frac{1}{3} - 2 + 1 = \frac{29}{6}.$$

47. Find $\displaystyle\int_0^{\pi/4} \sec t(\sec t + \tan t)\, dt.$

SOLUTION:

$$\int_0^{\pi/4} \sec t(\sec t + \tan t)\, dt = \int_0^{\pi/4} (\sec^2 t + \sec t \tan t)\, dt = \int_0^{\pi/4} \sec^2 t\, dt + \int_0^{\pi/4} \sec t \tan t\, dt$$

$$= [\tan t + \sec t]\Big|_0^{\pi/4} = \left(\tan \frac{\pi}{4} + \sec \frac{\pi}{4}\right) - (\tan 0 + \sec 0)$$

$$= 1 + \sqrt{2} - 0 - 1 = \sqrt{2}.$$

51. Determine the area of the region bounded by the x-axis and the graph of $f(x) = 1 + 2\sin x$ on $[0, \pi/2]$. Draw a sketch of this region.

SOLUTION:

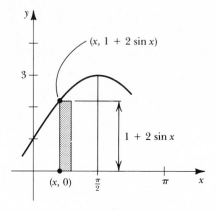

Since $f(x) = 1 + 2\sin x$ is nonnegative on $[0, \pi/2]$, the desired area can be found by evaluating

$$\int_0^{\pi/2} (1 + 2\sin x)\, dx = [x - 2\cos x]\Big|_0^{\pi/2} = \left(\frac{\pi}{2} - 2\cos\frac{\pi}{2}\right) - (0 - 2\cos 0) = \frac{\pi}{2} - 2(0) - 0 + 2 = 2 + \frac{\pi}{2}.$$

61. Find $f(x)$ if $f'(x) = \sin x - x$ and $f(0) = -1$.

SOLUTION: First evaluate $\int (\sin x - x)\, dx$. $f(x) = \int (\sin x - x)\, dx = -\cos x - \frac{1}{2}x^2 + C$.

Second, determine the value of C. $f(0) = -\cos 0 - \frac{1}{2}(0)^2 + C = -1 \implies -1 - 0 + C = -1 \implies C = 0$.

Thus $f(x) = -\cos x - \frac{1}{2}x^2$.

65. Find an equation of the curve passing through the points $(0,2)$ and $(1,3)$ with the property that $y'' = 6x - 2$.

SOLUTION: By finding the antiderivative of y'', a family of functions can be determined for y'. Thus $y' = \int (6x - 2)\, dx = 3x^2 - 2x + C_1$. Now proceed by finding a family of functions for y. So $y = \int (3x^2 - 2x + C_1)\, dx = x^3 - x^2 + C_1 x + C_2$.

To evaluate C_1 and C_2, substitute the points through which the curve must pass. Substitute $(0,2)$ to obtain $2 = 0^3 - 0^2 + C_1(0) + C_2 \implies C_2 = 2$ and $y = x^3 - x^2 + C_1 x + 2$. Substitute $(1,3)$ to obtain $3 = 1^3 - 1^2 + C_1(1) + 2 \implies C_1 = 1$ and $y = x^3 - x^2 + x + 2$, which is the desired equation.

73. An open construction elevator is rising at the rate of 3 feet per second. A hammer falls from the elevator when it is 100 feet from the ground. How long does it take the hammer to reach the ground?

SOLUTION: The acceleration of the hammer is $-32 \, \text{ft/sec}^2$. Thus $v(t) = \int -32 \, dt = -32t + C$. At $t = 0$ (when the hammer is dropped) the velocity of the hammer is 3 ft/sec, provided by the motion of the elevator. Thus $v(0) = -32t + C = 3 \implies C = 3$ and $v(t) = -32t + C$. Next $s(t) = \int (-32t + 3) \, dt = -16t^2 + 3t + C$. Now at $t = 0$, the altitude of the hammer was 100 ft. Thus $s(0) = -16(0)^2 + 3(0) + C = 100 \implies C = 100$ and $s(t) = -16t^2 + 3t + 100$.

When the hammer reaches the ground, $s(t) = 0$. To find the time at which it occurs, solve $-16t^2 + 3t + 100 = 0$. Applying the quadratic formula,

$$t = \frac{-3 \pm \sqrt{9 - 4(-16)(100)}}{2(-16)} = \frac{-3 \pm \sqrt{6409}}{-32}$$

and $t \approx -2.41$ or $t \approx 2.60$. Discarding the negative value, the hammer strikes the ground approximately 2.60 seconds after it is dropped. Note that the hammer does not <u>immediately</u> start falling when it is dropped as it has a positive velocity (upwards) when it is dropped.

―――――――――――――――――――――――――――――――――――――――**4.5**

Integration by Substitution

7. Evaluate $\int 3t^2 (t^3 + 4)^{1/2} \, dt$.

SOLUTION: Let $u = t^3 + 4$. Then $du = 3t^2 \, dt$ and

$$\int 3t^2 (t^3 + 4)^{1/2} \, dt = \int u^{1/2} \, du = \frac{2}{3} u^{3/2} + C = \frac{2}{3}(t^3 + 4)^{3/2} + C.$$

13. Evaluate $\int \sin 2x \, dx$.

SOLUTION: Let $u = 2x$. Then $du = 2 \, dx$ and $\frac{1}{2} du = dx$. So $\int \sin 2x \, dx = \int \sin u \left(\frac{1}{2} du \right) = \frac{1}{2} \int \sin u \, du = \frac{1}{2}(-\cos u) + C = -\frac{1}{2} \cos 2x + C.$

27. Evaluate $\displaystyle\int \frac{3x^2 + 1}{\sqrt[3]{x^3 + x}}\, dx$.

SOLUTION: $\displaystyle\int \frac{3x^2 + 1}{\sqrt[3]{x^3 + x}}\, dx = \int (3x^2 + 1)(x^3 + x)^{-1/3}\, dx$. Let $u = x^3 + x$. Then $du = (3x^2 + 1)\, dx$ and $\displaystyle\int (3x^2 + 1)(x^3 + x)^{-1/3}\, dx = \int u^{-1/3}\, du = \frac{3}{2}u^{2/3} + C = \frac{3}{2}(x^3 + x)^{2/3} + C.$

31. Evaluate $\displaystyle\int_0^{\pi/4} \tan x \sec^2 x \, dx$.

SOLUTION: Let $u = \tan x$. Then $du = \sec^2 x \, dx$. Also $x = 0 \implies u = \tan 0 = 0$ and $x = \pi/4 \implies u = \tan \dfrac{\pi}{4} = 1.$

Thus $\displaystyle\int_0^{\pi/4} \tan x \sec^2 x \, dx = \int_0^1 u \, du = \left[\frac{1}{2}u^2\right]\Big|_0^1 = \frac{1}{2}.$ Note that the integral can also be evaluated with the substitution $u = \sec x$, which produces the integral $\displaystyle\int_1^{\sqrt{2}} u \, du = \frac{1}{2}.$

37. Evaluate $\displaystyle\int_{-1}^1 \frac{x + 1}{(x^2 + 2x + 2)^3}\, dx$.

SOLUTION: $\displaystyle\int_{-1}^1 \frac{x + 1}{(x^2 + 2x + 2)^3}\, dx = \int_{-1}^1 (x + 1)(x^2 + 2x + 2)^{-3}\, dx.$

Let $u = x^2 + 2x + 2$. Then $du = (2x + 2)\, dx = 2(x + 1)\, dx \implies \dfrac{1}{2}du = (x + 1)\, dx$. Also $x = -1 \implies u = (-1)^2 + 2(-1) + 2 = 1$ and $x = 1 \implies u = (1)^2 + 2(1) + 2 = 5.$ Thus

$$\int_{-1}^1 (x + 1)(x^2 + 2x + 2)^{-3}\, dx = \int_1^5 u^{-3}\left(\frac{1}{2}\, du\right) = \frac{1}{2}\int_1^5 u^{-3}\, du = \frac{1}{2}\left[-\frac{1}{2}u^{-2}\right]\Big|_1^5$$

$$= -\frac{1}{4}(5^{-2} - 1^{-2}) = -\frac{1}{4}\left(\frac{1}{25} - 1\right) = \frac{6}{25}.$$

45. Evaluate $\displaystyle\int (z + 1)\sqrt{z - 1}\, dz$.

SOLUTION: Let $u = z - 1$. Then $du = dz$ and $u + 2 = z + 1$. Thus

$$\int (z + 1)(z - 1)^{1/2}\, dz = \int (u + 2)u^{1/2}\, du = \int (u^{3/2} + 2u^{1/2})\, du$$

$$= \frac{2}{5}u^{5/2} + \frac{4}{3}u^{3/2} + C = \frac{2}{15}\sqrt{u}\,(3u^2 + 10u) + C$$

$$= \frac{2}{15}\sqrt{z-1}\left(3(z-1)^2 + 10(z-1)\right) + C$$

$$= \frac{2}{15}(z-1)(3z+7)\sqrt{z-1} + C.$$

49. Evaluate $\displaystyle\int_1^2 \left(1 + \frac{1}{t^2}\right)^3 \frac{1}{t^3}\, dt.$

SOLUTION: $\displaystyle\int_1^2 \left(1 + \frac{1}{t^2}\right)^3 \frac{1}{t^3}\, dt = \int_1^2 (1 + t^{-2})^3 t^{-3}\, dt.$

Let $u = 1 + t^{-2}$. Then $du = -2t^{-3}\, dt \implies -\frac{1}{2}\, du = t^{-3}\, dt$. Also $t = 1 \implies u = 1 + 1^{-2} = 2$ and $t = 2 \implies u = 1 + 2^{-2} = 5/4$.
Thus

$$\int_1^2 (1 + t^{-2})^3 t^{-3}\, dt = \int_2^{5/4} u^3 \left(-\frac{1}{2}\, du\right) = -\frac{1}{2}\int_2^{5/4} u^3\, du$$

$$= -\frac{1}{2}\left[\frac{1}{4}u^4\right]\Big|_2^{5/4} = -\frac{1}{8}\left(\left(\frac{5}{4}\right)^4 - 2^4\right) = \frac{3471}{2048}.$$

55. Evaluate $\displaystyle\int_1^2 \frac{\sqrt{\sqrt{x} + 1}}{\sqrt{x}}\, dx.$

SOLUTION: $\displaystyle\int_1^2 \frac{\sqrt{\sqrt{x}+1}}{\sqrt{x}}\, dx = \int_1^2 (x^{1/2} + 1)^{1/2} x^{-1/2}\, dx.$

Let $u = x^{1/2} + 1$. Then $du = \frac{1}{2}x^{-1/2}\, dx \implies 2\, du = x^{-1/2}\, dx$. Also, $x = 1 \implies u = 1^{1/2} + 1 = 2$ and $x = 2 \implies u = \sqrt{2} + 1$. Thus

$$\int_1^2 \frac{\sqrt{\sqrt{x}+1}}{\sqrt{x}}\, dx = \int_2^{\sqrt{2}+1} u^{1/2}(2\, du) = 2\int_2^{\sqrt{2}+1} u^{1/2}\, du$$

$$= 2\left[\frac{2}{3}u^{3/2}\right]\Big|_2^{\sqrt{2}+1} = \frac{4}{3}\left((\sqrt{2}+1)^{3/2} - 2^{3/2}\right).$$

63. Evaluate $\displaystyle\int \frac{1}{x^2 + 6x + 9}\, dx.$

SOLUTION: This solution requires the recognition that $x^2 + 6x + 9 = (x+3)^2$.
So $\displaystyle\int \frac{1}{x^2 + 6x + 9}\, dx = \int (x+3)^{-2}\, dx$. Now let $u = x+3$. Then $du = dx$ and $\displaystyle\int \frac{1}{x^2 + 6x + 9}\, dx = \int u^{-2}\, du = -u^{-1} + C = \frac{-1}{x+3} + C.$

73. Find $f(x)$ given $f'(x) = (x+2)\sqrt{x^2+4x}$ and $f(0) = 0$.

SOLUTION: $f(x) = \int (x+2)(x^2+4x)^{1/2}\,dx$. Let $u = x^2 + 4x$. Then $du = (2x+4)\,dx = 2(x+2)\,dx \implies \dfrac{1}{2}\,du = (x+2)\,dx$.

Thus

$$f(x) = \int u^{1/2}\left(\frac{1}{2}\,du\right) = \frac{1}{2}\int u^{1/2}\,du = \frac{1}{2}\left(\frac{2}{3}u^{3/2}\right) + C = \frac{1}{3}(x^2+4x)^{3/2} + C.$$

To evaluate C, $f(0) = \dfrac{1}{3}\left(0^2 + 4(0)\right)^{3/2} + C = 0 \implies C = 0$ and the desired function is $f(x) = \dfrac{1}{3}(x^2+4x)^{3/2}$.

83. Show that if f is an even integrable function defined on an interval $[-a, a]$, then $\displaystyle\int_{-a}^{a} f(x)\,dx = 2\int_{0}^{a} f(x)\,dx$.

SOLUTION: Recall that if f is even then $f(-x) = f(x)$ for all x in the domain of f.

Then $\displaystyle\int_{-a}^{a} f(x)\,dx = \int_{-a}^{0} f(x)\,dx + \int_{0}^{a} f(x)\,dx = -\int_{0}^{-a} f(x)\,dx + \int_{0}^{a} f(x)\,dx$.

Consider $\displaystyle\int_{0}^{-a} f(x)\,dx$. Let $u = -x$. Then $du = -dx$. Also, $x = 0 \implies u = 0$ and $x = -a \implies u = a$. Thus

$$\int_{0}^{-a} f(x)\,dx = \int_{0}^{a} -f(-u)\,du = -\int_{0}^{a} f(-u)\,du = -\int_{0}^{a} f(u)\,du$$

$$\text{and} \qquad \int_{-a}^{a} f(x)\,dx = \int_{u=0}^{u=a} f(u)\,du + \int_{x=0}^{x=a} f(x)\,dx.$$

Now $\displaystyle\int_{u=0}^{u=a} f(u)\,du$ is equal to some real number k and $\displaystyle\int_{x=0}^{x=a} f(x)\,dx = k$ also since the letters u and x are arbitrary.

So $\displaystyle\int_{-a}^{a} f(x)\,dx = k + k = 2k = 2\int_{0}^{a} f(x)\,dx$.

The Natural Logarithm Function

5. Find the derivative of $f(x) = \ln(x^2+3)^2$.

SOLUTION: Applying the chain rule, obtain

$$f'(x) = \frac{1}{(x^2+3)^2} \cdot D_x\left[(x^2+3)^2\right] = \frac{1}{(x^2+3)^2} \cdot 2(x^2+3) \cdot D_x[x^2+3]$$

$$= \frac{2(x^2 + 3)}{(x^2 + 3)^2}(2x) = \frac{4x}{x^2 + 3}.$$

COMMENT: $f(x) = \ln(x^2 + 3)^2 = 2\ln(x^2 + 3)$ by the laws of logarithms. Thus
$f'(x) = 2 \cdot \dfrac{1}{x^2 + 3}(2x) = \dfrac{4x}{x^2 + 3}$. It helps to know the laws of logarithms. By applying them before
differentiating, the problem can often be converted to a simpler form.

13. Find the derivative of $f(x) = \ln(x + \sqrt{x^2 - 1})$.

SOLUTION: Apply the chain rule and obtain

$$f'(x) = \frac{1}{x + \sqrt{x^2 - 1}} \cdot D_x\left[x + (x^2 - 1)^{1/2}\right] = \frac{1}{x + \sqrt{x^2 - 1}}\left(1 + \frac{1}{2}(x^2 - 1)^{-1/2}(2x)\right)$$

$$= \frac{1}{x + \sqrt{x^2 - 1}}\left(1 + \frac{x}{\sqrt{x^2 - 1}}\right) = \frac{1}{x + \sqrt{x^2 - 1}} \cdot \frac{\sqrt{x^2 - 1} + x}{\sqrt{x^2 - 1}} = \frac{1}{\sqrt{x^2 - 1}}.$$

17. Find the derivative of $f(x) = \left(\ln\dfrac{1+x}{1-x}\right)^{1/2}$.

SOLUTION: Apply $\ln(a/b) = \ln a - \ln b$ to $f(x)$ and obtain

$$f(x) = \left(\ln\frac{1+x}{1-x}\right)^{1/2} = (\ln(1+x) - \ln(1-x))^{1/2}.$$

$$f'(x) = \frac{1}{2}(\ln(1+x) - \ln(1-x))^{-1/2} D_x[\ln(1+x) - \ln(1-x)]$$

$$= \frac{1}{2}\left(\ln\frac{1+x}{1-x}\right)^{-1/2}\left(\frac{1}{1+x}(1) - \frac{1}{1-x}(-1)\right)$$

$$= \frac{1}{2}\left(\ln\frac{1+x}{1-x}\right)^{-1/2}\left(\frac{1}{1+x} + \frac{1}{1-x}\right)$$

$$= \frac{1}{2}\left(\ln\frac{1+x}{1-x}\right)^{-1/2}\left(\frac{1-x+1+x}{1-x^2}\right) = \frac{1}{1-x^2}\left(\ln\frac{1+x}{1-x}\right)^{-1/2}.$$

25. Find the derivative of $f(x) = \ln|2x + 1|$.

SOLUTION: $f'(x) = \dfrac{1}{|2x + 1|} \cdot D_x|2x + 1|$.

Recall $D_x|x| = \begin{cases} 1, & \text{for } x > 0 \\ -1, & \text{for } x < 0 \end{cases} = \dfrac{|x|}{x}$, $x \neq 0$. Thus $D_x|2x + 1| = \dfrac{|2x + 1|}{2x + 1}(2)$. So $f'(x) =$
$\dfrac{1}{|2x + 1|} \cdot \dfrac{|2x + 1|}{2x + 1}(2) = \dfrac{2}{2x + 1}$.

29. Find the derivative of $f(x) = \cos(\ln x)$.

SOLUTION: Apply the chain rule and obtain $f'(x) = -\sin(\ln x) \cdot D_x [\ln x] = -\sin(\ln x) \cdot \dfrac{1}{x} = -\dfrac{1}{x}\sin(\ln x)$.

35. Find $D_x y$ if $\ln\left(\dfrac{x}{y}\right) + x^2 + y^2 = 3$.

SOLUTION: $\ln\left(\dfrac{x}{y}\right) + x^2 + y^2 = 3 \implies \ln x - \ln y + x^2 + y^2 = 3 \implies D_x[\ln x] - D_x[\ln y] +$

$D_x[x^2] + D_x[y^2] = D_x[3] \implies \dfrac{1}{x} - \dfrac{1}{y}D_x y + 2x + 2y\,D_x y = 0 \implies \left(2y - \dfrac{1}{y}\right)D_x y =$

$-\dfrac{1}{x} - 2x \implies D_x y = \dfrac{\dfrac{1}{x} + 2x}{\dfrac{1}{y} - 2y} = \dfrac{y(1 + 2x^2)}{x(1 - 2y^2)}.$

43. Evaluate $\displaystyle\int (\csc 2x + \cot 3x)\,dx$.

SOLUTION: $\displaystyle\int (\csc 2x + \cot 3x)\,dx = \int \csc 2x\,dx + \int \cot 3x\,dx$.

Consider the two integrals separately. $\displaystyle\int \csc 2x\,dx = \int \dfrac{\csc 2x(\csc 2x - \cot 2x)}{\csc 2x - \cot 2x}\,dx$. Let $u = $ $\csc 2x - \cot 2x$. Then $du = \left(-(\csc 2x \cot 2x)(2) + \csc^2 2x(2)\right)\,dx = 2\csc 2x(\csc 2x - \cot 2x)\,dx \implies$ $\dfrac{1}{2}\,du = \csc 2x(\csc 2x - \cot 2x)\,dx$.

So $\displaystyle\int \csc 2x\,dx = \int \dfrac{1}{u}\left(\dfrac{1}{2}\,du\right) = \dfrac{1}{2}\int \dfrac{1}{u}\,du = \dfrac{1}{2}\ln|u| + C = \dfrac{1}{2}\ln|\csc 2x - \cot 2x| + C$.

Now $\displaystyle\int \cot 3x\,dx = \int \dfrac{\cos 3x}{\sin 3x}\,dx$. Let $u = \sin 3x$. Then $du = (\cos 3x)(3)\,dx \implies \dfrac{1}{3}\,du =$ $\cos 3x\,dx$.

Then $\displaystyle\int \cot 3x\,dx = \int \dfrac{1}{u}\left(\dfrac{1}{3}\,du\right) = \dfrac{1}{3}\int \dfrac{1}{u}\,du = \dfrac{1}{3}\ln|u| + C = \dfrac{1}{3}\ln|\sin 3x| + C$. Thus

$$\int (\csc 2x + \cot 3x)\,dx = \dfrac{1}{2}\ln|\csc 2x - \cot 2x| + \dfrac{1}{3}\ln|\sin 3x| + C.$$

47. Evaluate $\displaystyle\int_2^3 \dfrac{\ln x}{x}\,dx$.

SOLUTION: Let $u = \ln x$. Then $du = \dfrac{1}{x}\,dx$. Also, $x = 2 \implies u = \ln 2$ and $x = 3 \implies$ $u = \ln 3$. Thus $\displaystyle\int_2^3 \dfrac{\ln x}{x}\,dx = \int_{\ln 2}^{\ln 3} u\,du = \left[\dfrac{1}{2}u^2\right]\Big|_{\ln 2}^{\ln 3} = \dfrac{1}{2}\left((\ln 3)^2 - (\ln 2)^2\right)$.

53. Evaluate $\displaystyle\int \frac{\cos x}{1 + \sin x}\, dx.$

SOLUTION: Let $u = 1 + \sin x$. Then $du = \cos x\, dx$ and $\displaystyle\int \frac{\cos x}{1 + \sin x}\, dx = \int \frac{1}{u}\, du = \ln|u| + C =$
$\ln|1 + \sin x| + C = \ln(1 + \sin x) + C.$
Note that $-1 \le \sin x \le 1 \implies 0 \le 1 + \sin x \le 2 \implies |1 + \sin x| = 1 + \sin x.$

57. Use logarithmic differentiation to find $D_x y$ if $y = \sqrt{x\sqrt{(x+1)\sqrt{x}}}.$

SOLUTION:

$$\ln y = \ln\left(x\left((x+1)x^{1/2}\right)^{1/2}\right)^{1/2} = \frac{1}{2}\ln\left(x\left((x+1)x^{1/2}\right)^{1/2}\right)$$

$$= \frac{1}{2}\left(\ln x + \ln\left((x+1)x^{1/2}\right)^{1/2}\right) = \frac{1}{2}\left(\ln x + \frac{1}{2}\ln\left((x+1)x^{1/2}\right)\right)$$

$$= \frac{1}{2}\left(\ln x + \frac{1}{2}\left(\ln(x+1) + \ln x^{1/2}\right)\right) = \frac{1}{2}\left(\ln x + \frac{1}{2}\left(\ln(x+1) + \frac{1}{2}\ln x\right)\right).$$

So

$$\frac{1}{y}D_x y = \frac{1}{2}\left(\frac{1}{x} + \frac{1}{2}\left(\frac{1}{x+1} + \frac{1}{2}\cdot\frac{1}{x}\right)\right) \implies$$

$$D_x y = \frac{1}{2}\left(\frac{1}{x} + \frac{1}{2}\left(\frac{2x + x + 1}{2x(x+1)}\right)\right) y$$

$$= \frac{1}{2}\left(\frac{1}{x} + \frac{3x+1}{4x(x+1)}\right) y = \frac{1}{2}\left(\frac{4(x+1) + (3x+1)}{4x(x+1)}\right) y$$

$$= \frac{7x+5}{8x(x+1)}\sqrt{x\sqrt{(x+1)\sqrt{x}}}.$$

63. Use L'Hôpital's rule to evaluate $\displaystyle\lim_{x\to\infty} \frac{\ln\sqrt{x}}{x^5}.$

SOLUTION: $\displaystyle\lim_{x\to\infty} \frac{\ln\sqrt{x}}{x^5} = \lim_{x\to\infty} \frac{\frac{1}{2}\ln x}{x^5} = \frac{1}{2}\lim_{x\to\infty} \frac{\ln x}{x^5}.$ Now $\displaystyle\lim_{x\to\infty} \ln x = \infty$ and $\displaystyle\lim_{x\to\infty} x^5 = \infty$
which yields the indeterminate form ∞/∞. Thus

$$\lim_{x\to\infty} \frac{\ln x}{x^5} = \lim_{x\to\infty} \frac{1/x}{5x^4} = \lim_{x\to\infty} \frac{1}{5x^5} = \frac{1}{5}\lim_{x\to\infty} \frac{1}{x^5} = 0.$$

So $\displaystyle\lim_{x\to\infty} \frac{\ln\sqrt{x}}{x^5} = \frac{1}{2}\cdot 0 = 0.$

79. Sketch the graph of $f(x) = x \ln x$.

SOLUTION: Since $\ln x$ is defined only for $x > 0$, the domain of f is $(0, \infty)$. Check for critical points by solving $f'(x) = 0$. $f'(x) = x \cdot \dfrac{1}{x} + \ln x = 1 + \ln x$. $f'(x) = 1 + \ln x = 0 \implies \ln x = -1 \implies -\ln x = 1 \implies \ln x^{-1} = 1 \implies x^{-1} = e \implies x = 1/e$. $f''(x) = 1/x$. $f''(1/e) = e > 0$ which indicates $f(x)$ has a minimum at $x = 1/e$ and $f(1/e) = \dfrac{1}{e} \ln \dfrac{1}{e} = -\dfrac{1}{e}$. Also there are no points of inflection and f is concave up.

Also $\lim\limits_{x \to 0+} x \ln x = \lim\limits_{x \to 0+} \dfrac{\ln x}{1/x} = \lim\limits_{x \to 0+} \dfrac{1/x}{-1/x^2} = \lim\limits_{x \to 0+} (-x) = 0$ by applying L'Hôpital's rule and clearly, $\lim\limits_{x \to \infty} x \ln x = \infty$.

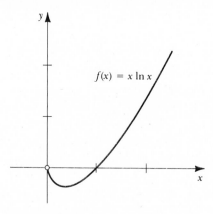

$f(x) = x \ln x$

83. Find an equation of the line tangent to the graph of $y = 3 \ln x + x$ at the point $(1, 1)$.

SOLUTION: Recall that to find the equation of a line one needs a point and the slope. The point is $(1, 1)$. To determine the slope, evaluate the derivative at $(1, 1)$. $\dfrac{dy}{dx} = 3 \cdot \dfrac{1}{x} + 1$.

$\dfrac{dy}{dx}\bigg|_{(1,1)} = 3 \cdot \dfrac{1}{1} + 1 = 4$.

Applying point-slope form, $y - 1 = 4(x - 1)$, and the equation of the tangent line is $y = 4x - 3$.

_____4.7

Improper Integrals

5. Determine whether $\displaystyle\int_3^\infty \dfrac{1}{x(\ln x)^2}\, dx$ converges or diverges and evaluate it if it converges.

SOLUTION: $\displaystyle\int_3^\infty \dfrac{1}{x(\ln x)^2}\, dx = \lim_{M \to \infty} \int_3^M \dfrac{1}{x}(\ln x)^{-2}\, dx$. Let $u = \ln x$. Then $du = \dfrac{1}{x}\, dx$ and

$$\lim_{M \to \infty} \int_3^M \dfrac{1}{x}(\ln x)^{-2}\, dx = \lim_{M \to \infty} \int_{x=3}^{x=M} u^{-2}\, du = \lim_{M \to \infty} \left[-u^{-1}\right]\bigg|_{x=3}^{x=M} = \lim_{M \to \infty} \left[-\dfrac{1}{\ln x}\right]\bigg|_3^M$$

$$= -\lim_{M \to \infty} \left(\frac{1}{\ln M} - \frac{1}{\ln 3} \right) = - \left(\lim_{M \to \infty} \frac{1}{\ln M} - \frac{1}{\ln 3} \right)$$

$$= - \left(0 - \frac{1}{\ln 3} \right) = \frac{1}{\ln 3}.$$

Thus $\int_3^\infty \dfrac{1}{x(\ln x)^2} \, dx$ converges to $\dfrac{1}{\ln 3}$.

17. Determine whether $\int_1^2 \dfrac{1}{(x-1)^2} \, dx$ converges or diverges and evaluate it if it converges.

SOLUTION: Since $\dfrac{1}{(x-1)^2}$ is undefined at $x = 1$,

$$\int_1^2 \frac{1}{(x-1)^2} \, dx = \lim_{M \to 1^+} \int_M^2 (x-1)^{-2} \, dx = \lim_{M \to 1^+} \left[-(x-1)^{-1} \right] \Big|_M^2$$

$$= -\lim_{M \to 1^+} \left(\frac{1}{2-1} - \frac{1}{M-1} \right) = -1 + \lim_{M \to 1^+} \frac{1}{M-1} = \infty.$$

Thus $\int_1^2 \dfrac{1}{(x-1)^2} \, dx$ diverges.

21. Determine whether $\int_0^{\pi/2} \sec x \, dx$ converges or diverges and evaluate it if it converges.

SOLUTION: Since $\sec \dfrac{\pi}{2}$ is undefined,

$$\int_0^{\pi/2} \sec x \, dx = \lim_{M \to \frac{\pi}{2}^-} \int_0^M \sec x \, dx = \lim_{M \to \frac{\pi}{2}^-} \int_0^M \frac{\sec x (\sec x + \tan x)}{\sec x + \tan x} \, dx$$

$$= \lim_{M \to \frac{\pi}{2}^-} \ln |\sec x + \tan x| \Big|_0^M = \lim_{M \to \frac{\pi}{2}^-} \left(\ln(\sec M + \tan M) - \ln(\sec 0 + \tan 0) \right)$$

$$= \lim_{M \to \frac{\pi}{2}^-} \left(\ln \frac{1 + \sin M}{\cos M} \right) - \ln 1 = \infty.$$

Thus $\int_0^{\pi/2} \sec x \, dx$ diverges.

27. Determine whether $\int_{-\infty}^{\infty} \dfrac{x}{(1+x^2)^3}\, dx$ converges or diverges and evaluate it if it converges.

SOLUTION: $\int_{-\infty}^{\infty} \dfrac{x}{(1+x^2)^3}\, dx = \int_{-\infty}^{a} x(1+x^2)^{-3}\, dx + \int_{a}^{\infty} x(1+x^2)^{-3}\, dx.$ First consider
$\int x(1+x^2)^{-3}\, dx.$ Let $u = 1 + x^2.$ Then $du = 2x\, dx$ and $\frac{1}{2} du = x\, dx.$ Thus $\int x(1+x^2)^{-3}\, dx =$
$\frac{1}{2} \int u^{-3}\, du = -\frac{1}{4} u^{-2} + C = -\frac{1}{2} \cdot \dfrac{1}{(1+x^2)^2} + C.$ So

$$\int_{-\infty}^{a} x(1+x^2)^{-3}\, dx = \lim_{M \to -\infty} \int_{M}^{a} x(1+x^2)^{-3}\, dx = -\frac{1}{2} \lim_{M \to -\infty} \left[\dfrac{1}{(1+x^2)^2} \right] \Big|_{M}^{a}$$

$$= -\frac{1}{2} \left(\dfrac{1}{(1+a^2)^2} - \lim_{M \to -\infty} \dfrac{1}{(1+M^2)^2} \right) = \dfrac{-1}{2(1+a^2)^2}.$$

Next,

$$\int_{a}^{\infty} x(1+x^2)^{-3}\, dx = \lim_{M \to \infty} \int_{a}^{M} x(1+x^2)^{-3}\, dx = -\frac{1}{2} \lim_{M \to \infty} \left[\dfrac{1}{(1+x^2)^2} \right] \Big|_{a}^{M}$$

$$= -\frac{1}{2} \left(\lim_{M \to \infty} \dfrac{1}{(1+M^2)^2} - \dfrac{1}{(1+a^2)^2} \right) = \dfrac{1}{2(1+a^2)^2}.$$

Thus $\int_{-\infty}^{\infty} \dfrac{x}{(1+x^2)^3}\, dx$ converges to $\dfrac{-1}{2(1+a^2)^2} + \dfrac{1}{2(1+a^2)^2} = 0.$

33. Determine whether $\int_{-\infty}^{0} \dfrac{1}{(x+2)^2}\, dx$ converges or diverges and evaluate it if it converges.

SOLUTION: Since $\dfrac{1}{(x+2)^2}$ is undefined at $x = -2,$

$$\int_{-\infty}^{0} \dfrac{1}{(x+2)^2}\, dx = \lim_{M \to -\infty} \int_{M}^{a} (x+2)^{-2}\, dx + \lim_{N \to -2^-} \int_{a}^{N} (x+2)^{-2}\, dx + \lim_{P \to -2^+} \int_{P}^{0} (x+2)^{-2}\, dx.$$

First, $\int (x+2)^{-2}\, dx = -(x+2)^{-1} + C$ by substituting $u = x + 2.$ Then

$$\lim_{M \to -\infty} \int_{M}^{a} (x+2)^{-2}\, dx = -\lim_{M \to -\infty} \left[\dfrac{1}{x+2} \right] \Big|_{M}^{a} = -\left(\dfrac{1}{a+2} - \lim_{M \to -\infty} \dfrac{1}{M+2} \right) = \dfrac{-1}{a+2}.$$

Next,

$$\lim_{N \to -2^-} \int_{a}^{N} (x+2)^{-2}\, dx = -\lim_{N \to -2^-} \left[\dfrac{1}{x+2} \right] \Big|_{a}^{N} = -\left(\lim_{N \to -2^-} \dfrac{1}{N+2} - \dfrac{1}{a+2} \right) = \infty.$$

Thus $\displaystyle\int_{-\infty}^{0} \frac{1}{(x+2)^2}\, dx$ diverges.

Note that recognizing $\dfrac{1}{(x+2)^2}$ is undefined at $x = -2$ is crucial. Ignoring that and blindly

evaluating $\displaystyle\lim_{M\to-\infty} \int_{M}^{0} \frac{1}{(x+2)^2}\, dx$ as a single integral will lead to an error.

37. Determine whether the region bounded by $y = 1/x^3$, the x-axis and $x = 1$ with $x \geq 1$ is finite.

SOLUTION: Since $y = 1/x^3 \geq 0$ for $x \geq 1$, the area can be found by evaluating $\displaystyle\int_{1}^{\infty} \frac{1}{x^3}\, dx$.

$$\int_{1}^{\infty} x^{-3}\, dx = \lim_{M\to\infty} \int_{1}^{M} x^{-3}\, dx = \lim_{M\to\infty} \left[-\frac{1}{2}x^{-2}\right]\Big|_{1}^{M} = -\frac{1}{2}\left(\lim_{M\to\infty} \frac{1}{M^2} - \frac{1}{1}\right) = \frac{1}{2}.$$

Thus the area is finite and is $\dfrac{1}{2}$.

_____Chapter 4

Review Exercises

7. Find the value of $\displaystyle\sum_{i=1}^{n} (2i - 1)$.

SOLUTION: To evaluate this sum, make use of the formulas in DEFINITION 4.3.

$$\sum_{i=1}^{n} (2i - 1) = 2\sum_{i=1}^{n} i - \sum_{i=1}^{n} 1 = 2\left(\frac{n(n+1)}{2}\right) - n = n(n+1) - n = n^2.$$

11. Express each of the following limits as a definite integral over the interval $[0, 2]$ and find its value.

b) $\displaystyle\lim_{n\to\infty} \sum_{i=1}^{n} (2x_i + 1)\frac{2}{n}$.

SOLUTION: b) $\displaystyle\lim_{n\to\infty} \sum_{i=1}^{n} (2x_i + 1)\frac{2}{n} = \int_{0}^{2} (2x + 1)\, dx$. Now

$$\lim_{n\to\infty} \sum_{i=1}^{n} (2x_i + 1)\frac{2}{n} = 4\lim_{n\to\infty} \frac{1}{n} \sum_{i=1}^{n} x_i + 2\lim_{n\to\infty} \frac{1}{n} \sum_{i=1}^{n} 1$$

$$= 4 \lim_{n \to \infty} \frac{1}{n} \sum_{i=1}^{n} \left(0 + \frac{2i}{n}\right) + 2 \lim_{n \to \infty} \frac{1}{n} \cdot n = 8 \lim_{n \to \infty} \frac{1}{n^2} \sum_{i=1}^{n} i + 2 \lim_{n \to \infty} 1$$

$$= 8 \lim_{n \to \infty} \frac{1}{n^2} \cdot \frac{n(n+1)}{2} + 2 = 4 \lim_{n \to \infty} \frac{n+1}{n} + 2 = 6.$$

17. Evaluate $\int 4(4x + 7)^3 \, dx$.

SOLUTION: Let $u = 7x + 7$. Then $du = 4 \, dx$ and $dx = du/4$. So

$$\int 4(4x + 7)^3 \, dx = \int 4u^3 \frac{du}{4} = \int u^3 \, du = \frac{1}{4}u^4 + C = \frac{1}{4}(4x + 7)^4 + C.$$

23. Evaluate $\int \left(\frac{1}{x^4} + \frac{1}{\sqrt[4]{x}}\right) dx$.

SOLUTION:

$$\int \left(\frac{1}{x^4} + \frac{1}{\sqrt[4]{x}}\right) dx = \int (x^{-4} + x^{-1/4}) \, dx = -\frac{1}{3}x^{-3} + \frac{4}{3}x^{3/4} + C.$$

25. Evaluate $\int_0^\pi (\cos t - t) \, dt$.

SOLUTION:

$$\int_0^\pi (\cos t - t) \, dt = \left[\sin t - \frac{1}{2}t^2\right] \Big|_0^\pi = \left(\sin \pi - \frac{1}{2}\pi^2\right) - (\sin 0 - 0) = -\frac{1}{2}\pi^2.$$

29. Evaluate $\int w^3 \sqrt{w^2 + 1} \, dw$.

SOLUTION: Let $u = w^2 + 1$. Then $du = 2w \, dw$, $dw = \frac{du}{2w}$ and $w^2 = u - 1$; so

$$\int w^3 \sqrt{w^2 + 1} \, dw = \int w^2 \sqrt{w^2 + 1} \, w \, dw = \int (u - 1)u^{1/2} \frac{du}{2} = \frac{1}{2} \int \left(u^{3/2} - u^{1/2}\right) du$$

$$= \frac{1}{2} \left(\frac{2}{5}u^{5/2} - \frac{2}{3}u^{3/2}\right) + C = \frac{1}{5}(w^2 + 1)^{5/2} - \frac{1}{3}(w^2 + 1)^{3/2} + C.$$

35. Evaluate $\displaystyle\int \frac{x-3}{x^2-6x+5}\,dx.$

SOLUTION: Let $u = x^2 - 6x + 5$. Then $du = 2(x-3)\,dx$, so

$$\int \frac{x-3}{x^2-6x+5}\,dx = \int \frac{1}{u}\frac{du}{2} = \frac{1}{2}\ln|u| + C = \frac{1}{2}\ln|x^2 - 6x + 5| + C.$$

39. Evaluate $\displaystyle\int_1^2 \frac{s}{(1+2s)^3}\,ds.$

SOLUTION: Let $u = 1 + 2s$. Then $du = 2\,ds$, $ds = du/2$, $s = 1 \implies u = 3$ and $s = 2 \implies u = 5$. Also $s = (u-1)/2$ so

$$\int_1^2 \frac{s}{(1+2s)^3}\,ds = \int_3^5 \frac{(u-1)/2}{u^3}\cdot\frac{du}{2} = \frac{1}{4}\int_3^5 \frac{u-1}{u^3}\,du$$

$$= \frac{1}{4}\int_3^5\left(\frac{u}{u^3} - \frac{1}{u^3}\right)du = \frac{1}{4}\int_3^5 (u^{-2} - u^{-3})\,du = \frac{1}{4}\Big[-u^{-1} + \frac{1}{2}u^{-2}\Big]\Big|_3^5$$

$$= \frac{1}{4}\left(\left(-\frac{1}{5} + \frac{1}{2}\left(\frac{1}{25}\right)\right) - \left(-\frac{1}{3} + \frac{1}{2}\left(\frac{1}{9}\right)\right)\right) = \frac{11}{450}.$$

45. Evaluate $\displaystyle\int \tan 4x\,dx.$

SOLUTION: $\displaystyle\int \tan 4x\,dx = \int \frac{\sin 4x}{\cos 4x}\,dx$ and let $u = \cos 4x$. Then $du = -4\sin 4x\,dx$ and $-\dfrac{du}{4} = \sin 4x\,dx$. Thus

$$\int \frac{\sin 4x}{\cos 4x}\,dx = \int \frac{1}{u}\left(-\frac{du}{4}\right) = -\frac{1}{4}\int \frac{du}{u} = -\frac{1}{4}\ln|u| + C$$

$$= -\frac{1}{4}\ln|\cos 4x| + C = \frac{1}{4}\ln|\sec 4x| + C.$$

53. Determine whether $\displaystyle\int_0^\infty \frac{1}{(x+1)^2}\,dx$ converges or diverges. If it converges, evaluate the integral.

SOLUTION:

$$\int_0^\infty \frac{1}{(x+1)^2}\,dx = \lim_{M\to\infty}\int_0^M (x+1)^{-2}\,dx = \lim_{M\to\infty}\Big[-(x+1)^{-1}\Big]\Big|_0^M$$

$$= -\lim_{M \to \infty} \left(\frac{1}{M+1} - \frac{1}{0+1} \right) = -\lim_{M \to \infty} \frac{1}{M+1} - 1 = -(0-1) = 1.$$

Thus the integral converges to 1.

59. Determine whether $\displaystyle\int_{-3}^{3} \frac{x\,dx}{\sqrt{9-x^2}}$ converges or diverges. If it converges, evaluate the integral.

SOLUTION:

$$\int_{-3}^{3} \frac{x\,dx}{\sqrt{9-x^2}} = \lim_{M \to -3+} \int_{M}^{a} x(9-x^2)^{-1/2}\,dx + \lim_{N \to 3-} \int_{a}^{N} x(9-x^2)^{-1/2}\,dx$$

where $-3 < a < 3$. Let $u = 9 - x^2$. Then $du = -2x\,dx$ and $-du/2 = x\,dx$. Thus

$$\lim_{M \to -3+} \int_{M}^{a} x(9-x^2)^{-1/2}\,dx + \lim_{N \to 3-} \int_{a}^{N} x(9-x^2)^{-1/2}\,dx$$

$$= \lim_{M \to -3+} \int_{x=M}^{x=a} u^{-1/2} \left(-\frac{du}{2} \right) + \lim_{N \to 3-} \int_{x=a}^{x=N} u^{-1/2} \left(-\frac{du}{2} \right)$$

$$= -\frac{1}{2} \left(\lim_{M \to -3+} \int_{x=M}^{x=a} u^{-1/2}\,du + \lim_{N \to 3-} \int_{x=a}^{x=N} u^{-1/2}\,du \right)$$

$$= -\frac{1}{2} \left(\lim_{M \to -3+} \left[2u^{1/2} \right] \Big|_{x=M}^{x=a} + \lim_{N \to 3-} \left[2u^{1/2} \right] \Big|_{x=a}^{x=N} \right)$$

$$= -\left(\lim_{M \to -3+} \left[\sqrt{9-x^2} \right] \Big|_{M}^{a} + \lim_{N \to 3-} \left[\sqrt{9-x^2} \right] \Big|_{a}^{N} \right)$$

$$= -\left(\lim_{M \to -3+} \left(\sqrt{9-a^2} - \sqrt{9-M^2} \right) + \lim_{N \to 3-} \left(\sqrt{9-N^2} - \sqrt{9-a^2} \right) \right)$$

$$= -\left((\sqrt{9-a^2} - 0) + (0 - \sqrt{9-a^2}) \right) = 0.$$

Thus the integral converges to 0.

71. Find the derivative of $x \displaystyle\int_{1}^{x} \ln t\,dt.$

SOLUTION: Apply the product rule and obtain

$$D_x \left[x \int_{1}^{x} \ln t\,dt \right] = x\,D_x \left[\int_{1}^{x} \ln t\,dt \right] + \left(\int_{1}^{x} \ln t\,dt \right)(D_x x)$$

$$= x \ln x + \int_{1}^{x} \ln t\,dt.$$

Note that $D_x \left[\displaystyle\int_1^x \ln t \, dt \right]$ is obtained by the application of the Fundamental Lemma of Calculus.

75. Find the area of the region bounded by the curve $y = (x - 2)^{2/3}$, the x-axis, and the lines $x = 1$ and $x = 10$. Make a sketch of the region.

SOLUTION:

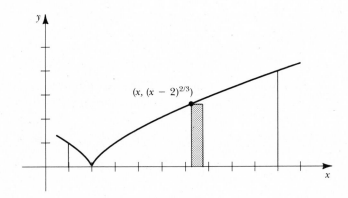

The area of the element is $(x - 2)^{2/3} dx$. Thus $A = \displaystyle\int_1^{10} (x - 2)^{2/3} dx$. Let $u = x - 2$. Then $du = dx$ and $x = 1 \implies u = -1$ and $x = 10 \implies u = 8$. Thus

$$A = \int_{-1}^{8} u^{2/3} du = \left[\frac{3}{5} u^{5/3} \right] \Big|_{-1}^{8} = \frac{3}{5} \left(8^{5/3} - (-1)^{5/3} \right) = \frac{3}{5}(32 + 1) = \frac{99}{5}.$$

5
Applications of the
Definite Integral

Sharpening your skills

To prepare for CHAPTER 5, it will help to review the process of evaluating definite integrals by using the Fundamental Theorem of Calculus. This is found in SECTION 4.3 of the text. Also review the material in SECTIONS 4.4–4.6, which present additional techniques, including substitution, for evaluating integrals. Some additional practice problems are presented below. The answers to these problems are found in APPENDIX B in this manual.

1. Evaluate each of the following:

   a) $\displaystyle\int_0^{2\pi} \pi(2x-3)^2\,dx,$

   b) $\displaystyle\int_{-1}^{1} \pi(x^2+4)^2\,dx,$

   c) $\displaystyle\int_0^{1} 2\pi x(x^2+3)\,dx,$

   d) $\displaystyle\int_0^{1} x(x^2-4)^6\,dx.$

$$5.1$$

Areas of Regions
in the Plane

COMMENT: A <u>strategy</u> for determining the area of a region in the plane is   i) Sketch the region. ii) Select an area element of width dx or dy.   iii) Determine the limits of integration and construct the integral from the element.   iv) Evaluate the integral.

Within this context, the embedding of the element refers to the top and bottom boundary functions in the case of a dx element or right and left in the case of a dy element. We say that the embedding changes when either of the boundary functions change.

1. Sketch the graphs $y = x^2 - 2x$, $x = 2$, $x = 4$, and $y = 0$, and then find the area of the region bounded by these graphs.

SOLUTION: i)

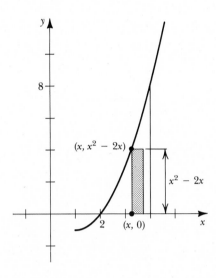

ii) Although it is possible to use either a dx element or dy element, a dx element is chosen since $y = x^2 - 2x$ cannot easily be solved for x. The area of the element is $(x^2 - 2x)\,dx$.

iii) The element traverses the area from $x = 2$ to $x = 4$ and does not switch its embedding. Thus the desired area is $\displaystyle\int_2^4 (x^2 - 2x)\,dx$.

iv)

$$\int_2^4 (x^2 - 2x)\,dx = \left[\frac{1}{3}x^3 - x^2\right]\Big|_2^4 = \left(\frac{1}{3}(64) - 16\right) - \left(\frac{1}{3}(8) - 4\right) = \frac{20}{3}.$$

7. Find the area bounded by $y = 1/x$, $x = -1$, $x = -5$, and $y = 0$.

SOLUTION: i)

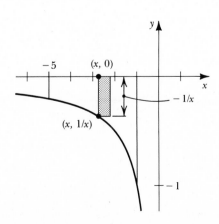

ii) Here it is best to select a dx element since a dy element would change its embedding. The area of the element is $-\dfrac{1}{x}\,dx$.

iii) The element traverses the area from $x = -5$ to $x = -1$. Thus the integral is $\displaystyle\int_{-5}^{-1} -\dfrac{1}{x}\,dx$.

iv)

$$\int_{-5}^{-1} -\frac{1}{x}\,dx = -\int_{-5}^{-1} \frac{1}{x}\,dx = -\ln|x|\,\Big|_{-5}^{-1} = -(\ln|-1| - \ln|-5|) = \ln 5.$$

15. Find the area bounded by $y = x^3$, $y = x^2$.

SOLUTION: i)

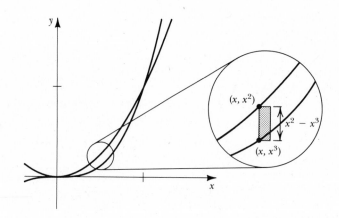

ii) Since the curves are given in the form $y = f(x)$, it is easier to use a dx element. The area of the element is $(x^2 - x^3)\,dx$.

iii) To find the limits, solve $y = x^3$ and $y = x^2$ simultaneously. $x^3 = x^2 \implies x^3 - x^2 = 0 \implies x^2(x - 1) = 0 \implies x = 0$ or $x = 1$. Thus the element traverses the area from $x = 0$ to $x = 1$. The integral is $\displaystyle\int_0^1 (x^2 - x^3)\,dx$.

iv)

$$\int_0^1 (x^2 - x^3)\,dx = \left[\frac{1}{3}x^3 - \frac{1}{4}x^4\right]\Big|_0^1 = \frac{1}{3} - \frac{1}{4} = \frac{1}{12}.$$

If you were to use a dy element, the equations of the curves would need to be solved for x. In the case of $y = x^3$, that poses no great problem: $x = y^{1/3}$. However, with $y = x^2$, $x = \pm y^{1/2}$ and one must select either the principal or negative square root. In this case, the principal root is correct. The integral that results is $\displaystyle\int_0^1 \left(y^{1/3} - y^{1/2}\right) dy$. It is left to the reader to show that this integral does evaluate to $\dfrac{1}{12}$.

25. Find the area bounded by $y = x$, $y = 1 - x$, and $y = -x/2$.

SOLUTION: i)

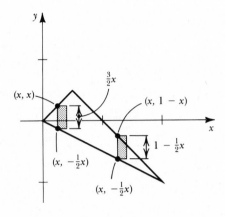

ii) In this case neither a dx nor a dy element avoids switching the embedding of the element. The selection of a dx element here is arbitrary as solving the equations of the boundary curves for x is trivial. The area of the first (left) element is $\left(x - \left(\dfrac{-x}{2} \right) \right) dx$ and that of the second is $\left(1 - x - \left(-\dfrac{x}{2} \right) \right) dx$.

iii) Since the first element traverses the area from $x = 0$ to $x = 1/2$ (obtained by solving $y = x$ and $y = -x/2$ simultaneously) and the second traverses from $x = 1/2$ to $x = 2$ (obtained by solving $y = 1 - x$ and $y = -x/2$ simultaneously), the area is the sum of the integrals

$$\int_0^{1/2} \frac{3}{2} x \, dx + \int_{1/2}^2 \left(1 - \frac{1}{2} x \right) dx.$$

iv)

$$\int_0^{1/2} \frac{3}{2} x \, dx = \left[\frac{3}{4} x^2 \right] \Big|_0^{1/2} = \frac{3}{4} \left(\frac{1}{4} \right) = \frac{3}{16}$$

and

$$\int_{1/2}^2 \left(1 - \frac{1}{2} x \right) dx = \left[x - \frac{1}{4} x^2 \right] \Big|_{1/2}^2$$

$$= \left(2 - \frac{1}{4}(4) \right) - \left(\frac{1}{2} - \frac{1}{4} \left(\frac{1}{4} \right) \right) = \frac{9}{16}.$$

Thus the desired area is $\dfrac{3}{16} + \dfrac{9}{16} = \dfrac{3}{4}$.

33. Find the area bounded by $y = \sin x$, $y = \tan x$, $x = \pi/4$.

SOLUTION: i)

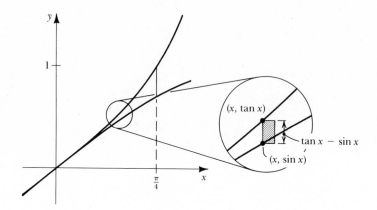

Note that $\tan x > \sin x$ on $\left(0, \dfrac{\pi}{4}\right)$ since $\tan x = \dfrac{\sin x}{\cos x}$ and $0 < \cos x < 1$ on $\left(0, \dfrac{\pi}{4}\right)$.

ii) The element to use here is a dx element. The area of the element is $(\tan x - \sin x)\, dx$.

iii) The element traverses the area from $x = 0$ to $x = \pi/4$. The area is described by the integral $\displaystyle\int_0^{\pi/4} (\tan x - \sin x)\, dx$.

iv)

$$\int_0^{\pi/4} (\tan x - \sin x)\, dx = \int_0^{\pi/4} \tan x\, dx - \int_0^{\pi/4} \sin x\, dx.$$

Now $\displaystyle\int \tan x\, dx = \int \dfrac{\sin x}{\cos x}\, dx$. If you make the substitution $u = \cos x$ and $du = -\sin x\, dx$, the integral becomes $\displaystyle\int -\dfrac{du}{u} = -\ln|u| + C = -\ln|\cos x| + C$. Thus

$$\int_0^{\pi/4} \tan x\, dx = -\ln|\cos x|\,\Big|_0^{\pi/4} = -\Big(\ln(\sqrt{2}/2) - \ln 1\Big)$$

$$= -\ln(\sqrt{2}/2) = \frac{1}{2}\ln 2.$$

Also $\displaystyle\int_0^{\pi/4} \sin x\, dx = [-\cos x]\,\Big|_0^{\pi/4} = -\left(\dfrac{\sqrt{2}}{2} - 1\right) = 1 - \dfrac{\sqrt{2}}{2}$. Thus the desired area is $\dfrac{1}{2}\ln 2 -$ $\left(1 - \dfrac{\sqrt{2}}{2}\right) = \dfrac{1}{2}(\sqrt{2} - 2 + \ln 2).$

43. Find the area bounded by $x = y^2$, $x + y = 2$.

SOLUTION: i)

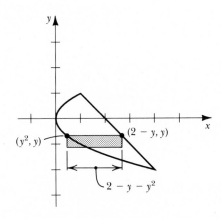

ii) A dy element is chosen here to avoid switching embedding and to avoid solving the boundary equations for y. The area of the element is $(2 - y - y^2)\,dy$.

iii) The element traverses the area from $y = -2$ to $y = 1$ (found by solving $x = y^2$ and $x + y = 2$ simultaneously), and thus the integral describing the area is $\displaystyle\int_{-2}^{1} (2 - y - y^2)\,dy$.

iv)

$$\int_{-2}^{1} (2 - y - y^2)\,dy = \left[2y - \frac{1}{2}y^2 - \frac{1}{3}y^3\right]\Big|_{-2}^{1}$$

$$= \left(2(1) - \frac{1}{2}(1) - \frac{1}{3}(1)\right) - \left(2(-2) - \frac{1}{2}(4) - \frac{1}{3}(-8)\right) = \frac{9}{2}.$$

47. Use integration to find the area of the region inside the triangle with vertices $(0,0)$, $(1,1)$ and $(1,0)$.

SOLUTION: In this problem the points of intersection are known but the equations of the boundary curves are not. Before applying the solution method, these equations must be determined.

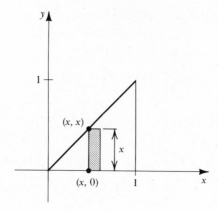

i) The equation of the line connecting $(0,0)$ and $(1,1)$ can be determined by the slope-intercept method. The slope is 1 and the y-intercept is 0 so the equation is $y = x$. The equations of the lines connecting the points $(0,0)$ and $(1,0)$ and the points $(1,0)$ and $(1,1)$ are horizontal and vertical with equations $y = 0$ and $x = 1$ respectively.

ii) The choice of a dx element is arbitrary. The area of the element is $(x - 0)\,dx$.

iii) The element traverses the area from $x = 0$ to $x = 1$. The integral is $\displaystyle\int_0^1 x\,dx$.

iv)

$$\int_0^1 x\,dx = \left[\frac{1}{2}x^2\right]\Big|_0^1 = \frac{1}{2}(1) - 0 = \frac{1}{2}.$$

_____5.2

Volumes of Solids with Known Cross Sections: Disks

---

1. Suppose S is a pyramid lying between the planes that pass through $x = 0$ and $x = 6$, and that every cross section of S perpendicular to the x-axis is a square with width $6 - x$,

$0 \leq x \leq 6$. Find the volume of S.

SOLUTION: i)

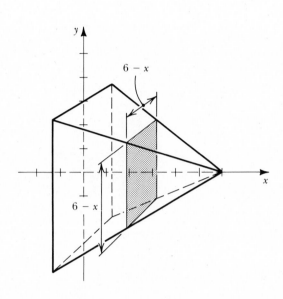

ii) The appropriate element here is a dx element since the cross section perpendicular to the x-axis is known. The volume of the cross section is $(6-x)^2\,dx$.

iii) The element traverses from $x = 0$ to $x = 6$ so the desired integral is $\displaystyle\int_0^6 (6-x)^2\,dx$.

iv) To evaluate $\displaystyle\int_0^6 (6-x)^2\,dx$, let $u = 6 - x$. Then $du = -dx$, $x = 0 \implies u = 6$ and $x = 6 \implies u = 0$. Thus obtain

$$\int_6^0 -u^2\,du = \left[-\frac{1}{3}u^3\right]\Big|_6^0 = -\frac{1}{3}(0 - 216) = 72.$$

11. Find the volume generated if the region bounded by the curves $y = x^2 + 2x + 1$, $x = 1$, $y = 0$ is revolved about the x-axis. Sketch the region to be revolved.

SOLUTION: i)

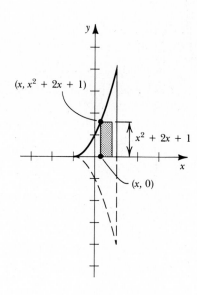

ii) A dx element will generate a disk. The volume of this element is

$$\pi \left((x+1)^2 \right)^2 \, dx = \pi (x+1)^4 \, dx.$$

iii) The element traverses the volume from $x = -1$ to $x = 1$. Thus the desired integral is

$$\int_{-1}^{1} \pi (x+1)^4 \, dx.$$

iv) With the substitution $u = x + 1$, $\displaystyle\int_{-1}^{1} \pi (x+1)^4 \, dx$ becomes

$$\int_{0}^{2} \pi u^4 \, du = \left[\frac{\pi}{5} u^5 \right]\Big|_{0}^{2} = \frac{\pi}{5}(32 - 0) = \frac{32\pi}{5}.$$

17. Find the volume generated if the region bounded by the curves $y = x^3$, $y = 1$, $x = 2$ is revolved about the x-axis. Sketch the region to be revolved.

SOLUTION: i)

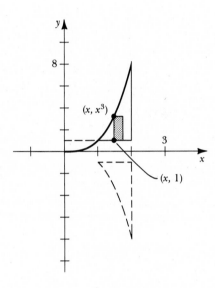

ii) A dx element is selected here. This element describes a washer with $r_1 = x^3 - 0$ and $r_2 = 1 - 0$ so the volume of the element is $\pi\left((x^3)^2 - 1^2\right) dx$.

iii) The element traverses the volume from $x = 1$ to $x = 2$, which generates the integral $\int_1^2 \pi(x^6 - 1)\, dx$.

iv)

$$\int_1^2 \pi(x^6 - 1)\, dx = \pi\left[\frac{1}{7}x^7 - x\right]\Big|_1^2$$

$$= \pi\left(\left(\frac{1}{7}(128) - 2\right) - \left(\frac{1}{7} - 1\right)\right) = \pi\left(\frac{127}{7} - 1\right) = \frac{120\pi}{7}.$$

23. Find the volume generated if the region bounded by the curves $y = \sec x$, $x = \dfrac{-\pi}{4}$, $x = \dfrac{\pi}{4}$ is revolved about the x-axis. Sketch the region to be revolved.

SOLUTION: i)

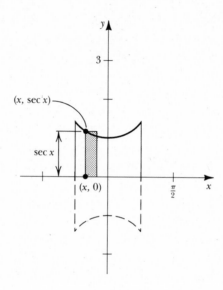

ii) A dx element generates a disk with $r = \sec x$. Thus the volume of the element is $\pi \sec^2 x \, dx$.

iii) The element traverses the region from $x = -\dfrac{\pi}{4}$ to $x = \dfrac{\pi}{4}$. The integral describing the volume is $\displaystyle\int_{-\pi/4}^{\pi/4} \pi \sec^2 x \, dx$.

iv)

$$\int_{-\pi/4}^{\pi/4} \pi \sec^2 x \, dx = \left[\pi \tan x\right]\Big|_{-\pi/4}^{\pi/4} = \pi \left(\tan \frac{\pi}{4} - \tan\left(-\frac{\pi}{4}\right)\right) = 2\pi.$$

33. Find the volume generated if the region bounded by the curves $y = \dfrac{\sqrt{x}}{\sqrt[4]{x^2 + 1}}$, $x = 0$, $x = 1$, $y = 0$ is revolved about the x-axis. Sketch the region to be revolved.

SOLUTION: i)

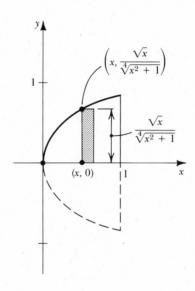

ii) The volume of the dx element is $\pi \left(\dfrac{\sqrt{x}}{\sqrt[4]{x^2 + 1}} \right)^2 dx$.

iii) The element traverses the volume from $x = 0$ to $x = 1$, which yields the integral

$$\int_0^1 \pi \frac{x}{\sqrt{x^2 + 1}}\, dx.$$

iv)

$$\int_0^1 \pi \frac{x}{\sqrt{x^2 + 1}}\, dx = \pi \int_0^1 x(x^2 + 1)^{-1/2}\, dx.$$

This integral will yield to the substitution $u = x^2 + 1$. Thus $du = 2x\, dx$, and the integral becomes

$$\pi \int_1^2 \frac{1}{2} u^{-1/2}\, du = \left[\pi u^{1/2} \right] \Big|_1^2 = \pi(\sqrt{2} - 1).$$

37. Find the volume generated if the region bounded by the curves $y = x + 1$, $y = 3x - 5$ and $y = 1$ is revolved about the x-axis. Sketch the region to be revolved.

SOLUTION: i)

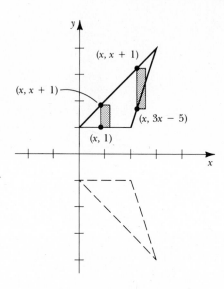

ii)   To produce a washer, use a dx element. Since the element switches embedding at $x = 2$, the volume must be split into two integrals. The volume of the element from $x = 0$ to $x = 2$ is $\pi\left((x+1)^2 - (1)^2\right)\,dx$, and the volume of the element from $x = 2$ to $x = 3$ is $\pi\left((x+1)^2 - (3x-5)^2\right)$.

iii)   The integrals describing the volume are

$$\int_0^2 \pi((x+1)^2 - 1)\,dx + \int_2^3 \pi\left((x+1)^2 - (3x-5)^2\right)\,dx.$$

iv)

$$\int_0^2 \pi((x+1)^2 - 1)\,dx + \int_2^3 \pi\left((x+1)^2 - (3x-5)^2\right)\,dx$$

$$= \pi \int_0^2 (x^2 + 2x)\,dx + \pi \int_2^3 (-3x^2 + 32x - 24)\,dx$$

$$= \pi \left(\left[\frac{1}{3}x^3 + x^2\right]\Big|_0^2 + 8\left[-\frac{1}{3}x^3 + 2x^2 - 3x\right]\Big|_2^3 \right)$$

$$= \pi \left(\left(\frac{1}{3}(8) + 4\right) - 0 + 8\left(\left(-\frac{1}{3}(27) + 2(9) - 3(3)\right) - \left(-\frac{1}{3}(8) + 2(4) - 3(2)\right)\right) \right)$$

$$= \pi \left(\frac{8}{3} + 4 + 8(-9 + 18 - 9 + \frac{8}{3} - 8 + 6)\right) = \pi \left(\frac{8}{3} + 4 + \frac{64}{3} - 16\right) = 12\pi.$$

41. Find the volume generated if the region bounded by $y = x^2$ and $y = x$ is revolved about the y-axis.

SOLUTION: i)

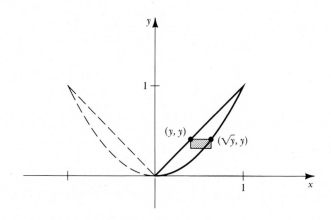

ii) This problem can be solved with a dy element. This produces a washer with $r_1 = \sqrt{y}$ and $r_2 = y$. Note that when $y = x^2$ is solved for x, $x = \pm\sqrt{y}$. A choice must be made between the principal and negative root. In this case, the principal root is needed.

iii) The integral is $\displaystyle\int_0^1 \pi \left((\sqrt{y})^2 - y^2\right)\, dy.$

iv)

$$\int_0^1 \pi \left((\sqrt{y})^2 - y^2\right)\, dy = \pi \int_0^1 (y - y^2)$$

$$= \pi \left[\frac{1}{2}y^2 - \frac{1}{3}y^3\right]\Big|_0^1 = \pi \left(\frac{1}{2} - \frac{1}{3}\right) = \frac{\pi}{6}.$$

47. Find the volume generated if the region bounded by $y = 2x - 1$, $y = -2x + 7$, and $y = x$ is revolved about the y-axis.

SOLUTION: i)

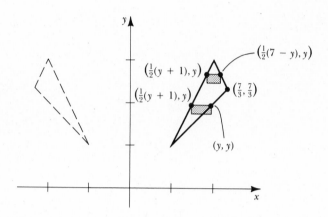

ii) A dy element will be used here which will result in a change of embedding. The volume of the first (lower) element is $\pi\left(y^2 - \left(\dfrac{y+1}{2}\right)^2\right) dy$. The volume of the second (upper) element

is $\pi\left(\left(\dfrac{7-y}{2}\right)^2 - \left(\dfrac{y+1}{2}\right)^2\right) dy$.

iii) The first element traverses the region from $y = 1$ to $y = 7/3$ and generates the integral $\displaystyle\int_1^{7/3}\left(y^2 - \left(\dfrac{y+1}{2}\right)^2\right) dy$. The second element traverses the region from $y = 7/3$ and $y = 3$

resulting in the integral $\displaystyle\int_{7/3}^3 \pi\left(\left(\dfrac{7-y}{2}\right)^2 - \left(\dfrac{y+1}{2}\right)^2\right) dy$.

iv) The desired volume is

$$V = \pi\int_1^{7/3}\left(y^2 - \left(\frac{y+1}{2}\right)^2\right) dy + \pi\int_{7/3}^3\left(\left(\frac{7-y}{2}\right)^2 - \left(\frac{y+1}{2}\right)^2\right) dy$$

$$= \pi\left[\frac{y^3}{3} - 2\frac{\left(\frac{y+1}{2}\right)^3}{3}\right]\Bigg|_1^{7/3} + \pi\left[-2\frac{\left(\frac{7-y}{2}\right)^3}{3} - 2\frac{\left(\frac{y+1}{2}\right)^3}{3}\right]\Bigg|_{7/3}^3$$

$$= \pi\left(\left(\frac{7^3}{3^4} - 2\cdot\frac{5^3}{3^4}\right) - \left(\frac{1^3}{3} - 2\cdot\frac{1^3}{3}\right) + \left(-2\cdot\frac{2^3}{3} - 2\cdot\frac{2^3}{3}\right) - \left(-2\cdot\frac{7^3}{3^4} - 2\cdot\frac{5^3}{3^4}\right)\right)$$

$$= \pi\left(\left(\frac{343}{81} - 2\cdot\frac{125}{81}\right) - \left(-\frac{1}{3}\right) + \left(-\frac{32}{3}\right) - \left(2\cdot\frac{343}{81} - 2\cdot\frac{125}{81}\right)\right) = \frac{64}{27}\pi.$$

53. A solid has its base in the xy-plane bounded by the graphs of $y = x^2$ and $y = 1$. Find the volume of the solid if each cross section perpendicular to the x-axis is a square.

SOLUTION: i)

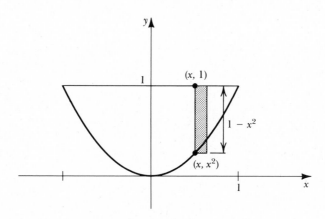

ii) A dx element is dictated here by the given cross section. The volume of the element is $(1 - x^2)^2\, dx$.

iii) The element traverses from $x = -1$ to $x = 1$ and the integral that describes the volume is $\int_{-1}^{1} (1 - x^2)^2\, dx$.

iv)

$$\int_{-1}^{1} (1 - x^2)^2\, dx = \int_{-1}^{1} (x^4 - 2x^2 + 1)\, dx = \left[\frac{1}{5}x^5 - \frac{2}{3}x^3 + x \right] \Bigg|_{-1}^{1}$$

$$= \left(\frac{1}{5} - \frac{2}{3} + 1 \right) - \left(-\frac{1}{5} + \frac{2}{3} - 1 \right) = \frac{2}{5} - \frac{4}{3} + 2 = \frac{16}{15}.$$

59. A water tower is in the shape of a sphere with radius 50 ft. The height of the water in the tank is 75 ft. How many gallons of water are in the tank? (One U.S. gallon is equivalent to 231 cubic inches.)

SOLUTION: i) The tower can be modeled by revolving the curve $x = \sqrt{50^2 - y^2}$ about the y-axis and using a dy element.

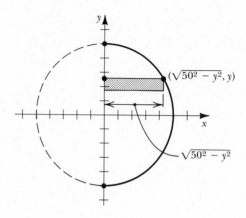

ii) The volume of the element is $\pi \left(\sqrt{50^2 - y^2} - 0 \right)^2 dy = \pi(2500 - y^2)$.

iii) The depth of the water is 75 feet, which would cause the element to range from $y = -50$ to $y = 25$. Thus the integral becomes $\displaystyle\int_{-50}^{25} \pi(2500 - y^2)\, dy$.

iv)

$$\int_{-50}^{25} \pi(2500 - y^2)\, dy = \pi \left[2500y - \frac{1}{3}y^3 \right] \Big|_{-50}^{25}$$

$$= \pi \left(\left(2500(25) - \frac{1}{3}(25)^3 \right) - \left(2500(-50) - \frac{1}{3}(-50)^3 \right) \right) = 140625\pi.$$

This result is in ft^3. To convert to gallons, perform the conversion

$$140625\pi \text{ ft}^3 \times 1728 \text{ in}^3/\text{ft}^3 \div 231 \text{ in}^3/\text{gal} = 1{,}051{,}948\pi \text{ gallons.}$$

67. A hole of radius 3 is bored through the center of a sphere with radius 4. How much volume has been removed?

SOLUTION: To model this situation, consider the curve $x^2 + y^2 = 4^2$ with $x \geq 0$ and revolve it around the y-axis. Selecting a dy element generates a washer element which can be used to determine the volume remaining.

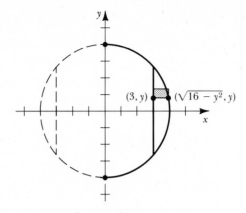

ii) The element has volume $\pi\left((\sqrt{16-y^2})^2 - 3^2\right)dy$.

iii) If you were to integrate over $y = -4$ to $y = 4$, this would calculate the volume of the entire sphere. To find the volume remaining, integrate from $y = -\sqrt{7}$ to $y = \sqrt{7}$ since the radius of the hole is 3 $(x = 3)$. The integral is $\displaystyle\int_{-\sqrt{7}}^{\sqrt{7}} \pi\left((\sqrt{16-y^2})^2 - 3^2\right)dy$.

iv)

$$V = \pi \int_{-\sqrt{7}}^{\sqrt{7}}(16 - y^2 - 9)\,dy = \pi \int_{-\sqrt{7}}^{\sqrt{7}}(7 - y^2)\,dy = \pi\left[7y - \frac{1}{3}y^3\right]\Bigg|_{-\sqrt{7}}^{\sqrt{7}}$$

$$= \pi\left(\left(7\sqrt{7} - \frac{1}{3}(\sqrt{7})^3\right) - \left(-7\sqrt{7} - \frac{1}{3}(-\sqrt{7})^3\right)\right) = \pi\left(14\sqrt{7} - \frac{14}{3}\sqrt{7}\right) = \frac{28\pi}{3}\sqrt{7}.$$

This is the remaining volume. Since the volume of the sphere is $\frac{4}{3}\pi r^3 = \frac{4}{3}\pi(4)^3 = \dfrac{256\pi}{3}$, the volume of the hole is

$$\frac{256\pi}{3} - \frac{28\pi\sqrt{7}}{3} = \frac{4\pi}{3}(64 - 7\sqrt{7}).$$

_____5.3

Volumes of Solids of Revolution: Shells

5. Use the method of shells to find the volume of the solid generated by revolving the region

bounded by $y = x^2$ and $y = \sqrt[3]{x}$ about the y-axis.

SOLUTION: First, sketch the region.

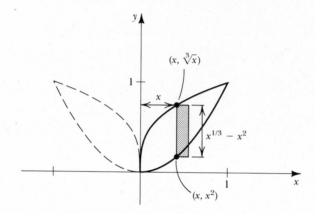

The volume generated is characterized by the integral

$$V = \int_0^1 2\pi x \left(x^{1/3} - x^2\right)\, dx = 2\pi \int_0^1 \left(x^{4/3} - x^3\right)\, dx$$

$$= 2\pi \left[\frac{3}{7}x^{7/3} - \frac{1}{4}x^4\right]\Big|_0^1 = 2\pi \left(\left(\frac{3}{7} - \frac{1}{4}\right) - (0 - 0)\right) = 2\pi \left(\frac{5}{28}\right) = \frac{5\pi}{14}.$$

11. Use the method of shells to find the volume of the solid generated by revolving the region bounded by $y = \frac{1}{2}x + 1$ and $x + y = 4$, and $y = 1$ about the y-axis.

SOLUTION:

The volume generated is characterized by the integral graph.

Determine the points of intersection. $x + y = 4$ and $y = 1 \implies x = 3$. $x + y = 4$ and $y = \frac{1}{2}x + 1 \implies x + \frac{1}{2}x + 1 = 4 \implies \frac{3}{2}x = 3 \implies x = 2$ and $y = 2$.

This volume can be determined by the sum of two integrals.

$$V = \int_0^2 2\pi x \left(\frac{1}{2}x + 1 - 1\right) dx + \int_2^3 2\pi x (4 - x - 1) dx$$

$$= 2\pi \left(\int_0^2 \frac{1}{2}x^2 \, dx + \int_2^3 (3x - x^2) \, dx\right)$$

$$= 2\pi \left(\left[\frac{1}{6}x^3\right]\Big|_0^2 + \left[\frac{3}{2}x^2 - \frac{1}{3}x^3\right]\Big|_2^3\right)$$

$$= 2\pi \left(\left(\frac{1}{6}(8) - 0\right) + \left(\left(\frac{3}{2}(9) - \frac{1}{3}(27)\right) - \left(\frac{3}{2}(4) - \frac{1}{3}(8)\right)\right)\right)$$

$$= 2\pi \left(-11 + \frac{27}{2}\right) = 2\pi \left(\frac{5}{2}\right) = 5\pi.$$

21. Use the method of shells to find the volume of the solid generated by revolving the region bounded by $y = 1/x$, $y = 1$, $y = 2$ and $x = 0$ about the x-axis.

SOLUTION:

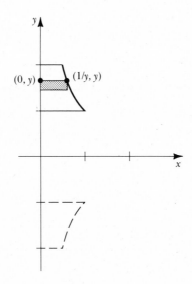

The height of the element is $\left(\frac{1}{y} - 0\right)$ and the radius of revolution of the element is y. The volume is found by evaluating the integral

$$V = \int_1^2 2\pi y \left(\frac{1}{y} - 0\right) dy = 2\pi \int_1^2 dy$$

$$= [2\pi y]\Big|_1^2 = 2\pi(2 - 1) = 2\pi.$$

33. Use either the method of disks or the method of shells to find the volume of the solid generated by revolving the region bounded by $y = 1 + \sqrt{x}$ and $x = 2y - 2$ about   a) the x-axis,   b) the y-axis.

SOLUTION:

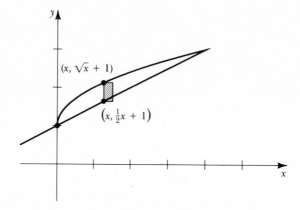

a) To determine the volume when revolved about the x-axis, use the method of disks. The element generates a washer.

$$V = \int_0^4 \pi\left((1+\sqrt{x})^2 - \left(\frac{1}{2}x+1\right)^2\right) dx = \pi \int_0^4 \left(1 + 2x^{1/2} + x - \frac{1}{4}x^2 - x - 1\right) dx$$

$$= \pi \int_0^4 \left(2x^{1/2} - \frac{1}{4}x^2\right) dx = \pi\left[\frac{4}{3}x^{3/2} - \frac{1}{12}x^3\right]\Big|_0^4$$

$$= \pi\left(\left(\frac{4}{3}(8) - \frac{1}{12}(64)\right) - 0\right) = \pi\left(\frac{32}{3} - \frac{16}{3}\right) = \frac{16\pi}{3}.$$

b) To find the volume when the region is revolved about the y-axis, use the method of shells. The height of the element is $(1+\sqrt{x}) - \left(\frac{1}{2}x + 1\right)$, and the radius of revolution is x.

$$V = \int_0^4 2\pi x\left((1+\sqrt{x}) - \left(\frac{1}{2}x+1\right)\right) dx = 2\pi \int_0^4 x\left(x^{1/2} - \frac{1}{2}x\right) dx$$

$$= 2\pi \int_0^4 \left(x^{3/2} - \frac{1}{2}x^2\right) dx = 2\pi\left[\frac{2}{5}x^{5/2} - \frac{1}{6}x^3\right]\Big|_0^4$$

$$= 2\pi\left(\left(\frac{2}{5}(32) - \frac{1}{6}(64)\right) - 0\right) = 2\pi\left(\frac{64}{5} - \frac{32}{3}\right) = 2\pi\left(\frac{192 - 160}{15}\right) = \frac{64\pi}{15}.$$

————————————————————————————————.5.4

Arc Length of
a Curve: Surfaces
of Revolution

COMMENT: You can consider an element of arc length, ds, which is expressed as $ds = \sqrt{(dx)^2 + (dy)^2}$. Then the length can be expressed as $\int_a^b ds = \int_a^b \sqrt{(dx)^2 + (dy)^2}$, where a and b are suitable limits of integration.

Note that $\sqrt{(dx)^2 + (dy)^2} = \sqrt{1 + (dy/dx)^2}\, dx$ and $\sqrt{(dx)^2 + (dy)^2} = \sqrt{1 + (dx/dy)^2}\, dy$, depending on which derivative is used.

3. Find the length of the curve $y = x^{3/2}$ for x in $[3, 15]$.

SOLUTION:

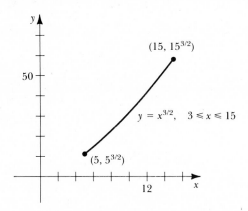

$L = \int_a^b \sqrt{(dx)^2 + (dy)^2}$ and $dy = \frac{3}{2}x^{1/2}\, dx$ so $L = \int_3^{15} \sqrt{1 + \frac{9}{4}x}\, dx$.

Let $u = 1 + \frac{9}{4}x$. Then $du = \frac{9}{4}\, dx$ and $\frac{4}{9}\, du = dx$. Also $x = 3 \implies u = 1 + \frac{9}{4}(3) = \frac{31}{4}$ and $x = 15 \implies u = 1 + \frac{9}{4}(15) = \frac{139}{4}$ and the integral becomes

$$\int_{31/4}^{139/4} u^{1/2} \left(\frac{4}{9}\, du\right) = \frac{4}{9} \int_{31/4}^{139/4} u^{1/2}\, du = \frac{4}{9} \left[\frac{2}{3}u^{3/2}\right]\Big|_{31/4}^{139/4}$$

$$= \frac{8}{27}\left(\left(\frac{139}{4}\right)^{3/2} - \left(\frac{31}{4}\right)^{3/2}\right) = \frac{8}{27}\left(\frac{139}{4}\sqrt{\frac{139}{4}} - \frac{31}{4}\sqrt{\frac{31}{4}}\right)$$

$$= \frac{8}{27}\left(\frac{139}{8}\sqrt{139} - \frac{31}{8}\sqrt{31}\right) = \frac{139}{27}\sqrt{139} - \frac{31}{27}\sqrt{31}.$$

9. Find the length of the curve $y = \dfrac{x^4 + 12}{12x}$ for x in $[1,3]$.

SOLUTION:

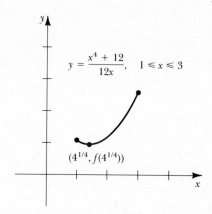

$$L = \int_a^b \sqrt{(dx)^2 + (dy)^2} \text{ and}$$

$$dy = \frac{12x(4x^3) - (x^4 + 12)(12)}{(12x)^2}\, dx = \frac{4x^4 - x^4 - 12}{12x^2}\, dx$$

$$= \frac{3(x^4 - 4)}{12x^2}\, dx = \frac{x^4 - 4}{4x^2}\, dx,$$

so

$$L = \int_1^3 \sqrt{1 + \left(\frac{x^4 - 4}{4x^2}\right)^2}\, dx = \int_1^3 \sqrt{1 + \frac{x^8 - 8x^4 + 16}{16x^4}}\, dx$$

$$= \int_1^3 \sqrt{\frac{x^8 + 8x^4 + 16}{16x^4}}\, dx = \int_1^3 \sqrt{\frac{(x^4 + 4)^2}{16x^4}}\, dx$$

$$= \int_1^3 \left|\frac{x^4 + 4}{4x^2}\right|\, dx = \int_1^3 \frac{x^4 + 4}{4x^2}\, dx$$

$$= \int_1^3 \left(\frac{1}{4}x^2 + x^{-2}\right) dx = \left[\frac{1}{12}x^3 - x^{-1}\right]\Big|_1^3$$

$$= \left(\frac{1}{12}(27) - \frac{1}{3}\right) - \left(\frac{1}{12} - 1\right) = \frac{17}{6}.$$

15. Find the length of the curve $y = \ln(\sec x)$ for x in $\left[0, \dfrac{\pi}{4}\right]$.

SOLUTION:

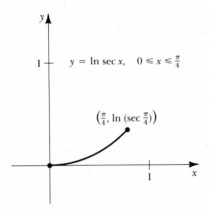

$L = \displaystyle\int_a^b \sqrt{(dx)^2 + (dy)^2}$ and $dy = \dfrac{1}{\sec x}(\sec x \tan x)\, dx = \tan x\, dx$ so

$$L = \int_0^{\pi/4} \sqrt{1 + \tan^2 x}\, dx = \int_0^{\pi/4} \sqrt{\sec^2 x}\, dx = \int_0^{\pi/4} |\sec x|\, dx$$

$$= \int_0^{\pi/4} \sec x\, dx = \int_0^{\pi/4} \frac{\sec x(\sec x + \tan x)}{\sec x + \tan x}\, dx.$$

Let $u = \sec x + \tan x$. Then $du = \left(\sec x \tan x + \sec^2 x\right) dx$, $x = 0 \implies u = 1$ and $x = \dfrac{\pi}{4} \implies u = \sqrt{2} + 1.$

Thus the integral becomes

$$\int_1^{1+\sqrt{2}} \frac{du}{u} = \ln|u|\,\Big|_1^{1+\sqrt{2}} = \ln(1 + \sqrt{2}) - \ln 1 = \ln(1 + \sqrt{2}).$$

21. Find the length of the curve $x^{2/3} + y^{2/3} = 1$ for x in $[0,1]$, $y \geq 0$.

SOLUTION:

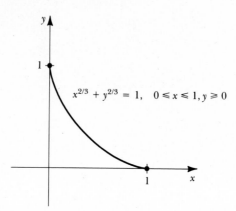

$x^{2/3} + y^{2/3} = 1, \quad 0 \leq x \leq 1, y \geq 0$

$L = \displaystyle\int_a^b \sqrt{(dx)^2 + (dy)^2}$ and $\dfrac{2}{3}x^{-1/3}\,dx + \dfrac{2}{3}y^{-1/3}\,dy = 0 \implies dy = \dfrac{-y^{1/3}}{x^{1/3}}\,dx$. Now $y^{2/3} = 1 - x^{2/3} \implies y^{1/3} = \pm\sqrt{1 - x^{2/3}}$. But $y \geq 0$, so $y^{1/3} = \sqrt{1 - x^{2/3}}$. Thus

$$L = \int_0^1 \sqrt{1 + \left(\frac{-\sqrt{1 - x^{2/3}}}{x^{1/3}}\right)^2}\,dx = \int_0^1 \sqrt{1 + \frac{1 - x^{2/3}}{x^{2/3}}}\,dx$$

$$= \int_0^1 \sqrt{\frac{1 - x^{2/3} + x^{2/3}}{x^{2/3}}}\,dx = \int_0^1 \sqrt{\frac{1}{x^{2/3}}}\,dx = \int_0^1 \left|x^{-1/3}\right|\,dx$$

$$= \int_0^1 x^{-1/3}\,dx = \left[\frac{3}{2}x^{2/3}\right]\Bigg|_0^1 = \frac{3}{2}(1 - 0) = \frac{3}{2}.$$

27. Find the area of the surface generated by revolving the curve $y = \sqrt{x + 1}$ on the interval $[1,5]$ about the x-axis.

SOLUTION:

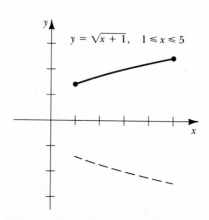

$y = \sqrt{x + 1}, \quad 1 \leq x \leq 5$

$S = \int_a^b 2\pi r \, ds$, where r is the radius of revolution and $ds = \sqrt{(dx)^2 + (dy)^2}$.

Now $r = \sqrt{x+1}$ and $dy = \frac{1}{2}(x+1)^{-1/2} \, dx$ so

$$S = \int_1^5 2\pi(x+1)^{1/2}\sqrt{1 + \left(\frac{1}{2}(x+1)^{-1/2}\right)^2} \, dx = 2\pi \int_1^5 (x+1)^{1/2}\left(1 + \frac{1}{4(x+1)}\right)^{1/2} \, dx$$

$$= 2\pi \int_1^5 (x+1)^{1/2}\left(\frac{4(x+1)+1}{4x+4}\right)^{1/2} \, dx = 2\pi \int_1^5 \left(\frac{(x+1)(4x+5)}{4(x+1)}\right)^{1/2} \, dx$$

$$= 2\pi \int_1^5 \left(\frac{4x+5}{4}\right)^{1/2} \, dx = \pi \int_1^5 (4x+5)^{1/2} \, dx.$$

Let $u = 4x + 5$. Then $du = 4 \, dx$ and $\frac{1}{4} \, du = dx$. Also $x = 1 \implies u = 9$ and $x = 5 \implies u = 25$. Thus

$$L = \pi \int_9^{25} u^{1/2}\left(\frac{1}{4} \, du\right) = \frac{\pi}{4} \int_1^5 u^{1/2} \, du = \frac{\pi}{4}\left[\frac{2}{3}u^{3/2}\right]\Big|_9^{25}$$

$$= \frac{\pi}{6}\left(25^{3/2} - 9^{3/2}\right) = \frac{49\pi}{3}.$$

———5.5

Moments and the
Center of Mass

3. Objects are placed along a line with coordinates and relative masses $x_1 = -1$, $m_1 = 3$; $x_2 = 0$, $m_2 = 1$; $x_3 = 2$, $m_3 = 4$; and $x_4 = 4$, $m_4 = 3$. Find   a) the moment of the system with respect to the origin and   b) the center of mass of the system.

SOLUTION: a) The moment of the system about the origin is found by evaluating $\sum_{i=1}^n m_i x_i$, so

$$M_p = \sum_{i=1}^4 m_i x_i = 3(-1) + 1(0) + 4(2) + 3(4) = 17.$$

b) The center of mass of the system is

$$\frac{M_p}{M} = \frac{17}{3+1+4+3} = \frac{17}{11}.$$

7. Objects are placed in the plane with the coordinates and relative masses $P_1(3,2)$, $m_1 = 3$; $P_2(2,-1)$, $m_2 = 2$; $P_3(5,-2)$, $m_3 = 4$; and $P_4(-2,0)$, $m_4 = 1$. Find   a) the moments of the system with respect to the axes and   b) determine the center of mass of the system.

SOLUTION: a) The moment with respect to the x-axis is

$$M_x = \sum_{i=1}^{n} m_i y_i = \sum_{i=1}^{4} m_i y_i = 3(2) + 2(-1) + 4(-2) + 1(0) = -4.$$

The moment with respect to the y-axis is

$$M_y = \sum_{i=1}^{n} m_i x_i = \sum_{i=1}^{4} m_i x_i = 3(3) + 2(2) + 4(5) + 1(-2) = 31.$$

b) The center of mass, $(\bar{x}, \bar{y})$ is calculated by

$$\bar{x} = \frac{M_y}{M} = \frac{31}{3+2+4+1} = \frac{31}{10} \quad \text{and} \quad \bar{y} = \frac{M_x}{M} = \frac{-4}{10} = -\frac{2}{5}.$$

Thus the center of mass is $\left(\dfrac{31}{10}, -\dfrac{2}{5} \right)$.

11. Find the centroid of the homogeneous lamina bounded by $y = x^2$ and $y = 1$.

SOLUTION:

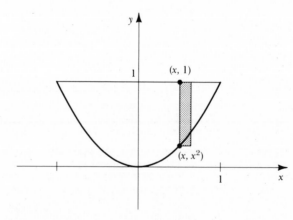

The center of mass, $(\bar{x}, \bar{y})$, is determined by evaluating

$$\bar{x} = \frac{\displaystyle\int_{-1}^{1} x(1 - x^2)\,dx}{\displaystyle\int_{-1}^{1} (1 - x^2)\,dx} \quad \text{and} \quad \bar{y} = \frac{\displaystyle\int_{-1}^{1} \left(1^2 - (x^2)^2\right)\,dx}{2\displaystyle\int_{-1}^{1} (1 - x^2)\,dx}.$$

Evaluate the integrals separately.

$$\int_{-1}^{1} x(1-x^2)\,dx = \int_{-1}^{1}(x-x^3)\,dx = \left[\frac{1}{2}x^2 - \frac{1}{4}x^4\right]\bigg|_{-1}^{1}$$

$$= \left(\frac{1}{2}-\frac{1}{4}\right) - \left(\frac{1}{2}-\frac{1}{4}\right) = 0.$$

$$\int_{-1}^{1}(1-x^2)\,dx = \left(x - \frac{1}{3}x^3\right)\bigg|_{-1}^{1} = \left(1-\frac{1}{3}\right) - \left(-1+\frac{1}{3}\right)$$

$$= 2 - \frac{2}{3} = \frac{4}{3}.$$

$$\int_{-1}^{1}(1-x^4)\,dx = \left[x - \frac{1}{5}x^5\right]\bigg|_{-1}^{1} = \left(1-\frac{1}{5}\right) - \left(-1+\frac{1}{5}\right)$$

$$= 2 - \frac{2}{5} = \frac{8}{5}.$$

Thus $(\bar{x},\bar{y}) = \left(\dfrac{0}{4/3}, \dfrac{8/5}{8/3}\right) = \left(0, \dfrac{3}{5}\right)$. Note that the fact that the centroid lies on the y-axis is not surprising since the lamina is symmetric with respect to the y-axis.

19. Find the centroid of the homogeneous lamina bounded by $y = x$, $y = 4 - x$ and $y = 0$.

SOLUTION:

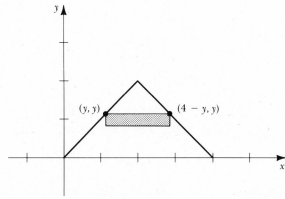

A dy element is chosen since a dx element would switch embedding. Since a dy element is used, the center of mass, $(\bar{x},\bar{y})$, is characterized by

$$\bar{x} = \frac{\displaystyle\int_a^b \left((f(y))^2 - (g(y))^2\right)\,dy}{2\displaystyle\int_a^b (f(y)-g(y))\,dy} = \frac{\displaystyle\int_0^2 \left((4-y)^2 - y^2\right)\,dy}{2\displaystyle\int_0^2 (4-2y)\,dy} \quad \text{and}$$

$$\bar{y} = \frac{\int_a^b y\,(f(y) - g(y))\,dy}{\int_a^b (f(y) - g(y))\,dy} = \frac{\int_0^2 y(4 - 2y)\,dy}{\int_0^2 (4 - 2y)\,dy}.$$

Evaluate the integrals separately.

$$\int_0^2 \left((4-y)^2 - y^2\right)\,dy = \int_0^2 \left(16 - 8y + y^2 - y^2\right)\,dy = 8\int_0^2 (2 - y)\,dy$$

$$= 8\left[2y - \frac{1}{2}y^2\right]\Big|_0^2 = 8(4 - 2) = 16.$$

$$\int_0^2 (4 - 2y)\,dy = [4y - y^2]\Big|_0^2 = (8 - 4) - 0 = 4.$$

$$\int_0^2 y(4 - 2y)\,dy = 2\int_0^2 \left(2y - y^2\right)\,dy = 2\left[y^2 - \frac{1}{3}y^3\right]\Big|_0^2$$

$$= 2\left(\left(4 - \frac{8}{3}\right) - 0\right) = \frac{8}{3}.$$

Thus $(\bar{x}, \bar{y}) = \left(\dfrac{16}{2(4)}, \dfrac{8/3}{4}\right) = \left(2, \dfrac{2}{3}\right).$

Work
_____5.6

3. A diesel locomotive on a freight train exerts the constant force of 8 T on a train while moving the train at 40 mph. How much work is done by the locomotive if the train travels as this speed for 1 mi?

SOLUTION: $W = \displaystyle\int_a^b f(x)\,dx$ and the force is constant at $8\,\text{tons} = 16000\,\text{lbs}$, so

$$W = \int_0^{5280} 16000\,dx = [16000x]\Big|_0^{5280}$$

$$= 16000(5280 - 0) = 8.448 \times 10^7 \text{ ft·lb}.$$

Note that the velocity of the train is irrelevant as long as it is constant and non-zero. The only factors involved in work are the force and the distance through which the force acts.

9. A spring is 10 in long and a force of 5 lbs is required to compress it to a length of 6 in. How much work is required to stretch it from its natural length of 10 in to a length of 20 in?

SOLUTION: The force law governing a spring is $F = kx$, where k is the spring constant and x is the distortion distance. If the natural length is 10 in and the spring is compressed to 6 in, $x = 4$ in and $F = 5$ lb. Thus $k = \dfrac{F}{x} = \dfrac{5}{4}$ lb/in and $F = \dfrac{5}{4}x$.

$$W = \int_0^{10} F\, dx = \int_0^{10} \frac{5}{4} x\, dx = \left[\frac{5}{8} x^2 \right] \Big|_0^{10}$$

$$= \frac{5}{8}(10^2 - 0) = 62.5 \,\text{in·lb}.$$

13. A 3-gal bucket full of water is at the bottom of a 100-ft well. How much work is required to lift this bucket to the top of the well, assuming that the bucket weighs 3 lbs when empty and that the rope weighs 4 oz/ft?

SOLUTION: Recall 1 gal ≈ 0.134 ft^3 and the density of water is 62.4 lb/ft^3, so 3 gal of water weigh approximately 25.08 lb. Thus a force of 28.08 lb must be exerted to lift the bucket of water, assuming that the weight of the rope is insignificant. If x measures the distance from the bottom of the well, the force needed to lift the rope is $0.25(100 - x)$. Thus the total force required is

$$F = 28.08 + 0.25(100 - x) = 28.08 + 25 - 0.25x = 53.08 - 0.25x,$$

and

$$W = \int_0^{100} (53.08 - 0.25x)\, dx = \left[53.08x - 0.125x^2 \right] \Big|_0^{100}$$

$$= \left(53.08(100) - 0.125(100)^2 \right) - 0 = 4058 \,\text{ft·lb}.$$

25. A service station has a 2000-gal cylindrical tank whose top is buried 2 ft below the ground, with the axis of the cylinder parallel to the ground. Once a week this tank is serviced by the supplier. In one week, 800 gal of gasoline are sold, so the service station has the choice of having the tank filled every other week or having it topped off each week. Which method of purchase will require the least work for the service station pumps?

SOLUTION: Consider a cross section with the center of the circle at the origin.

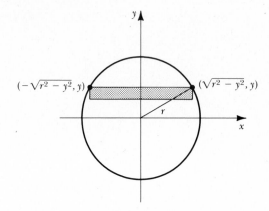

Since $V = \pi r^2 h$ and $V = 2000\,\mathrm{gal} = 268\,\mathrm{ft}^3$ and the volume of the element is

$$\left(\sqrt{r^2 - y^2} - \left(-\sqrt{r^2 - y^2}\right)\right) h\,dy = 2h\sqrt{r^2 - y^2}\,dy,$$

where r and h are constant. The amount of work needed to pump the gasoline from the top of the tank to the surface is the same in either case so that work can be ignored.

The amount of work needed to pump 800 gallons is $W_1 = \displaystyle\int_{y_1}^{r} 2wh\sqrt{r^2 - y^2}\,(r - y)\,dy$, where w is the density of the gasoline. If the tank is topped off every week, the work is $2W_1$. To pump 1600 gallons without topping, the first 800 gallons requires work W_1. The second 800 gallons must first be pumped to the position occupied by the first 800 gallons using work W_2. Then it must be pumped to the top of the tank using work W_1. Thus the total work is $2W_1 + W_2$ as opposed to $2W_1$ when the tank is topped off.

_____5.7

Fluid Pressure

5. A vertical gate on a dam is in the shape of a rectangle 10 ft wide and 5 ft deep with its width parallel to the surface of the water. Find the force of the water on the gate when the level of water in the dam is at the top of the gate.

SOLUTION: The total force on the plate is characterized by $F = \displaystyle\int_{a}^{b} wyf(y)\,dy$, where $f(y)\,dy$ is the cross-sectional area of the plate element, y is the depth of the plate element below the surface of the liquid, and w is the density of the liquid.

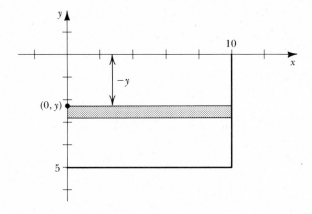

Thus

$$F = \int_{-5}^{0} w(0-y)10 \, dy = -10w \int_{-5}^{0} y \, dy = -10w \left[\frac{1}{2}y^2\right]\Big|_{-5}^{0}$$

$$= -5w\left(0^2 - (-5)^2\right) = 125w = 125(62.4) = 7800 \, \text{lb}.$$

9. A metal plate in the shape of the region $y = 4 - x^2$ and $y = 0$ is submerged vertically in a tank of water 6 ft deep with the flat edge of the plate on the bottom of the tank. The dimensions of the plate are given in feet. Find the force on the plate.

SOLUTION:

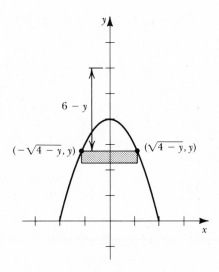

The force on the vertical plate can be characterized by

$$\int_{0}^{4} w(6-y)\left(\sqrt{4-y} - \left(-\sqrt{4-y}\right)\right) \, dy = 2w \int_{0}^{4} (6-y)(4-y)^{1/2} \, dy.$$

Let $u = 4 - y$. Then $du = -dy$ and $y = 0 \implies u = 4$, $y = 4 \implies u = 0$. Thus the integral becomes

$$2w \int_4^0 (6 - (4 - u))\, u^{1/2}(-du) = -2w \int_4^0 (2u^{1/2} + u^{3/2})\, du = -2w \left[\frac{4}{3}u^{3/2} + \frac{2}{5}u^{5/2} \right] \Bigg|_4^0$$

$$= -2w \left(\left(\frac{4}{3}(0) + \frac{2}{5}(0) \right) - \left(\frac{4}{3}(4)^{3/2} + \frac{2}{5}(4)^{5/2} \right) \right)$$

$$= 2w \left(\frac{32}{3} + \frac{64}{5} \right) = \frac{704w}{15} = 2928.64\,\text{lb.}$$

17. A pig trough 8 ft long has a cross section in the shape of an isosceles trapezoid with a lower base of 1 ft, an upper base of 2 ft, and an altitude of 1 ft. The trough is filled with swill of density $64\,\text{lb/ft}^3$. a) What is the total force on an end of the trough? b) What is the total force on the bottom of the trough?

SOLUTION:

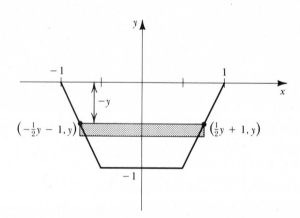

a) The slope of the line through $(1,0)$ and $\left(\frac{1}{2}, -1 \right)$ is $\dfrac{-1 - 0}{\frac{1}{2} - 1} = \dfrac{-1}{-1/2} = 2$. Thus the equation is $y - 0 = 2(x - 1) \implies y = 2x - 2$. Similarly the equation of the line through $(-1, 0)$ and $(-1/2, -1)$ is $y = -2x - 2$. Thus the force on the end can be characterized by

$$F = \int_{-1}^0 w(0 - y) \left(\left(\frac{1}{2}y + 1 \right) - \left(-\frac{1}{2}y - 1 \right) \right) dy = -w \int_{-1}^0 (y^2 + 2y)\, dy$$

$$= -w \left[\frac{1}{3}y^3 + y^2 \right] \Bigg|_{-1}^0 = -w \left(\left(\frac{1}{3}(0)^3 + (0)^2 \right) - \left(\frac{1}{3}(-1)^3 + (-1)^2 \right) \right)$$

$$= w \left(-\frac{1}{3} + 1 \right) = \frac{2}{3}w = 42.67\,\text{lb.}$$

b) The force on the bottom is

$$F = whA = 64(1)\left((1)(8)\right) = 512\,\text{lb}.$$

_____**Chapter 5**

Review Exercises

3. Sketch and find the area of the region determined by $y = 4 - x^2$ and $y = x^2 - 4$.

SOLUTION:

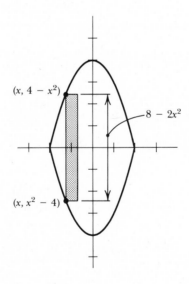

The area of the element is $(8 - 2x^2)\,dx$. Thus the area can be determined by evaluating
$$\int_{-2}^{2}(8 - 2x^2)\,dx$$

$$\int_{-2}^{2}(8 - 2x^2)\,dx = \left[8x - \frac{2}{3}x^3\right]\Bigg|_{-2}^{2} = \left(16 - \frac{2}{3}(8)\right) - \left(-16 - \frac{2}{3}(-8)\right)$$

$$= 32 - \frac{32}{3} = \frac{64}{3}.$$

11. Sketch and find the area of the region determined by $y = x$, $y = x + \sin x$, $x = 0$, and $x = \pi$.

SOLUTION:

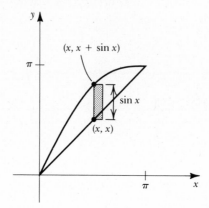

From the graph, the area of the element is $\sin x \, dx$. Thus the area can be determined by evaluating $\int_0^\pi \sin x \, dx$.

$$\int_0^\pi \sin x \, dx = [-\cos x]\Big|_0^\pi = -(\cos \pi - \cos 0) = -(-1 - 1) = 2.$$

15. Sketch the region determined by $y = x^2 + 2x + 2$, $x = 0$, $x = 2$ and $y = 0$. Use the method of disks to find the volume generated when the region is revolved about the x-axis.

SOLUTION:

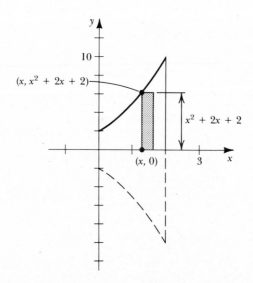

From the diagram, the volume of the element is $\pi(x^2 + 2x + 2)^2\, dx$. The volume is

$$\int_0^2 \pi(x^2 + 2x + 2)^2\, dx = \int_0^2 \pi(x^4 + 4x^3 + 8x^2 + 8x + 4)\, dx$$

$$= \pi\left[\frac{1}{5}x^5 + x^4 + \frac{8}{3}x^3 + 4x^2 + 4x\right]\Big|_0^2 = \pi\left(\left(\frac{32}{5} + 16 + \frac{64}{3} + 16 + 8\right) - 0\right)$$

$$= \pi\left(\frac{96 + 240 + 320 + 240 + 120}{15}\right) = \frac{1016\pi}{15}.$$

19. Sketch the region determined by $y^2 = 4x$, and $x = 4$. Use the method of disks to find the volume generated when the region is revolved about the line $x = 4$.

SOLUTION:

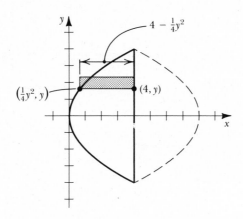

From the graph the volume can be characterized by $\displaystyle\int_{-4}^{4} \pi\left(4 - \frac{1}{4}y^2\right)^2 dy.$

$$\int_{-4}^{4} \pi\left(4 - \frac{1}{4}y^2\right)^2 dy = \pi\int_{-4}^{4}\left(16 - 2y^2 + \frac{1}{16}y^4\right) dy = \pi\left[16y - \frac{2}{3}y^3 + \frac{1}{80}y^5\right]\Big|_{-4}^{4}$$

$$= \pi\left(\left(64 - \frac{2}{3}(64) + \frac{1}{80}(1024)\right) - \left(-64 - \frac{2}{3}(-64) + \frac{1}{80}(-1024)\right)\right)$$

$$= \pi\left(128 - \frac{2}{3}(128) + \frac{1}{80}(2048)\right) = \pi\left(\frac{128}{3} + \frac{128}{5}\right) = \frac{1024\pi}{15}.$$

27. Sketch the region determined by $y = 2\sqrt{x}$, $x = 4$, and $y = 0$. Use the method of shells to find the volume generated when the region is revolved about the line $x = 4$.

SOLUTION:

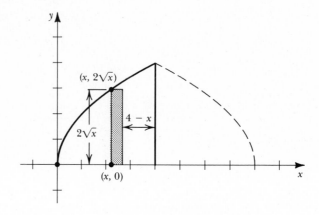

The volume can be characterized by $\displaystyle\int_0^4 2\pi(4 - x)(2\sqrt{x})\,dx.$

$$\int_0^4 2\pi(4 - x)(2\sqrt{x})\,dx = 4\pi \int_0^4 (4x^{1/2} - x^{3/2})\,dx = 4\pi \left[\frac{8}{3}x^{3/2} - \frac{2}{5}x^{5/2}\right]\Bigg|_0^4$$

$$= 4\pi \left(\left(\frac{8}{3}(4)^{3/2} - \frac{2}{5}(4)^{5/2}\right) - 0\right) = 4\pi\left(\frac{8}{3}(8) - \frac{2}{5}(32)\right)$$

$$= 4\pi \left(\frac{64}{3} - \frac{64}{5}\right) = \frac{512\pi}{15}.$$

Note that this is half of the volume determined in EXERCISE 19.

31. A solid has its base in the xy-plane bounded by the graphs of $x = y^2$ and $x = 4$. Find the volume of the solid if each cross section perpendicular to the x-axis is a square.

SOLUTION:

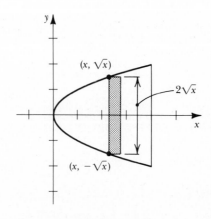

The volume of the element is $(2\sqrt{x})^2 \, dx$, so the volume can be characterized by $\int_0^4 (2\sqrt{x})^2 \, dx$.

$$\int_0^4 (2\sqrt{x})^2 \, dx = 4 \int_0^4 x \, dx = [2x^2] \Big|_0^4 = 2(16 - 0) = 32.$$

35. Find the length of the curve described by $y = \ln(\cos x)$ from $x = -\pi/4$ to $x = \pi/4$.

SOLUTION: $y = \ln(\cos x) \implies dy = \dfrac{1}{\cos x}(-\sin x)\,dx = -\tan x \, dx$, so

$$L = 2 \int_0^{\pi/4} \sqrt{(dx)^2 + (dy)^2} = 2 \int_0^{\pi/4} \sqrt{1 + \tan^2 x} \, dx = 2 \int_0^{\pi/4} \sqrt{\sec^2 x} \, dx$$

$$= 2 \int_0^{\pi/4} |\sec x| \, dx = 2 \int_0^{\pi/4} \sec x \, dx = 2 \int_0^{\pi/4} \frac{\sec x(\sec x + \tan x)}{\sec x + \tan x} \, dx$$

$$= 2 \int_0^{\pi/4} \frac{\sec^2 x + \sec x \tan x}{\sec x + \tan x} \, dx.$$

Let $u = \sec x + \tan x$. Then $du = (\sec^2 x + \sec x \tan x)\,dx$. $x = 0 \implies u = \sec 0 + \tan 0 = 1$ and $x = \frac{\pi}{4} \implies u = \sec \frac{\pi}{4} + \tan \frac{\pi}{4} = \sqrt{2} + 1$. Thus

$$2 \int_0^{\pi/4} \frac{\sec^2 x + \sec x \tan x}{\sec x + \tan x} \, dx = 2 \int_1^{\sqrt{2}+1} \frac{1}{u} \, du = 2 \ln |u| \Big|_1^{\sqrt{2}+1}$$

$$= 2 \left(\ln(\sqrt{2} + 1) - \ln 1 \right) = 2 \ln(\sqrt{2} + 1).$$

43. Find the centroid of the homogeneous lamina bounded by the graphs of $y = \sqrt{x}$ and $y = x$.

SOLUTION:

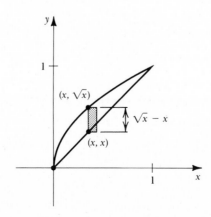

The centroid is determined by evaluating

$$\bar{x} = \frac{\displaystyle\int_0^1 x(\sqrt{x} - x)\,dx}{\displaystyle\int_0^1 (\sqrt{x} - x)\,dx} \quad \text{and} \quad \bar{y} = \frac{\displaystyle\int_0^1 \left((\sqrt{x})^2 - x^2\right)\,dx}{2\displaystyle\int_0^1 (\sqrt{x} - x)\,dx}.$$

Evaluate the three integrals separately.

$$\int_0^1 x(\sqrt{x} - x)\,dx = \int_0^1 (x^{3/2} - x^2)\,dx = \left[\frac{2}{5}x^{5/2} - \frac{1}{3}x^3\right]\Bigg|_0^1 = \frac{1}{15}.$$

$$\int_0^1 \left((\sqrt{x})^2 - x^2\right)\,dx = \int_0^1 (x - x^2)\,dx = \left[\frac{1}{2}x^2 - \frac{1}{3}x^3\right]\Bigg|_0^1 = \frac{1}{6}.$$

$$\int_0^1 (\sqrt{x} - x)\,dx = \int_0^1 (x^{1/2} - x)\,dx = \left[\frac{2}{3}x^{3/2} - \frac{1}{2}x^2\right]\Bigg|_0^1 = \frac{1}{6}.$$

Thus $(\bar{x}, \bar{y}) = \left(\dfrac{1/15}{1/6}, \dfrac{1/6}{2(1/6)}\right) = \left(\dfrac{2}{5}, \dfrac{1}{2}\right)$.

51. A conical tank with the vertex at the bottom has radius 5 ft and altitude 20 ft. If the water in the tank is 12 ft deep, find the work required to pump the water   a) over the top; b) to a point 10 ft above the top.

SOLUTION:

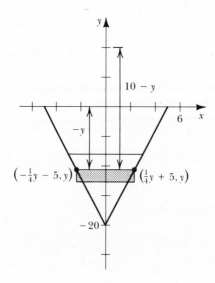

a) Placing the axis of the conical reservoir on the y-axis generates the graph above. The equation of the line through $(5,0)$ and $(0,-20)$ is $y = 4x - 20$ and that of the line through $(-5,0)$ and

$(0, -20)$ is $y = -4x - 20$. This yields a cross-sectional area of the element as $\pi \left(\frac{1}{4}y + 5\right)^2$. The work needed to lift this element to the top of the reservoir is

$$F = (62.4\,\text{lb/ft}^3)\left(\pi\left(\frac{1}{4}y + 5\right)^2\right)\Delta y,$$

where Δy is the thickness of the element.

The total work is determined by

$$W = \int_{-20}^{-8} 62.4\pi \left(\frac{1}{4}y + 5\right)^2 (0 - y)\, dy = -62.4\pi \int_{-20}^{-8} \left(\frac{1}{16}y^2 + \frac{5}{2}y + 25\right)(y)\, dy$$

$$= -62.4\pi \int_{-20}^{-8} \left(\frac{1}{16}y^3 + \frac{5}{2}y^2 + 25y\right) dy = -62.4\pi \left[\frac{1}{64}y^4 + \frac{5}{6}y^3 + \frac{25}{2}y^2\right]\Big|_{-20}^{-8}$$

$$= -62.4\pi \left(\left(\frac{1}{64}(4096) + \frac{5}{6}(-512) + \frac{25}{2}(64)\right) - \left(\frac{1}{64}(160{,}000) + \frac{5}{6}(-8000) + \frac{25}{2}(400)\right)\right)$$

$$= -62.4\pi(-396) = 24{,}710.4\pi.$$

Thus the amount of work necessary to raise the water to the top of the reservoir is $24{,}710.4\pi \approx 77{,}630\,\text{ft·lb}$.

b) To pump the water to a point 10 ft above the reservoir, evaluate

$$W = \int_{-20}^{-8} (62.4)\left(\pi\left(\frac{1}{4}y + 5\right)^2\right)(10 - y)\, dy = 62.4\pi \int_{-20}^{-8} \left(\frac{1}{16}y^2 + \frac{5}{2}y + 25\right)(10 - y)\, dy$$

$$= 62.4\pi \int_{-20}^{-8} \left(-\frac{1}{16}y^3 - \frac{15}{8}y^2 + 250\right) dy = 62.4\pi \left[-\frac{1}{64}y^4 - \frac{15}{24}y^3 + 250y\right]\Big|_{-20}^{-8}$$

$$= 62.4\pi \left(\left(-\frac{1}{64}(4096) - \frac{5}{8}(-512) - 2000\right) - \left(-\frac{1}{64}(160{,}000) - \frac{5}{8}(-8000) - 5000\right)\right)$$

$$= 62.4\pi(756) = 47174.4\pi.$$

Thus the work needed is $47174.4\pi \approx 148{,}203\,\text{ft·lb}$.

6
The Calculus of Inverse Functions

Sharpening your skills

In preparation for CHAPTER 6, you should review the material on the trigonometric functions in APPENDIX A of the text. Also review SECTION 4.6, which deals with the natural logarithm function, and SECTIONS 2.3–2.6 where techniques for differentiation are presented. Some practice problems are presented below. The answers are in APPENDIX B in this manual.

Practice Problems

1. Given $\sin x = \dfrac{3}{5}$ and $\cos y = \dfrac{5}{13}$ for $\dfrac{\pi}{2} \leq x \leq \pi$ and $0 \leq y \leq \dfrac{\pi}{2}$, find:

   a) $\cos x$ b) $\tan y$ c) $\csc y$ d) $\sin(x+y)$ e) $\cos(x-y)$ f) $\sin 2x$
   g) $\cos(y/2)$ h) $\sin(y-x)$.

2. Evaluate each of the following:

   a) $\displaystyle\int_0^2 \frac{dx}{3x}$,   b) $\displaystyle\int \frac{dx}{x \ln x}$.

3. Find $D_x y$ in each of the following:

   a) $y = \ln(2x^3)$,   b) $y = \ln x \sin^2 2x$.

_____6.1

Inverse Functions

5. Determine whether $f(x) = x^2 + 4$ is one-to-one.

SOLUTION: To determine whether $y = f(x) = x^2 + 4$ is one-to-one, solve the equation for x. Then $y - 4 = x^2$ and $x = \pm\sqrt{y-4}$. Since a given value for y can be produced by more than one value of x, for example $y = 5 \implies x = \pm 1$, $f(x) = x^2 + 4$ is not one-to-one.

9. Determine whether $f(x) = \dfrac{1}{x-1}$ is one-to-one.

SOLUTION: To determine whether $y = f(x) = \dfrac{1}{x-1}$ is one-to-one, solve for x. Then $y = \dfrac{1}{x-1} \implies x - 1 = \dfrac{1}{y} \implies x = \dfrac{1}{y} + 1$. If any non-zero value is substituted in the equation for y, it will generate exactly one value for x. Thus this function is one-to-one.

19. For $f(x) = \dfrac{1}{x-1}$, a) Give the domain and range of f. b) Find f^{-1} and give its domain and range. c) Sketch the graph of $y = f(x)$ and $y = f^{-1}(x)$ on the same set of axes.

SOLUTION: a) The domain of f is $\{x \in \mathbb{R} \mid x \neq 1\}$. To determine the range, solve $y = f(x) = \dfrac{1}{x-1}$ for x. From the SOLUTION to EXERCISE 9 above, $x = \dfrac{1}{y} + 1$ and it can be seen that the range is $\{y \in \mathbb{R} \mid y \neq 0\}$.

b) Then $f^{-1}(x) = \dfrac{1}{x} + 1$ and the domain is $\{x \in \mathbb{R} \mid x \neq 0\}$. The range will be the same as the domain of f, $\{y \in \mathbb{R} \mid y \neq 1\}$.

c)

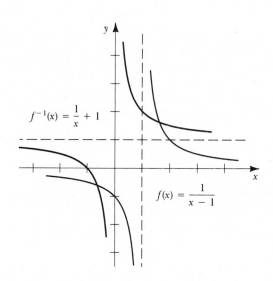

$f^{-1}(x) = \dfrac{1}{x} + 1$

$f(x) = \dfrac{1}{x-1}$

27. $f(x) = \dfrac{1}{x^2 + 1}$ describes a function that is not one-to-one. Determine a new function that is one-to-one by modifying the domain of the given function. Sketch the graph of the new function and its inverse on the same set of axes.

SOLUTION: The domain of f is $\mathbb{R}$. By solving $y = f(x) = \dfrac{1}{x^2 + 1}$ for x, determine the appropriate limitation on the domain to produce a one-to-one function. $y = \dfrac{1}{x^2 + 1} \implies x^2 + 1 = \dfrac{1}{y} \implies x^2 = \dfrac{1}{y} - 1 \implies x = \pm\sqrt{\dfrac{1}{y} - 1}$. Since a given value of y generates two values of x, one positive and the other negative, this suggests that restricting the domain of f to nonnegative reals will produce a one-to-one function. If the domain of f is $[0, \infty)$, then $x = \sqrt{\dfrac{1}{y} - 1}$ and f is one-to-one. Note that restricting the domain to $(-\infty, 0]$ also generates a one-to-one function.

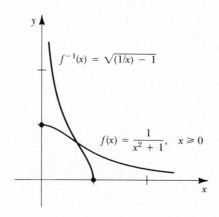

31. If $f(x) = x^3$ on $[1, 2]$, find $(f^{-1})'$ a) directly,   b) by using the derivative relation in the inverse function theorem.

SOLUTION: a) $f(x) = x^3 \implies f^{-1}(x) = x^{1/3}$. Thus $(f^{-1})'(x) = \dfrac{1}{3}x^{-2/3}$.

b) Since f is increasing and differentiable on $[1, 3]$, the inverse function theorem may be used and $D_y f^{-1}(y) = \dfrac{1}{D_x f(x)} = \dfrac{1}{D_x[x^3]} = \dfrac{1}{3x^2}$. Since $y = x^3 \implies x = y^{1/3} \implies x^2 = y^{2/3}$.

$D_y f^{-1}(y) = \dfrac{1}{3y^{2/3}} = \dfrac{1}{3}y^{-2/3}$ or $D_x f^{-1}(x) = \dfrac{1}{3}x^{-2/3}$.

39. Use the inverse function theorem to find the slope of the line tangent to the graph of f^{-1} at the point $(2, 0)$ if $f(x) = \sqrt{x+4} + x^3$.

SOLUTION: $D_x[f(x)] = \dfrac{1}{2}(x+4)^{-1/2}(1) + 3x^2 > 0$ for $x > -4$. Thus f is increasing and differentiable and the inverse function theorem may be applied.

Now $D_y f^{-1}(y) = \dfrac{1}{D_x[f(x)]} = \dfrac{1}{\dfrac{1}{2}(x+4)^{-1/2} + 3x^2}$, so $D_y f^{-1}(2) = \dfrac{1}{\dfrac{1}{2}(0+4)^{-1/2} + 3(0)^2} =$

$\dfrac{1}{\dfrac{1}{2} \cdot \dfrac{1}{2}} = 4.$

45. Show that $f(x) = \sqrt{1 - x^2}$, $0 \le x \le 1$ has the property that $f = f^{-1}$.

SOLUTION: Solve $y = f(x) = \sqrt{1 - x^2}$ for x to determine f^{-1}. $y = \sqrt{1 - x^2} \implies y^2 = 1 - x^2 \implies x^2 = 1 - y^2 \implies x = \pm\sqrt{1 - y^2}$. Since $0 \le x \le 1$, $x = \sqrt{1 - y^2}$. Also $0 \le y \le 1$. Thus $f^{-1}(x) = \sqrt{1 - x^2}$ with $0 \le x \le 1$ and clearly then $f = f^{-1}$.

51. Sketch the graph of f and its inverse and define $f^{-1}(x)$ if $f(x) = \begin{cases} -x + 2, & \text{if } x < 1 \\ -\dfrac{1}{2}x + \dfrac{3}{2}, & \text{if } x \geq 1. \end{cases}$

SOLUTION: Let $x < 1$. Then $-x > -1$ and $y = -x + 2 > 1$. $y = -x + 2 \implies x = -y + 2$.

Also $x \geq 1 \implies -x \leq -1 \implies -\dfrac{1}{2}x + \dfrac{3}{2} \leq -\dfrac{1}{2} + \dfrac{3}{2} \implies -\dfrac{1}{2}x + \dfrac{3}{2} \leq 1$ and $y = -\dfrac{1}{2}x + \dfrac{3}{2} \implies$

$y - \dfrac{3}{2} = -\dfrac{1}{2}x \implies -2y + 3 = x$. Thus $f^{-1}(x) = \begin{cases} -x + 2, & \text{if } x > 1 \\ -2x + 3, & \text{if } x \leq 1. \end{cases}$

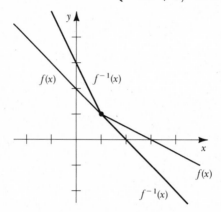

$$\rule{6cm}{0.4pt}\mathbf{6.2}$$

Inverse Trigonometric Functions

9. Find $\sin\left(\arccos\dfrac{5}{13}\right)$.

SOLUTION: Let $y = \arccos\dfrac{5}{13}$. Then $\sin\left(\arccos\dfrac{5}{13}\right) = \sin y$. Now $y = \arccos\dfrac{5}{13} \implies$

$\cos y = \dfrac{5}{13} \implies \sin y = \sqrt{1 - \cos^2 y} \implies \sin y = \sqrt{1 - (5/13)^2} = 12/13$. Thus

$\sin\left(\arccos\dfrac{5}{13}\right) = \dfrac{12}{13}$.

17. Find $\sin\left(\arccos\left(1/2\right) + \arctan\left(3/4\right)\right)$.

SOLUTION: Make use of the identity $\sin(A + B) = \sin A \cos B + \cos A \sin B$ and obtain

$$\sin\left(\arccos\left(1/2\right) + \arctan\left(3/4\right)\right) =$$

$$\sin\left(\arccos\left(1/2\right)\right)\cos\left(\arctan\left(3/4\right)\right) + \cos\left(\arccos\left(1/2\right)\right)\sin\left(\arctan\left(3/4\right)\right).$$

i) To evaluate $\sin(\arccos(1/2))$, let $y = \arccos(1/2)$. Then $\cos y = 1/2$ and $\sin(\arccos(1/2)) = \sin y = \sqrt{1 - \cos^2 y} = \sqrt{1 - \dfrac{1}{4}} = \dfrac{\sqrt{3}}{2}$.

ii) To evaluate $\cos(\arctan(3/4))$, let $y = \arctan(3/4)$. Then $\tan y = \dfrac{3}{4} = \dfrac{\sin y}{\cos y} = \dfrac{\sqrt{1 - \cos^2 y}}{\cos y}$.

So $3\cos y = 4\sqrt{1 - \cos^2 y} \implies 9\cos^2 y = 16(1 - \cos^2 y) \implies 25\cos^2 y = 16 \implies \cos y = \dfrac{4}{5}$.

iii) $\cos(\arccos(1/2)) = \dfrac{1}{2}$.

iv) To evaluate $\sin(\arctan(3/4))$, note that from above $\cos(\arctan(3/4))$. Then

$$\sin(\arctan(3/4)) = \sqrt{1 - (\cos(\arctan(3/4)))^2} = \sqrt{1 - (4/5)^2} = \dfrac{3}{5}.$$

Thus $\sin(\arccos(1/2) + \arctan(3/4)) = \dfrac{\sqrt{3}}{2} \cdot \dfrac{4}{5} + \dfrac{1}{2} \cdot \dfrac{3}{5} = \dfrac{1}{10}(3 + 4\sqrt{3})$.

27. Find the derivative of $f(x) = \arctan(x^2 - x + 3)$.

SOLUTION: Using the chain rule obtain

$$f'(x) = \frac{1}{1 + (x^2 - x + 3)^2} \cdot D_x\left[x^2 - x + 3\right] = \frac{2x - 1}{1 + (x^2 - x + 3)^2}.$$

35. Find the derivative of $f(x) = \text{arcsec}(\arctan(\sqrt{x}) + 1)$.

SOLUTION:

$$f'(x) = \frac{1}{|\arctan(\sqrt{x}) + 1|\sqrt{(\arctan(\sqrt{x}) + 1)^2 - 1}} \cdot D_x\left[\arctan(\sqrt{x}) + 1\right]$$

$$= \frac{1}{(\arctan(\sqrt{x}) + 1)\sqrt{(\arctan(\sqrt{x}) + 1)^2 - 1}} \cdot \frac{1}{1 + (\sqrt{x})^2} \cdot D_x\left[\sqrt{x}\right]$$

$$= \frac{1}{2\sqrt{x}\,(\arctan(\sqrt{x}) + 1)(1 + x)\sqrt{(\arctan(\sqrt{x}) + 1)^2 - 1}}.$$

39. Evaluate $\displaystyle\int_0^1 \frac{dx}{\sqrt{4 - x^2}}$.

SOLUTION: $\displaystyle\int_0^1 \frac{dx}{\sqrt{2^2 - x^2}} = \left[\arcsin\left(\frac{x}{2}\right)\right]\Big|_0^1 = \arcsin\left(\frac{1}{2}\right) - \arcsin(0) = \frac{\pi}{6} - 0 = \frac{\pi}{6}$.

45. Evaluate $\displaystyle\int \frac{dx}{x\sqrt{x^4 - 1}}$.

SOLUTION: $\displaystyle\int \frac{dx}{x\sqrt{x^4 - 1}} = \int \frac{x\,dx}{x^2\sqrt{(x^2)^2 - 1}}$. Let $u = x^2$. Then $du = 2x\,dx \implies \dfrac{du}{2} = x\,dx$.

So

$$\frac{x\,dx}{x^2\sqrt{x^4-1}} = \int \frac{du/2}{u\sqrt{u^2-1}} = \frac{1}{2}\cdot\frac{1}{1}\operatorname{arcsec}\frac{u}{1} + C = \frac{1}{2}\operatorname{arcsec}(x^2) + C.$$

51. Evaluate $\displaystyle\int \frac{5-x}{\sqrt{25-x^2}}\,dx.$

SOLUTION: $\displaystyle\int \frac{5-x}{\sqrt{25-x^2}}\,dx = 5\int \frac{dx}{\sqrt{25-x^2}} - \int \frac{x}{\sqrt{25-x^2}}\,dx.$ First

$$\int \frac{dx}{\sqrt{25-x^2}} = \int \frac{dx}{\sqrt{5^2-x^2}} = \arcsin\left(\frac{x}{5}\right) + C.$$

Then $\displaystyle\int \frac{x}{\sqrt{25-x^2}}\,dx = \int x(25-x^2)^{-1/2}\,dx.$ Let $u = 25 - x^2$. Then $du = -2x\,dx$ and $-\dfrac{1}{2}\,du = x\,dx.$ So

$$\int x(25-x^2)^{-1/2}\,dx = \int u^{-1/2}\left(-\frac{1}{2}\,du\right) = -\frac{1}{2}\int u^{-1/2}\,du$$

$$= -\frac{1}{2}(2u^{1/2}) + C = -\sqrt{25-x^2} + C.$$

Thus $\displaystyle\int \frac{5-x}{\sqrt{25-x^2}}\,dx = 5\arcsin\left(\frac{x}{5}\right) + \sqrt{25-x^2} + C.$

59. Prove the identity $\sin(\arccos x) = \cos(\arcsin x).$

SOLUTION: Let $y = \arccos x$. Then $\cos y = x$. Since $\sin^2 y + \cos^2 y = 1$, $\sin y = \pm\sqrt{1-\cos^2 y} = \pm\sqrt{1-x^2}$. Since $0 \le y = \arccos x \le \pi$, $\sin y \ge 0$ and $\sin y = \sqrt{1-x^2}$. Thus $\sin(\arccos x) = \sqrt{1-x^2}$. Let $w = \arcsin x$. Then $\sin w = x$. In a similar fashion, $\cos w = \pm\sqrt{1-\sin^2 w} = \pm\sqrt{1-x^2}$. Since $-\frac{\pi}{2} \le w = \arcsin x \le \frac{\pi}{2}$, $\cos w \ge 0$ and $\cos w = \sqrt{1-x^2}$. Thus $\cos(\arcsin x) = \sqrt{1-x^2}$ and $\sin(\arccos x) = \cos(\arcsin x)$.

63. Sketch the graph of $y = \dfrac{\pi}{2} + \arcsin(x)$.

SOLUTION: Since $-\dfrac{\pi}{2} \le \arcsin x \le \dfrac{\pi}{2}$, $0 \le \dfrac{\pi}{2} + \arcsin x \le \pi$.

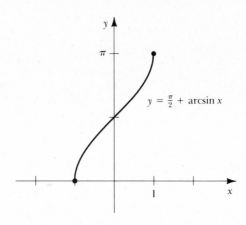

$y = \frac{\pi}{2} + \arcsin x$

71. Use L'Hôpital's rule to find $\displaystyle\lim_{x \to 0^+} \csc x \arcsin x$.

SOLUTION: In order to use L'Hôpital's rule, the limit must be rewritten. $\displaystyle\lim_{x \to 0^+} \csc x \arcsin x =$ $\displaystyle\lim_{x \to 0^+} \dfrac{\arcsin x}{\sin x}$, which produces the indeterminate form $0/0$, thus satisfying the hypotheses of L'Hôpital's rule.

So $\displaystyle\lim_{x \to 0^+} \dfrac{\arcsin x}{\sin x} = \lim_{x \to 0^+} \dfrac{\dfrac{1}{\sqrt{1 - x^2}}}{\cos x} = \lim_{x \to 0^+} \dfrac{1}{\cos x \sqrt{1 - x^2}} = 1$.

85. A camera on a tripod is filming the launching of a rocket at a distance of 5 mi from the launch pad. Five seconds after launch, the rocket is 2 mi directly over the pad and rising at a rate of 3 mi/sec. At what rate must the camera rotate to keep the rocket in view?

SOLUTION:

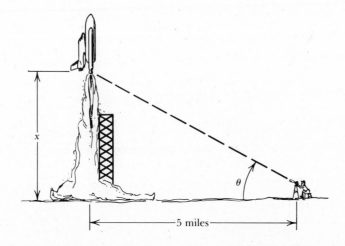

x

θ

5 miles

Find $\dfrac{d\theta}{dt}\bigg|_{t=5}$. Now $\tan\theta = x/5$ so $\theta = \arctan(x/5)$ and $\dfrac{d\theta}{dt} = \dfrac{d\theta}{dx}\cdot\dfrac{dx}{dt} = \dfrac{1/5}{1+(x/5)^2}\cdot\dfrac{dx}{dt} =$

$\dfrac{3/5}{1+(x^2/25)}$. At $t = 5$, $x = 2$. Thus $\dfrac{d\theta}{dt}\bigg|_{t=5} = \dfrac{3/5}{1+(4/25)} = \dfrac{3/5}{29/25} = \dfrac{15}{29}$. Thus the camera must

rotate at $\dfrac{15}{29}$ radians/sec.

89. Farmer MacDonald plans to use three pieces of straight fencing each 10 ft long to make a pen for pigs along the side of a 120 ft barn. The barn is to be one side of the pen; another side is to be parallel to the barn. What angle should the other sides make with the side of the barn to maximize the area enclosed?

SOLUTION:

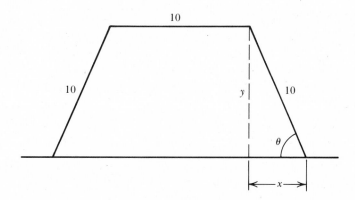

$A = 10y + 2\left(\dfrac{1}{2}xy\right) = 10y + xy = y(10 + x)$. Also $\sin\theta = y/10$ and $\cos\theta = x/10$ so $A = 10\sin\theta(10 + 10\cos\theta) = 100\sin\theta(1 + \cos\theta)$. To maximize A, determine the critical points.

$$\dfrac{dA}{d\theta} = 100\cos\theta(1 + \cos\theta) + 100\sin\theta(-\sin\theta) = 100\left(\cos\theta + \cos^2\theta - \sin^2\theta\right).$$

Now $\dfrac{dA}{d\theta} = 0 \implies \cos\theta + \cos^2\theta - \sin^2\theta = 0 \implies \cos\theta + \cos^2\theta - (1 - \cos^2\theta) = 0 \implies 2\cos^2\theta + \cos\theta - 1 = 0 \implies (2\cos\theta - 1)(\cos\theta + 1) = 0 \implies \cos\theta = 1/2$ or $\cos\theta = -1 \implies \theta = \arccos(1/2)$ or $\theta = \arccos(-1) \implies \theta = \pi/3 = 60°$ or $\theta = \pi = 180°$.

$$\dfrac{d^2 A}{d\theta^2} = 100\left(-\sin\theta + 2\cos\theta(-\sin\theta) - 2\sin\theta\cos\theta\right) = 100\left(-\sin\theta - 4\sin\theta\cos\theta\right).$$

$\dfrac{d^2 A}{d\theta^2}\bigg|_{\theta=\pi/3} = 100\left(-\sin\dfrac{\pi}{3} - 4\sin\dfrac{\pi}{3}\cos\dfrac{\pi}{3}\right) < 0$, which indicates the presence of a maximum at $\theta = \pi/3$.

$\dfrac{d^2 A}{d\theta^2}\bigg|_{\theta=\pi} = 100(-\sin \pi - 4 \sin \pi \cos \pi) = 0$, which is inconclusive. However, $\dfrac{dA}{d\theta} < 0$ on both sides of $\theta = \pi$, so there is neither a maximum nor a minimum at $\theta = \pi$. Thus the area is maximized at $\theta = 60°$, and the area is

$$A = 100 \sin \frac{\pi}{3}\left(1 + \cos \frac{\pi}{3}\right) = 100\frac{\sqrt{3}}{2}\left(1 + \frac{1}{2}\right)$$

$$= 50\sqrt{3}\left(\frac{3}{2}\right) = 75\sqrt{3} \approx 129.9 \,\text{ft}^2.$$

_____6.3

The Natural
Exponential Function

_____

5. Find $D_x y$ if $y = \dfrac{x}{e^x + e^{-x}}$.

SOLUTION: Apply the quotient rule and obtain

$$D_x y = \frac{(e^x + e^{-x})(1) - x(e^x - e^{-x})}{(e^x + e^{-x})^2} = \frac{e^x + e^{-x} - x(e^x - e^{-x})}{(e^x + e^{-x})^2}$$

$$= \frac{e^x - xe^x + e^{-x} + xe^{-x}}{(e^x + e^{-x})^2} = \frac{e^x(1 - x) + e^{-x}(1 + x)}{(e^x + e^{-x})^2}.$$

13. Find $D_x y$ if $y = e^{\sin x}$.

SOLUTION: Applying the chain rule, $D_x\left[e^{\sin x}\right] = e^{\sin x} \cos x$.

21. Find $D_x y$ if $e^{xy} = \ln x$.

SOLUTION: Differentiating implicitly, $D_x\left[e^{xy}\right] = D_x\left[\ln x\right] \implies e^{xy} \cdot D_x\left[xy\right] = \dfrac{1}{x} \implies$

$$e^{xy}(y + x\, D_x y) = \frac{1}{x} \implies y + x\, D_x y = \frac{1}{xe^{xy}} \implies D_x y = \frac{\left(\dfrac{1}{xe^{xy}} - y\right)}{x} = \frac{1 - xye^{xy}}{x^2 e^{xy}}.$$

25. Evaluate $\int_0^1 \dfrac{e^x + e^{-x}}{2}\, dx$.

SOLUTION: $\int_0^1 \dfrac{e^x + e^{-x}}{2}\, dx = \dfrac{1}{2}\left(\int_0^1 e^x\, dx + \int_0^1 e^{-x}\, dx \right).$

Let $u = -x$ in the second integral. Then $du = -dx$, $x = 0 \implies u = 0$ and $x = 1 \implies u = -1$, so the integral becomes

$$\frac{1}{2}\left([e^x]\Big|_0^1 - \int_0^{-1} e^u\, du \right) = \frac{1}{2}\left([e^x]\Big|_0^1 - [e^u]\Big|_0^{-1} \right) = \frac{1}{2}\left((e^1 - e^0) - (e^{-1} - e^0) \right) = \frac{1}{2}\left(e - \frac{1}{e} \right).$$

29. Evaluate $\int e^{\sin x} \cos x\, dx$.

SOLUTION: Let $u = \sin x$. Then $du = \cos x\, dx$ and $\int e^{\sin x} \cos x\, dx = \int e^u\, du = e^u + C = e^{\sin x} + C.$

35. Evaluate $\int \dfrac{x e^{\arctan(x^2)}}{1 + x^4}\, dx$.

SOLUTION: Let $u = \arctan(x^2)$. Then $du = \dfrac{1}{1 + (x^2)^2}(2x)\, dx$ and $\dfrac{1}{2}\, du = \dfrac{x}{1 + (x^2)^2}\, dx$, so the integral becomes $\int \dfrac{1}{2} e^u\, du = \dfrac{1}{2} e^u + C = \dfrac{1}{2} e^{\arctan(x^2)} + C.$

39. Sketch the graph of $f(x) = e^x + e^{-x}$.

SOLUTION: $f'(x) = e^x - e^{-x}$. Then $f'(x) = 0 \implies e^x = e^{-x} \implies e^{2x} = 1 \implies x = 0$. $f''(x) = e^x + e^{-x}$ and $f''(0) = e^0 + e^{-0} = 2 > 0$ so there is a minimum at $x = 0$. $f''(x) \neq 0$ since $f''(x) = e^x + e^{-x}$ for all x, so there are no points of inflection. Moreover, since $f''(x) > 0$ for all $x \in \mathbb{R}$, the curve is everywhere concave up.

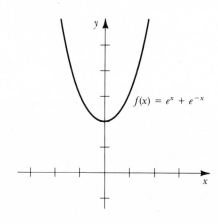

$f(x) = e^x + e^{-x}$

47. Sketch the graph of $f(x) = x^2 e^x$.

SOLUTION: $f'(x) = 2xe^x + x^2 e^x = xe^x(2 + x)$, so $f'(x) = 0 \implies x = 0$ or $x = -2$ since $e^x \neq 0$.

$$f''(x) = 2e^x + 2xe^x + 2xe^x + x^2 e^x = 2e^x + 4xe^x + x^2 e^x = e^x(x^2 + 4x + 2).$$

$f''(0) = 2e^2 > 0$ so there is a minimum at $x = 0$, and $f''(-2) = e^{-2}(4 - 8 + 2) < 0$ so there is a maximum at $x = -2$.

$f''(x) = 0 \implies x^2 + 4x + 2 = 0 \implies x = \dfrac{-4 \pm \sqrt{16 - 8}}{2} = \dfrac{-4 \pm \sqrt{8}}{2} = -2 \pm \sqrt{2}$. Since $f''(x) > 0$ for $x < -2 - \sqrt{2}$ or $x > -2 + \sqrt{2}$, the graph is concave up on these intervals, and since $f''(x) < 0$ for $-2 - \sqrt{2} < x < -2 + \sqrt{2}$, the graph is concave down on this interval. Also there are points of inflection at $x = -2 \pm \sqrt{2}$.

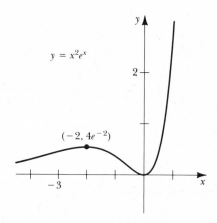

$y = x^2 e^x$

$(-2, 4e^{-2})$

59. Use L'Hôpital's rule to evaluate $\displaystyle \lim_{x \to \infty} \frac{x^3}{e^{x^2}}$.

SOLUTION: $\displaystyle \lim_{x \to \infty} \frac{x^3}{e^{x^2}}$ produces the indeterminate form ∞/∞. Thus $\displaystyle \lim_{x \to \infty} \frac{x^3}{e^{x^2}} = \lim_{x \to \infty} \frac{3x^2}{2xe^{x^2}} = \lim_{x \to \infty} \frac{3x}{2e^{x^2}}$, which yields the form ∞/∞. So $\displaystyle \lim_{x \to \infty} \frac{3x}{2e^{x^2}} = \lim_{x \to \infty} \frac{3}{4xe^{x^2}} = 0$, so $\displaystyle \lim_{x \to \infty} \frac{x^3}{e^{x^2}} = 0$.

65. Find the area of the region in the plane that is bounded by the x-axis, the y-axis, the line

$x = 1$, and the graph of $y = e^x$.

SOLUTION:

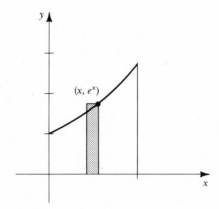

Since $y = e^x$ is nonnegative over $[0, 1]$, the desired area can be found by evaluating $\int_0^1 e^x\, dx$.

$$\int_0^1 e^x\, dx = [e^x]\Big|_0^1 = e^1 - e^0 = e - 1.$$

_____6.4

General Exponential and Logarithmic Functions

5. Find $D_x y$ if $y = (\sin x)^e$.

SOLUTION: Note that this problem is not one of the form $y = a^x$, but is of the form $y = (f(x))^n$, which indicates that the power rule and chain rule should be used. Thus $D_x[(\sin x)^e] = e(\sin x)^{e-1} \cdot D_x[\sin x] = e\cos x(\sin x)^{e-1}$.

11. Find $D_x y$ if $y = \log_{10}(x^2 + 1)$.

SOLUTION: Apply the formula $D_x[\log_a x] = \dfrac{1}{x \ln a}$ and the chain rule to obtain

$$D_x\left[\log_{10}(x^2 + 1)\right] = \frac{1}{(x^2 + 1)\ln 10} \cdot D_x\left[x^2 + 1\right] = \frac{2x}{(x^2 + 1)\ln 10}.$$

19. Find $D_x y$ if $y = \log_4 \dfrac{\sqrt{x^2 + 2x}}{\sqrt[3]{x^4 - 5}}$.

SOLUTION: The problem can be simplified by using the laws of logarithms.

$$D_x\left[\log_4 \frac{\sqrt{x^2 + 2x}}{\sqrt[3]{x^4 - 5}}\right] = D_x\left[\log_4(x^2 + 2x)^{1/2} - \log_4(x^4 - 5)^{1/3}\right]$$

$$= \frac{1}{2} D_x \left[\log_4(x^2 + 2x) \right] - \frac{1}{3} D_x \left[\log_4(x^4 - 5) \right]$$

$$= \frac{1}{2} \cdot \frac{1}{(x^2 + 2x) \ln 4} D_x \left[x^2 + 2x \right] - \frac{1}{3} \cdot \frac{1}{(x^4 - 5) \ln 4} D_x \left[x^4 - 5 \right]$$

$$= \frac{1}{\ln 4} \left(\frac{2x + 2}{2(x^2 + 2x)} - \frac{4x^3}{3(x^4 - 5)} \right)$$

$$= \frac{1}{\ln 4} \left(\frac{3(2x + 2)(x^4 - 5) - 8x^3(x^2 + 2x)}{6(x^2 + 2x)(x^4 - 5)} \right)$$

$$= -\frac{1}{\ln 4} \left(\frac{2x^5 + 10x^4 + 30x + 30}{6(x^2 + 2x)(x^4 - 5)} \right) = -\frac{1}{\ln 4} \left(\frac{x^5 + 5x^4 + 15x + 15}{3(x^2 + 2x)(x^4 - 5)} \right).$$

25. Find $D_x \left[(\cos x)^x \right]$.

SOLUTION: This is neither a function of the form $y = a^x$ nor a function of the form $y = (f(x))^n$. This problem may be attacked through logarithmic differentiation. $y = (\cos x)^x \implies \ln y = x \ln(\cos x) \implies D_x \left[\ln y \right] = D_x \left[x \ln(\cos x) \right] \implies \frac{1}{y} D_x y = \ln(\cos x) + x \cdot \frac{1}{\cos x}(-\sin x) \implies D_x y = y \left(\ln(\cos x) - x \tan x \right) = (\cos x)^x \left(\ln(\cos x) - x \tan x \right).$

29. Find $D_x y$ if $y \log_{10} x = x \log_{10} y$.

SOLUTION: Apply implicit differentiation along with the product rule and obtain
$D_x \left[y \log_{10} x \right] = D_x \left[x \log_{10} y \right] \implies y \cdot \frac{1}{x \ln 10} + (D_x y)(\log_{10} x) = \log_{10} y + x \cdot \frac{1}{y \ln 10} D_x y \implies$
$D_x y \left(\log_{10} x - \frac{x}{y \ln 10} \right) = \log_{10} y - \frac{y}{x \ln 10} \implies$

$$D_x y = \frac{\log_{10} y - \dfrac{y}{x \ln 10}}{\log_{10} x - \dfrac{x}{y \ln 10}} = \frac{xy \ln 10 \log_{10} y - y^2}{xy \ln 10 \log_{10} x - x^2} = \frac{y}{x} \left(\frac{x \ln 10 \log_{10} y - y}{y \ln 10 \log_{10} x - x} \right).$$

33. Evaluate $\displaystyle\int_0^1 3^{2x} \, dx$.

SOLUTION: Let $u = 3^{2x}$. Then $du = 3^{2x} \ln 3 (2 \, dx)$ and $\frac{1}{2 \ln 3} du = 3^{2x} \, dx$. Also, $x = 0 \implies u = 3^0 = 1$ and $x = 1 \implies u = 3^2 = 9$.

Thus $\displaystyle\int_0^1 3^{2x} \, dx = \int_1^9 \frac{1}{2 \ln 3} \, du = \frac{1}{2 \ln 3} \int_1^9 du = \frac{1}{2 \ln 3}[u] \Big|_1^9 = \frac{1}{2 \ln 3}(9 - 1) = \frac{4}{\ln 3}.$

47. Sketch the graph of $f(x) = \log_2(\log_2 x)$.

SOLUTION: The domain of f is $(1, \infty)$ since the domain of the logarithm function is $(0, \infty)$, but $\log_2 x \leq 0$ for $0 < x \leq 1$. To determine the critical points, solve $f'(x) = 0$.

$$f'(x) = \frac{1}{(\log_2 x)\ln 2} \cdot D_x[\log_2 x] = \frac{1}{(\log_2 x)\ln 2} \cdot \frac{1}{x \ln 2} = \frac{1}{x \log_2 x(\ln 2)^2}$$

so $f'(x) = 0 \implies \dfrac{1}{x \log_2 x(\ln 2)^2} = 0$, which is impossible, so there are no critical points. Moreover, since $x > 1$, $f'(x) > 0$ so the function is increasing.

To determine concavity, solve $f''(x) = 0$.

$$f''(x) = \frac{1}{(\ln 2)^2} D_x\left[\frac{1}{x \log_2 x}\right] = \frac{1}{(\ln 2)^2} \cdot \frac{-\left(\log_2 x + x \cdot \dfrac{1}{x \ln 2}\right)}{(x \log_2 x)^2} = \frac{-\left(\log_2 x + \dfrac{1}{\ln 2}\right)}{(\ln 2)^2 (x \log_2 x)^2}.$$

$f''(x) = 0 \implies \log_2 x + \dfrac{1}{\ln 2} = 0 \implies \log_2 x = -\dfrac{1}{\ln 2} \implies x = 2^{-1/\ln 2} \approx 0.37 < 1$, so there are no points of inflection. Moreover, $f''(x) < 0$ for $x > 1$, so the curve is concave down.

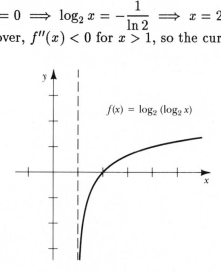

$$f(x) = \log_2(\log_2 x)$$

51. Use L'Hôpital's rule to evaluate $\displaystyle\lim_{x \to \infty} \frac{\log_2 x}{x}$.

SOLUTION: As written, this limit produces the indeterminate form ∞/∞, which satisfies the hypotheses of L'Hôpital's rule. Thus $\displaystyle\lim_{x \to \infty} \frac{\log_2 x}{x} = \lim_{x \to \infty} \frac{1/(x \ln 2)}{1} = \frac{1}{\ln 2} \lim_{x \to \infty} \frac{1}{x} = 0.$

55. Suppose $f'(x) = x^x$ and $g(x) = f(2x)$. Find $g'(x)$.

SOLUTION: Use the chain rule to obtain $D_x[g(x)] = D_x[f(2x)] = f'(2x) \cdot D_x[2x] = 2f'(2x) = 2(2x)^{2x}$.

63. Show that $f(x) = (1 + \frac{1}{x})^x$ is an increasing function when x is positive.

SOLUTION: To show $f(x) = \left(1 + \frac{1}{x}\right)^x$ is increasing when $x > 0$, show $f'(x) > 0$.

Let $y = (1 + x^{-1})^x$ and apply logarithmic differentiation. Then $\ln y = x \ln(1 + x^{-1})$ and

$$\frac{1}{y} D_x y = \ln(1 + x^{-1}) + x \cdot \frac{1}{1 + x^{-1}}(-x^{-2}) \implies D_x y = y \left(\ln \left(1 + \frac{1}{x}\right) - \frac{1/x}{1 + \frac{1}{x}} \right) \implies D_x y =$$

$$y \left(\ln \left(1 + \frac{1}{x}\right) - \frac{1}{x + 1} \right).$$

Since $y = \left(1 + \frac{1}{x}\right)^x > 0$ for $x > 0$, it remains to show $\ln \left(1 + \frac{1}{x}\right) - \frac{1}{x + 1} > 0$ for $x > 0$.

Let $g(x) = \ln \left(1 + \frac{1}{x}\right) - \frac{1}{x + 1} = \ln \left(\frac{x + 1}{x}\right) - \frac{1}{x + 1} = \ln(x + 1) - \ln x - (x + 1)^{-1}$. Then

$$g'(x) = \frac{1}{x + 1} - \frac{1}{x} + (x + 1)^{-2}(1) = \frac{1}{x + 1} - \frac{1}{x} + \frac{1}{(x + 1)^2}$$

$$= \frac{x(x + 1) - (x + 1)^2 + x}{x(x + 1)^2} = \frac{x^2 + x - x^2 - 2x - 1 + x}{x(x + 1)^2}$$

$$= \frac{-1}{x(x + 1)^2},$$

which indicates that $\ln \left(1 + \frac{1}{x}\right) - \frac{1}{x + 1}$ is decreasing for $x > 0$. Also,

$$\lim_{x \to \infty} \left(\ln \left(1 + \frac{1}{x}\right) - \frac{1}{x + 1} \right) = \ln 1 - 0 = 0.$$

Since $g(x)$ is decreasing and $\lim_{x \to \infty} g(x) = 0$, $g(x) > 0$ for $x > 0$.

Thus $D_x \left[\left(1 + \frac{1}{x}\right)^x \right] > 0$ for $x > 0$, and $f(x) = \left(1 + \frac{1}{x}\right)^x$ is increasing for $x > 0$.

_____6.5

Additional
Indeterminate Forms

5. Evaluate $\lim_{x \to 0^+} (x + e^x)^{1/x}$.

SOLUTION: This limit yields the indeterminate form 1^∞. To evaluate this limit, rewrite $(x + e^x)^{1/x} = \exp \left(\ln(x + e^x)^{1/x} \right) = \exp \left((1/x) \ln(x + e^x) \right)$. Thus

$$\lim_{x \to 0^+} (x + e^x)^{1/x} = \lim_{x \to 0^+} \exp \left(\frac{1}{x} \ln(x + e^x) \right) = \exp \left(\lim_{x \to 0^+} \frac{1}{x} \ln(x + e^x) \right)$$

since the exponential function is continuous.

Now $\lim\limits_{x\to 0^+} \dfrac{\ln(x + e^x)}{x}$ yields the indeterminate form $0/0$, which allows the use of L'Hôpital's rule. So

$$\lim_{x\to 0^+} \frac{\ln(x + e^x)}{x} = \lim_{x\to 0^+} \frac{\frac{1}{x + e^x}(1 + e^x)}{1} = \lim_{x\to 0^+} \frac{1 + e^x}{x + e^x} = \lim_{x\to 0^+} \frac{1 + e^0}{0 + e^0} = 2.$$

Thus $\lim\limits_{x\to 0^+} (x + e^x)^{1/x} = e^2$.

11. Evaluate $\lim\limits_{x\to 2^+} (x^2 - 4)^{(x-2)}$.

SOLUTION: This limit produces the indeterminate form 0^0. Rewrite the limit as

$$\lim_{x\to 2^+} (x^2 - 4)^{(x-2)} = \lim_{x\to 2^+} \exp\left(\ln(x^2 - 4)^{(x-2)}\right) = \exp\left(\lim_{x\to 2^+}\left(\ln(x^2 - 4)^{(x-2)}\right)\right)$$

since $f(x) = e^x$ is continuous. Now

$$\lim_{x\to 2^+}\left(\ln(x^2 - 4)^{(x-2)}\right) = \lim_{x\to 2^+} (x - 2)\ln(x^2 - 4) = \lim_{x\to 2^+} \frac{\ln(x^2 - 4)}{\frac{1}{x - 2}}$$

which yields the indeterminate form $-\infty/\infty$. Apply L'Hôpital's rule and obtain

$$\lim_{x\to 2^+} \frac{\frac{1}{x^2 - 4}\cdot 2x}{-(x - 2)^{-2}} = \lim_{x\to 2^+} \frac{-2x(x - 2)^2}{x^2 - 4} = \lim_{x\to 2^+} \frac{-2x(x - 2)}{x + 2} = 0.$$

Thus $\lim\limits_{x\to 2^+}\left(\ln(x^2 - 4)^{(x-2)}\right) = 0$ and $\lim\limits_{x\to 2^+} (x^2 - 4)^{(x-2)} = e^0 = 1$.

17. Evaluate $\lim\limits_{x\to\infty} \left(e^{-x}\right)^{e^x}$.

SOLUTION: Rewrite the limit and obtain $\lim\limits_{x\to\infty} \exp\left(\ln\left(e^{-x}\right)^{e^x}\right) = \exp\left(\lim\limits_{x\to\infty} \ln\left(e^{-x}\right)^{e^x}\right)$ since $f(x) = e^x$ is continuous. Now

$$\lim_{x\to\infty} \ln\left(e^{-x}\right)^{e^x} = \lim_{x\to\infty} e^x \ln\left(e^{-x}\right) = \lim_{x\to\infty} e^x(-x\ln e)$$

$$= \lim_{x\to\infty} (-xe^x) = -\infty \quad\text{and}$$

$$\lim_{x\to\infty} \left(e^{-x}\right)^{e^x} = e^{\lim_{x\to\infty}(-xe^x)} = 0.$$

23. Evaluate $\lim\limits_{x\to\infty}\left(1+\dfrac{1}{2x}\right)^x$ using the fact that $\lim\limits_{x\to\infty}\left(1+\dfrac{1}{x}\right)^x = e$.

SOLUTION: Let $u = 2x$. Then $x = u/2$ and as $x \to \infty$, $u \to \infty$ also. Thus

$$\lim_{x\to\infty}\left(1+\frac{1}{2x}\right)^x = \lim_{\substack{x\to\infty\\u\to\infty}}\left(1+\frac{1}{u}\right)^{u/2} = \lim_{u\to\infty}\left(\left(1+\frac{1}{u}\right)^u\right)^{1/2} = \left(\lim_{u\to\infty}\left(1+\frac{1}{u}\right)^u\right)^{1/2}$$

since $f(x) = \sqrt{x}$ is continuous for $x > 0$.

So $\lim\limits_{x\to\infty}\left(1+\dfrac{1}{2x}\right)^x = e^{1/2} = \sqrt{e}$.

27. Sketch the graph of $f(x) = x^x$.

SOLUTION: The domain of the function is $(0,\infty)$. To determine critical points, solve $f'(x) = 0$. $y = x^x \implies \ln y = x\ln x \implies \dfrac{1}{y}D_x y = \ln x + x\cdot\dfrac{1}{x} \implies D_x y = y(1+\ln x) = x^x(1+\ln x)$.
So $f'(x) = 0 \implies 1 + \ln x = 0 \implies \ln x = -1 \implies x = e^{-1} = 1/e$.
$f''(x) = D_x\,[x^x](1+\ln x) + x^x\left(1+\dfrac{1}{x}\right) = x^x(1+\ln x)^2 + x^x\left(1+\dfrac{1}{x}\right) > 0$ for $x > 0$, so f is concave up, and there are no points of inflection. Also, the critical point at $x = 1/e$ is a minimum.
$\lim\limits_{x\to 0}x^x = \lim\limits_{x\to 0}e^{\ln x^x} = e^{\lim\limits_{x\to 0}x\ln x}$. Now $\lim\limits_{x\to 0}x\ln x = \lim\limits_{x\to 0}\dfrac{\ln x}{x^{-1}} = \lim\limits_{x\to 0}\dfrac{1/x}{-x^{-2}} = \lim\limits_{x\to 0}\dfrac{-x^2}{x} = 0$ so $\lim\limits_{x\to 0}x^x = e^0 = 1$.

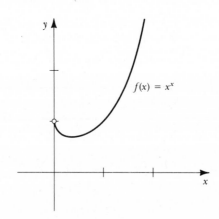

$f(x) = x^x$

29. If the interest on an investment, $A(0)$, is compounded m times a year, and the interest rate is i, the total amount of investment at the end of t years is

$$A(t) = A(0)\left(1+\frac{i}{m}\right)^{mt}.$$

Find $A(t)$ if the compounding is continuous (that is, if $m \to \infty$).

SOLUTION: Evaluate $\lim\limits_{m \to \infty} A(0)\left(1 + \dfrac{i}{m}\right)^{mt}$. Let $u = m/i$. Then $m \to \infty \implies u \to \infty$ since i is fixed. So

$$\lim_{m \to \infty} A(0)\left(1 + \frac{i}{m}\right)^{mt} = A(0)\lim_{u \to \infty}\left(1 + \frac{1}{u}\right)^{uit} = A(0)\lim_{u \to \infty}\left(\left(1 + \frac{1}{u}\right)^{u}\right)^{it}$$

$$= A(0)\left(\lim_{u \to \infty}\left(1 + \frac{1}{u}\right)^{u}\right)^{it}$$

since the power function is continuous.

Now $\lim\limits_{u \to \infty}\left(1 + \dfrac{1}{u}\right)^{u} = e$ from EXAMPLE 6 in SECTION 6.5. Thus $\lim\limits_{m \to \infty} A(0)\left(1 + \dfrac{i}{m}\right)^{mt} = A(0)e^{it}$.

_____6.6

Exponential Growth and Decay
_____

5. The number of bacteria present in a certain culture doubles every 4 hr.   Suppose there are 1000 present at time $t = 0$,   a) Find an expression for the number present at any time t. b) How many bacteria will be present after 7 hr?

SOLUTION: a) Let $N(t)$ be the number of bacteria at time t for $t \geq 0$. Then $N(0) = 1000$ and $\dfrac{N'(t)}{N(t)} = k$. Thus $\displaystyle\int \dfrac{N'(t)}{N(t)}\,dt = \int k\,dt \implies \ln|N(t)| = kt + c \implies \ln(N(t)) = kt + c \implies N(t) = e^{kt+c} = e^{kt}e^{c} = Ce^{kt}$.

Now $N(0) = Ce^{0} = 1000 \implies C = 1000$ and $N(t) = 1000e^{kt}$.

Also since the number doubles every four hours, if $N(t) = 1000e^{kt}$, then $N(t+4) = 1000e^{k(t+4)}$, and $2(1000e^{kt}) = 1000e^{k(t+4)} \implies 2e^{kt} = e^{k(t+4)} \implies 2 = \dfrac{e^{kt+4k}}{e^{kt}} = e^{4k} \implies \ln 2 = \ln e^{4k} = 4k\ln e = 4k \implies k = \dfrac{1}{4}\ln 2$.

Thus $N(t) = 1000e^{\frac{t}{4}\ln 2} = 1000\left(e^{\ln 2}\right)^{t/4} = 1000\left(2^{t/4}\right)$.

b) After 7 hours, the number of bacteria will be $N(7) = 1000\left(2^{7/4}\right) \approx 3364$ bacteria.

13. Five hundred gallons of pesticide is accidentally spilled into a lake with a volume of 8×10^{7} gal and uniformly mixes with the water. A river flows into the lake bringing 10,000 gal of

fresh water per minute, and the uniform mixture flows out of the lake at the same rate. How long will it take to reduce the pesticide in the lake to a safe level of 1 part per billion?

SOLUTION: Let $A(t)$ be the amount of pesticide in the lake at time $t > 0$. No pesticide flows into the lake, but pesticide flows out at a (negative) rate of $\dfrac{-10^4 \text{ gal/min}}{8 \times 10^7 \text{ gal}} A(t) \text{ gal}$. The amount is described by the equation $\dfrac{dA}{dt} = -1.25 \times 10^{-4} A(t)$, $A(0) = 500$. Thus, $A(t) = 500e^{-1.25 \times 10^{-4}t}\text{gal}$. To reduce the pesticide concentration to 1 part per billion, the amount must decrease to A, where $\dfrac{A}{8 \times 10^7} = \dfrac{1}{1 \times 10^9}$ or $A = 8 \times 10^{-2}$. This occurs when

$$A(t) = 500e^{-1.25 \times 10^{-4}t} = 8 \times 10^{-2},$$

or, solving for t, when $t = -\dfrac{1}{1.25 \times 10^{-4}} \ln\left(\dfrac{8 \times 10^{-2}}{500}\right)$ or approximately, $t \approx 69{,}922.69 \text{ min}$ or $t \approx 48.56 \text{ day}$.

19. A sample of wood is found to contain carbon with one part $^{14}_{6}\text{C}$ to 1.35×10^{12} parts $^{12}_{6}\text{C}$. Assuming that the ratio at the time the tree died was one part $^{14}_{6}\text{C}$ to 10^{12} parts $^{12}_{6}\text{C}$, and that the half-life of $^{14}_{6}\text{C}$ is 5730 years, estimate the age of the sample.

SOLUTION: Let $A(t)$ be the amount of $^{14}_{6}\text{C}$ per 10^{12} parts of $^{12}_{6}\text{C}$ in the sample at time t. Then $A(t) = A(0)e^{kt} = e^{kt}$ since $A(0) = 1$. Then $A(t + 5730) = \dfrac{1}{2}A(t) \implies \dfrac{A(t + 5730)}{A(t)} = \dfrac{e^{k(t+5730)}}{e^{kt}} = e^{5730k} = \dfrac{1}{2} \implies (e^k)^{5730} = \dfrac{1}{2} \implies e^k = \left(\dfrac{1}{2}\right)^{1/5730} = 2^{-1/5730}$. Thus $A(t) = (2^{-1/5730})t$.

Since the tree has 1 part $^{14}_{6}\text{C}$ per 1.35×10^{12} parts of $^{12}_{6}\text{C}$, the sample has $1/1.35$ parts $^{14}_{6}\text{C}$ per 10^{12} parts $^{12}_{6}\text{C}$. Find t so that $A(t) = (2^{-1/5730})^t = \dfrac{1}{1.35}$. Then $t \ln 2^{-1/5730} = \ln\dfrac{1}{1.35} = -\ln 1.35 \implies t = \dfrac{-\ln 1.35}{-\dfrac{1}{5730}\ln 2} = 5730\dfrac{\ln 1.35}{\ln 2} \approx 2480.6 \text{ yrs}.$

_____**6.7**

Separable Differential Equations

_____

5. Find the general solution to $y' = \dfrac{\sin x + x^2}{\cos y - 1}$.

SOLUTION: Apply separation of variables to $\dfrac{dy}{dx} = \dfrac{\sin x + x^2}{\cos y - 1}$ and obtain

$\int (\cos y - 1)\, dy = \int (\sin x + x^2)\, dx$. Then $\sin y - y = -\cos x + \dfrac{1}{3}x^3 + C$ and

$y - \sin y = \cos x - \dfrac{1}{3}x^3 + C$ is the desired solution.

11. Find the general solution to $y + e^x y' = 0$.

SOLUTION: $y + e^x y' = 0 \implies e^x \dfrac{dy}{dx} = -y \implies \dfrac{e^x}{dx} = \dfrac{-y}{dy} \implies \int \dfrac{dy}{y} = \int \dfrac{-dx}{e^x} =$

$-\int e^{-x}\, dx \implies \ln|y| = e^{-x} + C$, which is the desired general solution.

17. Find the solution to $y' = e^y \cos x$ if $y(\pi) = 0$.

SOLUTION: $\dfrac{dy}{dx} = e^y \cos x \implies \int e^{-y}\, dy = \int \cos x\, dx \implies -e^{-y} = \sin x + C$, and $e^{-y} =$
$-\sin x + C$. Now $\ln e^{-y} = \ln(-\sin x + C) \implies -y = \ln(-\sin x + C) \implies y = -\ln(-\sin x + C)$.
Substitute $y(\pi) = 0$ and obtain $0 = -\ln(-\sin \pi + C)$. Then $\ln C = 0 \implies C = 1$, and the
desired solution is $y = -\ln(1 - \sin x)$.

25. The dispersion of information among a population can be modeled by the differential equation $\dfrac{dP}{dt} = k(1 - P)$, where P denotes the proportion of the population aware of the information at time t, and k is a positive constant. Suppose that 10% of the population learns of a tax rebate on the 7:00 AM news and that 50% is aware of the rebate by noon. What percentage will know about the rebate before the 6:00 PM news?

SOLUTION: Apply separation of variables to $\dfrac{dP}{dt} = k(1 - P)$ and obtain $\int \dfrac{dP}{1 - P} = \int k\, dt$.
Thus $-\ln(1 - P) = kt + C \implies \ln(1 - P) = -kt + C \implies e^{\ln(1-P)} = e^{-kt+C} \implies 1 - P =$
$e^{-kt}e^C \implies 1 - P = Ce^{-kt} \implies -P = -1 + Ce^{-kt} \implies P = 1 + Ce^{-kt}$.
Now let t be the time after 7:00 AM. Then $P(0) = 1 + Ce^{k(0)} = 0.1 \implies C = -0.9$, and
$P(t) = 1 - 0.9e^{-kt}$. Also, $P(5) = 1 - 0.9e^{-k(5)} = 0.5 \implies 0.9e^{-5k} = 0.5 \implies e^{-5k} = 5/9 \implies$
$\ln e^{-5k} = \ln(5/9) \implies -5k = \ln(5/9) \implies k = -\dfrac{1}{5}\ln\dfrac{5}{9}$. Thus $P(t) = 1 - 0.9e^{\frac{t}{5}\ln\frac{5}{9}} =$
$1 - 0.9\left(e^{\ln\frac{5}{9}}\right)^{t/5} = 1 - 0.9\left(\dfrac{5}{9}\right)^{t/5}$, and $P(11) = 1 - 0.9\left(\dfrac{5}{9}\right)^{11/5} \approx 0.753$. By the 6 PM news,
approximately 75.3% of the population will know about the rebate.

29. A body is found floating face down in Lake Gotchaheny (a lake with a constant temperature of $62°$F). When the body was taken from the water at 11:50 AM, its temperature was $66°$F. The temperature of the body when first found at 11:00 AM was $67°$F. When did the victim meet his demise? (Assume that the victim was a normal $98.6°$F before going to the watery grave.)

SOLUTION: Using Newton's Law of Cooling, $\dfrac{dT(t)}{dt} = k\,(T(t) - L)$, where $T(t)$ is the temperature of the object at time t and L is the ambient temperature. Applying separation of variables, $\displaystyle\int \frac{dT}{T-L} = \int t\,dt \implies \ln|T-L| = kt + C$. Since $T \geq L$, $\ln(T-L) = kt + C$ and $T - L = e^{kt+C} = e^{kt}e^C = Ce^{kt}$.

So $T = Ce^{kt} + L$. Let $t = 0$ at 11:00 AM with $T = 67$. Then at $t = 50$, $T = 66$. Thus $67 = Ce^{k\cdot 0} + 62 \implies 5 = C$ and $66 = 5e^{50k} + 62 \implies e^{50k} = \dfrac{4}{5} \implies 50k = \ln 0.8 \implies k = \dfrac{1}{50}\ln 0.8$.

So $T = 5e^{\frac{t}{50}\ln 0.8} + 62 = 5\left(e^{\ln 0.8}\right)^{t/50} + 62 = 5(0.8)^{t/50} + 62$. To find t when $T = 98.6$,

$98.6 = 5(0.8)^{t/50} + 62 \implies 36.6 = 5(0.8)^{t/50} \implies 7.32 = (0.8)^{t/50} \implies \ln 7.32 = \dfrac{t}{50}\ln 0.8 \implies$

$t = 50\dfrac{\ln 7.32}{\ln 0.8} \approx -446.$

Therefore the victim met his demise approximately 446 minutes or 7 hr 26 min before 11:00 AM, or approximately 3:34 AM.

6.8

Hyperbolic Functions

---

5. Differentiate $f(x) = \cosh(\ln x)$.

SOLUTION: Apply the chain rule and obtain $f'(x) = \sinh(\ln x)\cdot D_x[\ln x] = \dfrac{\sinh(\ln x)}{x}$.

11. Differentiate $f(x) = e^{\sinh x^2}$.

SOLUTION: Apply the chain rule and obtain

$$f'(x) = e^{\sinh x^2}\cdot D_x\left[\sinh x^2\right] = e^{\sinh x^2}\cosh x^2 \cdot D_x\left[x^2\right]$$

$$= 2x\cosh x^2 e^{\sinh x^2}.$$

15. Differentiate $f(x) = \dfrac{\tanh x}{1 + x^2}$.

SOLUTION: Apply the quotient rule and obtain $f'(x) = \dfrac{(1+x^2)\operatorname{sech}^2 x - 2x\tanh x}{(1+x^2)^2}$.

17. Evaluate $\displaystyle\int \frac{\cosh\sqrt{x}}{\sqrt{x}}\,dx$.

SOLUTION: Let $u = \sqrt{x} = x^{1/2}$. Then $du = \dfrac{1}{2}x^{-1/2}\,dx$ and $2\,du = \dfrac{1}{\sqrt{x}}\,dx$. Thus

$$\int \frac{\cosh\sqrt{x}}{\sqrt{x}}\,dx = \int \cosh u(2\,du) = 2\int \cosh u\,du = 2\sinh u + C = 2\sinh\sqrt{x} + C.$$

23. Evaluate $\int \dfrac{\cosh x}{\sinh^2 x}\, dx$.

SOLUTION: Let $u = \sinh x$. Then $du = \cosh x\, dx$ and

$$\int \frac{\cosh x}{\sinh^2 x}\, dx = \int \frac{1}{u^2}\, du = \int u^{-2}\, du = -u^{-1} + C = \frac{-1}{\sinh x} + C = -\operatorname{csch} x + C.$$

29. Evaluate $\displaystyle\lim_{x \to 0} \frac{\ln \cosh x}{x}$.

SOLUTION: $\displaystyle\lim_{x \to 0} \ln \cosh x = \lim_{x \to 0} \ln \left(\frac{e^x + e^{-x}}{2} \right) = 0$, so the hypotheses of L'Hôpital's rule are satisfied and

$$\lim_{x \to 0} \frac{\ln \cosh x}{x} = \lim_{x \to 0} \frac{\dfrac{1}{\cosh x} \cdot D_x[\cosh x]}{1}$$

$$= \lim_{x \to 0} \frac{\sinh x}{\cosh x} = \lim_{x \to 0} \tanh x = \frac{e^0 - e^0}{e^0 + e^0} = 0.$$

45. Find the volume generated by rotating $y = \cosh x$ from $(0, 1)$ to $(a, \cosh a)$ about the x-axis.

SOLUTION:

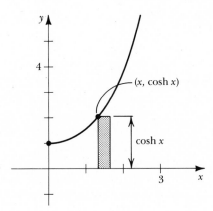

Rotation about the x-axis generates a disk and $V = \displaystyle\int_0^a \pi \cosh^2 x\, dx = \pi \int \cosh^2 x\, dx$. From

EXERCISE 40, $\cosh \dfrac{x}{2} = \sqrt{\dfrac{\cosh x + 1}{2}} \implies \cosh^2 \dfrac{x}{2} = \dfrac{\cosh x + 1}{2}$, so

$$\pi \int_0^a \cosh^2 x\, dx = \pi \int_0^a \frac{1 + \cosh 2x}{2}\, dx = \frac{\pi}{2} \left[x + \frac{1}{2} \sinh 2x \right]\Big|_0^a$$

$$= \frac{\pi}{2}\left((a + \frac{1}{2}\sinh 2a) - (0 + \sinh 0)\right) = \frac{\pi}{2}(a + \frac{1}{2}\sinh 2a).$$

47. Show that the length of the curve $y = \cosh x$ from $(0,1)$ to $(a, \cosh a)$ is $\sinh a$.

SOLUTION:

$$\sqrt{(dx)^2 + (dy)^2} = \sqrt{1 + \sinh^2 x}\, dx$$

$$= \sqrt{\cosh^2 x - \sinh^2 x + \sinh^2 x}\, dx = \sqrt{\cosh^2 x}\, dx$$

$$= |\cosh x|\, dx = \cosh x\, dx.$$

Thus $L = \displaystyle\int_0^a \cosh x\, dx = [\sinh x]\Big|_0^a = \sinh a - \sinh 0 = \sinh a.$

_____**6.9**

Inverse Hyperbolic Functions

5. Differentiate $f(x) = \sinh x^2 \operatorname{arcsinh} x^2$.

SOLUTION: Using the product rule and the chain rule obtain

$$f'(x) = (\cosh x^2)(2x)(\operatorname{arcsinh} x^2) + (\sinh x^2)\left(\frac{1}{\sqrt{1 + (x^2)^2}}\right)(2x)$$

$$= 2x\left(\cosh x^2 \operatorname{arcsinh} x^2 + \frac{\sinh x^2}{\sqrt{1 + x^4}}\right).$$

13. Evaluate $\displaystyle\int \frac{x\, dx}{\sqrt{x^4 + 9}}$.

SOLUTION: $\displaystyle\int \frac{x\, dx}{\sqrt{x^4 + 9}} = \int \frac{x\, dx}{\sqrt{(x^2)^2 + 3^2}}$. Let $u = x^2$. Then $du = 2x\, dx$ and $\frac{1}{2}du = x\, dx$.

Thus $\displaystyle\int \frac{x\, dx}{\sqrt{(x^2)^2 + 3^2}} = \int \frac{\frac{1}{2}du}{\sqrt{u^2 + 3^2}} = \frac{1}{2}\operatorname{arcsinh}\frac{u}{3} + C = \frac{1}{2}\operatorname{arcsinh}\frac{x^2}{3} + C.$

17. Evaluate $\displaystyle\int \frac{e^x\,dx}{1-e^{2x}}$.

SOLUTION: $\displaystyle\int \frac{e^x\,dx}{1-e^{2x}} = \int \frac{e^x\,dx}{1-(e^x)^2}$. Let $u = e^x$. Then $du = e^x\,dx$ and $\displaystyle\int \frac{e^x\,dx}{1-(e^x)^2} =$

$\displaystyle\int \frac{du}{1-u^2} = \begin{cases} \operatorname{arctanh} u + C, & \text{for } |u| < 1 \\ \operatorname{arccoth} u + C, & \text{for } |u| > 1 \end{cases} = \begin{cases} \operatorname{arctanh}(e^x) + C, & \text{for } e^x < 1 \\ \operatorname{arccoth}(e^x) + C, & \text{for } e^x > 1 \end{cases} =$

$\begin{cases} \operatorname{arctanh}(e^x) + C, & \text{for } x < 0 \\ \operatorname{arccoth}(e^x) + C, & \text{for } x > 0. \end{cases}$

27. Verify: $\operatorname{arcsech} x = \ln\left(\dfrac{1+\sqrt{1-x^2}}{x}\right)$ for $x > 0$.

SOLUTION: Let $y = \operatorname{arcsech} x$. Then $x = \operatorname{sech} y = \dfrac{2}{e^y + e^{-y}}$. So $(e^y + e^{-y})x = 2$ or $xe^{2y} - 2e^y + x = 0$. Apply the quadratic formula to obtain

$$e^y = \frac{2 \pm \sqrt{4 - 4x^2}}{2x} \qquad \text{or} \qquad y = \ln\left(\frac{1 \pm \sqrt{1-x^2}}{x}\right).$$

Since $x > 0$, $y = \ln\left(\dfrac{1+\sqrt{1-x^2}}{x}\right)$ and $\operatorname{arcsech} x = \ln\left(\dfrac{1+\sqrt{1-x^2}}{x}\right)$.

31. Evaluate $\displaystyle\lim_{x\to 0^+} x \operatorname{arcsech} x$.

SOLUTION: Since $\operatorname{arcsech} x = \ln\left(\dfrac{1+\sqrt{1-x^2}}{x}\right)$ from EXERCISE 27 above,

$$\lim_{x\to 0^+} x \operatorname{arcsech} x = \lim_{x\to 0^+} x \ln\frac{1+\sqrt{1-x^2}}{x} = \lim_{x\to 0^+} \frac{\ln\dfrac{1+\sqrt{1-x^2}}{x}}{1/x},$$

which yields the indeterminate form ∞/∞. Applying L'Hôpital's rule, the limit becomes

$$\lim_{x\to 0^+} \frac{\dfrac{1}{\dfrac{1+\sqrt{1-x^2}}{x}} \cdot \dfrac{x\left(\frac{1}{2}(1-x^2)^{-1/2}(-2x)\right) - \left(1+(1-x^2)^{1/2}\right)}{x^2}}{-1/x^2}$$

$$= \lim_{x\to 0^+} \frac{x}{1+\sqrt{1-x^2}} \cdot \frac{(1-x^2)^{-1/2}(-x^2 - \sqrt{1-x^2} - 1 + x^2)}{x^2} \cdot \frac{-x^2}{1}$$

$$= \lim_{x \to 0^+} \frac{x(1 + \sqrt{1 - x^2})}{(1 + \sqrt{1 - x^2})\sqrt{1 - x^2}} = \frac{0(1 + \sqrt{1})}{(1 + \sqrt{1})(\sqrt{1})} = 0.$$

Thus $\lim_{x \to 0^+} x \operatorname{arcsech} x = 0$.

35. Show that $\operatorname{arctanh} \dfrac{3}{5} = \operatorname{arcsinh} \dfrac{3}{4} = \operatorname{arccosh} \dfrac{5}{4}$.

SOLUTION: Let $x = \operatorname{arcsinh} \dfrac{3}{4}$. Then $\sinh x = \dfrac{3}{4}$. Since $\cosh^2 x - \sinh^2 x = 1$, $\cosh^2 x = 1 + (3/4)^2 = 25/16$ and $\cosh x = \dfrac{5}{4}$. But then $x = \operatorname{arccosh} \dfrac{5}{4}$.

Also, $\tanh x = \dfrac{\sinh x}{\cosh x} = \dfrac{3/4}{5/4} = \dfrac{3}{5}$, so $x = \operatorname{arctanh} \dfrac{3}{5}$. Thus $x = \operatorname{arctanh} \dfrac{3}{5} = \operatorname{arcsinh} \dfrac{3}{4} = \operatorname{arccosh} \dfrac{5}{4}$.

Chapter 6
Review Exercises

5. Consider $f(x) = x^2 + 1$, $x \geq 0$.

    a) Show that the function is one-to-one.

    b) Find f^{-1} and give its domain and range.

    c) Sketch the graphs of $y = f(x)$ and $y = f^{-1}(x)$ on the same set of axes.

    d) Use the derivative relation in the Inverse Function Theorem to determine the derivative of f^{-1}.

SOLUTION: a) To show f is one-to-one, show that if $f(x_1) = f(x_2)$, then $x_1 = x_2$. Let $f(x_1) = f(x_2)$. Then $x_1^2 + 1 = x_2^2 + 1$ and $x_1^2 = x_2^2$. Thus $x_1 = \pm x_2$. But if $x_1 = -x_2$ and $x_1 \geq 0$, then $x_2 \leq 0$, which is impossible since $x_2 \geq 0$. Thus $x_1 = x_2$ and hence f is one-to-one. Note that the restriction of the domain to $[0, \infty)$ is crucial. If negative values were also permitted, then f would <u>not</u> be one-to-one.

b) To find f^{-1}, let $y = x^2 + 1$ and solve for x. $y = x^2 + 1 \implies y - 1 = x^2 \implies x = \pm\sqrt{y - 1}$. But since $x \geq 0$, discard the negative square root and $x = \sqrt{y - 1}$. Thus $f^{-1}(x) = \sqrt{x - 1}$. Since the domain of f is $[0, \infty)$, the range of f^{-1} is $[0, \infty)$. The range of f is $[1, \infty)$ so the domain of f^{-1} is $[1, \infty)$.

c)

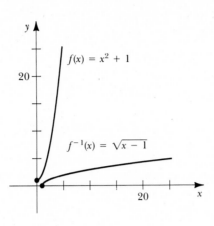

d) $f^{-1}(y) = \sqrt{y-1}$ and the Inverse Function Theorem states

$$D_y\left[f^{-1}(y)\right] = \frac{1}{D_x f(x)}.$$

Thus

$$D_y[\sqrt{y-1}] = \frac{1}{D_x[x^2+1]} = \frac{1}{2x} = \frac{1}{2\sqrt{y-1}},$$

since $x = \sqrt{y-1}$ from above.

11. Find dy/dx if $y = e^{x^3}$.

SOLUTION: $D_x\left[e^{x^3}\right] = e^{x^3} D_x[x^3] = 3x^2 e^{x^3}.$

17. Find dy/dx if $y = xe^{\tan x}$.

SOLUTION:

$$D_x\left[xe^{\tan x}\right] = x D_x\left[e^{\tan x}\right] + e^{\tan x} D_x x$$

$$= xe^{\tan x}(D_x \tan x) + e^{\tan x} = e^{\tan x}(x \sec^2 x + 1).$$

25. Find dy/dx if $y = x^e$.

SOLUTION: Note that this uses a direct application of the power rule $(D_x[x^n] = nx^{n-1}$, $n \neq 0)$. Thus $\dfrac{dy}{dx} = ex^{e-1}.$

29. Find dy/dx if $y = e^x \sinh(2x - 1)$.

SOLUTION:

$$D_x\left[e^x \sinh(2x-1)\right] = e^x D_x\left[\sinh(2x-1)\right] + \sinh(2x-1)D_x[e^x]$$

$$= e^x \cosh(2x - 1)D_x[2x - 1] + e^x \sinh(2x - 1)$$

$$= e^x \left(2 \cosh(2x - 1) + \sinh(2x - 1)\right).$$

33. Find dy/dx if $\ln(x + y) = \arctan(x/y)$.

SOLUTION:

$$D_x\left[\ln(x + y)\right] = D_x\left[\arctan(x/y)\right] \implies$$

$$\frac{1}{x + y}D_x[x + y] = \frac{1}{1 + (x/y)^2}D_x[x/y] \implies$$

$$\frac{1}{x + y}\left(1 + \frac{dy}{dx}\right) = \frac{1}{1 + (x/y)^2} \cdot \frac{y - x\left(\frac{dy}{dx}\right)}{y^2} \implies$$

$$\frac{1}{x + y} + \frac{dy/dx}{x + y} = \frac{y^2}{y^2 + x^2} \cdot \frac{y - x\left(\frac{dy}{dx}\right)}{y^2} \implies$$

$$\left(\frac{1}{x + y} + \frac{x}{y^2 + x^2}\right)\frac{dy}{dx} = \frac{y}{y^2 + x^2} - \frac{1}{x + y} \implies$$

$$\frac{y^2 + x^2 + x^2 + xy}{(x + y)(y^2 + x^2)} \cdot \frac{dy}{dx} = \frac{xy + y^2 - y^2 - x^2}{(y^2 + x^2)(x + y)} \implies$$

$$\frac{dy}{dx} = \frac{xy - x^2}{(y^2 + x^2)(x + y)} \cdot \frac{(x + y)(y^2 + x^2)}{y^2 + 2x^2 + xy} \implies$$

$$\frac{dy}{dx} = \frac{x(y - x)}{y^2 + 2x^2 + xy}.$$

41. Evaluate $\displaystyle\int \frac{e^x \, dx}{\sqrt{1 - e^{2x}}}$.

SOLUTION: Let $u = e^x$. Then $u^2 = (e^x)^2 = e^{2x}$ and $du = e^x \, dx$. Thus

$$\int \frac{e^x \, dx}{\sqrt{1 - e^{2x}}} = \int \frac{du}{\sqrt{1 - u^2}} = \arcsin u + C = \arcsin e^x + C.$$

45. Evaluate $\displaystyle\int_{-1}^{1} 2^x \, dx$.

SOLUTION: Let $u = 2^x$. Then $du = 2^x \ln 2 \, dx$ and $du/\ln 2 = 2^x \, dx$. Also $x = -1 \implies u = 2^{-1} = 1/2$ and $x = 1 \implies u = 2^1 = 2$.

Thus

$$\int_{-1}^{1} 2^x \, dx = \int_{1/2}^{2} \frac{du}{\ln 2} = \frac{1}{\ln 2} \int_{1/2}^{2} du = \left[\frac{1}{\ln 2} \cdot u \right] \Big|_{1/2}^{2}$$

$$= \frac{1}{\ln 2} \left(2 - \frac{1}{2} \right) = \frac{3}{2} \cdot \frac{1}{\ln 2} = \frac{3}{2 \ln 2}.$$

51. Evaluate $\lim_{x \to 0^+} x^{\ln x}$.

SOLUTION: To evaluate this limit, rewrite the limit as

$$\lim_{x \to 0^+} x^{\ln x} = \lim_{x \to 0^+} \exp \left(\ln(x^{\ln x}) \right) = \exp \left(\lim_{x \to 0^+} \ln(x^{\ln x}) \right).$$

Now

$$\lim_{x \to 0^+} \ln(x^{\ln x}) = \lim_{x \to 0^+} (\ln x)(\ln x) = \lim_{x \to 0^+} (\ln x)^2 = \infty.$$

Thus $\exp \left(\lim_{x \to 0^+} \ln(x^{\ln x}) \right) = \infty$ and $\lim_{x \to 0^+} x^{\ln x} = \infty.$

57. Evaluate $\lim_{x \to \infty} \left(\tan \frac{1}{x} \right)^x$.

SOLUTION: Rewrite $\lim_{x \to \infty} \left(\tan \frac{1}{x} \right)^x = \lim_{x \to \infty} \exp \left(\ln(\tan(1/x))^x \right) = \exp \left(\lim_{x \to \infty} \ln(\tan(1/x))^x \right).$

Now

$$\lim_{x \to \infty} \ln \left(\tan \frac{1}{x} \right)^x = \lim_{x \to \infty} x \ln \left(\tan \frac{1}{x} \right) = \infty(-\infty) = -\infty$$

so $\exp \left(\lim_{x \to \infty} \ln(\tan(1/x))^x \right) = 0$ and $\lim_{x \to \infty} \left(\tan \frac{1}{x} \right)^x = 0.$

65. Sketch the graph of $f(x) = \sinh 2x$.

SOLUTION: The graph of f is obtained from the graph of $g(x) = \sinh x$ by horizontally compressing the graph by a factor of $1/2$.

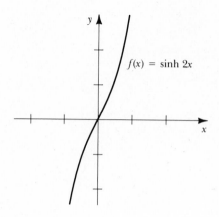

69. Find the general solution of the differential equation $y' = e^{x+y}$.

SOLUTION: $y' = e^{x+y} \implies \dfrac{dy}{dx} = e^x e^y$. Apply separation of variables and obtain $e^{-y}\, dy = e^x\, dx$. Thus

$$\int e^{-y} dy = \int e^x dx$$
$$e^{-y} = -e^x + C$$
$$\ln e^{-y} = \ln |-e^x + C|$$
$$-y \ln e = \ln |-e^x + C|$$
$$-y = \ln |-e^x + C|$$
$$y = -\ln |-e^x + C|$$

is the desired general solution.

75. Find the solution to the differential equation $2x(y+1) - yy' = 0$ with $y(1) = 0$.

SOLUTION: $2x(y+1) - yy' = 0 \implies 2x(y+1) = y\frac{dy}{dx}$. Apply separation of variables and obtain

$$\frac{y\, dy}{y+1} = 2x\, dx \implies$$

$$\left(1 + \frac{-1}{y+1}\right) dy = 2x\, dx \implies$$

$$\int \left(1 - \frac{1}{y+1}\right) dy = \int 2x\, dx \implies$$

$$y - \ln |y+1| = x^2 + C.$$

Applying $y(1) = 0$, $0 - \ln |0+1| = 1^2 + C \implies 0 - \ln 1 = 1 + C \implies 0 = 1 + C \implies C = -1$. Thus the desired solution is $y - \ln |y+1| = x^2 - 1$.

7
Techniques of Integration

Sharpening your skills

In preparation for your study of CHAPTER 7 you should review the basic techniques of integration presented in SECTIONS 4.3–4.6. Also review the material in SECTIONS 6.2–6.4 dealing with differentiation and integration of expressions including inverse trigonometric functions and exponential and logarithmic functions. Finally, review the material presented in SECTIONS 6.8 and 6.9 on differentiation and integration of hyperbolic and inverse hyperbolic functions. You may find it helpful to make a list of formulas for differentiation and integration and keep it at hand when working on the problems in this chapter. Some additional practice problems are given below. The answers are found in APPENDIX B in this manual.

Practice Problems

1. Find $D_x y$ for each of the following.
   a) $y = \sinh(2x)\cosh(\ln x)$
   b) $y = \log_{10}(\tanh x)$
   c) $y = x\arcsin(2x)$
   d) $y = e^x \arctan x$.

2. Evaluate each of the following:
   a) $\displaystyle\int \frac{dx}{\sqrt{9 - 4x^2}}$
   b) $\displaystyle\int_0^4 e^{-4x}\, dx$
   c) $\displaystyle\int_0^{\sqrt{3}} \frac{dx}{1 + x^2}$
   d) $\displaystyle\int \tanh 2x \, dx$.

7.1
Integration by Parts

9. Evaluate $\displaystyle\int \arccos x \, dx$.

SOLUTION: Let $u = \arccos x$ and $dv = dx$. Then $du = \dfrac{-1}{\sqrt{1-x^2}}\, dx$ and $v = x$, so

$$\int \arccos x\, dx = x \arccos x - \int \frac{-x}{\sqrt{1-x^2}}\, dx.$$ To evaluate $\displaystyle\int \frac{-x}{\sqrt{1-x^2}}\, dx$, let $w = 1 - x^2$. Then

$dw = -2x\, dx$ and $\dfrac{1}{2} dw = -x\, dx$. Thus

$$\int \frac{-x}{\sqrt{1-x^2}}\, dx = \frac{1}{2} \int \frac{dw}{w^{1/2}} = \frac{1}{2} \int w^{-1/2}\, dw = w^{1/2} + C = \sqrt{1-x^2} + C.$$

Hence $\displaystyle\int \arccos x\, dx = x \arccos x - \sqrt{1-x^2} + C.$

17. Evaluate $\displaystyle\int x^3 \ln x^2\, dx = 2 \int x^3 \ln x\, dx.$

SOLUTION: Let $u = \ln x$ and $dv = x^3\, dx$. Then $du = \dfrac{1}{x}\, dx$ and $v = \dfrac{1}{4}x^4$, so

$$\int x^3 \ln x^2\, dx = 2 \int x^3 \ln x\, dx = 2 \left(\frac{1}{4}x^4 \ln x - \int \frac{1}{4}x^4 \left(\frac{1}{x}\, dx \right) \right)$$

$$= \frac{1}{2}x^4 \ln x - \frac{1}{2} \int x^3\, dx = \frac{1}{2}x^4 \ln x - \frac{1}{8}x^4 + C.$$

25. Evaluate $\displaystyle\int e^x \sin x\, dx.$

SOLUTION: Let $u = e^x$ and $dv = \sin x\, dx$. Then $du = e^x\, dx$ and $v = -\cos x$, so $\displaystyle\int e^x \sin x\, dx =$

$-e^x \cos x - \displaystyle\int -\cos x(e^x\, dx) = -e^x \cos x + \int e^x \cos x\, dx.$

To evaluate $\displaystyle\int e^x \cos x\, dx$, let $u = e^x$ and $dv = \cos x\, dx$. Then $du = e^x\, dx$ and $v = \sin x$, so

$\displaystyle\int e^x \cos x\, dx = e^x \sin x - \int \sin x(e^x\, dx)$. It appears that this is circular, but examine the entire

problem at this point. $\displaystyle\int e^x \sin x\, dx = -e^x \cos x + \left(e^x \sin x - \int e^x \sin x\, dx \right)$ and $2 \displaystyle\int e^x \sin x\, dx =$

$e^x(\sin x - \cos x) + C.$ So $\displaystyle\int e^x \sin x\, dx = \frac{e^x}{2}(\sin x - \cos x) + C.$

31. Evaluate $\displaystyle\int_0^{\pi/6} \sin 2x \sin 3x\, dx.$

SOLUTION: Let $u = \sin 2x$ and $dv = \sin 3x\, dx$. Then $du = 2 \cos 2x\, dx$ and $v = -\dfrac{1}{3} \cos 3x$, so

$$\int_0^{\pi/6} \sin 2x \sin 3x\, dx = -\frac{1}{3} \left[\sin 2x \cos 3x \right]\Big|_0^{\pi/6} - \int_0^{\pi/6} -\frac{1}{3} \cos 3x(2 \cos 2x\, dx)$$

$$= -\frac{1}{3}\left(\sin\frac{\pi}{3}\cos\frac{\pi}{2} - \sin 0\cos 0\right) + \frac{2}{3}\int_0^{\pi/6}\cos 3x\cos 2x\, dx$$

$$= \frac{2}{3}\int_0^{\pi/6}\cos 3x\cos 2x\, dx.$$

To evaluate $\displaystyle\int_0^{\pi/6}\cos 3x\cos 2x\, dx$, let $u = \cos 2x$ and $dv = \cos 3x\, dx$. Then $du = -2\sin 2x\, dx$ and $v = \frac{1}{3}\sin 3x$, and

$$\int_0^{\pi/6}\cos 3x\cos 2x\, dx = \frac{1}{3}[\cos 2x\sin 3x]\Big|_0^{\pi/6} - \int_0^{\pi/6}\frac{1}{3}\sin 3x(-2\sin 2x\, dx)$$

$$= \frac{1}{3}\left(\cos\frac{\pi}{3}\sin\frac{\pi}{2} - \cos 0\sin 0\right) + \frac{2}{3}\int_0^{\pi/6}\sin 2x\sin 3x\, dx$$

$$= \frac{1}{6} + \frac{2}{3}\int_0^{\pi/6}\sin 2x\sin 3x\, dx.$$

Thus

$$\int_0^{\pi/6}\sin 2x\sin 3x\, dx = \frac{2}{3}\left(\frac{1}{6} + \frac{2}{3}\int_0^{\pi/6}\sin 2x\sin 3x\, dx\right) \implies$$

$$\int_0^{\pi/6}\sin 2x\sin 3x\, dx = \frac{1}{9} + \frac{4}{9}\int_0^{\pi/6}\sin 2x\sin 3x\, dx \implies$$

$$\frac{5}{9}\int_0^{\pi/6}\sin 2x\sin 3x\, dx = \frac{1}{9} \implies \int_0^{\pi/6}\sin 2x\sin 3x\, dx = \frac{1/9}{5/9} = \frac{1}{5}.$$

35. Evaluate $\displaystyle\int e^{\sqrt{x}}\, dx$.

SOLUTION: Let $w = \sqrt{x}$. Then $dw = \frac{1}{2}x^{-1/2}\, dx$ and $2\sqrt{x}\, dw = 2w\, dw = dx$, so $\displaystyle\int e^{\sqrt{x}}\, dx = \int e^w(2w\, dw) = 2\int we^w\, dw$. Let $u = w$ and $dv = e^w\, dw$. Then $du = dw$ and $v = e^w$, so $\displaystyle\int we^w\, dw = we^w - \int e^w\, dw = we^w - e^w + C$. Thus $\displaystyle\int e^{\sqrt{x}}\, dx = 2(we^w - e^w + C) = 2e^w(w - 1) + C = 2e^{\sqrt{x}}(\sqrt{x} - 1) + C$.

39. Evaluate $\displaystyle\int x3^x\, dx$.

SOLUTION: Let $u = x$ and $dv = 3^x\, dx$. Then $du = dx$ and $v = \frac{1}{\ln 3}3^x$, so $\displaystyle\int x3^x\, dx = \frac{x}{\ln 3}3^x - \int\frac{1}{\ln 3}3^x\, dx = \frac{x}{\ln 3}3^x - \frac{1}{(\ln 3)^2}3^x + C$.

45. Evaluate $\displaystyle\int \ln(x + \sqrt{x^2 + 1})\, dx$.

SOLUTION: Let $u = \ln(x + \sqrt{x^2 + 1})$ and $dv = dx$. Then

$$du = \frac{1}{x + \sqrt{x^2 + 1}}\left(1 + \frac{1}{2}(x^2 + 1)^{-1/2}(2x)\right) dx = \frac{1 + \dfrac{x}{\sqrt{x^2 + 1}}}{x + \sqrt{x^2 + 1}}\, dx = \frac{1}{\sqrt{x^2 + 1}}\, dx$$

and $v = x$, so

$$\int \ln(x + \sqrt{x^2 + 1})\, dx = x \ln(x + \sqrt{x^2 + 1}) - \int x \frac{1}{\sqrt{x^2 + 1}}\, dx.$$

Let $w = x^2 + 1$. Then $dw = 2x\, dx$ and $\dfrac{1}{2}\, dw = x\, dx$. Thus

$$\int x(x^2 + 1)^{-1/2}\, dx = \int w^{-1/2}\left(\frac{1}{2}\, dw\right) = \frac{1}{2}\int w^{-1/2}\, dw = w^{1/2} + C = \sqrt{x^2 + 1} + C.$$

Thus $\displaystyle\int \ln(x + \sqrt{x^2 + 1})\, dx = x \ln(x + \sqrt{x^2 + 1}) - \sqrt{x^2 + 1} + C.$

51. Determine the area of the region bounded by $y = \arctan x$, $x = -1$, $x = 1$, $y = 0$. Sketch a graph of the region.

SOLUTION:

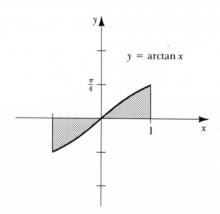

To calculate the area, evaluate $\displaystyle -\int_{-1}^{0} \arctan x\, dx + \int_{0}^{1} \arctan x\, dx = 2\int_{0}^{1} \arctan x\, dx$ since $f(x) = \arctan x$ is symmetric with respect to the origin, and $\arctan x < 0$ for $-1 < x < 0$. Let $u = \arctan x$ and $dv = dx$. Then $du = \dfrac{dx}{1 + x^2}$ and $v = x$, so

$$2\int_{0}^{1} \arctan x\, dx = 2\left([x \arctan x]\Big|_{0}^{1} - \int_{0}^{1} \frac{x}{1 + x^2}\, dx\right) = 2\left((\arctan 1 - 0) - \int_{0}^{1} x(1 + x^2)^{-1}\, dx\right).$$

To evaluate $\int_0^1 x(1+x^2)^{-1}\,dx$, let $w = 1+x^2$. Then $dw = 2x\,dx$ and $\frac{1}{2}\,dw = x\,dx$, so the integral

becomes $\int_{x=0}^{x=1} w^{-1}\left(\frac{1}{2}\,dw\right) = \frac{1}{2}\ln|w|\Big|_{x=0}^{x=1} = \frac{1}{2}[\ln(1+x^2)]\Big|_0^1 = \frac{1}{2}(\ln 2 - \ln 1)$. Thus

$$A = 2\int_0^1 \arctan x\,dx = 2\left(\frac{\pi}{4} - \frac{1}{2}\ln 2\right) = \frac{\pi}{2} - \ln 2.$$

57. Use the Method of Disks to determine the volume generated if the region bounded by $y = \ln x$, $y = \dfrac{x-1}{e-1}$ and $y = 0$ is revolved about the x-axis.

SOLUTION: First sketch the region and determine the limits of integration.

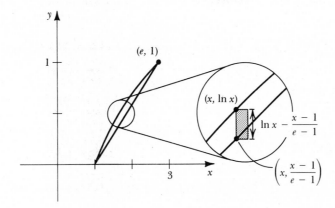

The points of intersection are $(1,0)$ and $(e,1)$. The desired volume can be characterized by the integral

$$\int_1^3 \left(\pi(\ln x)^2 - \pi\left(\frac{x-1}{e-1}\right)^2\right)dx = \pi\left(\int_1^e (\ln x)^2\,dx - \frac{1}{(e-1)^2}\int_1^e (x-1)^2\,dx\right).$$

Consider $\int_1^e (\ln x)^2\,dx$. Let $u = (\ln x)^2$ and $dv = dx$. Then $du = 2\ln x\left(\frac{1}{x}\right)$ and $v = x$, so

$$\int_1^e (\ln x)^2\,dx = \left[x(\ln x)^2\right]\Big|_1^e - \int_1^e 2\ln x\left(\frac{1}{x}\right)(x\,dx)$$

$$= (e(\ln e)^2 - (\ln 1)^2) - 2\int_1^e \ln x\,dx.$$

To evaluate $\int_1^e \ln x\,dx$, let $u = \ln x$ and $dv = dx$. Then $du = \frac{1}{x}\,dx$ and $v = x$, and $\int_1^e \ln x\,dx =$
$[x\ln x]\Big|_1^e - \int_1^e x\left(\frac{1}{x}\,dx\right) = (e\ln e - \ln 1) - \int_1^e dx = e - [x]\Big|_1^e = e - (e-1) = 1$. Thus $\int_1^e (\ln x)^2\,dx =$
$e - 2(1) = e - 2$.

Also $\displaystyle\int_1^e (x-1)^2\,dx = \frac{1}{3}\left[(x-1)^3\right]\Big|_1^e = \frac{1}{3}\left((e-1)^3 - 0\right) = \frac{1}{3}(e-1)^3.$

$$V = \pi\left(e - 2 - \frac{1}{(e-1)^2}\left(\frac{1}{3}(e-1)^3\right)\right) = \pi\left(e - 2 - \frac{1}{3}(e-1)\right) = \pi\left(\frac{2}{3}e - \frac{5}{3}\right) = \frac{\pi}{3}(2e - 5).$$

65. Derive the reduction formula $\displaystyle\int (\ln x)^n\,dx = x(\ln x)^n - n\int (\ln x)^{n-1}\,dx.$

SOLUTION: Let $u = (\ln x)^n$ and $dv = dx$. Then $du = n(\ln x)^{n-1}\left(\dfrac{1}{x}\,dx\right)$ and $v = x + C$.

Thus $\displaystyle\int (\ln x)^n\,dx = x(\ln x)^n - \int xn(\ln x)^{n-1}\left(\frac{1}{x}\,dx\right) = x(\ln x)^n - n\int (\ln x)^{n-1}\,dx$, which is the desired result.

_____7.2

Integrals of Products of Trigonometric Functions

3. Evaluate $\displaystyle\int_0^{\pi/2} \sin^2 2x \cos^3 2x\,dx.$

SOLUTION:

$$\int_0^{\pi/2} \sin^2 2x \cos^3 2x\,dx = \int_0^{\pi/2} \sin^2 2x \cos^2 2x \cos 2x\,dx$$

$$= \int_0^{\pi/2} \sin^2 2x \left(1 - \sin^2 2x\right)\cos 2x\,dx = \int_0^{\pi/2} \left(\sin^2 2x - \sin^4 2x\right)\cos 2x\,dx.$$

Let $u = \sin 2x$. Then $du = 2\cos 2x\,dx$ and $\dfrac{1}{2}\,du = \cos 2x\,dx$. When $x = 0$, $u = \sin 0 = 0$ and

when $x = \dfrac{\pi}{2}$, $u = \sin 2\left(\dfrac{\pi}{2}\right) = 0$. Thus $\displaystyle\int_0^{\pi/2} \sin^2 2x \cos^3 2x\,dx = \int_0^0 (u^2 - u^4)\left(\frac{1}{2}\,du\right) = 0$ due to the limits of integration.

9. Evaluate $\displaystyle\int_0^\pi \cos^4 5x\,dx.$

SOLUTION:

$$\int_0^\pi \cos^4 5x\,dx = \int_0^\pi \left(\cos^2 5x\right)^2\,dx = \int_0^\pi \left(\frac{1 + \cos 2(5x)}{2}\right)^2\,dx$$

$$= \frac{1}{4} \int_0^\pi \left(1 + 2\cos 10x + \cos^2 10x\right) dx = \frac{1}{4} \int_0^\pi \left(1 + 2\cos 10x + \frac{1}{2} + \frac{1}{2}\cos 20x\right) dx$$

$$= \frac{1}{4}\left(\left[\frac{3}{2}x\right]\Big|_0^\pi + 2\left[\frac{1}{10}\sin 10x\right]\Big|_0^\pi + \frac{1}{2}\left[\frac{1}{20}\sin 20x\right]\Big|_0^\pi\right)$$

$$= \frac{1}{4}\left(\frac{3}{2}\pi + \frac{1}{5}\left(\sin 10\pi - \sin 0\right) + \frac{1}{40}\left(\sin 20\pi - \sin 0\right)\right) = \frac{3\pi}{8}.$$

15. Evaluate $\int \sec^4 x \tan^3 x \, dx$.

SOLUTION:

$$\int \sec^4 x \tan^3 x \, dx = \int \sec^2 x \sec^2 x \tan^3 x \, dx$$

$$= \int \sec^2 x \left(1 + \tan^2 x\right) \tan^3 x \, dx = \int \sec^2 x \left(\tan^3 x + \tan^5 x\right) dx.$$

Let $u = \tan x$. Then $du = \sec^2 x \, dx$ and the integral becomes $\int \left(u^3 + u^5\right) du = \frac{1}{4}u^4 + \frac{1}{6}u^6 + C = \frac{1}{4}\tan^4 x + \frac{1}{6}\tan^6 x + C.$

21. Evaluate $\int \cot^5 x \csc x \, dx$.

SOLUTION:

$$\int \cot^5 x \csc x \, dx = \int \left(\cot^2 x\right)^2 \cot x \csc x \, dx$$

$$= \int \left(\csc^2 x - 1\right)^2 \cot x \csc x \, dx$$

$$= \int \left(\csc^4 x - 2\csc^2 x + 1\right) \cot x \csc x \, dx.$$

Let $u = \csc x$. Then $du = -\csc x \cot x \, dx$, and the integral becomes

$$\int -(u^4 - 2u^2 + 1) du = -\left(\frac{1}{5}u^5 - \frac{2}{3}u^3 + u\right) + C = -\left(\frac{1}{5}\csc^5 x - \frac{2}{3}\csc^3 x + \csc x\right) + C.$$

31. Evaluate $\int \cos^2 x \tan x \, dx$.

SOLUTION:

$$\int \cos^2 x \tan x \, dx = \int \cos^2 x \left(\frac{\sin x}{\cos x}\right) dx = \int \cos x \sin x \, dx = \int \frac{1}{2}\sin 2x \, dx$$

$$= \frac{1}{2}\left(-\frac{1}{2}\cos 2x\right) + C = -\frac{1}{4}\cos 2x + C.$$

39. Evaluate $\displaystyle\int \frac{\cot x}{\csc^4 x}\,dx$.

SOLUTION:

$$\int \frac{\cot x}{\csc^4 x}\,dx = \int \frac{\cos x/\sin x}{1/\sin^4 x}\,dx = \int \sin^3 x \cos x\,dx.$$

Let $u = \sin x$. Then $du = \cos x\,dx$ and the integral becomes $\displaystyle\int u^3\,du = \frac{1}{4}u^4 + C = \frac{1}{4}\sin^4 x + C.$

43. Evaluate $\displaystyle\int \sin 2x \cos 3x\,dx$.

SOLUTION: Use the trigonometric identity $\sin a \cos b = \dfrac{1}{2}(\sin(a+b) + \sin(a-b))$ and rewrite the integral as

$$\int \sin 2x \cos 3x\,dx = \int \frac{1}{2}(\sin(2x+3x) + \sin(2x-3x))\,dx$$

$$= \frac{1}{2}\int(\sin 5x + \sin(-x))\,dx = \frac{1}{2}\int(\sin 5x - \sin x)\,dx$$

$$= \frac{1}{2}\left(-\frac{1}{5}\cos 5x + \cos x\right) + C.$$

Note that $\sin(-x) = -\sin x$ since $f(x) = \sin x$ is an odd function.

53. Use the Method of Disks to determine the volume generated by revolving the region bounded by $y = \tan x$, $y = 0$ and $x = \pi/4$ about the x-axis.

SOLUTION:

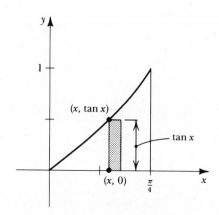

$$V = \int_0^\pi \pi \tan^2 x \, dx = \pi \int_0^\pi (\sec^2 x - 1) \, dx = \pi [\tan x - x] \Big|_0^{\pi/4}$$

$$= \pi \left(\left(\tan \frac{\pi}{4} - \frac{\pi}{4} \right) - (\tan 0 - 0) \right) = \pi \left(1 - \frac{\pi}{4} \right).$$

55. Derive the reduction formula

$$\int (\sin x)^n \, dx = -\frac{1}{n}(\sin x)^{n-1} \cos x + \frac{n-1}{n} \int (\sin x)^{n-2} \, dx.$$

SOLUTION: Let $u = (\sin x)^{n-1}$ and $dv = \sin x \, dx$. Then $du = (n-1)(\sin x)^{n-2} \cos x \, dx$ and $v = -\cos x + C$. So

$$\int (\sin x)^n \, dx = -(\sin x)^{n-1} \cos x - \int (n-1)(\sin x)^{n-2}(-\cos x)^2 \, dx$$

$$= -(\sin x)^{n-1} \cos x + (n-1) \int (\sin x)^{n-2}(\cos x)^2 \, dx$$

$$= -(\sin x)^{n-1} \cos x + (n-1) \int (\sin x)^{n-2} \left(1 - (\sin x)^2\right) \, dx$$

$$= -(\sin x)^{n-1} \cos x + (n-1) \left(\int (\sin x)^{n-2} \, dx - \int (\sin x)^n \, dx \right).$$

Now

$$\int (\sin x)^n \, dx = -(\sin x)^{n-1} \cos x + (n-1) \int (\sin x)^{n-2} \, dx - (n-1) \int (\sin x)^n \, dx \implies$$

$$n \int (\sin x)^n \, dx = -(\sin x)^{n-1} \cos x + (n-1) \int (\sin x)^{n-2} \, dx \implies$$

$$\int (\sin x)^n \, dx = -\frac{1}{n}(\sin x)^{n-1} \cos x + \frac{n-1}{n} \int (\sin x)^{n-2} \, dx,$$

which is the desired reduction formula.

61. Find the centroid of the homogeneous lamina that is bounded by the graphs of

$y = \sin x$, $y = \cos x$, $x = 0$ and $x = \pi/4$.

SOLUTION:

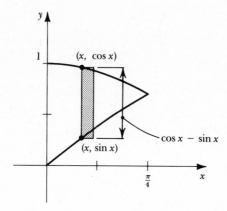

$$\bar{x} = \frac{\displaystyle\int_0^\pi x(\cos x - \sin x)\,dx}{\displaystyle\int_0^\pi (\cos x - \sin x)\,dx} \quad \text{and} \quad \bar{y} = \frac{\displaystyle\int_0^\pi \left(\cos^2 x - \sin^2 x\right)\,dx}{2\displaystyle\int_0^\pi (\cos x - \sin x)\,dx}.$$

Evaluate the integrals one at a time. For the first integral let $u = x$, $dv = (\cos x - \sin x)\,dx$. Then $du = dx$, $v = \sin x + \cos x$ and

$$\int_0^{\pi/4} x(\cos x - \sin x)\,dx = \left[x(\sin x + \cos x) - \int (\sin x + \cos x)\,dx \right]\Bigg|_0^{\pi/4}$$

$$= \left[x(\sin x + \cos x) - (-\cos x + \sin x) \right]\Bigg|_0^{\pi/4}$$

$$= \left(\frac{\pi}{4}\left(\sin\frac{\pi}{4} + \cos\frac{\pi}{4} \right) - \left(-\cos\frac{\pi}{4} + \sin\frac{\pi}{4} \right) \right) - (0 - (-\cos 0 + \sin 0))$$

$$= \frac{\pi\sqrt{2}}{4} - 1.$$

Next,

$$\int_0^\pi \left(\cos^2 x - \sin^2 x \right)\,dx = \int_0^\pi \cos 2x\,dx = \left[\frac{1}{2}\sin 2x \right]\Bigg|_0^{\pi/4}$$

$$= \frac{1}{2}\left(\sin\frac{\pi}{2} - \sin 0 \right) = \frac{1}{2}.$$

Finally, $\int_0^\pi (\cos x - \sin x)\, dx = [\sin x + \cos x]\Big|_0^{\pi/4} = \left(\sin \dfrac{\pi}{4} + \cos \dfrac{\pi}{4}\right) - (\sin 0 + \cos 0) = \sqrt{2} - 1.$

So

$$\bar{x} = \dfrac{\dfrac{\pi\sqrt{2}}{4} - 1}{\sqrt{2} - 1} = \dfrac{\pi\sqrt{2} - 4}{4(\sqrt{2} - 1)} \cdot \dfrac{\sqrt{2} + 1}{\sqrt{2} + 1}$$

$$= \dfrac{2\pi + (\pi - 4)\sqrt{2} - 4}{4} \qquad \text{and}$$

$$\bar{y} = \dfrac{\dfrac{1}{2}}{2(\sqrt{2} - 1)} = \dfrac{1}{4(\sqrt{2} - 1)} \cdot \dfrac{\sqrt{2} + 1}{\sqrt{2} + 1} = \dfrac{\sqrt{2} + 1}{4}.$$

Thus the centroid is $\left(\dfrac{2(\pi - 2) + (\pi - 4)\sqrt{2}}{4}, \dfrac{\sqrt{2} + 1}{4}\right).$

—— **7.3**

Trigonometric Substitution

13. Evaluate $\displaystyle\int_1^2 \dfrac{\sqrt{x^2 - 1}}{x}\, dx.$

SOLUTION: Let $x = \sec\theta$. Then $dx = \sec\theta \tan\theta\, d\theta$ and $\theta = \operatorname{arcsec} x$. Now $x = 1 \implies \theta = \operatorname{arcsec} 1 = 0$ and $x = 2 \implies \theta = \operatorname{arcsec} 2 = \pi/3$. Thus

$$\int_1^2 \dfrac{\sqrt{x^2 - 1}}{x}\, dx = \int_0^{\pi/3} \dfrac{\sqrt{\sec^2\theta - 1}}{\sec\theta} \sec\theta \tan\theta\, d\theta$$

$$= \int_0^{\pi/3} \sqrt{\tan^2\theta} \tan\theta\, d\theta = \int_0^{\pi/3} |\tan\theta| \tan\theta\, d\theta = \int_0^{\pi/3} \tan^2\theta\, d\theta.$$

Note that since $0 \le \theta \le \pi/3$, $\tan\theta \ge 0$ and thus $|\tan\theta| = \tan\theta$. So

$$\int_0^{\pi/3} \tan^2\theta\, d\theta = \int_0^{\pi/3} (\sec^2\theta - 1)\, d\theta$$

$$= [\tan\theta - \theta]\Big|_0^{\pi/3} = \left(\tan\dfrac{\pi}{3} - \dfrac{\pi}{3}\right) - (\tan 0 - 0) = \sqrt{3} - \dfrac{\pi}{3}.$$

19. Evaluate $\displaystyle\int_0^\infty \frac{1}{(x+1)^2 + 1}\, dx$.

SOLUTION: Let $x + 1 = \tan\theta$. Then $dx = \sec^2\theta\, d\theta$ and $\theta = \arctan(x+1)$. Now as $x \to \infty$, $\theta \to \pi/2$ and $x = 0 \implies \theta = \arctan 1 = \pi/4$. Thus

$$\int_0^\infty \frac{1}{(x+1)^2 + 1}\, dx = \int_{\pi/4}^{\pi/2} \frac{1}{\tan^2\theta + 1}\, \sec^2\theta\, d\theta$$

$$= \int_{\pi/4}^{\pi/2} \frac{1}{\sec^2\theta}\, \sec^2\theta\, d\theta = \int_{\pi/4}^{\pi/2} d\theta = [\theta]\Big|_{\pi/4}^{\pi/2} = \frac{\pi}{2} - \frac{\pi}{4} = \frac{\pi}{4}.$$

25. Evaluate $\displaystyle\int e^x \sqrt{1 - e^{2x}}\, dx$.

SOLUTION: Since $\displaystyle\int e^x\sqrt{1 - e^{2x}}\, dx = \int \sqrt{1 - (e^x)^2}\, e^x\, dx$ contains a factor of the form $\sqrt{a^2 - u^2}$, let $e^x = \sin\theta$. Then $e^x\, dx = \cos\theta\, d\theta$, so the integral becomes

$$\int \sqrt{1 - \sin^2\theta}\, \cos\theta\, d\theta = \int \sqrt{\cos^2\theta}\, \cos\theta\, d\theta = \int |\cos\theta|\, \cos\theta\, d\theta.$$

Now since $-\dfrac{\pi}{2} \le \arcsin x \le \dfrac{\pi}{2}$ and $\theta = \arcsin e^x$, $0 < \theta \le \dfrac{\pi}{2}$ for $e^x \ge 0$. Thus $\cos\theta \ge 0$ and $|\cos\theta| = \cos\theta$ and the integral becomes

$$\int \cos^2\theta\, d\theta = \int \frac{1 + \cos 2\theta}{2}\, d\theta = \frac{1}{2}\Big(\theta + \frac{1}{2}\sin 2\theta\Big) + C$$

$$= \frac{1}{2}(\theta + \sin\theta\cos\theta) = \frac{1}{2}\left(\arcsin e^x + \sin(\arcsin e^x)\cos(\arcsin e^x)\right) + C$$

$$= \frac{1}{2}\left(\arcsin e^x + e^x\sqrt{1 - e^{2x}}\right) + C,$$

since $\cos(\arcsin e^x) = \sqrt{1 - (\sin(\arcsin e^x))^2} = \sqrt{1 - (e^x)^2} = \sqrt{1 - e^{2x}}$.

29. Find the area of the region bounded by $y = \dfrac{1}{x^2 + 1}$, the x-axis, and the lines $x = -2$ and $x = 2$.

SOLUTION:

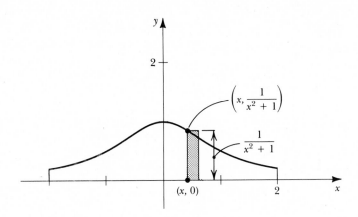

Since $f(x) = \dfrac{1}{x^2+1}$ is even, $(f(-x) = f(x))$ and thus its graph is symmetric with respect to the y-axis; the area bounded by the curve and the x-axis between $x = -2$ and $x = 2$ is twice the area bounded by the curve and the x-axis between $x = 0$ and $x = 2$. Thus the area is characterized by the integral $2 \displaystyle\int_0^1 \dfrac{1}{x^2+1}\, dx$.

Let $x = \tan\theta$. Then $dx = \sec^2\theta\, d\theta$, $x = 0 \implies \theta = \arctan 0 = 0$ and $x = 2 \implies \theta = \arctan 2$. Thus

$$A = 2\int_0^{\arctan 2} \frac{1}{\tan^2\theta + 1}\sec^2\theta\, d\theta = 2\int_0^{\arctan 2} d\theta$$

$$= [2\theta]\Big|_0^{\arctan 2} = 2(\arctan 2 - \arctan 0) = 2\arctan 2 \approx 2.21.$$

37. Find the arc length of the graph of $f(x) = \ln x$ from $x = 1$ to $x = e$.

SOLUTION: $L = \displaystyle\int_a^b \sqrt{(dx)^2 + (dy)^2}$ so

$$L = \int_1^e \sqrt{1 + \frac{1}{x^2}}\, dx = \int_1^e \sqrt{\frac{x^2+1}{x^2}}\, dx = \int_1^e \frac{\sqrt{x^2+1}}{|x|}\, dx = \int_1^e \frac{\sqrt{x^2+1}}{x}\, dx$$

since $1 \le x \le e$.

Since the integral contains a factor of the form $\sqrt{x^2 + a^2}$, let $x = a\tan\theta = \tan\theta$. So $dx = \sec^2\theta\, d\theta$, $x = 1 \implies \theta = \arctan 1 = \pi/4$ and $x = e \implies \theta = \arctan e$. Thus the integral becomes

$$\int_{\pi/4}^{\arctan e} \frac{\sqrt{\tan^2\theta + 1}}{\tan\theta}\sec^2\theta\, d\theta = \int_{\pi/4}^{\arctan e} \frac{|\sec\theta|}{\tan\theta}\sec^2\theta\, d\theta = \int_{\pi/4}^{\arctan e} \frac{\sec^3\theta}{\tan\theta}\, d\theta$$

since $\frac{\pi}{4} \leq \theta \leq \arctan e \implies \sec \theta > 0$. So

$$\int_{\pi/4}^{\arctan e} \frac{\sec^3 \theta}{\tan \theta} \, d\theta = \int_{\pi/4}^{\arctan e} \frac{\sec \theta (\tan^2 \theta + 1)}{\tan \theta} \, d\theta$$

$$= \int_{\pi/4}^{\arctan e} \left(\sec \theta \tan \theta + \frac{\sec \theta}{\tan \theta} \right) d\theta = \left[\sec \theta \right] \Big|_{\pi/4}^{\arctan e} + \int_{\pi/4}^{\arctan e} \csc \theta \, d\theta$$

$$= \sec(\arctan e) - \sec \frac{\pi}{4} + \int_{\pi/4}^{\arctan e} \frac{\csc \theta (\csc \theta - \cot \theta)}{\csc \theta - \cot \theta} \, d\theta$$

$$= \sqrt{e^2 + 1} - \sqrt{2} + \ln |\csc \theta - \cot \theta| \, \Big|_{\pi/4}^{\arctan e}$$

$$= \sqrt{e^2 + 1} - \sqrt{2} + \left(\ln |\csc(\arctan e) - \cot(\arctan e)| - \ln \left| \csc \frac{\pi}{4} - \cot \frac{\pi}{4} \right| \right)$$

$$= \sqrt{e^2 + 1} - \sqrt{2} + \ln \left| \frac{\sqrt{e^2 + 1}}{e} - \frac{1}{e} \right| - \ln |\sqrt{2} - 1|$$

$$= \sqrt{e^2 + 1} - \sqrt{2} + \ln \left| \sqrt{e^2 + 1} - 1 \right| - \ln e - \ln(\sqrt{2} - 1)$$

$$= \sqrt{e^2 + 1} - \sqrt{2} - 1 + \ln \left(\frac{-1 + \sqrt{e^2 + 1}}{\sqrt{2} - 1} \right).$$

41. The velocity of an object moving along a straight line is given by $v(t) = \sqrt{25 - t^2}$ cm/sec. Find the distance traveled by the object during the time interval $[0, 5]$.

SOLUTION: The distance traveled, $s(t)$, is characterized by $\int_0^5 \sqrt{(5)^2 - t^2} \, dt$. Since the integral contains a factor of the form $\sqrt{a^2 - t^2}$, let $t = a \sin \theta = 5 \sin \theta$. Then $dt = 5 \cos \theta \, d\theta$, $t = 0 \implies \theta = \sin^{-1} \frac{0}{5} = 0$ and $t = 5 \implies \theta = \sin^{-1} \frac{5}{5} = \frac{\pi}{2}$. So

$$s = \int_0^{\pi/2} \sqrt{25 - (5 \sin \theta)^2} (5 \cos \theta \, d\theta) = 25 \int_0^{\pi/2} \sqrt{\cos^2 \theta} \cos \theta \, d\theta$$

$$= 25 \int_0^{\pi/2} |\cos \theta| \cos \theta \, d\theta = 25 \int_0^{\pi/2} \cos^2 \theta \, d\theta.$$

Since $0 \leq \theta \leq \frac{\pi}{2}$, $\cos \theta \geq 0$ and $|\cos \theta| = \cos \theta$. Continuing,

$$25 \int_0^{\pi/2} \cos^2 \theta \, d\theta = 25 \int_0^{\pi/2} \frac{1 + \cos 2\theta}{2} \, d\theta = \frac{25}{2} \left[\theta + \frac{1}{2} \sin 2\theta \right] \Big|_0^{\pi/2}$$

$$= \frac{25}{2}\left(\left(\frac{\pi}{2}+\frac{1}{2}\sin\pi\right)-\left(0+\frac{1}{2}\sin 0\right)\right)=\frac{25\pi}{4}.$$

Thus the distance traveled is $\dfrac{25\pi}{4}$ cm.

45. Find the volume of the torus generated by revolving about the y-axis the circle with equation $(x-2)^2+y^2=1$.

SOLUTION: The graph of $(x-2)^2+y^2=1$ is a circle with center at $(2,0)$ and radius 1.

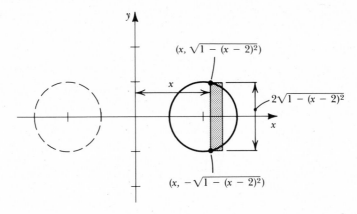

Use a shell with height $2\sqrt{1-(x-2)^2}$ and radius of revolution x to obtain

$$V=\int_1^3 2\pi x 2\sqrt{1-(x-2)^2}\,dx.$$

Since the integral contains the factor of the form $\sqrt{1-(x-2)^2}$, let $x-2=\sin\theta$ with $x=2+\sin\theta$ and $dx=\cos\theta\,d\theta$; $x=1\implies x-2=-1\implies\theta=-\pi/2$ and $x=3\implies x-2=1\implies\theta=\pi/2$. The integral is thus

$$V=4\pi\int_{-\pi/2}^{\pi/2}(2+\sin\theta)\sqrt{1-\sin^2\theta}\,\cos\theta\,d\theta=4\pi\int_{-\pi/2}^{\pi/2}(2+\sin\theta)\cos^2\theta\,d\theta$$

$$=4\pi\int_{-\pi/2}^{\pi/2}(1+\cos 2\theta+\cos^2\theta\sin\theta)d\theta$$

$$=4\pi\left[\theta+\frac{1}{2}\sin 2\theta-\frac{\cos^3\theta}{3}\right]\Bigg|_{-\pi/2}^{\pi/2}=4\pi^2.$$

_____7.4
Partial Fractions
_____

3. Evaluate $\displaystyle\int_3^4 \frac{1}{x^2 - 3x + 2}\, dx$.

SOLUTION: Since $\displaystyle\int_3^4 \frac{1}{x^2 - 3x + 2}\, dx = \int_3^4 \frac{1}{(x-2)(x-1)}\, dx$, $\dfrac{1}{x^2 - 3x + 2}$ has a partial fraction decomposition of the form $\dfrac{A}{x-2} + \dfrac{B}{x-1}$. Then

$$\frac{A}{x-2} + \frac{B}{x-1} = \frac{A(x-1) + B(x-2)}{(x-2)(x-1)} = \frac{(A+B)x + (-A - 2B)}{(x-2)(x-1)}.$$

Since $(A+B)x + (-A - 2B) = 0x + 1$, $A + B = 0$ and $-A - 2B = 1$.
Now $A + B = 0 \implies A = -B$, so $-(-B) - 2B = 1 \implies -B = 1 \implies B = -1$ and $A = 1$.
Thus

$$\int_3^4 \frac{1}{x^2 - 3x + 2}\, dx = \int_3^4 \left(\frac{1}{x-2} + \frac{-1}{x-1} \right) dx$$

$$= \int_3^4 \frac{dx}{x-2} - \int_3^4 \frac{dx}{x-1} = \ln|x-2| \Big|_3^4 - \ln|x-1| \Big|_3^4$$

$$= (\ln 2 - \ln 1) - (\ln 3 - \ln 2) = \ln 2 - \ln 3 + \ln 2 = \ln \frac{4}{3}.$$

9. Evaluate $\displaystyle\int \frac{x^3 + x^2 + x}{x^2 + 2x + 1}\, dx$.

SOLUTION: Since the degree of the numerator is greater than the degree of the denominator, simplify using polynomial long division. Thus

$$\int \frac{x^3 + x^2 + x}{x^2 + 2x + 1}\, dx = \int \left(x - 1 + \frac{2x+1}{x^2 + 2x + 1} \right) dx$$

$$= \int (x-1)\, dx + \int \frac{2x+1}{(x+1)^2}\, dx = \frac{1}{2}x^2 - x + C + \int \frac{2x+1}{(x+1)^2}\, dx.$$

Now $\dfrac{2x+1}{(x+1)^2}$ has a decomposition of the form $\dfrac{A}{x+1} + \dfrac{B}{(x+1)^2}$. Then

$$\frac{A}{x+1} + \frac{B}{(x+1)^2} = \frac{A(x+1) + B}{(x+1)^2} = \frac{Ax + (B+A)}{(x+1)^2}$$

and $Ax + (B + A) = 2x + 1 \implies A + B = 1$ and $A = 2$. But $A = 2 \implies B = -1$, so

$$\int \frac{2x + 1}{(x + 1)^2} \, dx = \int \left(\frac{2}{x + 1} + \frac{-1}{(x + 1)^2} \right) dx$$

$$= 2 \int \frac{dx}{x + 1} - \int \frac{dx}{(x + 1)^2} = 2 \ln |x + 1| + C - \int \frac{dx}{(x + 1)^2}.$$

To evaluate $\int \frac{dx}{(x + 1)^2}$, let $u = x + 1$. Then $du = dx$. Thus the integral becomes

$$\int \frac{du}{u^2} = \int u^{-2} \, du = -u^{-1} + C = \frac{-1}{x + 1} + C.$$

Thus

$$\int \frac{x^3 + x^2 + x}{x^2 + 2x + 1} \, dx = \frac{1}{2}x^2 - x + 2 \ln |x + 1| + \frac{1}{x + 1} + C$$

$$= \frac{1}{2}x^2 - x + \frac{1}{x + 1} + \ln(x + 1)^2 + C.$$

17. Evaluate $\int \frac{1}{x^3 + x^2 + x + 1} \, dx$.

SOLUTION:

$$\int \frac{1}{x^3 + x^2 + x + 1} \, dx = \int \frac{1}{x^2(x + 1) + (x + 1)} \, dx = \int \frac{dx}{(x^2 + 1)(x + 1)}.$$

Now $\dfrac{1}{(x^2 + 1)(x + 1)}$ has a decomposition of the form $\dfrac{A}{x + 1} + \dfrac{B}{x^2 + 1} + \dfrac{Cx}{x^2 + 1}$ and

$$\frac{A}{x + 1} + \frac{B}{x^2 + 1} + \frac{Cx}{x^2 + 1} = \frac{A(x^2 + 1) + B(x + 1) + Cx(x + 1)}{(x + 1)(x^2 + 1)}$$

$$= \frac{(A + C)x^2 + (B + C)x + (A + B)}{(x + 1)(x^2 + 1)}.$$

Now $(A + C)x^2 + (B + C)x + (A + B) = 0x^2 + 0x + 1 \implies A = -C$, $B = -C$ and $A + B = 1$. But $A = -C$ and $B = -C \implies A = B$ so $2A = 1$ and $A = 1/2$. Thus

$$\int \frac{dx}{x^3 + x^2 + x + 1} = \int \left(\frac{1/2}{x + 1} + \frac{1/2}{x^2 + 1} + \frac{(-1/2)x}{x^2 + 1} \right) dx$$

$$= \frac{1}{2} \left(\int \frac{dx}{x + 1} + \int \frac{dx}{x^2 + 1} - \int \frac{x}{x^2 + 1} \right) dx.$$

Evaluating the integrals separately,

$$\int \frac{dx}{x+1} = \ln|x+1| + C.$$

$$\int \frac{dx}{x^2+1} = \arctan x + C.$$

To evaluate $\int x(x^2+1)^{-1}\,dx$, let $u = x^2+1$. Then $du = 2x\,dx$ and

$$\int x(x^2+1)^{-1}\,dx = \frac{1}{2}\int u^{-1}\,du = \frac{1}{2}\ln|u| + C = \frac{1}{2}\ln|x^2+1| + C = \ln\sqrt{x^2+1} + C.$$

Thus

$$\int \frac{1}{x^3+x^2+x+1}\,dx = \frac{1}{2}\left(\ln|x+1| - \ln\sqrt{x^2+1} + \arctan x\right) + C.$$

27. Evaluate $\displaystyle\int \frac{\cos x}{\sin x(\sin x - 1)}\,dx.$

SOLUTION: Let $u = \sin x$. Then $du = \cos x\,dx$ and the integral becomes $\displaystyle\int \frac{du}{u(u-1)}$. Now

$$\frac{1}{u(u-1)} = \frac{A}{u} + \frac{B}{u-1} = \frac{A(u-1) + Bu}{u(u-1)} = \frac{(A+B)u - A}{u(u-1)}.$$

Thus $(A+B)u - A = 0u + 1 \implies A + B = 0$ and $-A = 1$. Thus $A = -1$ and $B = 1$, so

$$\int \frac{du}{u(u-1)} = \int \left(-\frac{1}{u} + \frac{1}{u-1}\right)du = -\ln|u| + \ln|u-1| + C$$

$$= \ln\left|\frac{u-1}{u}\right| + C = \ln\left|\frac{\sin x - 1}{\sin x}\right| + C.$$

31. Evaluate $\displaystyle\int \frac{dx}{1 + \sqrt{x+1}}.$

SOLUTION: Let $u = (x+1)^{1/2}$. Then $du = \frac{1}{2}(x+1)^{-1/2}\,dx$ and $dx = 2(x+1)^{1/2}\,du = 2u\,du$.
Thus

$$\int \frac{dx}{1+\sqrt{x+1}} = \int \frac{2u\,du}{1+u} = 2\int\left(1 - \frac{1}{1+u}\right)du$$

by the use of polynomial long division. So

$$2\int\left(1 + \frac{-1}{1+u}\right)du = 2\left(u - \ln|u+1|\right) + C$$

$$= 2\left(\sqrt{x+1} - \ln\left|\sqrt{x+1} + 1\right|\right) + C = 2\left(\sqrt{x+1} - \ln(1 + \sqrt{x+1})\right) + C.$$

35. Find the volume of the solid obtained if the region described by $f(x) = \dfrac{1}{x^2 - x - 6}$ between the lines $x = 0$ and $x = 2$ (see EXERCISE 33) is revolved about the x-axis.

SOLUTION:

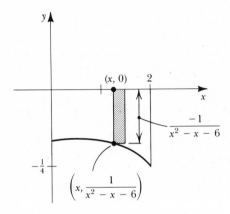

Using the Method of Disks,

$$V = \int_0^2 \pi\left(0 - \frac{1}{x^2 - x - 6}\right)^2 dx = \pi\int_0^2 \frac{1}{(x-3)^2(x+2)^2}\,dx.$$

This integral has the decomposition

$$\frac{A}{x-3} + \frac{B}{(x-3)^2} + \frac{C}{x+2} + \frac{D}{(x+2)^2}$$

$$= \frac{A(x-3)(x+2)^2 + B(x+2)^2 + C(x+2)(x-3)^2 + D(x-3)^2}{(x-3)^2(x+2)^2}.$$

Now

$$A(x-3)(x+2)^2 + B(x+2)^2 + C(x+2)(x-3)^2 + D(x-3)^2 = 1.$$

$x = 3 \implies 25B = 1 \implies B = 1/25.$ $x = -2 \implies 25D = 1 \implies D = 1/25.$

$$x = 0 \implies -12A + \frac{4}{25} + 18C + \frac{9}{25} = 1 \implies$$

$$-12A + 18C = \frac{12}{25} \implies A = -\frac{1}{12}\left(\frac{12}{25} - 18C\right) = -\frac{1}{25} + \frac{3}{2}C.$$

$$x = 1 \implies -18A + \frac{9}{25} + 12C + \frac{4}{25} = 1 \implies$$

$$-18\left(-\frac{1}{25}+\frac{3}{2}C\right)+12C=\frac{12}{25}\implies\frac{18}{25}-15C=\frac{12}{25}\implies$$

$$-15C=-\frac{6}{25}\implies C=\frac{2}{125}.$$

Thus

$$A=-\frac{1}{25}+\frac{3}{2}\cdot\frac{2}{125}=\frac{-5}{125}+\frac{3}{125}=\frac{-2}{125}.$$

So

$$V=\pi\int_0^2\left(\frac{-2/125}{x-3}+\frac{1/25}{(x-3)^2}+\frac{2/125}{x+2}+\frac{1/25}{(x+2)^2}\right)dx$$

$$=\pi\left[-\frac{2}{125}\ln|x-3|-\frac{1/25}{x-3}+\frac{2}{125}\ln|x+2|-\frac{1/25}{x+2}\right]\Bigg|_0^2$$

$$=\frac{\pi}{125}\left[2\ln\left|\frac{x+2}{x-3}\right|-\frac{5(2x-1)}{x^2-x-6}\right]\Bigg|_0^2$$

$$=\frac{\pi}{125}\left(\left(2\ln|4|+\frac{5(3)}{4}\right)-\left(2\ln\left(\frac{2}{3}\right)-\frac{5}{6}\right)\right)$$

$$=\frac{\pi}{125}\left(2\ln 6+\frac{55}{12}\right).$$

43. Evaluate $\displaystyle\int\frac{dx}{\cos x+\sin x+1}$.

SOLUTION: Use the substitutions in EXERCISE 39 to obtain

$$\int\frac{\dfrac{2\,du}{1+u^2}}{\dfrac{1-u^2}{1+u^2}+\dfrac{2u}{1+u^2}+1}=\int\frac{\dfrac{2\,du}{1+u^2}}{\dfrac{1-u^2+2u+1+u^2}{1+u^2}}=\int\frac{2\,du}{2u+2}$$

$$=\int\frac{du}{u+1}=\ln|u+1|+C=\ln\left|1+\tan\frac{x}{2}\right|+C.$$

_____**7.5**

Integrals Involving
Quadratic Polynomials

_____

3. Evaluate $\int \dfrac{1}{(x^2 + 2x + 10)^2}\, dx$.

SOLUTION: Complete the square in $x^2 + 2x + 10$ and obtain $x^2 + 2x + 1 - 1 + 10 = (x+1)^2 + 3^2$.
The integral becomes $\int \dfrac{1}{((x+1)^2 + 3^2)^2}\, dx$, which will yield to a substitution of $x + 1 = 3\tan\theta$.
Then $dx = 3\sec^2\theta\, d\theta$ and

$$\int \frac{1}{((x+1)^2 + 3^2)^2}\, dx = \int \frac{1}{((3\tan\theta)^2 + 3^2)^2} 3\sec^2\theta\, d\theta$$

$$= \int \frac{3\sec^2\theta}{(9\sec^2\theta)^2}\, d\theta = \int \frac{1}{27\sec^2\theta}\, d\theta$$

$$= \frac{1}{27}\int \cos^2\theta\, d\theta = \frac{1}{27}\int \frac{1 + \cos 2\theta}{2}\, d\theta = \frac{1}{54}\left(\theta + \frac{1}{2}\sin 2\theta\right) + C$$

$$= \frac{1}{54}\left(\arctan \frac{x+1}{3} + \sin\left(\arctan \frac{x+1}{3}\right)\cos\left(\arctan \frac{x+1}{3}\right)\right) + C$$

$$= \frac{1}{54}\left(\arctan \frac{x+1}{3} + \frac{x+1}{\sqrt{x^2 + 2x + 10}} \cdot \frac{3}{\sqrt{x^2 + 2x + 10}}\right) + C$$

$$= \frac{1}{54}\left(\arctan \frac{x+1}{3} + \frac{3(x+1)}{x^2 + 2x + 10}\right) + C.$$

15. Evaluate $\int \dfrac{x-3}{(x^2+1)(x^2+x+2)}\, dx$.

SOLUTION:

$$\frac{x-3}{(x^2+1)(x^2+x+2)} = \frac{A}{x^2+1} + \frac{Bx}{x^2+1} + \frac{C}{x^2+x+2} + \frac{Dx}{x^2+x+2}.$$

Thus

$$A(x^2 + x + 2) + Bx(x^2 + x + 2) + C(x^2 + 1) + Dx(x^2 + 1) = x - 3.$$

Now

$$x = 0 \implies 2A + C = -3 \implies C = -3 - 2A$$

$$x = 1 \implies 4A + 4B + 2C + 2D = -2 \implies$$
$$2A + 2B + C + D = -1 \implies$$
$$2A + 2B - 3 - 2A + D = -1 \implies$$
$$2B + D = 2 \implies D = 2 - 2B,$$
$$x = -1 \implies 2A - 2B + 2C - 2D = -4 \implies$$
$$A - B + C - D = -2 \implies A - B - 3 - 2A - 2 + 2B = -2 \implies$$
$$-A + B = 3 \implies B = 3 + A$$
$$x = -2 \implies 4A - 8B + 5C - 10D = -5 \implies$$
$$4A - 8(3 + A) + 5(-3 - 2A) - 10\left(2 - 2(3 + A)\right) = -5 \implies$$
$$4A - 24 - 8A - 15 - 10A - 20 + 60 + 20A = -5 \implies$$
$$6A + 1 = -5 \implies 6A = -6 \implies A = -1.$$

Thus

$$B = 3 - 1 = 2,$$
$$C = -3 - 2(-1) = -3 + 2 = -1, \qquad \text{and}$$
$$D = 2 - 2(2) = -2.$$

So

$$\int \frac{x - 3}{(x^2 + 1)(x^2 + x + 2)}\, dx$$

$$= \int \frac{-1}{x^2 + 1}\, dx + \int \frac{2x}{x^2 + 1}\, dx + \int \frac{-1}{x^2 + x + 2}\, dx + \int \frac{-2x}{x^2 + x + 2}\, dx.$$

Consider each of the integrals separately. To evaluate $\int \dfrac{dx}{x^2 + 1}$, let $x = \tan\theta$. Then $dx = \sec^2\theta\, d\theta$ and $\int \dfrac{dx}{x^2 + 1} = \arctan x + C.$

To evaluate $\int \dfrac{2x}{x^2 + 1}\, dx$, let $u = x^2 + 1$. Then $du = 2x\, dx$ and

$$\int \frac{2x}{x^2 + 1}\, dx = \int \frac{du}{u} = \ln|u| + C = \ln\left|x^2 + 1\right| + C = \ln(x^2 + 1) + C.$$

Now $\int \dfrac{-1}{x^2 + x + 2}\, dx + \int \dfrac{-2x}{x^2 + x + 2}\, dx = -\int \dfrac{2x + 1}{x^2 + x + 2}\, dx.$ Let $u = x^2 + x + 2$. Then $du = (2x + 1)\, dx$ and the integral becomes

$$-\int \frac{1}{u}\, du = -\ln|u| + C = -\ln\left|x^2 + x + 2\right| + C.$$

Thus

$$\int \frac{x-3}{(x^2+1)(x^2+x+2)}\,dx = -\arctan x + \ln(x^2+1) - \ln\left|x^2+x+2\right| + C$$

$$= -\arctan x + \ln\left|\frac{x^2+1}{x^2+x+2}\right| + C.$$

21. Evaluate $\displaystyle\int \frac{\sqrt{x}}{1+\sqrt[3]{x}}\,dx$.

SOLUTION: Let $z = x^{1/6}$. Then $z^3 = (x^{1/6})^3 = x^{1/2}$ and $z^2 = (x^{1/6})^2 = x^{1/3}$. Also $dz = \frac{1}{6}x^{-5/6}\,dx$ and $dx = 6x^{5/6}\,dz = 6z^5\,dz$. Thus

$$\int \frac{\sqrt{x}}{1+\sqrt[3]{x}}\,dx = \int \frac{z^3}{1+z^2}(6z^5\,dz) = 6\int \frac{z^8}{1+z^2}\,dz$$

$$= 6\int\left(z^6 - z^4 + z^2 - 1 + \frac{1}{1+z^2}\right)dz$$

$$= 6\left(\frac{1}{7}z^7 - \frac{1}{5}z^5 + \frac{1}{3}z^3 - z + \arctan z\right) + C$$

$$= 6\left(\frac{1}{7}x^{7/6} - \frac{1}{5}x^{5/6} + \frac{1}{3}x^{1/2} - x^{1/6} + \arctan(x^{1/6})\right) + C.$$

———**7.6**

Numerical Integration

5. Approximate $\displaystyle\int_{-1}^{1} \sin \pi x^2\,dx$ with $n = 4$ using (a) the trapezoidal rule and (b) Simpson's rule.

SOLUTION: (a) $h = \dfrac{1-(-1)}{4} = \dfrac{1}{2}$, so $x_0 = -1$, $x_1 = -1/2$, $x_2 = 0$, $x_3 = 1/2$, and $x_4 = 1$. Thus

$$\int_{-1}^{1} \sin \pi x^2\,dx \approx \frac{1/2}{2}\left(\sin\left(\pi(-1)^2\right) + 2\sin\left(\pi\left(-\frac{1}{2}\right)^2\right)\right.$$

$$\left. +2\sin\left(\pi(0)^2\right) + 2\sin\left(\pi\left(\frac{1}{2}\right)^2\right) + \sin\left(\pi(1)^2\right)\right)$$

$$= \frac{1}{4}\left(2\sin\pi + 4\sin\frac{\pi}{4} + 2\sin 0\right)$$

$$= \frac{1}{4}\left(4\left(\frac{\sqrt{2}}{2}\right)\right) \approx 0.7071.$$

(b) As in (a), $h = 1/2$ and $x_0 = -1$, $x_1 = -1/2$, $x_2 = 0$, $x_3 = 1/2$ and $x_4 = 1$. Thus

$$\int_{-1}^{1}\sin\pi x^2\, dx \approx \frac{1/2}{3}\left(\sin\left(\pi(-1)^2\right) + 4\sin\left(\pi\left(-\frac{1}{2}\right)^2\right)\right.$$

$$\left. +2\sin\left(\pi(0)^2\right) + 4\sin\left(\pi\left(\frac{1}{2}\right)^2\right) + \sin\left(\pi(1)^2\right)\right)$$

$$= \frac{1}{6}\left(2\sin\pi + 8\sin\frac{\pi}{4} + 2\sin 0\right)$$

$$= \frac{1}{6}\left(8\left(\frac{\sqrt{2}}{2}\right)\right) = \frac{2}{3}\sqrt{2} \approx 0.9428.$$

9. Use the trapezoidal rule with $n = 4$ to find an approximation to the length of the cosine curve from $x = 0$ to $x = \pi/2$.

SOLUTION: $L = \int_{a}^{b}\sqrt{(dx)^2 + (dy)^2}$ and $dy/dx = -\sin x$ so $L = \int_{0}^{\pi/2}\sqrt{1 + \sin^2 x}\, dx$. With $n = 4$, $h = \frac{\frac{\pi}{2} - 0}{4} = \frac{\pi}{8}$ and $x_0 = 0$, $x_1 = \frac{\pi}{8}$, $x_2 = \frac{\pi}{4}$, $x_3 = \frac{3\pi}{8}$ and $x_4 = \frac{\pi}{2}$. Thus

$$L \approx \frac{\pi/8}{2}\left(\sqrt{1 + (\sin 0)^2} + 2\sqrt{1 + \left(\sin\frac{\pi}{8}\right)^2}\right.$$

$$\left. +2\sqrt{1 + \left(\sin\frac{\pi}{4}\right)^2} + 2\sqrt{1 + \left(\sin\frac{3\pi}{8}\right)^2} + \sqrt{1 + \left(\sin\frac{\pi}{2}\right)^2}\right)$$

$$\approx \frac{\pi}{16}\left(1 + 2(1.0707) + 2(1.2247) + 2(1.3614) + 1.4142\right) \approx 1.9101.$$

11. Use Simpson's rule with $n = 4$ to find an approximation to the length of the cosine curve from $x = 0$ to $x = \pi/2$.

SOLUTION: As in EXERCISE 9, $h = \pi/8$ and $x_0 = 0$, $x_1 = \pi/8$, $x_2 = \pi/4$, $x_3 = 3\pi/3$ and $x_4 = \pi/2$. So

$$L \approx \frac{\pi/8}{3} \left(\sqrt{1 + (\sin 0)^2} + 4\sqrt{1 + \left(\sin\frac{\pi}{8}\right)^2} + 2\sqrt{1 + \left(\sin\frac{\pi}{4}\right)^2} \right.$$

$$\left. + 4\sqrt{1 + \left(\sin\frac{3\pi}{8}\right)^2} + \sqrt{1 + \left(\sin\frac{\pi}{2}\right)^2} \right)$$

$$\approx \frac{\pi}{24}\left(1 + 4(1.0707) + 2(1.2247) + 4(1.3614) + 1.4142\right) \approx \frac{\pi}{24}(14.5924) \approx 1.9101.$$

17. Use THEOREM 7.24 to find an upper bound for the error in using the trapezoidal rule with $n = 4$, $h = 1/2$, to approximate $\int_1^3 \ln x\, dx$.

SOLUTION: The upper bound for the error in using the trapezoidal approximation is

$$\frac{(b-a)M}{12}h^2 = \frac{(3-1)M}{12}\left(\frac{1}{2}\right)^4 = \frac{1}{24}M,$$

where $M \geq |f''(x)|$ for all x in $[1,3]$.

Now $f'(x) = 1/x$ and $|f''(x)| = \left|-1/x^2\right| = 1/x^2$ which is decreasing on $[1,3]$ and thus achieves its maximum at $x = 1$, so $M = 1/1^2 = 1$ and the upper bound for the error is $1/24 \approx 0.0417$.

23. Suppose that the grade-point averages of all college students in the United States are normally distributed with mean equal to 2.4 and standard deviation equal to 0.8. Find, to within 10^{-3}, the probability that a randomly chosen student has a grade-point average   a) between 1.6 and 3.2.

SOLUTION: a) $P = \int_{1.6}^{3.2} \dfrac{\exp\left(-\dfrac{1}{2}\left(\dfrac{x - 2.4}{0.8}\right)^2\right)}{0.8\sqrt{2\pi}}\, dx.$ Let $z = \dfrac{x - 2.4}{0.8}$. Then $dz = \dfrac{1}{0.8}\, dx$ and

$$P = \int_{1.6}^{3.2} \frac{e^{-z^2/2}}{\sqrt{2\pi}}\, dz = \frac{1}{2\sqrt{2\pi}} \int_{-1}^{1} e^{-z^2/2}\, dz = \frac{2}{\sqrt{2\pi}} \int_0^1 e^{-z^2/2}\, dz.$$

Since the maximum error is to be 10^{-3}, analyze

$$\frac{(b-a)M}{180}h^4 = \frac{M}{180}h^4 \quad \text{with } M \geq \left|f^{(4)}(z)\right| \text{ for } z \in [0,1]$$

$$f'(z) = \frac{2}{\sqrt{2\pi}} e^{-z^2/2}(-z)$$

$$f''(z) = \frac{-2}{\sqrt{2\pi}} e^{-z^2/2} + \frac{2}{\sqrt{2\pi}} e^{-z^2/2}(-z)(-z) = \frac{2}{\sqrt{2\pi}} e^{-z^2/2}(z^2 - 1)$$

$$f^{(3)}(z) = \frac{2}{\sqrt{2\pi}}e^{-z^2/2}(2z) + \frac{2}{\sqrt{2\pi}}e^{-z^2/2}(-z)(z^2-1) = \frac{2}{\sqrt{2\pi}}e^{-z^2/2}(-z^3+3z)$$

$$f^{(4)}(z) = \frac{2}{\sqrt{2\pi}}e^{-z^2/2}(-3z^2+3) + \frac{2}{\sqrt{2\pi}}e^{-z^2/2}(-z)(-z^3+3z)$$

$$= \frac{2}{\sqrt{2\pi}}e^{-z^2/2}(z^4-6z^2+3).$$

Now for $0 \le z \le 1$, $e^{z^2/2} \ge 1$, so $0 < e^{-z^2/2} \le 1$. Consider $g(z) = z^4 - 6z^2 + 3$. $g'(z) = 4z^3 - 12z = 4z(z^2-3)$. Thus g has critical points at $z = 0$ or $z = \pm\sqrt{3}$ and for $0 \le z \le 1$, $g(z)$ is decreasing; thus $g(0) = 3$ is the maximum on the interval $[0,1]$ and $g(1) = -2$ is the minimum. So 3 is the maximum of $|g(z)|$. Thus $|f^{(4)}(z)| \le (1)(3) = 3$ on $[0,1]$ and

$$\frac{3}{180}h^4 < 10^{-3} \implies h^4 < 60 \times 10^{-3} \implies$$

$$h < \sqrt[4]{0.06} \approx 0.4949.$$

So if $\frac{1}{n} = h < 0.4949$, the error will be less than 10^{-3}. Choose $n > \frac{1}{0.4949} \approx 2.02$. Since n must be even to use Simpson's rule, $n = 4$ will suffice and $h = 1/4$.
So the desired approximation is

$$\frac{1/4}{3} \cdot \frac{2}{\sqrt{2\pi}}\left(e^0 + 4e^{-1/32} + 2e^{-1/8} + 4e^{-9/32} + e^{-1/2}\right) \approx 0.6827$$

and the probability that a randomly chosen grade point average is between 1.6 and 3.2 is 0.6827 to within 10^{-3}.

_____Chapter 7

Review Exercises

5. Evaluate $\displaystyle\int \frac{x}{\sqrt{1+x^2}}\, dx$.

SOLUTION: Let $u = 1 + x^2$. Then $du = 2x\, dx$ and $du/2 = x\, dx$. Thus

$$\int \frac{x}{\sqrt{1+x^2}}\, dx = \int \frac{1}{\sqrt{u}}\frac{du}{2} = \frac{1}{2}\int u^{-1/2}\, du = \frac{1}{2}(2u^{1/2}) + C = \sqrt{1+x^2} + C.$$

11. Evaluate $\displaystyle\int \cos^5 x\sqrt{\sin x}\, dx$.

SOLUTION:

$$\int \cos^5 x(\sin x)^{1/2}\, dx = \int \cos x \cos^4 x(\sin x)^{1/2}\, dx = \int \cos x(\cos^2 x)^2(\sin x)^{1/2}\, dx$$

$$= \int \cos x (1 - \sin^2 x)^2 (\sin x)^{1/2} \, dx = \int \cos x (1 - 2\sin^2 x + \sin^4 x)(\sin x)^{1/2} \, dx$$

$$= \int \left((\sin x)^{1/2} - 2(\sin x)^{5/2} + (\sin x)^{9/2} \right) \cos x \, dx.$$

Let $u = \sin x$. Then $du = \cos x \, dx$ and the integral becomes

$$\int (u^{1/2} - 2u^{5/2} + u^{9/2}) \, du = \frac{2}{3} u^{3/2} - \frac{4}{7} u^{7/2} + \frac{2}{11} u^{11/2} + C$$

$$= \frac{2}{3} (\sin x)^{3/2} - \frac{4}{7} (\sin x)^{7/2} + \frac{2}{11} (\sin x)^{11/2} + C$$

$$= \frac{2}{231} \sqrt{\sin x} (77 \sin x - 66 \sin^3 x + 21 \sin^5 x) + C.$$

17. Evaluate $\displaystyle \int \frac{x^3}{\sqrt{x^2 - 1}} \, dx.$

SOLUTION: Let $u = x^2 - 1$. Then $du = 2x \, dx$ and $du/2 = x \, dx$. Also $x^2 = u + 1$. Thus the integral becomes

$$\int \frac{x^3}{\sqrt{x^2 - 1}} \, dx = \int \frac{x^2}{\sqrt{x^2 - 1}} x \, dx = \int \frac{u + 1}{\sqrt{u}} \frac{du}{2} = \frac{1}{2} \int (u + 1) u^{-1/2} \, du$$

$$= \frac{1}{2} \int (u^{1/2} + u^{-1/2}) \, du = \frac{1}{2} \left(\frac{2}{3} u^{3/2} + 2u^{1/2} \right) + C$$

$$= \frac{1}{3} (x^2 - 1)^{3/2} + (x^2 - 1)^{1/2} + C = \frac{1}{3} \sqrt{x^2 - 1} \left((x^2 - 1) + 3 \right) + C$$

$$= \frac{1}{3} \sqrt{x^2 - 1} (x^2 + 2) + C.$$

23. Evaluate $\displaystyle \int \frac{x^3 + 2x + 1}{x^3 + x} \, dx.$

SOLUTION: By using polynomial long division, $\dfrac{x^3 + 2x + 1}{x^3 + x} = 1 + \dfrac{x + 1}{x^3 + x}$, so

$$\int \frac{x^3 + 2x + 1}{x^3 + x} \, dx = \int \left(1 + \frac{x + 1}{x^3 + x} \right) \, dx = x + \int \frac{x + 1}{x(x^2 + 1)} \, dx + C.$$

To evaluate $\displaystyle \int \frac{x + 1}{x(x^2 + 1)} \, dx$, use the method of partial fractions.

$$\frac{x + 1}{x(x^2 + 1)} = \frac{A}{x} + \frac{B}{x^2 + 1} + \frac{Cx}{x^2 + 1} = \frac{A(x^2 + 1) + Bx + Cx^2}{x(x^2 + 1)}$$

$$= \frac{Ax^2 + A + Bx + Cx^2}{x(x^2 + 1)} = \frac{(A + C)x^2 + Bx + A}{x(x^2 + 1)},$$

so $x + 1 = (A + C)x^2 + Bx + A$. Thus $A = 1$, $B = 1$, and $C = -A = -1$, so

$$\int \frac{x + 1}{x(x^2 + 1)} \, dx = \int \left(\frac{1}{x} + \frac{1}{x^2 + 1} + \frac{-x}{x^2 + 1} \right) dx$$

$$= \int \frac{1}{x} \, dx + \int \frac{1}{x^2 + 1} \, dx - \int \frac{x}{x^2 + 1} \, dx$$

$$= \ln |x| + \arctan x - \frac{1}{2} \ln \left| x^2 + 1 \right| = \ln |x| - \ln \sqrt{x^2 + 1} + \arctan x$$

$$= \ln \sqrt{\frac{x^2}{x^2 + 1}} + \arctan x.$$

Thus $\displaystyle \int \frac{x^3 + 2x + 1}{x^3 + x} \, dx = x + \ln \sqrt{\frac{x^2}{x^2 + 1}} + \arctan x + C.$

33. Evaluate $\displaystyle \int \frac{2x}{x^2 + 6x - 7} \, dx.$

SOLUTION: $\displaystyle \int \frac{2x}{x^2 + 6x - 7} \, dx = 2 \int \frac{x}{(x + 7)(x - 1)} \, dx.$ To evaluate $\displaystyle \int \frac{x}{(x + 7)(x - 1)} \, dx$, use the method of partial fractions.

$$\frac{x}{(x + 7)(x - 1)} = \frac{A}{x + 7} + \frac{B}{x - 1} = \frac{A(x - 1) + B(x + 7)}{(x + 7)(x - 1)}$$

$$= \frac{Ax - A + Bx + 7B}{(x + 7)(x - 1)} = \frac{(A + B)x - A + 7B}{(x + 7)(x - 1)}.$$

So $x = (A + B)x - A + 7B \implies A + B = 1$ and $-A + 7B = 0$.
$A = 7B \implies 7B + B = 1 \implies B = 1/8$. Thus $A = 7/8$. Hence

$$\int \frac{x}{(x + 7)(x - 1)} \, dx = \int \frac{7/8}{x + 7} \, dx + \int \frac{1/8}{x - 1} \, dx = \frac{7}{8} \ln |x + 7| + \frac{1}{8} \ln |x - 1| + C,$$

and

$$\int \frac{2x}{x^2 + 6x - 7} \, dx = 2 \left(\frac{7}{8} \ln |x + 7| + \frac{1}{8} \ln |x - 1| \right) + C = \frac{7}{4} \ln |x + 7| + \frac{1}{4} \ln |x - 1| + C.$$

37. Evaluate $\displaystyle \int x^5 e^{-x^2} \, dx.$

SOLUTION: Apply integration by parts. Let $u = x^4$ and $dv = xe^{-x^2} \, dx$. Then $du = 4x^3 \, dx$ and $v = -\frac{1}{2} e^{-x^2}$, so

$$\int x^5 e^{-x^2} \, dx = x^4 \left(-\frac{1}{2} e^{-x^2} \right) + \int \frac{1}{2} e^{-x^2} (4x^3) \, dx.$$

Now $\int \frac{1}{2}e^{-x^2}(4x^3)\,dx = 2\int x^3 e^{-x^2}\,dx$.

To evaluate $\int x^3 e^{-x^2}\,dx$, apply integration by parts again with $u = x^2$ and $dv = xe^{-x^2}\,dx$. Then $du = 2x\,dx$ and $v = -\frac{1}{2}e^{-x^2}$. Thus

$$\int x^3 e^{-x^2}\,dx = x^2\left(-\frac{1}{2}e^{-x^2}\right) - \int -\frac{1}{2}e^{-x^2}(2x\,dx)$$

$$= -\frac{1}{2}x^2 e^{-x^2} + \int xe^{-x^2}\,dx = -\frac{1}{2}x^2 e^{-x^2} - \frac{1}{2}e^{-x^2} + C.$$

So

$$\int x^5 e^{-x^2}\,dx = -\frac{1}{2}x^4 e^{-x^2} + 2\left(-\frac{1}{2}x^2 e^{-x^2} - \frac{1}{2}e^{-x^2}\right) + C = -\frac{1}{2}e^{-x^2}(x^4 + 2x^2 + 2) + C.$$

43. Evaluate $\int \dfrac{dx}{x^3 - 4x^2}$.

SOLUTION: $\int \dfrac{dx}{x^3 - 4x^2} = \int \dfrac{dx}{x^2(x-4)}$. Apply the method of partial fractions.

$$\frac{1}{x^2(x-4)} = \frac{A}{x} + \frac{B}{x^2} + \frac{C}{x-4} = \frac{Ax(x-4) + B(x-4) + Cx^2}{x^2(x-4)} \implies$$

$$Ax^2 - 4Ax + Bx - 4B + Cx^2 = 1 \implies$$

$$(A+C)x^2 + (-4A+B)x - 4B = 1 \implies$$

$A + C = 0$, $-4A + B = 0$ and $-4B = 1$. Thus $B = -1/4$, $-4A = 1/4 \implies A = -1/16$ and $C = 1/16$, so

$$\int \frac{dx}{x^2(x-4)} = \int \left(\frac{-1/16}{x} + \frac{-1/4}{x^2} + \frac{1/16}{x-4}\right)dx = -\frac{1}{16}\int \frac{dx}{x} - \frac{1}{4}\int x^{-2}\,dx + \frac{1}{16}\int \frac{dx}{x-4}$$

$$= -\frac{1}{16}\ln|x| + \frac{1}{4}x^{-1} + \frac{1}{16}\ln|x-4| + C = \frac{1}{16}\ln\left|\frac{x-4}{x}\right| + \frac{1}{4x} + C.$$

45. Evaluate $\int x^3(16 - x^2)^{3/2}\,dx$.

SOLUTION: $\int x^3(16-x^2)^{3/2}\,dx = \int x^2(16-x^2)^{3/2}\,x\,dx$, so let $u = 16-x^2$. Then $du = -2x\,dx$ and $-\frac{1}{2}du = x\,dx$. Also $x^2 = 16 - u$. Thus the integral becomes

$$\int (16-u)u^{3/2}\left(-\frac{1}{2}\,du\right) = -\frac{1}{2}\int (16u^{3/2} - u^{5/2})\,du = -\frac{1}{2}\left(\frac{32}{5}u^{5/2} - \frac{2}{7}u^{7/2}\right) + C$$

$$= \frac{1}{7}u^{7/2} - \frac{16}{5}u^{5/2} + C = \frac{1}{7}(16 - x^2)^{7/2} - \frac{16}{5}(16 - x^2)^{5/2} + C.$$

COMMENT: This integral can also be evaluated by the substitution $u = 4\sin x$. However, the solution presented is shorter and thus, preferred.

53. Evaluate $\int \dfrac{\sin(\ln x)\cos(\ln x)}{x}\,dx$.

SOLUTION: Let $u = \ln x$. Then $du = \dfrac{1}{x}\,dx$ and

$$\int \frac{\sin(\ln x)\cos(\ln x)}{x}\,dx = \int \sin u \cos u\,du = \int \frac{1}{2}\sin 2u\,du = -\frac{1}{4}\cos 2u + C.$$

Thus

$$\int \frac{\sin(\ln x)\cos(\ln x)}{x}\,dx = -\frac{1}{4}\cos(2(\ln x)) + C.$$

COMMENT: To evaluate $\int \sin u \cos u\,du$, the substitution $w = \sin u$ or $w = \cos u$ can also be made.

61. Evaluate $\int e^{3x}\sin 2x\,dx$.

SOLUTION: Apply integration by parts with $u = \sin 2x$ and $dv = e^{3x}\,dx$. Then $du = 2\cos 2x$ and $v = \frac{1}{3}e^{3x}$, so

$$\int e^{3x}\sin 2x\,dx = (\sin 2x)\left(\frac{1}{3}e^{3x}\right) - \int \frac{2}{3}e^{3x}\cos 2x\,dx.$$

To evaluate $\int e^{3x}\cos 2x\,dx$, let $u = \cos 2x$ and $dv = e^{3x}\,dx$. Then $du = -2\sin 2x$ and $v = \frac{1}{3}e^{3x}$, so

$$\int e^{3x}\cos 2x\,dx = (\cos 2x)\left(\frac{1}{3}e^{3x}\right) - \int -\frac{2}{3}e^{3x}\sin 2x\,dx.$$

Thus

$$\int e^{3x}\sin 2x\,dx = \frac{1}{3}e^{3x}\sin 2x - \frac{2}{3}\left(\frac{1}{3}e^{3x}\cos 2x + \frac{2}{3}\int e^{3x}\sin 2x\,dx\right) \implies$$

$$\int e^{3x}\sin 2x\,dx = \frac{1}{3}e^{3x}\sin 2x - \frac{2}{9}e^{3x}\cos 2x - \frac{4}{9}\int e^{3x}\sin 2x\,dx \implies$$

$$\frac{13}{9} \int e^{3x} \sin 2x \, dx = \frac{1}{9} e^{3x} (3 \sin 2x - 2 \cos 2x) \implies$$

$$\int e^{3x} \sin 2x \, dx = \frac{1}{13} e^{3x} (3 \sin 2x - 2 \cos 2x) + C.$$

67. Evaluate $\int x \arctan \sqrt{x} \, dx$.

SOLUTION: Apply integration by parts with $u = \arctan \sqrt{x}$ and $dv = x \, dx$. Then $du = \frac{1}{1 + (\sqrt{x})^2} \cdot \frac{1}{2} x^{-1/2} dx$ and $v = \frac{1}{2} x^2$, so

$$\int x \arctan \sqrt{x} \, dx = \frac{1}{2} x^2 \arctan \sqrt{x} - \int \frac{1}{2} x^2 \cdot \frac{1}{1 + x} \cdot \frac{1}{2} x^{-1/2} dx$$

$$= \frac{1}{2} x^2 \arctan \sqrt{x} - \frac{1}{4} \int \frac{x^{3/2}}{1 + x} \, dx.$$

To evaluate $\int \frac{x^{3/2}}{1 + x} \, dx$, let $u = x^{1/2}$. Then $du = \frac{1}{2} x^{-1/2} dx \implies 2x^{1/2} \, du = dx \implies 2u \, du = dx$ and

$$\int \frac{x^{3/2}}{1 + x} \, dx = \int \frac{u^3}{1 + u^2} (2u \, du) = 2 \int \frac{u^4}{1 + u^2} \, du = 2 \int \left(u^2 - 1 + \frac{1}{1 + u^2} \right) du$$

$$= 2 \left(\frac{1}{3} u^3 - u + \arctan u \right) + C = 2 \left(\frac{1}{3} x^{3/2} - x^{1/2} + \arctan \sqrt{x} \right) + C.$$

Thus

$$\int x \arctan \sqrt{x} \, dx = \frac{1}{2} x^2 \arctan \sqrt{x} - \frac{1}{4} \left(2 \left(\frac{1}{3} x^{3/2} - x^{1/2} + \arctan \sqrt{x} \right) \right) + C$$

$$= \frac{1}{2} x^2 \arctan \sqrt{x} - \frac{1}{6} x^{3/2} + \frac{1}{2} x^{1/2} - \frac{1}{2} \arctan \sqrt{x} + C$$

$$= \frac{1}{2} (x^2 - 1) \arctan \sqrt{x} - \frac{1}{6} \sqrt{x} (x - 3) + C.$$

69. Evaluate $\int \frac{3x^2}{\sqrt{4x^2 - 1}} \, dx$.

SOLUTION: Let $\sec u = 2x$. Then $\sec u \tan u \, du = 2 \, dx$ and

$$\int \frac{3x^2}{\sqrt{4x^2 - 1}} \, dx = 3 \int \frac{\left(\frac{1}{2} \sec u \right)^2}{\sqrt{\sec^2 u - 1}} \cdot \frac{1}{2} \sec u \tan u \, du = \frac{3}{8} \int \frac{\sec^3 u \tan u}{\sqrt{\tan^2 u}} \, du$$

$$= \frac{3}{8} \int \sec^3 u \, du = \frac{3}{8} \int \sec u (\sec^2 u) \, du.$$

To evaluate $\int \sec u \sec^2 u \, du$, use integration by parts with $w = \sec u$ and $dv = \sec^2 u \, du$. Then $dw = \sec u \tan u \, du$ and $v = \tan u$, so

$$\int \sec u (\sec^2 u) \, du = \tan u \sec u - \int \tan^2 u \sec u \, du \implies$$

$$\int \sec^3 u \, du = \tan u \sec u - \int (\sec^2 u - 1) \sec u \, du \implies$$

$$\int \sec^3 u \, du = \tan u \sec u - \int \sec^3 u \, du + \int \sec u \, du \implies$$

$$2 \int \sec^3 u \, du = \tan u \sec u + \int \sec u \, du \implies$$

$$\int \sec^3 u \, du = \frac{1}{2} (\tan u \sec u + \ln |\sec u + \tan u|) + C.$$

Thus

$$\int \frac{3x^2}{\sqrt{4x^2 - 1}} \, dx = \frac{3}{8} \left(\frac{1}{2} (\tan u \sec u + \ln |\sec u + \tan u|) \right) + C$$

$$= \frac{3}{16} \left(\tan(\operatorname{arcsec} 2x) \sec(\operatorname{arcsec} 2x) + \ln |\sec(\operatorname{arcsec} 2x) + \tan(\operatorname{arcsec} 2x)| \right) + C$$

$$= \frac{3}{16} \left(2x\sqrt{4x^2 - 1} + \ln \left| 2x + \sqrt{4x^2 - 1} \right| \right) + C.$$

77. Evaluate $\int \tan^3 2x \, dx$.

SOLUTION:

$$\int \tan^3 2x \, dx = \int \tan 2x (\sec^2 2x - 1) \, dx = \int \tan 2x \sec^2 2x \, dx - \int \tan 2x \, dx$$

$$= \int \tan 2x \sec^2 2x \, dx - \int \frac{\sin 2x}{\cos 2x} \, dx.$$

Let $u = \tan 2x$ and $w = \cos 2x$. Then $du = 2 \sec^2 2x \, dx$ and $dw = -2 \sin 2x \, dx$, so

$$\int \tan^3 2x \, dx = \frac{1}{2} \int u \, du + \frac{1}{2} \int \frac{dw}{w} = \frac{1}{4} u^2 + \frac{1}{2} \ln |w| + C$$

$$= \frac{1}{4} \tan^2 2x + \frac{1}{2} \ln |\cos 2x| + C.$$

81. Evaluate $\int \cos 2x \sin 3x \, dx$.

SOLUTION:

$$\cos 2x \sin 3x \, dx = \int \frac{1}{2}(\sin 5x + \sin x) \, dx$$

$$= \frac{1}{2}\left(-\frac{1}{5}\cos 5x - \cos x\right) + C = -\frac{1}{2}\left(\frac{1}{5}\cos 5x + \cos x\right) + C.$$

COMMENT: Recall $\sin a \cos b = \frac{1}{2}\left(\sin(a+b) + \sin(a-b)\right)$.

87. Evaluate $\int \frac{\cosh(\ln x)}{x} \, dx$.

SOLUTION: Let $u = \ln x$. Then $du = \frac{1}{x} \, dx$ and

$$\int \frac{\cosh(\ln x)}{x} \, dx = \int \cosh u \, du = \sinh u + C = \sinh(\ln x) + C$$

$$= \frac{e^{\ln x} - e^{-\ln x}}{2} + C = \frac{x - \frac{1}{x}}{2} + C = \frac{x^2 - 1}{2x} + C.$$

COMMENT: Another way of evaluating this is to note that $\cosh(\ln x) = \dfrac{e^{\ln x} + e^{-\ln x}}{2} = \dfrac{1}{2}\left(x + \dfrac{1}{x}\right).$

93. Evaluate $\int \frac{\sqrt{x}}{1 + \sqrt[4]{x}} \, dx$.

SOLUTION: Let $u = x^{1/4}$. Then $u^2 = x^{1/2}$ and $du = \frac{1}{4}x^{-3/4}dx \implies dx = 4x^{3/4}du \implies dx = 4u^3 \, du$. Thus

$$\int \frac{\sqrt{x}}{1 + \sqrt[4]{x}} \, dx = \int \frac{u^2}{1 + u}(4u^3 \, du) = 4 \int \frac{u^5}{1 + u} \, du$$

$$= 4 \int \left(u^4 - u^3 + u^2 - u + 1 - \frac{1}{u+1} \right) \, du$$

$$= 4 \left(\frac{1}{5} u^5 - \frac{1}{4} u^4 + \frac{1}{3} u^3 - \frac{1}{2} u^2 + u - \ln |u+1| \right) + C$$

$$= 4 \left(\frac{1}{5} x^{5/4} - \frac{1}{4} x + \frac{1}{3} x^{3/4} - \frac{1}{2} x^{1/2} + x^{1/4} - \ln(x^{1/4} + 1) \right) + C.$$

105. Find the volume of the solid generated by revolving about the x-axis the region bounded by the x-axis, the lines $x = -2$ and $x = 2$, and the graph of $y = 4/(x^2 + 4)$.

SOLUTION:

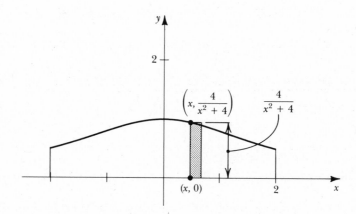

From the graph, the volume of the element is $\pi \left(\dfrac{4}{x^2 + 4} \right)^2 \, dx$. The volume is determined by

$\displaystyle\int_{-2}^{2} \pi \left(\dfrac{4}{x^2 + 4} \right)^2 \, dx$. Let $x = 2 \tan \theta$. Then $dx = 2 \sec^2 \theta \, d\theta$. Also $x = -2 \implies 2 \tan \theta = -2 \implies \theta = -\pi/4$ and $x = 2 \implies \theta = \pi/4$.

Thus

$$\int_{-2}^{2} \pi \left(\frac{4}{x^2 + 4} \right)^2 \, dx = 16\pi \int_{-\pi/4}^{\pi/4} \frac{2 \sec^2 \theta \, d\theta}{\left((2 \tan \theta)^2 + 2^2 \right)^2} = 32\pi \int_{-\pi/4}^{\pi/4} \frac{\sec^2 \theta \, d\theta}{\left(4(\tan^2 \theta + 1) \right)^2}$$

$$= 2\pi \int_{-\pi/4}^{\pi/4} \frac{\sec^2 \theta \, d\theta}{\sec^4 \theta} = 2\pi \int_{-\pi/4}^{\pi/4} \cos^2 \theta \, d\theta = \pi \int_{-\pi/4}^{\pi/4} (1 + \cos 2\theta) \, d\theta$$

$$= \pi \left[\theta + \frac{1}{2} \sin 2\theta \right] \Bigg|_{-\pi/4}^{\pi/4} = \pi \left(\left(\frac{\pi}{4} + \frac{1}{2} \sin \frac{\pi}{2} \right) - \left(-\frac{\pi}{4} + \frac{1}{2} \sin \left(-\frac{\pi}{2} \right) \right) \right)$$

$$= \pi \left(\frac{\pi}{2} + 1 \right).$$

113. Approximate $\int_1^3 \dfrac{\sin^2 x}{x}\, dx$ with $n = 8$ by using a) The Trapezoidal Rule and b) Simpson's Rule.

SOLUTION: a) $h = \dfrac{3-1}{8} = \dfrac{1}{4}$ so

$$\int_1^3 \frac{\sin^2 x}{x}\, dx \approx \frac{1/4}{2}\left(\frac{\sin^2 1}{1} + 2\frac{\sin^2(5/4)}{5/4} + 2\frac{\sin^2(3/2)}{3/2} + 2\frac{\sin^2(7/4)}{7/4} + 2\frac{\sin^2 2}{2} \right.$$

$$\left. + 2\frac{\sin^2(9/4)}{9/4} + 2\frac{\sin^2(5/2)}{5/2} + 2\frac{\sin^2(11/4)}{11/4} + \frac{\sin^2 3}{3} \right)$$

$$\approx 0.125(0.70807 + 1.44091 + 1.32666 + 1.10654 + 0.82682$$

$$+ 0.53813 + 0.28653 + 0.10593 + 0.00663) \approx 0.7933.$$

b)

$$\int_1^3 \frac{\sin^2 x}{x}\, dx \approx \frac{1/4}{3}\left(\frac{\sin^2 1}{1} + 4\frac{\sin^2(5/4)}{5/4} + 2\frac{\sin^2(3/2)}{3/2} + 4\frac{\sin^2(7/4)}{7/4} + 2\frac{\sin^2 2}{2} \right.$$

$$\left. + 4\frac{\sin^2(9/4)}{9/4} + 2\frac{\sin^2(5/2)}{5/2} + 4\frac{\sin^2(11/4)}{11/4} + \frac{\sin^2 3}{3} \right)$$

$$\approx 0.08333(0.70807 + 2.88182 + 1.32666 + 2.21309 + 0.82682$$

$$+ 1.07626 + 0.28653 + 0.21187) \approx 0.7948.$$

8

Sequences and Series

Sharpening your skills

To prepare for this chapter, review the material in SECTION 1.9 on evaluating limits at infinity and L'Hôpital's rule in SECTION 3.5. Also review the material on evaluating sums in SECTION 2.1. Some practice problems are included below. The answers for these problems are in APPENDIX B in this manual.

Practice Problems

1. Evaluate each of the following.

   a) $\lim\limits_{x \to \infty} \dfrac{4x^3 - 7}{8x + 3x^2 - 5x^3}$,

   b) $\lim\limits_{x \to \infty} \dfrac{x^2 + 3x}{5x^4 + 3}$,

   c) $\lim\limits_{x \to \infty} \dfrac{3x^3 + 4x^2 - 8}{x^2 - 2}$,

   d) $\lim\limits_{x \to \infty} \dfrac{2x^2 - 3}{\sqrt{x^4 + x^3}}$.

2. Evaluate each of the following.

   a) $\sum\limits_{i=1}^{6} (2i^2 + 1)$,

   b) $\sum\limits_{i=0}^{4} \left(\sin \dfrac{\pi}{4} i \right)$,

   c) $\sum\limits_{i=0}^{3} (-1)^{i+1} e^i$,

   d) $\sum\limits_{i=1}^{n} (i^2 - 4i + 2)$.

_____8.1

Infinite Sequences

5. Given the nth term of a sequence, $a_n = \dfrac{n}{n+4}$, $n \geq 1$: a) List the first three terms of the sequence. b) Determine if the sequence is convergent. c) If the sequence is convergent, give its limit. d) Determine if the sequence is bounded.

SOLUTION: a) $a_0 = \dfrac{0}{0+4} = 0$, $a_1 = \dfrac{1}{1+4} = \dfrac{1}{5}$, and $a_2 = \dfrac{2}{2+4} = \dfrac{1}{3}$ are the first three terms of the sequence. b) The sequence does converge. c) Examine $\lim\limits_{n \to \infty} a_n$.

$$\lim_{n \to \infty} \dfrac{n}{n} \dfrac{1}{1 + \dfrac{4}{n}} = \lim_{n \to \infty} \dfrac{1}{1 + \frac{4}{n}} = 1,$$

and the sequence converges to 1.   d) The sequence is bounded since it is convergent. Moreover, it is bounded below by 0 since $a_n \geq 0$ for all n and the sequence is bounded above by 1 since $a_n < 1$ for all n.

9. Given the nth term of a sequence, $a_n = \dfrac{n^3 + 2n^2 - 1}{n^2 + n}$:   a) List the first three terms of the sequence.   b) Determine if the sequence is convergent.   c) If the sequence is convergent, give its limit.   d) Determine if the sequence is bounded.

SOLUTION: a) The first three terms of the sequence are:

$$a_1 = \frac{1 + 2 - 1}{1 + 1} = 1,$$

$$a_2 = \frac{8 + 2(4) - 1}{4 + 2} = \frac{5}{2},$$

$$a_3 = \frac{27 + 2(9) - 1}{9 + 3} = \frac{44}{12} = \frac{11}{3}.$$

b) The sequence diverges since

$$\lim_{n \to \infty} \frac{n^3 + 2n^2 - 1}{n^2 + n} = \lim_{n \to \infty} \frac{n^2}{n^2} \cdot \frac{n + 2 - \dfrac{1}{n^2}}{1 + \dfrac{1}{n}} = \lim_{n \to \infty} \frac{n + 2 - \dfrac{1}{n^2}}{1 + \dfrac{1}{n}} = \infty.$$

d) Since $a_1 = 1$ and the sequence is increasing, it is bounded below by 1. However, the sequence is not bounded above.

17. Given the nth term of a sequence, $a_n = \dfrac{\ln n}{n^2} - 1$:   a) List the first three terms of the sequence.   b) Determine if the sequence is convergent.   c) If the sequence is convergent, give its limit.   d) Determine if the sequence is bounded.

SOLUTION: a) The first three terms of the sequence are:

$$a_1 = \frac{\ln 1}{1} - 1 = -1,$$

$$a_2 = \frac{\ln 2}{4} - 1,$$

$$a_3 = \frac{\ln 3}{9} - 1.$$

b) The sequence does converge.   c)

$$\lim_{n \to \infty} \frac{\ln n}{n^2} - 1 = -1 + \lim_{n \to \infty} \frac{\ln n}{n^2}.$$

Now $\lim\limits_{n\to\infty} \dfrac{\ln n}{n^2}$ yields the indeterminate form $\dfrac{\infty}{\infty}$ which satisfies the hypothesis of L'Hôpital's rule. Thus

$$\lim_{n\to\infty} \frac{\ln n}{n^2} = \lim_{n\to\infty} \frac{1/n}{2n} = \lim_{n\to\infty} \frac{1}{2n^2} = 0$$

and the sequence converges to -1. d) Since the sequence converges, it is bounded. Since $\dfrac{\ln n}{n^2} \geq 0$ and $a_1 = -1$, the sequence is bounded below by -1. Also since $\dfrac{\ln n}{n^2}$ is decreasing, the sequence is bounded above by $a_2 = \dfrac{\ln 2}{4} - 1$.

23. Given the nth term of a sequence, $a_1 = 1$, $a_n = \dfrac{a_{n-1}}{2}$, if $n \geq 2$: a) List the first three terms of the sequence. b) Determine if the sequence is convergent. c) If the sequence is convergent, give its limit. d) Determine if the sequence is bounded.

SOLUTION: a) The first three terms of the sequence are

$$a_1 = 1 = \left(\frac{1}{2}\right)^0$$

$$a_2 = \frac{a_1}{2} = \frac{1}{2} = \left(\frac{1}{2}\right)^1$$

$$a_3 = \frac{a_2}{2} = \frac{1/2}{2} = \frac{1}{4} = \left(\frac{1}{2}\right)^2 .$$

b) The sequence converges.   c) An alternative (non-recursive) way of defining this sequence is $a_n = \left(\frac{1}{2}\right)^{n-1}$. Thus $\lim\limits_{n\to\infty} a_n = \lim\limits_{n\to\infty} \left(\dfrac{1}{2}\right)^{n-1} = 0$ since this sequence is of the form r^n where $|r| < 1$.   d) Since the sequence converges it is bounded. As the sequence is decreasing, it is bounded above by $a_1 = 1$. The sequence is bounded below by 0.

37. Given the nth term of a sequence, $a_n = \dfrac{n}{n^2 + 1}\cos n\pi$: a) List the first three terms of the sequence. b) Determine if the sequence is convergent. c) If the sequence is convergent, give its limit. d) Determine if the sequence is bounded.

SOLUTION: a) The first three terms of the sequence are:

$$a_1 = \frac{1}{1+1}\cos\pi = -\frac{1}{2},$$

$$a_2 = \frac{2}{4+1}\cos 2\pi = \frac{2}{5},$$

$$a_3 = \frac{3}{9+1}\cos 3\pi = -\frac{3}{10}.$$

b) The sequence does converge. c) $\lim_{n\to\infty} a_n = \lim_{n\to\infty} \frac{n}{n^2+1} \cos n\pi$. Now, $|\cos n\pi| \leq 1$, so

$$\frac{-n}{n^2+1} \leq \frac{n}{n^2+1} \cos n\pi \leq \frac{n}{n^2+1}$$ and $\lim_{n\to\infty} \frac{-n}{n^2+1} = \lim_{n\to\infty} \frac{-1/n}{1+\frac{1}{n^2}} = 0$. Also $\lim_{n\to\infty} \frac{n}{n^2+1} =$

$\lim_{n\to\infty} \frac{1/n}{1+\frac{1}{n^2}} = 0$. Thus by the sandwiching theorem, $\lim_{n\to\infty} \frac{n}{n^2+1} \cos n\pi = 0$ and the sequence

converges. d) Since the sequence converges, it is bounded. The sequence alternates but in absolute value, it is decreasing. Thus the upper bound is $a_2 = \frac{2}{5}$ and the lower bound is $a_1 = -\frac{1}{2}$.

43. Given the nth term of a sequence, $a_1 = 1$, $a_n = \frac{a_{n-1}}{n^2}$, if $n \geq 2$: a) List the first three terms of the sequence. b) Determine if the sequence is convergent. c) If the sequence is convergent, give its limit. d) Determine if the sequence is bounded.

SOLUTION: a) The first three terms of the sequence are:

$$a_1 = 1 = \frac{1}{1^2} = \frac{1}{(1!)^2},$$

$$a_2 = \frac{a_1}{2^2} = \frac{1}{4} = \frac{1}{2^2 \cdot 1^2} = \frac{1}{(2!)^2}$$

$$a_3 = \frac{a_2}{3^2} = \frac{1/4}{9} = \frac{1}{36} = \frac{1}{3^2 \cdot 2^2 \cdot 1^2} = \frac{1}{(3!)^2}.$$

b) The sequence does converge. c) From (a), a non-recursive definition of a_n is $a_n = \frac{1}{(n!)^2}$. Clearly $\lim_{n\to\infty} a_n = 0$ and the sequence converges to 0. d) Since the sequence converges, it is bounded. Moreover, since $a_n > 0$ for all n and $\lim_{n\to\infty} a_n = 0$, the lower bound of the sequence is 0. Since the sequence is decreasing, i.e., $a_{n+1} < a_n$ for all n and $a_n = 1$, the upper bound of the sequence is 1.

47. The population of a certain city was 250,000 at the end of 1987. It has been estimated that in each year following 1987, 50,000 people will enter the city and 15% of the people living in the city at the beginning of the year leave the city during the year. Let x_n denote the population of the city at the end of n years after 1987. Find a formula for x_n in terms of n and determine $\lim_{n\to\infty} x_n$.

SOLUTION: Let n be the year after 1987. Then $x_0 = 250,000$ and $x_n = x_{n-1} + 50,000 - 0.15x_{n-1} = 0.85x_{n-1} + 50,000$. Consider the first terms of the sequence:

$$x_0 = 250,000$$

$$x_1 = 0.85(250{,}000) + 50{,}000 = 5(0.85)(50{,}000) + 50{,}000$$
$$x_2 = 0.85\left(0.85(250{,}000) + 50{,}000\right) + 50{,}000$$
$$= 5(0.85)^2(50{,}000) + (0.85)^1(50{,}000) + (0.85)^0(50{,}000)$$

This suggests

$$x_n = \left(5(0.85)^n + (0.85)^{n-1} + \cdots + (0.85)^0\right)(50{,}000) = 50{,}000\left(5(0.85)^n + \sum_{i=0}^{n-1}(0.85)^i\right).$$

To prove this, proceed by induction on n.

i) For $n = 0$, $x_0 = 50{,}000\left(5(0.85)^{1-1}\right) = 250{,}000$.

ii) Suppose true for $n = k$; that is,

$$x_k = 50{,}000\left(5(0.85)^k + \sum_{i=0}^{k-1}(0.85)^i\right).$$

Show $x_{k+1} = 50{,}000\left(5(0.85)^k + \sum_{i=0}^{k-1}(0.85)^i\right)$. Now

$$x_{k+1} = (0.85)(x_k) + 50{,}000 = 0.85\left(50{,}000\left(5(0.85)^k + \sum_{i=0}^{k-1}(0.85)^i\right)\right) + 50{,}000$$

$$= 50{,}000\left(5(0.85)^{k+1} + \sum_{i=0}^{k-1}(0.85)^{i+1} + 1\right) = 50{,}000\left(5(0.85)^{k+1} + \sum_{i=1}^{k}(0.85)^i + (0.85)^0\right)$$

$$= 50{,}000\left(5(0.85)^{k+1} + \sum_{i=0}^{k}(0.85)^i\right).$$

Thus by the Principle of Math Induction,

$$x_n = 50{,}000\left(5(0.85)^n + \sum_{i=0}^{n-1}(0.85)^i\right).$$

65. The sequence $\{F_n\}$ described in EXERCISE 46 is called a *Fibonacci sequence.* Consider the sequence $\{x_n\}$, where $x_n = \dfrac{F_{n+1}}{F_n}$. Assuming that $\lim\limits_{n\to\infty} x_n = x$ exists, show that $x = \dfrac{1 + \sqrt{5}}{2}$. This number is called the *golden ratio* and, among its many applications, gives the average monthly increase rate in the rabbit population described in

EXERCISE 46. (*Hint:* Divide $F_{n+1} = F_n + F_{n-1}$ by F_n to obtain a relationship between x_n and x_{n-1}. Then show that $x = 1 + \frac{1}{x}$ and solve for x.)

SOLUTION:

$$x_n = \frac{F_{n+1}}{F_n} = \frac{F_n + F_{n-1}}{F_n} = 1 + \frac{F_{n-1}}{F_n} = 1 + \frac{1}{F_n/F_{n-1}} = 1 + \frac{1}{x_{n-1}},$$

so $x_n = 1 + \frac{1}{x_{n-1}}$. Thus $x = \lim_{n\to\infty} x_n = \lim_{n\to\infty}\left(1 + \frac{1}{x_{n-1}}\right) = 1 + \frac{1}{\lim_{n\to\infty} x_{n-1}} = 1 + \frac{1}{x}$. Then

$x = 1 + \frac{1}{x} \implies x^2 = x + 1 \implies x^2 - x - 1 = 0 \implies x = \frac{1 \pm \sqrt{1+4}}{2} = \frac{1 \pm \sqrt{5}}{2}$. Since $x_n > 0$,

$\lim_{n\to\infty} x_n = x \geq 0$; thus discard $x = \frac{1 - \sqrt{5}}{2}$. That leaves $x = \frac{1 + \sqrt{5}}{2}$.

Infinite Series

8.2

3. Determine whether the series $\sum_{n=1}^{\infty} \left(\frac{2}{3}\right)^n$ converges or diverges.

SOLUTION: $\sum_{n=1}^{\infty} \left(\frac{2}{3}\right)^n = \sum_{n=1}^{\infty} \frac{2}{3}\left(\frac{2}{3}\right)^{n-1}$. This is an example of a geometric series with $a = \frac{2}{3}$

and $r = \frac{2}{3}$. Since $|r| < 1$, the series $\sum_{n=1}^{\infty} \left(\frac{2}{3}\right)^n$ is convergent. Moreover,

$$\sum_{n=1}^{\infty} \left(\frac{2}{3}\right)^n = \frac{a}{1-r} = \frac{2/3}{1 - \frac{2}{3}} = \frac{2/3}{1/3} = 2.$$

11. Determine whether the series $\sum_{n=1}^{\infty} \left(\frac{1}{2^n} - \frac{1}{2^{n+1}}\right)$ converges or diverges.

SOLUTION:

$$\sum_{n=1}^{\infty} \left(\frac{1}{2^n} - \frac{1}{2^{n+1}}\right) = \sum_{n=1}^{\infty} \frac{1}{2^n}\left(1 - \frac{1}{2}\right) = \sum_{n=1}^{\infty} \frac{1}{2}\left(\frac{1}{2}\right)^n$$

$$= \sum_{n=1}^{\infty} \frac{1}{2}\left(\frac{1}{2}\right)\left(\frac{1}{2}\right)^{n-1} = \sum_{n=1}^{\infty} \frac{1}{4}\left(\frac{1}{2}\right)^{n-1},$$

which is a geometric series with $a = 1/4$ and $r = 1/2$. Since $|r| < 1$, the series converges to

$$\frac{a}{1-r} = \frac{1/4}{1-(1/2)} = \frac{1/4}{1/2} = \frac{1}{2}.$$

19. Find the sum of the infinite series $\displaystyle\sum_{n=0}^{\infty} 3^n \cdot 5^{-n}$.

SOLUTION:

$$\sum_{n=0}^{\infty} 3^n \cdot 5^{-n} = \sum_{n=0}^{\infty} 3^n \cdot \frac{1}{5^n} = \sum_{n=0}^{\infty} \frac{3^n}{5^n} = \sum_{n=0}^{\infty} \left(\frac{3}{5}\right)^n.$$

Let $m = n+1$. Then $m-1 = n$ and when $n = 0$, $m = 1$. Thus the series becomes $\displaystyle\sum_{m=1}^{\infty} \left(\frac{3}{5}\right)^{m-1}$,

which is a geometric series with $a = 1$ and $r = 3/5$. Since $|r| < 1$, the series converges to

$\dfrac{a}{1-r} = \dfrac{1}{1-(3/5)} = \dfrac{1}{2/5} = \dfrac{5}{2}$. Thus $\displaystyle\sum_{n=0}^{\infty} 3^n \cdot 5^{-n} = \frac{5}{2}$.

23. Find the sum of the infinite series $\displaystyle\sum_{n=2}^{\infty} \frac{1}{n^2 - 1}$.

SOLUTION: $\displaystyle\sum_{n=2}^{\infty} \frac{1}{n^2 - 1} = \sum_{n=2}^{\infty} \frac{1}{(n-1)(n+1)}$. Let $m = n - 1$. Then $n + 1 = m + 2$ and

when $n = 2$, $m = 1$. Thus $\displaystyle\sum_{n=2}^{\infty} \frac{1}{n^2 - 1} = \sum_{m=1}^{\infty} \frac{1}{m(m+2)}$. The partial fraction decomposition of

$\dfrac{1}{m(m+2)}$ is $\dfrac{A}{m} + \dfrac{B}{m+2}$ and $A(m+2) + Bm = 1$. If $m = 0$, $2A = 1 \implies A = 1/2$ and if

$m = -2$, $-2B = 1 \implies B = -1/2$. So

$$\sum_{n=2}^{\infty} \frac{1}{n^2 - 1} = \sum_{m=1}^{\infty} \left(\frac{1/2}{m} - \frac{1/2}{m+2}\right) = \sum_{m=1}^{\infty} \frac{1}{2}\left(\frac{1}{m} - \frac{1}{m+2}\right),$$

and

$$S_m = \frac{1}{2}\left(1 - \frac{1}{3}\right) + \frac{1}{2}\left(\frac{1}{2} - \frac{1}{4}\right) + \frac{1}{2}\left(\frac{1}{3} - \frac{1}{5}\right) + \cdots$$

$$+ \frac{1}{2}\left(\frac{1}{m-2} - \frac{1}{m}\right) + \frac{1}{2}\left(\frac{1}{m-1} - \frac{1}{m+1}\right) + \frac{1}{2}\left(\frac{1}{m} - \frac{1}{m+2}\right)$$

$$= \frac{1}{2}\left(1 + \frac{1}{2} - \frac{1}{m+1} - \frac{1}{m+2}\right).$$

Thus $\lim\limits_{m\to\infty} S_m = \lim\limits_{m\to\infty} \dfrac{1}{2}\left(\dfrac{3}{2} - \dfrac{1}{m+1} - \dfrac{1}{m+2}\right) = \dfrac{3}{4}$ and $\sum\limits_{n=2}^{\infty} \dfrac{1}{n^2-1} = \dfrac{3}{4}$.

29. Show that the series $\sum\limits_{n=1}^{\infty} \ln\left(\dfrac{n}{n+1}\right)$ diverges.

SOLUTION: For each n,

$$S_n = \ln\dfrac{1}{2} + \ln\dfrac{2}{3} + \ln\dfrac{3}{4} + \cdots + \ln\dfrac{n-1}{n} + \ln\dfrac{n}{n+1}$$

$$= (\ln 1 - \ln 2) + (\ln 2 - \ln 3) + (\ln 3 - \ln 4) + \cdots + (\ln(n-1) - \ln n) + (\ln n - \ln(n+1))$$

$$= \ln 1 - \ln(n+1) = -\ln(n+1).$$

Thus the sequence $\{S_n\}$ does not converge since the logarithm function is unbounded; therefore, $\sum\limits_{n=1}^{\infty} \ln\dfrac{n}{n+1}$ diverges.

39. The government claims to be able to stimulate the economy substantially by giving each taxpayer a $50 tax rebate. They reason that 90% of this amount will be spent, that 90% of the amount spent will again be spent, and so on. If this is true, how much total expenditure will result from this $50 rebate?

SOLUTION: This describes a sequence where $a_1 = 0.9(50)$ and $a_n = 0.9a_{n-1}$ for $n \geq 2$. The total expenditure from the $50 rebate is $\sum\limits_{n=1}^{\infty} a_n$. To determine a non-recursive form of a_n, examine the first few terms of the sequence.

$$a_1 = 0.9(50)$$
$$a_2 = 0.9(a_1) = 0.9\,(0.9(50)) = (0.9)^2(50)$$
$$a_n = 50(0.9)^n.$$

Now

$$\sum\limits_{n=1}^{\infty} 50(0.9)^n = \sum\limits_{n=1}^{\infty} 50(0.9)(0.9)^{n-1} = \sum\limits_{n=1}^{\infty} 45(0.9)^{n-1},$$

which is a geometric series with $a = 45$ and $r = 0.9$. This series converges to $\dfrac{a}{1-r} = \dfrac{45}{1-0.9} = \dfrac{45}{0.1} = 450$. Thus the $50 rebate will produce a total expenditure of $450.

51. Complete the steps in the following proof that the harmonic series $\sum_{n=1}^{\infty} \frac{1}{n}$ diverges. Suppose $\sum_{n=1}^{\infty} \frac{1}{n} = S$. Find $\sum_{n=1}^{\infty} \frac{1}{2n}$ and show that $\sum_{n=1}^{\infty} \frac{1}{2n} < \sum_{n=1}^{\infty} \frac{1}{2n-1}$. Use this to construct the contradiction that $S > \frac{1}{2}S + \frac{1}{2}S$.

SOLUTION: Assuming that $\sum_{n=1}^{\infty} \frac{1}{n} = S$, then $\sum_{n=1}^{\infty} \frac{1}{2n} = \frac{1}{2}\sum_{n=1}^{\infty} \frac{1}{n} = \frac{1}{2}S$.

Since $\frac{1}{2n} < \frac{1}{2n-1}$ for all n, $\sum_{n=1}^{\infty} \frac{1}{2n} < \sum_{n=1}^{\infty} \frac{1}{2n-1}$. Now

$$\sum_{n=1}^{\infty} \frac{1}{n} = 1 + \frac{1}{2} + \frac{1}{3} + \frac{1}{4} + \cdots = \left(1 + \frac{1}{3} + \frac{1}{5} + \cdots\right) + \left(\frac{1}{2} + \frac{1}{4} + \frac{1}{6} + \cdots\right)$$

$$= \sum_{n=1}^{\infty} \left(\frac{1}{2n-1} + \frac{1}{2n}\right).$$

Thus $\sum_{n=1}^{\infty} \frac{1}{n} - \sum_{n=1}^{\infty} \frac{1}{2n} = S - \frac{1}{2}S = \frac{1}{2}S = \sum_{n=1}^{\infty} \frac{1}{2n-1}$. But then $\frac{1}{2}S = \sum_{n=1}^{\infty} \frac{1}{2n} < \sum_{n=1}^{\infty} \frac{1}{2n-1} < \frac{1}{2}S$ and $S < \frac{1}{2}S + \frac{1}{2}S$, which is impossible.

Thus the assumption that $\sum_{n=1}^{\infty} \frac{1}{n} = S$ is incorrect.

_____**8.3**

Infinite Series
with Positive Terms

3. Use the comparison and limit comparison tests to determine whether $\sum_{n=1}^{\infty} \frac{1}{n^2 + 2n + 2}$ converges or diverges.

SOLUTION: Recall that $\sum_{n=1}^{p} \frac{1}{n^p}$, the p-series, converges if $p > 1$ and diverges if $p \leq 1$. Thus

$\sum_{n=1}^{\infty} \frac{1}{n^2}$ converges. Now $\sum_{n=1}^{\infty} \frac{1}{n^2 + 2n + 2}$ is a series consisting of positive terms and $n^2 + 2n + 2 \geq$

$n^2 \implies \frac{1}{n^2 + 2n + 2} \leq \frac{1}{n^2}$ and, by the comparison test, $\sum_{n=1}^{\infty} \frac{1}{n^2 + 2n + 2}$ converges.

11. Use the comparison and limit comparison tests to determine whether $\displaystyle\sum_{n=1}^{\infty} \frac{\cos n\pi + 2}{n^2}$ converges or diverges.

SOLUTION: Since $-1 \le \cos n\pi \le 1$, $1 \le \cos n\pi + 2 \le 3$ and $\displaystyle\sum_{n=1}^{\infty} \frac{\cos n\pi + 2}{n^2}$ is a series of

positive terms with $\dfrac{\cos n\pi + 2}{n^2} \le \dfrac{3}{n^2}$ for all n. Now $\displaystyle\sum_{n=1}^{\infty} \frac{3}{n^2}$ converges since $\displaystyle\sum_{n=1}^{\infty} \frac{1}{n^2}$ converges.

Thus by the comparison test, $\displaystyle\sum_{n=1}^{\infty} \frac{\cos n\pi + 2}{n^2}$ converges.

15. Use the comparison and limit comparison tests to determine whether $\displaystyle\sum_{n=1}^{\infty} \frac{n!}{(n+1)!}$ converges or diverges.

SOLUTION:

$$\sum_{n=1}^{\infty} \frac{n!}{(n+1)!} = \sum_{n=1}^{\infty} \frac{n!}{(n+1)n!} = \sum_{n=1}^{\infty} \frac{1}{n+1},$$

so let $a_n = \dfrac{1}{n+1}$ and $b_n = \dfrac{1}{n}$.

Then $\displaystyle\lim_{n\to\infty} \frac{a_n}{b_n} = \lim_{n\to\infty} \frac{1/(n+1)}{1/n} = \lim_{n\to\infty} \frac{n}{n+1} = 1.$

Thus by the limit comparison test and the fact that $\displaystyle\sum_{n=1}^{\infty} \frac{1}{n}$ diverges, $\displaystyle\sum_{n=1}^{\infty} \frac{n!}{(n+1)!}$ diverges.

23. Use the integral test to determine whether $\displaystyle\sum_{n=1}^{\infty} \frac{\ln n}{n}$ converges or diverges.

SOLUTION: Let $f(x) = \dfrac{\ln x}{x}$. Then $f'(x) = \dfrac{x(1/x) - (\ln x)(1)}{x^2} = \dfrac{1 - \ln x}{x^2}$. Now $f'(x) < 0$

for $x > e$ so $f(x) = \dfrac{\ln x}{x}$ is decreasing and continuous on $[e, \infty)$. Now $f(n) = a_n$ for all

n and $\displaystyle\sum_{n=1}^{\infty} \frac{\ln n}{n}$ is a series of positive terms. Consider $\displaystyle\sum_{n=3}^{\infty} \frac{\ln n}{n}$ using the integral test. Now

$\displaystyle\int_3^{\infty} \frac{\ln x}{x}\, dx = \lim_{M\to\infty} \int_3^M \frac{\ln x}{x}\, dx.$ To integrate, let $u = \ln x$. Then $du = \dfrac{1}{x}\, dx$ and

$$\int \frac{\ln x}{x}\, dx = \int u\, du = \frac{1}{2}u^2 + C = \frac{1}{2}(\ln x)^2 + C.$$

Thus

$$\int_3^\infty \frac{\ln x}{x}\, dx = \lim_{M\to\infty}\left(\frac{1}{2}(\ln M)^2 - \frac{1}{2}(\ln 3)^2\right) = \frac{1}{2}\left(\lim_{M\to\infty}\ln M\right)^2 - \frac{1}{2}(\ln 3)^2 = \infty.$$

Thus $\displaystyle\sum_{n=3}^\infty \frac{\ln n}{n}$ diverges, so $\displaystyle\sum_{n=1}^\infty \frac{\ln n}{n}$ diverges.

29. Use the integral test to determine whether $\displaystyle\sum_{n=1}^\infty \frac{n}{(1+n^2)^2}$ converges or diverges.

SOLUTION: Let $f(x) = \dfrac{x}{(1+x^2)^2}$. Then $f(n) = a_n$ for all n and

$$f'(x) = \frac{(1+x^2)^2 - x\left(2(1+x^2)(2x)\right)}{\left((1+x^2)^2\right)^2}$$

$$= \frac{(1+x^2)\left((1+x^2) - 4x^2\right)}{(1+x^2)^4} = \frac{1-3x^2}{(1+x^2)^3} < 0$$

for $x \geq 1$. Thus $f(x)$ is decreasing and continuous on $[1,\infty)$.

Also $\displaystyle\sum_{n=1}^\infty \frac{n}{(1+n^2)^2}$ is a series of positive terms. So $\displaystyle\int_1^\infty \frac{x}{(1+x^2)^2}\, dx = \lim_{M\to\infty}\int_1^M \frac{x}{(1+x^2)^2}\, dx$.

Let $u = 1 + x^2$. Then $du = 2x\, dx$ and

$$\int \frac{x}{(1+x^2)^2}\, dx = \frac{1}{2}\int \frac{du}{u^2} = -\frac{1}{2}u^{-1} + C = \frac{-1}{2(1+x^2)} + C$$

So $\displaystyle\int_1^\infty \frac{x}{(1+x^2)^2}\, dx = \lim_{M\to\infty}\left[\frac{-1}{2(1+x^2)}\right]\Bigg|_1^M$

$$= -\frac{1}{2}\left(\lim_{M\to\infty}\frac{1}{1+M^2} - \frac{1}{1+1^2}\right) = -\frac{1}{2}\left(0 - \frac{1}{2}\right) = \frac{1}{4}.$$

Thus by the integral test, $\displaystyle\sum_{n=1}^\infty \frac{n}{(1+n^2)^2}$ converges.

33. Determine whether $\displaystyle\sum_{n=1}^\infty \left(\left(\frac{2}{3}\right)^n + \frac{1}{n}\right)$ converges or diverges.

SOLUTION: Let $a_n = \left(\dfrac{2}{3}\right)^n + \dfrac{1}{n}$ and $b_n = \dfrac{1}{n}$. Clearly $a_n > b_n$ for all n, so by the comparison test and the fact that $\displaystyle\sum_{n=1}^\infty \frac{1}{n}$ diverges, $\displaystyle\sum_{n=1}^\infty \left(\left(\frac{2}{3}\right)^n + \frac{1}{n}\right)$ diverges.

39. Determine whether $\sum\limits_{n=2}^{\infty} (\ln n)^{-n}$ converges or diverges.

SOLUTION: $\sum\limits_{n=2}^{\infty} (\ln n)^{-n} = \sum\limits_{n=2}^{\infty} \dfrac{1}{(\ln n)^n}$, so let $a_n = \dfrac{1}{(\ln n)^n}$ and $b_n = \dfrac{1}{2^n}$. Now $\ln 8 > 2$, so

for $n \geq 8$, $\ln n > 2 \implies (\ln n)^n > 2^n \implies \dfrac{1}{(\ln n)^n} < \dfrac{1}{2^n}$. Thus since $\sum\limits_{n=2}^{\infty} (\ln n)^{-n}$ is a series of

positive terms and by the comparison test, $\sum\limits_{n=2}^{\infty} (\ln n)^{-n}$ converges since $\sum\limits_{n=1}^{\infty} \dfrac{1}{2^n}$ converges.

45. A biologist examines a circular plate for a certain type of bacteria by drawing concentric circles of radius n, for positive integers n. The number of bacteria between the $(n-1)$-st circle and the n-th circle is inversely proportional to the area of the n-th circle. (The constant of proportionality is independent of n.) Show that the number of bacteria on the plate is finite without assuming that the plate has finite radius.

SOLUTION: The area of the n-th circle is πn^2. Let a_n be the number of bacteria between the $(n-1)$-st circle and the n-th circle. Then $a_n = k\left(\dfrac{1}{\pi n^2}\right)$. Show that $\sum\limits_{n=1}^{\infty} \dfrac{k}{\pi n^2}$ is finite. Let $b_n = 1/n^2$. Then

$$\lim_{n\to\infty} \frac{a_n}{b_n} = \lim_{n\to\infty} \frac{k/(\pi n^2)}{1/n^2} = \lim_{n\to\infty} \frac{k}{\pi} = \frac{k}{\pi},$$

which is finite. Thus by the limit comparison test and the fact that $\sum\limits_{n=1}^{\infty} \dfrac{1}{n^2}$ converges, $\sum\limits_{n=1}^{\infty} \dfrac{k}{\pi n^2}$ converges and the number of bacteria on the plate is finite regardless of the radius of the plate.

57. Use the result of EXERCISE 56 to determine the number of terms required to approximate to within 10^{-3} the sum of the following convergent series. a) $\sum\limits_{n=1}^{\infty} \dfrac{1}{n^2}$.

SOLUTION: The error in approximating $S = \sum\limits_{n=1}^{\infty} a_n$ by $S_N = \sum\limits_{n=1}^{N} a_n$ is $S - S_N = \sum\limits_{n=N+1}^{\infty} a_n$

where $\sum\limits_{n=1}^{\infty} a_n$ is a series of positive terms and by the result in EXERCISE 56, $S - S_N < \int_N^{\infty} f(x)\,dx$,

where f is continuous and decreasing and $f(n) = a_n$ for each n. Thus $\int_N^{\infty} f(x)\,dx$ can be used

as an upper bound for the error. In each of the following, find M so that $10^{-3} > \int_N^{\infty} f(x)\,dx$. Then $S - S_M < 10^{-3}$.

a) Let $f(x) = 1/x^2$, which is decreasing and continuous on $[1, \infty)$. Now

$$\int_N^\infty x^{-2}\, dx = \lim_{M \to \infty} \int_N^M x^{-2}\, dx = \lim_{M \to \infty} [-x^{-1}]\Big|_N^M = -\left(\lim_{M \to \infty} \frac{1}{M} - \frac{1}{N}\right) = \frac{1}{N}.$$

Set $10^{-3} > \dfrac{1}{N}$. Then $N > 10^3$, so 1000 terms are necessary to guarantee the approximation is within 10^{-3}.

_____8.4

Alternating Series

_____

7. Determine whether $\displaystyle\sum_{n=0}^\infty (-1)^n \frac{n+2}{4n+5}$ converges or diverges.

SOLUTION: $\displaystyle\lim_{n \to \infty} \frac{n+2}{4n+5} = \lim_{n \to \infty} \frac{1 + (2/n)}{4 + (5/n)} = \frac{1}{4}$; thus $\displaystyle\lim_{n \to \infty} a_n = \lim_{n \to \infty} (-1)^n \frac{n+2}{4n+5} \neq 0$ and $\displaystyle\sum_{n=0}^\infty (-1)^n \frac{n+2}{4n+5}$ diverges.

13. Determine whether $\displaystyle\sum_{n=2}^\infty (-1)^n \frac{1}{\ln n}$ converges or diverges.

SOLUTION: $\displaystyle\lim_{n \to \infty} a_n = \lim_{n \to \infty} \frac{1}{\ln n} = 0$ and $\ln(n+1) > \ln n \implies \displaystyle\sum_{n=2}^\infty (-1)^n \frac{1}{\ln n}$ converges.

21. Determine whether $\displaystyle\sum_{n=1}^\infty \frac{(-1)^n (1000)^n}{n!}$ converges or diverges.

SOLUTION: $\displaystyle\lim_{n \to \infty} a_n = \lim_{n \to \infty} \frac{(1000)^n}{n!}$. As $n \to \infty$, n becomes greater than 1000, so let $n > 1000$. Then $\dfrac{1000}{n+1} < 1$ and

$$a_{n+1} = \frac{1000^{n+1}}{(n+1)!} = \frac{1000}{n+1} \cdot \frac{1000^n}{n!} = \frac{1000}{n+1} a_n < a_n.$$

Also

$$a_n = \frac{1000^{1000}}{1000!} \left(\frac{1000}{1001}\right)\left(\frac{1000}{1002}\right)\left(\frac{1000}{1003}\right) \cdots \left(\frac{1000}{n}\right) < \frac{1000^{1000}}{1000!} \cdot \frac{1000}{n}.$$

Now

$$\lim_{n \to \infty} \frac{1000^{1000}}{1000!} \cdot \frac{1000}{n} = \frac{1000^{1001}}{1000!} \lim_{n \to \infty} \frac{1}{n} = 0.$$

Thus $\lim_{n \to \infty} a_n = 0$ and $\displaystyle\sum_{n=1}^{\infty} \frac{(-1)^n (1000)^n}{n!}$ converges.

25. Determine whether $\displaystyle\sum_{n=1}^{\infty} (-1)^{n-1} \frac{\pi^n}{n e^n}$ converges or diverges.

SOLUTION: $\displaystyle\lim_{n \to \infty} a_n = \lim_{n \to \infty} \frac{\pi^n}{n e^n} = \lim_{n \to \infty} \frac{(\pi/e)^n}{n}$ which yields the indeterminate form $\dfrac{\infty}{\infty}$.

Apply L'Hôpital's rule and obtain $\displaystyle\lim_{n \to \infty} \frac{(\pi/e)^n}{n} = \lim_{n \to \infty} \frac{n(\pi/e)^{n-1}}{1} = \infty$ since $\pi/e > 1$. Thus

$\displaystyle\sum_{n=1}^{\infty} (-1)^{n-1} \frac{\pi^n}{n e^n}$ diverges.

29. Determine whether $\displaystyle\sum_{n=1}^{\infty} (-1)^n \frac{n^3}{n^3 + e^n}$ converges or diverges.

SOLUTION: Consider $f(x) = \dfrac{x^3}{x^3 + e^x}$. Then

$$f'(x) = \frac{(x^3 + e^x)(3x^2) - x^3(3x^2 + e^x)}{(x^3 + e^x)^2} = \frac{3x^5 + 3x^2 e^x - 3x^5 - x^3 e^x}{(x^3 + e^x)^2}$$

$$= \frac{x^2 e^x(3 - x)}{(x^3 + e^x)^2} < 0 \quad \text{for } x > 3,$$

so $f(x)$ is decreasing for $x > 3$. Thus $a_{n+1} < a_n$ for $n > 3$.

Now $\displaystyle\lim_{n \to \infty} \frac{n^3}{n^3 + e^n}$ yields the indeterminate form $\dfrac{\infty}{\infty}$. Thus

$$\lim_{n \to \infty} \frac{n^3}{n^3 + e^n} = \lim_{n \to \infty} \frac{3n^2}{3n^2 + e^n} = \lim_{n \to \infty} \frac{6n}{6n + e^n} = \lim_{n \to \infty} \frac{6}{6 + e^n} = 0$$

by repeated applications of L'Hôpital's rule; thus $\displaystyle\sum_{n=1}^{\infty} (-1)^n \frac{n^3}{n^3 + e^n}$ converges.

35. Determine whether $\displaystyle\sum_{n=1}^{\infty} \frac{(-1)^n (n!)^2}{(2n)!}$ diverges or converges.

SOLUTION: $a_n = \dfrac{(n!)^2}{(2n)!}$ and

$$a_{n+1} = \frac{((n+1)!)^2}{(2(n+1))!} = \frac{(n+1)^2 (n!)^2}{(2n+2)(2n+1)(2n)!} = \frac{(n+1)^2}{(2n+2)(2n+1)} a_n < a_n,$$

since $\dfrac{n+1}{2(n+1)} < 1$ and $\dfrac{n+1}{2(n+1)-1} < 1$.

Now $\displaystyle\lim_{n\to\infty} a_n = \lim_{n\to\infty} \dfrac{(n!)^2}{(2n)!} = \lim_{n\to\infty} \dfrac{n!}{2n(2n-1)\cdots(n+1)}$.

$$a_n = \frac{n!}{2n(2n-1)\cdots(n+1)} = \frac{n!}{2n(2n-1)(2n-2)\cdots(2n-(n-2))(2n-(n-1))}$$

$$= \frac{n(n-1)(n-2)\cdots(n-(n-2))(n-(n-1))}{2n\left(2\left(n-\frac{1}{2}\right)\right)(2(n-1))\cdots\left(2\left(n-\frac{1}{2}(n-2)\right)\right)\left(2\left(n-\frac{1}{2}(n-1)\right)\right)}$$

$$= \frac{n(n-1)(n-2)\cdots(n-(n-2))(n-(n-1))}{2^n\left(n\left(n-\frac{1}{2}\right)(n-1)\cdots\left(n-\frac{1}{2}(n-2)\right)\left(n-\frac{1}{2}(n-1)\right)\right)} < \frac{1}{2^n}$$

since $\dfrac{n-1}{n-(1/2)} < 1, \dfrac{n-2}{n-1} < 1, \ldots, \dfrac{n-(n-2)}{n-\frac{1}{2}(n-2)} < 1$ and $\dfrac{n-(n-1)}{n-\frac{1}{2}(n-1)} < 1$. Since $\displaystyle\lim_{n\to\infty}\frac{1}{2^n} = 0$

and $0 < a_n < \dfrac{1}{2^n}$ for all n, $\displaystyle\lim_{n\to\infty} a_n = 0$ and thus $\displaystyle\sum_{n=1}^{\infty} \frac{(-1)^n(n!)^2}{(2n)!}$ converges by the alternating series test.

39. Determine the number of terms of the series $\displaystyle\sum_{n=2}^{\infty} \frac{(-1)^n}{\ln n}$ that are required to produce an approximation to the infinite sum that is accurate to within 10^{-4}.

SOLUTION: $\quad a_n = \dfrac{1}{\ln n}$ so set $\dfrac{1}{\ln n} = 10^{-4}$ since $|S - S_n| < a_{n+1}$. Then $\ln n = 10^4$ and $n = e^{10^4} \approx 8.8 \times 10^{4342}$.
If $n \ge e^{10^4} + 1$, the approximation will be within 10^{-4}.

45. Determine an approximation to the sum of the series $\displaystyle\sum_{n=0}^{\infty} \frac{(-1)^n}{4^n + 1}$ to within 10^{-4}.

SOLUTION: To determine the number of terms required, set $\dfrac{1}{4^n + 1} = 10^{-4}$.

Then $4^n + 1 = 10^4 \implies 4^n = -1 + 10^4 \implies n\ln 4 = \ln(-1 + 10^4) \implies n = \dfrac{\ln(-1 + 10^4)}{\ln 4} \approx 6.6$, which indicates that 7 terms are needed ($n = 6$).

$$S_7 = \frac{1}{4^0 + 1} - \frac{1}{4^1 + 1} + \frac{1}{4^2 + 1} + \cdots - \frac{1}{4^7 + 1}$$

$$\approx 0.5 - 0.2 + 0.05882 - 0.01538 + 0.00389 - 0.00097 + 0.00024 \approx 0.3466.$$

Thus $S = 0.3466$ accurate to within 10^{-4}.

_____**8.5**

Absolute Convergence

5. Determine whether $\displaystyle\sum_{n=1}^{\infty}(-1)^{n-1}\frac{n}{n^2+1}$ is divergent, conditionally convergent or absolutely convergent.

SOLUTION: $\displaystyle\lim_{n\to\infty}\frac{n}{n^2+1} = 0$ so proceed by considering $\displaystyle\sum_{n=1}^{\infty}\left|(-1)^{n-1}\frac{n}{n^2+1}\right| = \sum_{n=1}^{\infty}\frac{n}{n^2+1}$.

Use the limit comparison test with $b_n = 1/n$. Then

$$\lim_{n\to\infty}\frac{a_n}{b_n} = \lim_{n\to\infty}\frac{n/(n^2+1)}{1/n} = \lim_{n\to\infty}\frac{n}{n^2+1}\cdot\frac{n}{1}$$

$$= \lim_{n\to\infty}\frac{n^2}{n^2+1} = \lim_{n\to\infty}\frac{1}{1+(1/n^2)} = 1 < \infty,$$

so $\displaystyle\sum_{n=1}^{\infty}\frac{n}{n^2+1}$ diverges since $\displaystyle\sum_{n=1}^{\infty}\frac{1}{n}$ diverges. Thus $\displaystyle\sum_{n=1}^{\infty}(-1)^{n-1}\frac{n}{n^2+1}$ is not absolutely convergent.

To show conditional convergence, show $a_{n+1} < a_n$. Let $f(x) = \dfrac{x}{x^2+1}$. Then $f(n) = a_n$ for all n. Now $f'(x) = \dfrac{(x^2+1)(1) - x(2x)}{(x^2+1)^2} = \dfrac{1-x^2}{(x^2+1)^2} < 0$ for $x > 1$, so f is decreasing for $x > 1$ and $a_{n+1} < a_n$. Therefore $\displaystyle\sum_{n=1}^{\infty}(-1)^{n-1}\frac{n}{n^2+1}$ is conditionally convergent.

15. Determine whether $\displaystyle\sum_{n=1}^{\infty}(-1)^{n-1}\frac{n}{e^n}$ is divergent, conditionally convergent or absolutely convergent.

SOLUTION: $\displaystyle\lim_{n\to\infty}a_n = \lim_{n\to\infty}\frac{n}{e^n} = \lim_{n\to\infty}\frac{1}{e^n} = 0$ by using L'Hôpital's rule. Proceed by examining $\displaystyle\sum_{n=1}^{\infty}\left|(-1)^{n-1}\frac{n}{e^n}\right| = \sum_{n=1}^{\infty}\frac{n}{e^n}$. Applying the ratio test,

$$\lim_{n\to\infty}\left|\frac{a_{n+1}}{a_n}\right| = \lim_{n\to\infty}\frac{(n+1)/e^{n+1}}{n/e^n} = \lim_{n\to\infty}\frac{n+1}{e^{n+1}}\cdot\frac{e^n}{n}$$

$$= \lim_{n\to\infty}\frac{n+1}{ne} = \lim_{n\to\infty}\frac{1+(1/n)}{e} = \frac{1}{e} < 1.$$

Thus $\sum_{n=1}^{\infty} (-1)^{n-1} \dfrac{n}{e^n}$ converges absolutely.

19. Determine whether $\sum_{n=1}^{\infty} \dfrac{(-1)^{2n-1}}{n}$ is divergent, conditionally convergent or absolutely convergent.

SOLUTION: $\lim\limits_{n \to \infty} \dfrac{1}{n} = 0$ so proceed to examine $\sum_{n=1}^{\infty} \left| \dfrac{(-1)^{2n+1}}{n} \right| = \sum_{n=1}^{\infty} \dfrac{1}{n}$. This is the harmonic

series, which diverges. Thus $\sum_{n=1}^{\infty} \dfrac{(-1)^{2n-1}}{n}$ is not absolutely convergent. This series is a series of

negative terms. Thus if it is not absolutely convergent, it diverges, so $\sum_{n=1}^{\infty} \dfrac{(-1)^{2n-1}}{n}$ is divergent.

23. Determine whether $\sum_{n=0}^{\infty} (-1)^n \dfrac{n^2}{\pi^n}$ is divergent, conditionally convergent or absolutely convergent.

SOLUTION:
$$\lim_{n \to \infty} |a_n| = \lim_{n \to \infty} \dfrac{n^2}{\pi^n} = \lim_{n \to \infty} \dfrac{2n}{n\pi^{n-1}} = \lim_{n \to \infty} \dfrac{2}{n(n-1)\pi^{n-2}} = 0$$
by two applications of L'Hôpital's rule.
Applying the ratio test,
$$\lim_{n \to \infty} \left| \dfrac{a_{n+1}}{a_n} \right| = \lim_{n \to \infty} \dfrac{(n+1)^2/\pi^{n+1}}{n^2/\pi^n} = \lim_{n \to \infty} \dfrac{(n+1)^2}{\pi^{n+1}} \cdot \dfrac{\pi^n}{n^2}$$

$$= \lim_{n \to \infty} \dfrac{(n+1)^2}{\pi n^2} = \lim_{n \to \infty} \dfrac{\left(1 + \dfrac{1}{n} \right)^2}{\pi} = \dfrac{1}{\pi} < 1.$$

Thus $\sum_{n=0}^{\infty} (-1)^n \dfrac{n^2}{\pi^n}$ is absolutely convergent.

37. Determine whether $\sum_{n=1}^{\infty} \dfrac{(-1)^n n^n}{(2n)!}$ is divergent, conditionally convergent or absolutely convergent.

SOLUTION: Consider $\sum_{n=1}^{\infty} \left| \dfrac{(-1)^n n^n}{(2n)!} \right| = \sum_{n=1}^{\infty} \dfrac{n^n}{(2n)!}$. Apply the ratio test and examine

$$\lim_{n \to \infty} \left| \dfrac{a_{n+1}}{a_n} \right| = \lim_{n \to \infty} \dfrac{(n+1)^{n+1}/(2(n+1))!}{n^n/(2n)!} = \lim_{n \to \infty} \dfrac{(n+1)^{n+1}}{(2n+2)(2n+1)(2n)!} \cdot \dfrac{(2n)!}{n^n}$$

$$= \lim_{n \to \infty} \frac{(n+1)^{n+1}}{(2n+2)(2n+1)n^n} = \lim_{n \to \infty} \frac{n+1}{(2n+2)(2n+1)} \cdot \frac{(n+1)^n}{n^n}$$

$$= \lim_{n \to \infty} \frac{1}{2(2n+1)} \cdot \left(\frac{n+1}{n}\right)^n = \lim_{n \to \infty} \frac{1}{2(2n+1)} \lim_{n \to \infty} \left(\frac{n+1}{n}\right)^n = 0(e) = 0.$$

Now

$$\lim_{n \to \infty} \left(\frac{n+1}{n}\right)^n = \lim_{n \to \infty} \left(1 + \frac{1}{n}\right)^n = e$$

from EXAMPLE 6 in SECTION 6.5.

$$\lim_{n \to \infty} \frac{a_{n+1}}{a_n} = 0 \cdot e = 0 < 1 \text{ and } \sum_{n=1}^{\infty} \frac{(-1)^n n^n}{(2n)!} \text{ converges absolutely.}$$

41. Determine whether $\displaystyle\sum_{n=1}^{\infty} \left(\frac{-n}{n^2+1}\right)^n$ is divergent, conditionally convergent or absolutely convergent.

SOLUTION: $\displaystyle\sum_{n=1}^{\infty} \left(\frac{-n}{n^2+1}\right)^n = \sum_{n=1}^{\infty} (-1)^n \left(\frac{n}{n^2+1}\right)^n$. Now $\displaystyle\lim_{n \to \infty} \left(\frac{n}{n^2+1}\right)^n = 0$ so proceed to

examine $\displaystyle\sum_{n=1}^{\infty} \left| (-1)^n \left(\frac{n}{n^2+1}\right)^n \right| = \sum_{n=1}^{\infty} \left(\frac{n}{n^2+1}\right)^n.$

Apply the root test and obtain

$$\lim_{n \to \infty} |a_n|^{1/n} = \lim_{n \to \infty} \left(\left(\frac{n}{n^2+1}\right)^n \right)^{1/n} = \lim_{n \to \infty} \frac{n}{n^2+1} = \lim_{n \to \infty} \frac{1/n}{1 + \frac{1}{n^2}} = 0$$

and $\displaystyle\sum_{n=1}^{\infty} \left(\frac{-n}{n^2+1}\right)^n$ converges absolutely.

45. Use the root test to test the convergence of $\displaystyle\sum_{n=1}^{\infty} \left(\frac{n-1}{3n+1}\right)^n.$

SOLUTION:

$$\lim_{n \to \infty} |a_n|^{1/n} = \lim_{n \to \infty} \left| \left(\frac{n-1}{3n+1}\right)^n \right|^{1/n} = \lim_{n \to \infty} \left(\left(\frac{n-1}{3n+1}\right)^n \right)^{1/n}$$

$$= \lim_{n \to \infty} \frac{n-1}{3n+1} = \lim_{n \to \infty} \frac{1 - \frac{1}{n}}{3 + \frac{1}{n}} = \frac{1}{3},$$

so $\displaystyle\sum_{n=1}^{\infty}\left(\frac{n-1}{3n+1}\right)^n$ converges absolutely.

_____8.6

Power Series
_____

5. Find the radius of convergence and the interval of convergence of $\displaystyle\sum_{n=0}^{\infty}\frac{x^n}{n!}$.

SOLUTION: Apply the ratio test and obtain

$$\lim_{n\to\infty}\left|\frac{a_{n+1}}{a_n}\right| = \lim_{n\to\infty}\left|\frac{x^{n+1}/(n+1)!}{x^n/n!}\right| = \lim_{n\to\infty}\left|\frac{x^{n+1}}{(n+1)!}\cdot\frac{n!}{x^n}\right|$$

$$= \lim_{n\to\infty}\frac{|x|}{n} = |x|\lim_{n\to\infty}\frac{1}{n} = |x|\cdot 0 = 0,$$

regardless of the value of x. Thus the series converges for all x, the radius of convergence is ∞, and the interval of convergence is **IR**.

13. Find the radius of convergence and the interval of convergence of $\displaystyle\sum_{n=1}^{\infty}\frac{2^n x^n}{n}$.

SOLUTION: Apply the ratio test and obtain

$$\lim_{n\to\infty}\left|\frac{a_{n+1}}{a_n}\right| = \lim_{n\to\infty}\left|\frac{2^{n+1}x^{n+1}/(n+1)}{2^n x^n/n}\right| = \lim_{n\to\infty}\left|\frac{2^{n+1}x^{n+1}n}{2^n x^n(n+1)}\right|$$

$$= \lim_{n\to\infty}\frac{|2x|\,n}{n+1} = |2x|\lim_{n\to\infty}\frac{n}{n+1} = |2x|.$$

Since the series converges for $0 \le \displaystyle\lim_{n\to\infty}\left|\frac{a_{n+1}}{a_n}\right| < 1$, set $0 \le |2x| < 1 \implies -1 < 2x < 1 \implies$ $-1/2 < x < 1/2$, so the radius of convergence is $1/2$.
At $x = -1/2$,

$$\sum_{n=1}^{\infty}\frac{2^n x^n}{n} = \sum_{n=1}^{\infty}\frac{2^n\left(-\frac{1}{2}\right)^n}{n} = \sum_{n=1}^{\infty}\frac{(-1)^n}{n},$$

which is the alternating harmonic series, a convergent series.

At $x = 1/2$, $\displaystyle\sum_{n=1}^{\infty}\frac{2^n x^n}{n} = \sum_{n=1}^{\infty}\frac{2^n\left(\frac{1}{2}\right)^n}{n} = \sum_{n=1}^{\infty}\frac{1}{n}$, the harmonic series, which is divergent.

Thus the interval of convergence is $\left[-\dfrac{1}{2}, \dfrac{1}{2}\right)$.

19. Find the radius of convergence and the interval of convergence of $\displaystyle\sum_{n=0}^{\infty}(n+2)^2(x-2)^n$.

SOLUTION: Apply the ratio test and obtain

$$\lim_{n\to\infty}\left|\frac{a_{n+1}}{a_n}\right| = \lim_{n\to\infty}\left|\frac{((n+1)+2)^2(x-2)^{n+1}}{(n+2)^2(x-2)^n}\right| = \lim_{n\to\infty}\frac{(n+3)^2}{(n+2)^2}|x-2|$$

$$= |x-2|\lim_{n\to\infty}\frac{\left(1+\dfrac{3}{n}\right)^2}{\left(1+\dfrac{2}{n}\right)^2} = |x-2|\cdot 1 = |x-2|.$$

Since the series converges if $0 \le \displaystyle\lim_{n\to\infty}\left|\frac{a_{n+1}}{a_n}\right| < 1$, set $0 \le |x-2| < 1$.

Then $-1 < x-2 < 1 \implies 1 < x < 3$ and the radius of convergence is 1. To determine convergence at the endpoints of the interval, set $x = 1$ and $x = 3$.

For $x = 1$, $\displaystyle\sum_{n=0}^{\infty}(n+2)^2(x-2)^n = \sum_{n=0}^{\infty}(n+2)^2(-1)^n$, which is clearly divergent as $\displaystyle\lim_{n\to\infty}(n+2)^2 \ne 0$.

Similarly at $x = 3$, $\displaystyle\sum_{n=0}^{\infty}(n+2)^2(1)^n$ diverges.

Thus the interval of convergence is $(1,3)$.

25. Find the radius of convergence and the interval of convergence of $\displaystyle\sum_{n=1}^{\infty}\frac{(2x+1)^n}{\sqrt{n}}$.

SOLUTION: Apply the ratio test and obtain

$$\lim_{n\to\infty}\left|\frac{a_{n+1}}{a_n}\right| = \lim_{n\to\infty}\left|\frac{(2x+1)^{n+1}/\sqrt{n+1}}{(2x+1)^n/\sqrt{n}}\right| = \lim_{n\to\infty}\frac{|2x+1|\sqrt{n}}{\sqrt{n+1}}$$

$$= |2x+1|\lim_{n\to\infty}\frac{\sqrt{1}}{\sqrt{1+\dfrac{1}{n}}} = |2x+1|\cdot 1 = |2x+1|.$$

Since the series converges if $0 \le \displaystyle\lim_{n\to\infty}\left|\frac{a_{n+1}}{a_n}\right| < 1$, set $0 \le |2x+1| < 1$. Then $-1 < 2x+1 < 1 \implies -2 < 2x < 0 \implies -1 < x < 0$ and the radius of convergence is 1/2. To determine convergence at the endpoints, set $x = 0$ and $x = -1$.

For $x = 0$, $\displaystyle\sum_{n=1}^{\infty} \frac{(2x+1)^n}{\sqrt{n}} = \sum_{n=1}^{\infty} \frac{1^n}{n^{1/2}}$, a divergent p-series. For $x = -1$, $\displaystyle\sum_{n=1}^{\infty} \frac{(2x+1)^n}{\sqrt{n}} =$

$\displaystyle\sum_{n=1}^{\infty} \frac{(-1)^n}{n^{1/2}}$, an alternating series which converges by the alternating series test since $\dfrac{1}{\sqrt{n+1}} <$

$\dfrac{1}{\sqrt{n}}$. Thus the interval of convergence is $[-1, 0)$.

29. Find the domain of $f(x) = \displaystyle\sum_{n=0}^{\infty} \frac{(x-1)^n}{n^2 + 2}$.

SOLUTION: To find the domain, determine the interval of convergence of the power series. Apply the ratio test and obtain

$$\lim_{n\to\infty} \left| \frac{a_{n+1}}{a_n} \right| = \lim_{n\to\infty} \left| \frac{(x-1)^{n+1}/\left((n+1)^2 + 2\right)}{(x-1)^n/(n^2+2)} \right| = \lim_{n\to\infty} \frac{|x-1|\,(n^2+2)}{(n+1)^2 + 2}$$

$$= |x-1| \lim_{n\to\infty} \frac{1 + \dfrac{2}{n^2}}{\left(1 + \dfrac{1}{n}\right)^2 + \dfrac{2}{n^2}} = |x-1| \cdot 1 = |x-1|.$$

Now $0 \le |x-1| < 1 \implies -1 < x - 1 < 1 \implies 0 < x < 2$.

When $x = 0$, $\displaystyle\sum_{n=0}^{\infty} \frac{(x-1)^n}{n^2+2} = \sum_{n=0}^{\infty} \frac{(-1)^n}{n^2+2}$, which converges absolutely by the comparison test since

$\dfrac{1}{n^2+2} < \dfrac{1}{n^2}$ for all n. Similarly, when $x = 2$, $\displaystyle\sum_{n=0}^{\infty} \frac{(x-1)^n}{n^2+2} = \sum_{n=0}^{\infty} \frac{1^n}{n^2+2}$, which also converges.

Thus the domain of f is $[0, 2]$.

37. Find the values of x for which $\displaystyle\sum_{n=0}^{\infty} \frac{2^n}{x^n}$ converges.

SOLUTION: Apply the ratio test and obtain

$$\lim_{n\to\infty} \left| \frac{a_{n+1}}{a_n} \right| = \lim_{n\to\infty} \left| \frac{2^{n+1}/x^{n+1}}{2^n/x^n} \right| = \lim_{n\to\infty} \frac{2}{|x|} = \frac{2}{|x|}.$$

Since the series converges for $0 \le \displaystyle\lim_{n\to\infty} \left| \frac{a_{n+1}}{a_n} \right| < 1$, set $0 < \dfrac{2}{|x|} < 1 \implies \dfrac{x}{2} > 1$ or $\dfrac{x}{2} < -1 \implies$

$x > 2$ or $x < -2$.

When $x = 2$, $\displaystyle\sum_{n=0}^{\infty} \frac{2^n}{x^n} = \sum_{n=0}^{\infty} \frac{2^n}{2^n} = \sum_{n=0}^{\infty} 1$, which diverges. When $x = -2$, $\displaystyle\sum_{n=0}^{\infty} \frac{2^n}{x^n} = \sum_{n=0}^{\infty} \frac{2^n}{(-2)^n} =$

$\displaystyle\sum_{n=0}^{\infty} (-1)^n$, which diverges. Thus $\displaystyle\sum_{n=0}^{\infty} \frac{2^n}{x^n}$ converges for $|x| > 2$, i.e., $x < -2$ or $x > 2$.

45. Find the interval of convergence of the power series $\sum\limits_{n=1}^{\infty} \dfrac{n^n x^n}{n!}$. (Hint: Use Stirling's formula given in EXERCISE 60 of SECTION 8.3 when considering convergence at the endpoints.)

SOLUTION:

$$\lim_{n\to\infty} \left| \frac{a_{n+1}x^{n+1}}{a_n x^n} \right| = \lim_{n\to\infty} \left| \frac{(n+1)^{n+1}x^{n+1}/(n+1)!}{n^n x^n/n!} \right| = |x| \lim_{n\to\infty} \left(\frac{n+1}{n} \right)^n = |x|\, e.$$

The limit was calculated in EXAMPLE 6 of SECTION 6.5. The series converges for $-1/e < x < 1/e$.

At $x = 1/e$, the series is $\sum\limits_{n=0}^{\infty} \dfrac{n^n e^{-n}}{n!}$. By Stirling's formula, the terms are asymptotically

$$\frac{n^n e^{-n}}{n!} \sim \frac{(n/e)^n}{\sqrt{2\pi n}(n/e)^n} = \frac{1}{\sqrt{2\pi n}};$$

thus the limit comparison test against the divergent p-series $\sum\limits_{n=1}^{\infty} \dfrac{1}{\sqrt{n}}$ implies that the given series diverges.

At $x = 1/e$, the (alternating) series is $\sum\limits_{n=0}^{\infty}(-1)^n \dfrac{n^n e^{-n}}{n!}$. By the preceding analysis, this series does not converge absolutely, but the terms do have the limit zero.

To see that the terms of the alternating series decrease, consider

$$\frac{a_{n+1}}{a_n} = \frac{(n+1)^{n+1}e^{-n+1}/(n+1)!}{n^n e^{-n}/n!} = \frac{\left(1+\frac{1}{n}\right)^n}{e}.$$

With $f(x) = \left(1+\dfrac{1}{x}\right)^x$, $f'(x) = \left(1+\dfrac{1}{x}\right)^x \left(\dfrac{1}{x}\right) \left(\dfrac{\ln\left(1+(1/x)\right)}{1/x} - \dfrac{1}{1+(1/x)} \right)$.

By EXERCISE 89a) of SECTION 4.6 of the text, $\dfrac{\ln(1+z)}{z} > \dfrac{1}{1+z}$, so $f'(x) > 0$ and f is increasing. Consequently a_{n+1}/a_n increases to its limit 1; thus, $a_{n+1}/a_n < 0$, so the terms of the alternating series decrease. The series converges conditionally at $x = -1/e$.

The interval of convergence is $-1/e \le x < 1/e$.

COMMENT: The difficulty here is to show that $(1+(1/n))^n$ increases to e. Numerical evidence of this is demonstrated in Table 6.1, page 463 of the text.

Differentiation and Integration of Power Series

3. Find a power series representation for $f(x) = \dfrac{1}{2 - x}$.

SOLUTION: $\dfrac{1}{2 - x} = \dfrac{1}{2} \cdot \dfrac{1}{1 - \dfrac{1}{2}x}$ so let $u = \dfrac{1}{2}x$. Then

$$\frac{1}{2} \cdot \frac{1}{1 - \dfrac{1}{2}x} = \frac{1}{2} \cdot \frac{1}{1 - u} = \frac{1}{2} \sum_{n=0}^{\infty} u^n$$

$$= \sum_{n=0}^{\infty} \frac{1}{2} u^n = \sum_{n=0}^{\infty} \frac{1}{2} \left(\frac{1}{2}x\right)^n = \sum_{n=0}^{\infty} \frac{1}{2} \left(\frac{1}{2}\right)^n x^n$$

$$= \sum_{n=0}^{\infty} \left(\frac{1}{2}\right)^{n+1} x^n = \sum_{n=0}^{\infty} \frac{x^n}{2^{n+1}}.$$

9. Find a power series representation for $f(x) = \dfrac{1}{1 - x^2}$.

SOLUTION: Let $u = x^2$. Then

$$\frac{1}{1 - x^2} = \frac{1}{1 - u} = \sum_{n=0}^{\infty} u^n = \sum_{n=0}^{\infty} (x^2)^n = \sum_{n=0}^{\infty} x^{2n}.$$

15. Find a power series representation for $f(x) = x \ln(1 + x)$.

SOLUTION: Consider $g(x) = \ln(1 + x)$. Then

$$g'(x) = \frac{1}{1 + x} = \frac{1}{1 - (-x)} = \sum_{n=0}^{\infty} (-x)^n$$

so

$$\ln(1 + x) = \int_0^x \frac{dt}{1 + t} = \int_0^x \frac{dt}{1 - (-t)} = \int_0^x \sum_{n=0}^{\infty} (-t)^n \, dt$$

$$= \sum_{n=0}^{\infty} \int_0^x (-1)^n t^n \, dt = \sum_{n=0}^{\infty} \frac{(-1)^n}{n+1} x^{n+1}.$$

Thus

$$f(x) = x \ln(1+x) = x \sum_{n=0}^{\infty} (-1)^n \frac{x^{n+1}}{n+1}$$

$$= \sum_{n=0}^{\infty} (-1)^n \frac{x^{n+2}}{n+1}.$$

21. Show that if $0 < x < 1$, then $\left| \dfrac{1}{1+x} - \displaystyle\sum_{i=0}^{n} (-1)^i x^i \right| < x^{n+1}.$

SOLUTION: If $0 < x < 1$, then

$$\frac{1}{1+x} = \frac{1}{1-(-x)} = \sum_{i=0}^{\infty} (-x)^i = \sum_{i=0}^{\infty} (-1)^i x^i,$$

an alternating convergent series. Now

$$\left| \sum_{i=0}^{\infty} (-1)^i x^i - \sum_{i=0}^{n} (-1)^i x^i \right| = |S - S_n| < a_{n+1} = x^{n+1}$$

by COROLLARY 8.32.

25. Use a power series representation to approximate $\displaystyle\int_0^{0.1} \ln(x+1)\, dx.$

SOLUTION: As in EXERCISE 15 above,

$$\ln(1+x) = \int_0^x \frac{dt}{1+t} = \int_0^x \sum_{n=0}^{\infty} (-1)^n t^n \, dt$$

$$= \sum_{n=0}^{\infty} \int_0^x (-1)^n t^n \, dt = \sum_{n=0}^{\infty} (-1)^n \frac{x^{n+1}}{n+1}.$$

Thus

$$\int_0^{0.1} \ln(x+1)\, dx = \int_0^{0.1} \sum_{n=0}^{\infty} (-1)^n \frac{x^{n+1}}{n+1} \, dx = \sum_{n=0}^{\infty} \int_0^{0.1} (-1)^n \frac{x^{n+1}}{n+1} \, dx$$

$$= \sum_{n=0}^{\infty} (-1)^n \frac{x^{n+2}}{(n+2)(n+1)} \Big|_0^{0.1}$$

$$= \sum_{n=0}^{\infty} (-1)^n \frac{(0.1)^{n+2}}{(n+2)(n+1)} - \sum_{n=0}^{\infty} (-1)^n \frac{0^{n+2}}{(n+2)(n+1)}$$

$$= \sum_{n=0}^{\infty} (-1)^n \frac{(0.1)^{n+2}}{(n+2)(n+1)}.$$

This is a convergent alternating series, so the error in approximating the series by a partial sum is less than the first term deleted. Since $a_2 = \dfrac{10^{-4}}{4.3} < 10^{-4}$, then

$$S_1 = \frac{(0.1)^2}{2.1} - \frac{(0.1)^3}{3.2} \approx 0.0048.$$

Thus $\displaystyle\int_0^{0.1} \ln(1+x)\,dx = 0.0048$ accurate to within 10^{-4}.

29. Use the technique of partial fractions to decompose $\dfrac{1}{1-x^2}$ and obtain a power series representation. Compare this series with the one found in EXERCISE 9.

SOLUTION: The partial fraction decompostion of $\dfrac{1}{1-x^2}$ is $\dfrac{A}{1-x} + \dfrac{B}{1+x}$. Then $A(1+x) + B(1-x) = 1$ and $x = 1 \implies 2A = 1 \implies A = 1/2$. Also $x = -1 \implies -2B = 1 \implies B = -1/2$. Thus

$$\frac{1}{1-x^2} = \frac{1/2}{1-x} + \frac{-1/2}{1+x} = \frac{1}{2}\sum_{n=0}^{\infty} x^n - \frac{1}{2}\sum_{n=0}^{\infty} (-x)^n$$

$$= \frac{1}{2}\left(\sum_{n=0}^{\infty} x^n - \sum_{n=0}^{\infty}(-1)^n x^n\right) = \frac{1}{2}\sum_{n=0}^{\infty}\left(x^n + (-1)^{n+1} x^n\right)$$

$$= \frac{1}{2}\left((x^1 - x^1) + (x^2 + x^2) + (x^3 - x^3) + \cdots\right)$$

$$= \frac{1}{2}\left(2x^2 + 2x^4 + \cdots\right) = x^2 + x^4 + \cdots = \sum_{n=0}^{\infty} x^{2n},$$

which is the same result as was obtained in EXERCISE 9.

35. Consider the functions f and g defined by

$$f(x) = \sum_{n=0}^{\infty} \frac{(-1)^{n+1} x^{2n+1}}{(2n+1)!} \qquad \text{and} \qquad g(x) = \sum_{n=0}^{\infty} \frac{(-1)^n x^{2n}}{(2n)!}.$$

Compute $f'(x)$ and $g'(x)$.

SOLUTION:

$$f(x) = \sum_{n=0}^{\infty} \frac{(-1)^{n+1} x^{2n+1}}{(2n+1)!} = \frac{-x}{1!} + \frac{x^3}{3!} - \frac{x^5}{5!} + \frac{x^7}{7!} - \cdots$$

so

$$f'(x) = -1 + \frac{3x^2}{3!} - \frac{5x^4}{5!} + \frac{7x^6}{7!} - \cdots = -1 + \frac{x^2}{2!} - \frac{x^4}{4!} + \frac{x^6}{6!} - \cdots$$

$$= \sum_{n=0}^{\infty} \frac{(-1)^n x^{2n}}{(2n)!} = g(x).$$

Next

$$g(x) = \frac{(-1)^n x^{2n}}{(2n)!} = 1 - \frac{x^2}{2!} + \frac{x^4}{4!} - \frac{x^6}{6!} + \cdots.$$

Then

$$g'(x) = -\frac{2x}{2!} + \frac{4x^3}{4!} - \frac{6x^5}{5!} + \cdots = -\frac{x}{1!} + \frac{x^3}{3!} - \frac{x^5}{5!} + \cdots$$

$$= \sum_{n=0}^{\infty} \frac{(-1)^n x^{2n+1}}{(2n+1)!} = \sum_{n=0}^{\infty} \frac{(-1)(-1)^{n-1} x^{2n+1}}{(2n+1)!}$$

$$= -\sum_{n=0}^{\infty} \frac{(-1)^{n+1} x^{2n+1}}{(2n+1)!} = -f(x).$$

So $f'(x) = g(x)$ and $g'(x) = -f(x)$, which is behavior like that of $f(x) = \sin x$ and $g(x) = \cos x$.

_____8.8

Taylor Polynomials and Taylor Series

5. Find the first four terms of the Maclaurin series for $f(x) = \arctan x$.

SOLUTION: The Maclaurin series for f is $f(x) = \sum_{n=0}^{\infty} \frac{f^{(n)}(0)}{n!} x^n$, so find the first three derivatives of f.

$$f'(x) = \frac{1}{1 + x^2} = (1 + x^2)^{-1}$$

$$f''(x) = -(1 + x^2)^{-2}(2x) = -2x(1 + x^2)^{-2}$$
$$f'''(x) = -2(1 + x^2)^{-2} - 2x\left(-2(1 + x^2)^{-3}(2x)\right) = -2(1 + x^2)^{-2} + 8x^2(1 + x^2)^{-3}$$
$$= -2(1 + x^2)^{-3}\left((1 + x^2) - 4x^2\right) = -2(1 + x^2)^{-3}(1 - 3x^2).$$

Thus

$$a_0 = \frac{f(0)}{0!}x^0 = \frac{\arctan 0}{1} = 0,$$

$$a_1 = \frac{f'(0)}{1!}x^1 = \frac{(1 + 0^2)^{-1}}{1}x = x,$$

$$a_2 = \frac{f''(0)}{2!}x^2 = \frac{-2(0)(1 + 0^2)^{-2}}{2}x^2 = 0 \quad \text{and}$$

$$a_3 = \frac{f'''(0)}{3!}x^3 = \frac{-2(1 + 0^2)^{-3}\left(1 - 3(0)^2\right)}{6}x^3 = -\frac{1}{3}x^3.$$

11. Find the first three Maclaurin polynomials for $f(x) = \arctan x$.

SOLUTION: If M_n denotes the n-th degree Maclaurin polynomial for f, then

$$M_n(x) = \sum_{i=0}^{n} \frac{f^{(i)}(0)}{i!}x^i,$$

which is the sum of the first n terms of the Maclaurin series. In EXERCISE 5 above the first four terms of the Maclaurin series for $f(x) = \arctan x$ were calculated. Thus

$$M_0(x) = 0,$$
$$M_1(x) = 0 + x = x,$$
$$M_2(x) = 0 + x + 0 = x, \quad \text{and}$$
$$M_3(x) = 0 + x + 0 + \frac{-1}{3}x^3 = x - \frac{1}{3}x^3.$$

17. Find the fourth Taylor polynomial for $f(x) = \tan x$ about $a = \pi/4$. Find the remainder.

SOLUTION: $P_4(x) = \sum_{i=0}^{4} \frac{f^{(i)}(a)}{i!}(x - a)^i$, so first calculate the first four derivatives of f.

$$f'(x) = \sec^2 x$$
$$f''(x) = 2\sec x \sec x \tan x = 2\sec^2 x \tan x$$
$$f'''(x) = 4\sec x(\sec x \tan x)\tan x + 2\sec^2 x \sec^2 x = 4\sec^2 x \tan^2 x + 2\sec^4 x$$
$$= 2\sec^2 x \left(2\tan^2 x + \tan^2 x + 1\right) = 2\sec^2 x(3\tan^2 x + 1)$$

$$f^{(4)}(x) = 4 \sec x \sec x \tan x (3 \tan^2 x + 1) + 2 \sec^2 x (6 \tan x \sec^2 x)$$
$$= 4 \sec^2 x \tan x (3 \tan^2 x + 1) + 12 \sec^4 x \tan x = 4 \sec^2 x \tan x (3 \tan^2 x + 1 + 3 \sec^2 x)$$
$$= 4 \sec^2 x \tan x (6 \tan^2 x + 4) = 8 \sec^2 x \tan x (3 \tan^2 x + 2).$$

So

$$P_4(x) = \frac{\tan \frac{\pi}{4}}{0!} \left(x - \frac{\pi}{4} \right)^0 + \frac{\sec^2 \frac{\pi}{4}}{1!} \left(x - \frac{\pi}{4} \right)^1$$

$$+ \frac{2 \sec^2 \frac{\pi}{4} \tan \frac{\pi}{4}}{2!} \left(x - \frac{\pi}{4} \right)^2 + \frac{2 \sec^2 \frac{\pi}{4} \left(3 \tan^2 \frac{\pi}{4} + 1 \right)}{3!} \left(x - \frac{\pi}{4} \right)^3$$

$$+ \frac{8 \sec^2 \frac{\pi}{4} \tan \frac{\pi}{4} \left(3 \tan^2 \frac{\pi}{4} + 2 \right)}{4!} \left(x - \frac{\pi}{4} \right)^4$$

$$= 1 + 2 \left(x - \frac{\pi}{4} \right) + \frac{4}{2!} \left(x - \frac{\pi}{4} \right)^2 + \frac{4(3+1)}{3!} \left(x - \frac{\pi}{4} \right)^3 + \frac{16(3+2)}{4!} \left(x - \frac{\pi}{4} \right)^4$$

$$= 1 + 2 \left(x - \frac{\pi}{4} \right) + 2 \left(x - \frac{\pi}{4} \right)^2 + \frac{8}{3} \left(x - \frac{\pi}{4} \right)^3 + \frac{10}{3} \left(x - \frac{\pi}{4} \right)^4.$$

$R_4(x) = \dfrac{f^{(5)}(\xi)}{(3+1)!} (x - a)^{3+1}$, so

$$f^{(5)}(x) = 16 \sec x \sec x \tan x \tan x (3 \tan^2 x + 2)$$
$$+ 8 \sec^2 x \sec^2 x (3 \tan^2 x + 2) + 8 \sec^2 x \tan x (6 \tan x \sec^2 x)$$
$$= 8(2 \sec^2 x \tan^2 x (3 \tan^2 x + 2) + \sec^4 x (3 \tan^2 x + 2) + 6 \sec^4 x \tan^2 x)$$
$$= 8 \sec^2 x \left(2 \tan^2 x (3 \tan^2 x + 2) + \sec^2 x (3 \tan^2 x + 2) + 6 \sec^2 x \tan^2 x \right)$$
$$= 8 \sec^2 x (6 \tan^4 x + 4 \tan^2 x + 3 \tan^4 x + 2 \tan^2 x + 3 \tan^2 x + 2 + 6 \tan^4 x + 6 \tan^2 x)$$
$$= 8 \sec^2 x (15 \tan^4 x + 15 \tan^2 x + 2).$$

Thus

$$R_4(x) = \frac{8 \sec^2 \xi (15 \tan^4 \xi + 15 \tan^2 \xi + 2)}{5!} \left(x - \frac{\pi}{4} \right)^5$$

$$= \frac{\sec^2 \xi (15 \tan^4 \xi + 15 \tan^2 \xi + 2)}{15} \left(x - \frac{\pi}{4} \right)^5,$$

for some ξ between $\pi/4$ and x.

25. Determine the Maclaurin series for $f(x) = \sin 3x$.

SOLUTION: $a_0 = \dfrac{\sin 3(0)}{0!} x^0 = 0.$

$$f'(x) = 3\cos 3x \qquad \text{so} \qquad a_1 = \frac{3\cos 3(0)}{1!}x = 3x$$

$$f''(x) = -9\sin 3x \qquad \text{so} \qquad a_2 = \frac{-9\sin 3(0)}{2!}x^2 = 0$$

$$f'''(x) = -27\cos 3x \qquad \text{so} \qquad a_3 = \frac{-27\cos 3(0)}{3!}x^3 = \frac{-27}{3!}x^3$$

$$f^{(4)}(x) = 81\sin 3x \qquad \text{so} \qquad a_4 = \frac{81\sin 3(0)}{4!}x^4 = 0$$

$$f^{(5)}(x) = 243\cos 3x \qquad \text{so} \qquad a_5 = \frac{243\cos 3(0)}{5!}x^5 = \frac{243}{4!}x^5.$$

Now

$$M_5(x) = 3x + \frac{-27}{3!}x^3 + \frac{243}{4!}x^5 = \frac{3^1}{1!}x + \frac{-(3)^3}{3!}x^3 + \frac{3^5}{5!}x^5$$

$$= (-1)^0\frac{3^{2(0)+1}}{(2(0)+1)!}x^{0+1} + (-1)^1\frac{3^{2(1)+1}}{(2(1)+1)!}x^{2(1)+1} + (-1)^2\frac{3^{2(2)+1}}{(2(2)+1)!}x^{2(2)+1}$$

$$= \sum_{i=0}^{2}(-1)^i\frac{3^{2i+1}}{(2i+1)!}x^{2i+1},$$

which indicates that the desired Maclaurin series is $\displaystyle\sum_{n=0}^{\infty}(-1)^n\frac{3^{2n+1}}{(2n+1)!}x^{2n+1}$.

31. Determine the Maclaurin series for $f(x) = 2^x$.

SOLUTION: $a_0 = \dfrac{2^0}{0!}x^0 = 1$. Now $f'(x) = 2^x\ln 2$ and $f^{(n)}(x) = 2^x(\ln 2)^n$. Thus the Maclaurin series expansion is $\displaystyle\sum_{n=0}^{\infty}\frac{2^0(\ln 2)^n}{n!}x^n = \sum_{n=0}^{\infty}\frac{(\ln 2)^n}{n!}x^n$.

37. Determine the Taylor series about $a = 1$ for $f(x) = e^x$.

SOLUTION: $f(x) = e^x \implies f'(x) = e^x$ and $f^{(n)}(x) = e^x$. Thus the desired Taylor series is $\displaystyle\sum_{n=0}^{\infty}\frac{e^1}{n!}(x-1)^n = \sum_{n=0}^{\infty}\frac{e}{n!}(x-1)^n$.

43. Use a Taylor polynomial for the function $f(x) = \sqrt{x}$ about $a = 4$ to find an approximation to $\sqrt{4.1}$ that is accurate to within 10^{-8}.

SOLUTION: $f(x) = \sqrt{x}$ so $P_0(4.1) = \dfrac{4^{1/2}}{0!}(4.1-4)^0 = 2$. $f'(x) = \frac{1}{2}x^{-1/2}$ so

$$P_1(4.1) = 2 + \frac{\frac{1}{2}(4)^{-1/2}}{1!}(4.1-4) = 2 + 0.25(0.1) = 2.025.$$

Then $f''(x) = -\dfrac{1}{4}x^{-3/2}$ so

$$P_2(4.1) = 2.025 + \frac{-\frac{1}{4}(4)^{-3/2}}{2!}(4.1 - 4)^2 = 2.025 - \frac{1}{8}\left(\frac{1}{8}\right)(0.1)^2$$

$$= 2.025 - 0.000156250 = 2.024843750.$$

Furthermore, $f'''(x) = \dfrac{3}{8}x^{-5/2}$ so

$$P_3(4.1) = 2.024843750 + \frac{\frac{3}{8}(4)^{-5/2}}{3!}(4.1 - 4)^3$$

$$= 2.024843750 + 0.000001953 = 2.024845703.$$

Next, $f^{(4)}(x) = -\frac{15}{16}x^{-7/2}$, so

$$P_4(4.1) = 2.024845703 + \frac{(-15/16)(4)^{-7/2}}{4!}$$

$$= 2.024845703 - 0.000000003 = 2.024845673,$$

so $\sqrt{4.1} = 2.02484567$ to within 10^{-8} since the Taylor series is an alternating series.

45. Use a Taylor polynomial to approximate $\sin 5°$ to an accuracy of 10^{-4}.

SOLUTION: $f(x) = \sin x$ and $5° = \pi/36$ radians. Let $a = 0$, so $P_0(\pi/36) = \dfrac{\sin 0}{0!}\left(\dfrac{\pi}{36} - 0\right)^0 = 0$.

Now $f'(x) = \cos x$, so $P_1\left(\frac{\pi}{36}\right) = 0 + \dfrac{\cos 0}{1!}\left(\dfrac{\pi}{36} - 0\right)^1 = 0.08726$. Since $f''(x) = -\sin x$, $P_2\left(\frac{\pi}{36}\right) = 0.08726 + \dfrac{-\sin 0}{2!}\left(\dfrac{\pi}{36} - 0\right)^2 = 0.08726$.

Since $f'''(x) = -\cos x$, so $P_3\left(\frac{\pi}{36}\right) = 0.08726 + \dfrac{-\cos 0}{3!}\left(\dfrac{\pi}{36} - 0\right)^3 = 0.08726 - 0.00011 = 0.087155$.

Since $f^{(4)}(x) = \sin x$ and $\sin 0 = 0$, proceed to $P_5(x)$. $f^{(5)}(x) = \cos x$, so

$$P_5\left(\frac{\pi}{36}\right) = 0.087155 + \frac{\cos 0}{5!}\left(\frac{\pi}{36} - 0\right)^5$$

$$= 0.087155 + 0.000000042 = 0.087155.$$

Thus $\sin 5° = 0.08716$ to within 10^{-4} since the Maclaurin series is an alternating series.

_____8.9

Applications of Taylor Polynomials and Series

_____

5. Find a power series representation for $f(x) = (3x + 2)^{3/2}$ and determine the radius of convergence.

SOLUTION:

$$f(x) = (3x + 2)^{3/2} = 2^{3/2} \left(\frac{3}{2}x + 1 \right)^{3/2}$$

$$= 2^{3/2} \left(1 + \sum_{n=1}^{\infty} \frac{\frac{3}{2}\left(\frac{3}{2} - 1\right) \cdots \left(\frac{3}{2} - n + 1\right)}{n!} \left(\frac{3}{2}x\right)^n \right)$$

is the power series representation using the binomial series. This series converges for $\left| \frac{3}{2}x \right| < 1$ or $-1 < \frac{3}{2}x < 1 \implies -\frac{2}{3} < x < \frac{2}{3} \implies |x| < \frac{2}{3}$, so the radius of convergence is 2/3.

7. Approximate $\int_0^{1/2} \sqrt[3]{1 + x^2}\, dx$ to within 10^{-4}.

SOLUTION: Using a binomial series,

$$(1 + x^2)^{1/3} = 1 + \sum_{n=1}^{\infty} \frac{\frac{1}{3}\left(\frac{1}{3} - 1\right) \cdots \left(\frac{1}{3} - n + 1\right)}{n!} (x^2)^n.$$

Thus

$$\int_0^{1/2} \sqrt[3]{1 + x^2}\, dx = \int_0^{1/2} \left(1 + \sum_{n=1}^{\infty} \frac{\frac{1}{3}\left(\frac{1}{3} - 1\right) \cdots \left(\frac{1}{3} - n + 1\right)}{n!} x^{2n} \right) dx$$

$$= \left[x + \sum_{n=1}^{\infty} \frac{\frac{1}{3}\left(\frac{1}{3} - 1\right) \cdots \left(\frac{1}{3} - n + 1\right)}{n!} \cdot \frac{1}{2n + 1} x^{2n+1} \right]\Bigg|_0^{1/2}$$

$$= \frac{1}{2} + \sum_{n=1}^{\infty} \frac{\frac{1}{3}\left(\frac{1}{3}-1\right)\cdots\left(\frac{1}{3}-n+1\right)}{n!\,(2n+1)} \left(\frac{1}{2}\right)^{2n+1}.$$

Since this is an alternating series, the partial sum S_n will approximate the limit of the series to within 10^{-4} when $a_{n+1} < 10^{-4}$. Since $a_3 < 10^{-4}$, then $S_2 = \frac{1/3}{1(3)}\left(\frac{1}{2}\right)^2 - \frac{(1/3)(2/3)}{2!5}\left(\frac{1}{2}\right)^5 =$ 0.5132 approximates $\int_0^{1/2} \sqrt[3]{1+x^2}\,dx$ to within 10^{-4}.

13. Write $e^{2+\pi i}$ in the form $a + bi$, where a and b are real numbers.

SOLUTION: $e^{2+\pi i} = e^2 e^{\pi i} = e^2\left(\cos\pi + i\sin\pi\right) = e^2(-1+0i) = -e^2 + 0i.$

_____Chapter 8

Review Exercises

5. Given $a_n = \sqrt[n]{n+1}$, determine:
   a) if the sequence is bounded;
   b) whether the sequence converges or diverges;
   c) the limit if the sequence converges.

SOLUTION: a) The sequence is bounded above by 2 and is bounded below by 1.

b) Since the sequence is decreasing and is bounded below, the sequence does converge. To show that the sequence is decreasing, consider $y = \sqrt[x]{x+1}$ for $x \geq 1$. Then $\ln y = \ln(x+1)^{1/x} = \frac{1}{x}\ln(x+1)$ and $\frac{1}{y}\frac{dy}{dx} = \frac{-1}{x^2}\ln(x+1) + \frac{1}{x(x+1)} \implies$

$$\frac{dy}{dx} = \frac{(x-(x+1)\ln(x+1))\,y}{x^2(x+1)} = \frac{\sqrt[x]{x+1}\,(x-(x+1)\ln(x+1))}{x^2(x+1)} < 0$$

for $x \geq 2$.

c) Evaluate $\lim\limits_{n\to\infty} \sqrt[n]{n+1}$. Consider $\lim\limits_{n\to\infty} e^{\ln \sqrt[n]{n+1}} = e^{\lim_{n\to\infty} \ln \sqrt[n]{n+1}}$. Now

$$\lim_{n\to\infty} \ln(n+1)^{1/n} = \lim_{n\to\infty} \frac{\ln(n+1)}{n} = \lim_{n\to\infty} \frac{1/n+1}{1} = 0,$$

by L'Hôpital's rule. Thus $\lim\limits_{n\to\infty} \sqrt[n]{n+1} = e^0 = 1$ and the sequence converges to 1.

15. Given $a_1 = 1$, $a_n = \frac{a_{n-1}}{3}$ if $n \geq 2$, determine:
   a) if the sequence is bounded;

   b) whether the sequence converges or diverges;

   c) the limit if the sequence converges.

SOLUTION: a) The sequence is bounded above by 1 and is bounded below by 0.

b) The sequence converges because it is decreasing and bounded below. It is decreasing since $a_n > 0$ and $a_n = \dfrac{a_{n-1}}{3}$, so $a_n < a_{n-1}$.

c) $\displaystyle \lim_{n \to \infty} a_n = \lim_{n \to \infty} \frac{1}{3^{n-1}} = 0$ since $a_n = \dfrac{1}{3^{n-1}}$.

21. Determine whether $\displaystyle \sum_{n=0}^{\infty} \frac{1}{e^n}$ is divergent, conditionally convergent or absolutely convergent.

SOLUTION: This is a series of positive terms. Applying the ratio test,

$$\lim_{n \to \infty} \left| \frac{1/e^{n+1}}{1/e^n} \right| = \lim_{n \to \infty} \left| \frac{e^n}{e^{n+1}} \right| = \lim_{n \to \infty} \frac{1}{e} = \frac{1}{e} < 1.$$

Thus the series converges absolutely.

27. Determine whether $\displaystyle \sum_{n=1}^{\infty} \frac{n!}{n^n}$ is divergent, conditionally convergent or absolutely convergent.

SOLUTION: Apply the ratio test.

$$\lim_{n \to \infty} \left| \frac{(n+1)!/(n+1)^{n+1}}{n!/n^n} \right| = \lim_{n \to \infty} \left| \frac{(n+1)!n^n}{n!(n+1)^{n+1}} \right| = \lim_{n \to \infty} \frac{(n+1)n^n}{(n+1)^n}$$

$$= \lim_{n \to \infty} \frac{n^n}{(n+1)^n} = \lim_{n \to \infty} \left(\frac{n}{n+1} \right)^n = \lim_{n \to \infty} \frac{1}{\left(1 + \dfrac{1}{n} \right)^n} = \frac{1}{e} < 1,$$

and $\displaystyle \sum_{n=1}^{\infty} \frac{n!}{n^n}$ converges absolutely.

35. Determine whether $\displaystyle \sum_{n=1}^{\infty} \frac{(-1)^n n}{(2n+1)^2}$ is divergent, conditionally convergent or absolutely convergent.

SOLUTION: Consider $\left| \dfrac{(-1)^n n}{(2n+1)^2} \right| = \dfrac{n}{(2n+1)^2} = \dfrac{n}{4n^2 + 4n + 1}$ and apply the limit comparison test with $\displaystyle \sum_{n=1}^{\infty} \frac{1}{n}$. Now

$$\lim_{n \to \infty} \frac{\dfrac{n}{4n^2 + 4n + 1}}{1/n} = \lim_{n \to \infty} \frac{n^2}{4n^2 + 4n + 1} = \frac{1}{4} > 0.$$

Since $\sum_{n=1}^{\infty} \frac{1}{n}$ diverges, $\sum_{n=1}^{\infty} \frac{n}{(2n+1)^2}$ diverges, and thus $\sum \frac{(-1)^n n}{(2n+1)^2}$ does not converge absolutely.

To show conditional convergence, show $|a_{n+1}| < |a_n|$. Consider $y = \frac{x}{(2x+1)^2}$ for $x \geq 1$. Then

$$\frac{dy}{dx} = \frac{(2x+1)^2 - x(2(2x+1)(2))}{(2x+1)^4} = \frac{(2x+1) - 4x}{(2x+1)^3} = \frac{1 - 2x}{(2x+1)^3} < 0$$

for $x \geq 1$. Thus $a_n = \frac{n}{(2n+1)^2}$ is decreasing and $\sum_{n=1}^{\infty} \frac{(-1)^n n}{(2n+1)^2}$ converges conditionally.

41. For $\sum_{n=1}^{\infty} \frac{x^n}{n^3 + n + 1}$ find:

a) the radius and
b) the interval of convergence.

SOLUTION: a) Applying the ratio test,

$$\lim_{n\to\infty} \left| \frac{a_{n+1}}{a_n} \right| = \lim_{n\to\infty} \left| \frac{x^{n+1}/((n+1)^3 + (n+1) + 1)}{x^n/(n^3 + n + 1)} \right| = \lim_{n\to\infty} |x| \frac{n^3 + n + 1}{(n+1)^3 + n + 2}$$

$$= |x| \lim_{n\to\infty} \frac{n^3 + n + 1}{(n+1)^3 + n + 2} = |x|.$$

Since the series converges for $0 \leq \lim_{n\to\infty} \left| \frac{a_{n+1}}{a_n} \right| < 1$, set $0 \leq |x| < 1 \implies -1 < x < 1$, so the radius of convergence is 1.

b) At $x = 1$, $\sum_{n=1}^{\infty} \frac{x^n}{n^3 + n + 1} = \sum_{n=1}^{\infty} \frac{1}{n^3 + n + 1}$ converges by comparison with $\sum_{n=1}^{\infty} \frac{1}{n^3}$, a convergent p-series.

Similarly, at $x = -1$, $\sum_{n=1}^{\infty} \frac{(-1)^n}{n^3 + n + 1}$ converges. Thus the interval of convergence is $[-1, 1]$.

47. For $\sum_{n=0}^{\infty} 3^n(x-3)^n$ find:

a) the radius and
b) the interval of convergence.

SOLUTION: a) Apply the ratio test and obtain

$$\lim_{n\to\infty} \left| \frac{3^{n+1}(x-3)^{n+1}}{3^n(x-3)^n} \right| = \lim_{n\to\infty} |3(x-3)| = |3(x-3)|.$$

Thus the series converges for $0 \le |3(x-3)| < 1 \implies -1 < 3(x-3) < 1 \implies -\frac{1}{3} < x - 3 < \frac{1}{3}$, so the radius of convergence is $1/3$.

b) $-\frac{1}{3} < x - 3 < \frac{1}{3} \implies \frac{8}{3} < x < \frac{10}{3}$. At $x = 10/3$,

$$\sum_{n=0}^{\infty} 3^n (x-3)^n = \sum_{n=0}^{\infty} 3^n \left(\frac{10}{3} - 3\right)^n = \sum_{n=0}^{\infty} 3^n \left(\frac{1}{3}\right)^n = \sum_{n=0}^{\infty} 1$$

which diverges. Also at $x = 8/3$,

$$\sum_{n=0}^{\infty} 3^n (x-3)^n = \sum_{n=0}^{\infty} 3^n \left(\frac{8}{3} - 3\right)^n = \sum_{n=0}^{\infty} (3)^n \left(-\frac{1}{3}\right)^n = \sum_{n=0}^{\infty} (-1)^n$$

which diverges. Thus the interval of convergence is $(8/3, 10/3)$.

55. Find an approximation to $\displaystyle\sum_{n=1}^{\infty} \frac{(-1)^{n-1}}{n3^n}$ that is accurate to within 10^{-5}.

SOLUTION: Since this is an alternating convergent sequence, calculate terms until $|a_i| < 10^{-5}$; in particular $a_9 = \frac{1}{9(3^9)} \approx 6 \times 10^{-6}$, so

$$S_8 = \frac{1}{3^1} - \frac{1}{2(3)^2} + \frac{1}{3(3)^3} + \cdots - \frac{1}{8(3)^8} \approx 0.28768.$$

Thus $\displaystyle\sum_{n=1}^{\infty} \frac{(-1)^{n-1}}{n3^n} \approx 0.28768.$

63. Find a power-series representation for $f(x) = \cosh x$.

SOLUTION:

$$\cosh x = \frac{e^x + e^{-x}}{2} = \frac{1}{2}(e^x + e^{-x}) = \frac{1}{2}\left(\sum_{n=0}^{\infty} \frac{x^n}{n!} + \sum_{n=0}^{\infty} \frac{(-x)^n}{n!}\right)$$

$$= \frac{1}{2}\left(\sum_{n=0}^{\infty} \frac{x^n}{n!} + \sum_{n=0}^{\infty} \frac{(-1)^n x^n}{n!}\right) = \frac{1}{2}\left(\sum_{n=0}^{\infty} \left(\frac{x^n}{n!} + \frac{(-1)^n x^n}{n!}\right)\right)$$

$$= \frac{1}{2}\sum_{n=0}^{\infty} \frac{1}{n!}(x^n + (-1)^n x^n) = \frac{1}{2}\sum_{n=0}^{\infty} \frac{1}{n!}(2x^{2n}) = \sum_{n=0}^{\infty} \frac{x^{2n}}{n!}.$$

67. a) Find the fourth Taylor polynomial about $\pi/4$ for $f(x) = \sec x$.

b) Use the polynomial found in part a) to approximate $\sec 0.8$.

SOLUTION: a)

$$f(x) = \sec x$$
$$f'(x) = \sec x \tan x$$
$$f''(x) = (\sec x \tan x)\tan x + \sec x \sec^2 x = \tan^2 x \sec x + \sec^3 x$$
$$= \sec x(\tan^2 x + \sec^2 x) = \sec x(2\sec^2 x - 1) = 2\sec^3 x - \sec x$$
$$f'''(x) = 6\sec^2 x \sec x \tan x - \sec x \tan x = \tan x(6 = sec^3 x - \sec x)$$
$$f^{(4)}(x) = \sec^2 x(6\sec^3 x - \sec x) + \tan x(18\sec^2 x \sec x \tan x - \sec x \tan x)$$
$$= \sec^2 x(6\sec^3 x - \sec x) + \tan^2 x(18\sec^3 x - \sec x)$$
$$= \sec^2 x(6\sec^3 x - \sec x) + (\sec^2 x - 1)(18\sec^3 x - \sec x)$$
$$= \sec^2 x(24\sec^3 x - 2\sec x) - \sec x(18\sec^2 x - 1)$$
$$= 2\sec^3 x(12\sec^2 x - 1) - \sec x(18\sec^2 x - 1).$$

Thus

$$P_4(x) = \frac{\sec \frac{\pi}{4}}{0!}\left(x - \frac{\pi}{4}\right)^0 + \frac{\sec \frac{\pi}{4}\tan \frac{\pi}{4}}{1!}\left(x - \frac{\pi}{4}\right)^1 + \frac{2\sec^3 \frac{3\pi}{4} - \sec \frac{3\pi}{4}}{2!}\left(x - \frac{\pi}{4}\right)^2$$

$$+ \frac{\tan \frac{\pi}{4}\left(6\sec^3 \frac{\pi}{4} - \sec \frac{\pi}{4}\right)}{3!}\left(x - \frac{\pi}{4}\right)^3$$

$$+ \frac{2\sec^3 \frac{\pi}{4}\left(12\sec^2 \frac{\pi}{4} - 1\right) - \sec \frac{\pi}{4}\left(18\sec^2 \frac{\pi}{4} - 1\right)}{4!}\left(x - \frac{\pi}{4}\right)^4$$

$$= \sqrt{2} + \sqrt{2}\left(x - \frac{\pi}{4}\right) + \frac{4\sqrt{2} - \sqrt{2}}{2}\left(x - \frac{\pi}{4}\right)^2 + \frac{12\sqrt{2} - \sqrt{2}}{6}\left(x - \frac{\pi}{4}\right)^3$$

$$+ \frac{92\sqrt{2} - 35\sqrt{2}}{24}\left(x - \frac{\pi}{4}\right)^4$$

$$= \sqrt{2}\left(1 + \left(x - \frac{\pi}{4}\right) + \frac{3}{2}\left(x - \frac{\pi}{4}\right)^2 + \frac{11}{6}\left(x - \frac{\pi}{4}\right)^3 + \frac{19}{8}\left(x - \frac{\pi}{4}\right)^4\right).$$

b)

$$P_4(0.8) = \sqrt{2}\left(1 + \left(0.8 - \frac{\pi}{4}\right) + \frac{3}{2}\left(0.8 - \frac{\pi}{4}\right)^2 + \frac{11}{6}\left(0.8 - \frac{\pi}{4}\right)^3 + \frac{19}{8}\left(0.8 - \frac{\pi}{4}\right)^4\right)$$

$$\approx 1.4142136(1 + 0.0146018 + 0.0003198 + 0.0000057 + 0.0000001) \approx 1.4353242.$$

69. Find the Maclaurin series for $f(x) = \dfrac{x - 1}{x + 1}$.

SOLUTION:

$$f(x) = \frac{x - 1}{x + 1} = 1 + \frac{-2}{x + 1} = 1 - 2\left(\frac{1}{x + 1}\right)$$

$$= 1 - 2\left(\frac{1}{1-(-x)}\right) = 1 - 2\sum_{n=0}^{\infty}(-x)^n = 1 - 2\sum_{n=0}^{\infty}(-1)^n x^n.$$

75. Find the values of x for which the series $\sum_{n=1}^{\infty}\frac{1}{n}\left(\frac{x-1}{x}\right)^n$ converges.

SOLUTION: Applying the ratio test,

$$\lim_{n\to\infty}\left|\frac{a_{n+1}}{a_n}\right| = \lim_{n\to\infty}\left|\frac{\frac{1}{n+1}\left(\frac{x-1}{x}\right)^{n+1}}{\frac{1}{n}\left(\frac{x-1}{x}\right)^n}\right| = \lim_{n\to\infty}\left|\frac{n}{n+1}\cdot\frac{x-1}{x}\right|$$

$$= \left|\frac{x-1}{x}\right|\lim_{n\to\infty}\frac{n}{n+1} = \left|\frac{x-1}{x}\right|.$$

Thus the series converges for $0 \le \left|\frac{x-1}{x}\right| < 1 \implies -1 < \frac{x-1}{x} < 1$.

Suppose $x > 0$. Then $-x < x - 1 < x \implies -2x < -1 < 0 \implies x > 1/2$.

Suppose $x < 0$. Then $-x > x - 1 > x \implies -2x > -1 > 0$, which is impossible since $-1 \not> 0$. Thus $x \not< 0$.

Clearly $x = 0$, so $\sum_{n=1}^{\infty}\frac{1}{n}\left(\frac{x-1}{x}\right)^n$ converges for $x > 1/2$.

At $x = 1/2$,

$$\sum_{n=1}^{\infty}\frac{1}{n}\left(\frac{x-1}{x}\right)^n = \sum_{n=1}^{\infty}\frac{1}{n}\left(\frac{\frac{1}{2}-1}{1/2}\right)^n = \sum_{n=1}^{\infty}\frac{1}{n}(-1)^n$$

which is the alternating harmonic series which does converge. Thus $\sum_{n=1}^{\infty}\frac{1}{n}\left(\frac{x-1}{x}\right)^n$ converges for $x \ge 1/2$.

9
Polar Coordinates and Parametric Equations

Sharpening your skills

You should review material on the Cartesian coordinate system and trigonometric functions in APPENDIX A, on functions and graphing in CHAPTERS 1 and 2, and on tangent lines in SECTION 2.1. You will also need to calculate area and arc length by integration. Many of the integrals will involve trigonometric functions or their powers.

Perhaps the problems below will help you review these topics. The section numbers refer to places in the text where the necessary tool is presented.

Practice Problems

1. Plot the points on an xy-graph. a) $(0, -2)$, b) $(-3, 1)$, c) $(\pi, \sqrt{2})$. (See APPENDIX A.2)

2. Calculate the values   a) $\sin \frac{7\pi}{6}$, b) $\cos\left(-\frac{3\pi}{4}\right)$, c) $4\cos\left(\frac{27\pi}{2}\right)$, d) $\sin\left(-\frac{5\pi}{6}\right)$. (See APPENDIX A.3)

3. Find all values of θ for which   a) $\sin \theta = -\frac{1}{2}$, b) $2\cos \theta = -1$, c) $\tan \theta = -\sqrt{3}$,
   d) $2\cos \theta = -\sqrt{3}$ and $2\sin \theta = 1$. (See APPENDIX A.3)

4. Sketch the graphs of   a) $y = -2x^2$, b) $x^2 + y^2 = 4$, c) $3x - 2y = 6$.   (See SECTIONS 1.2–1.4)

5. Find the equation of the tangent line to the graph of $y = 3x^2$ at the point $(-1, 3)$.   (See SECTION 2.1)

6. Determine maxima and minima and where the function increases and decreases for $f(x) = 3 + 4\cos x$. Sketch the graph of this function on a Cartesian coordinate system.   (See SECTIONS 2.9–2.12)

7. Evaluate the integrals

   a) $\displaystyle\int_{\pi/4}^{2\pi/3} (3 + 4\cos \theta)^2 \, d\theta$, b) $\displaystyle\int \sec^3 \theta \, d\theta$.   (See SECTIONS 7.1–7.3)

The Polar Coordinate System

1. Plot the points whose polar coordinates are   a) $\left(3, \frac{\pi}{6}\right)$ d) $\left(2, -\frac{\pi}{3}\right)$.

SOLUTION: a) The point is a distance 3 from the pole on a ray which makes an angle of $\frac{\pi}{6}$ with the polar axis.

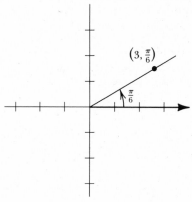

d) The point is a distance 2 from the pole on a ray that makes an angle of $-\frac{\pi}{3}$ with the polar axis.

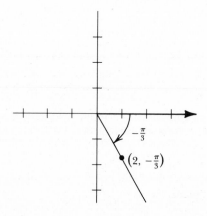

5. Give four other sets of polar coordinates that describe the points with polar coordinates
   a) $(2, 0)$ b) $\left(-1, \frac{\pi}{2}\right)$.

SOLUTION: If a point has polar coordinates (r, θ), then the coordinates $(-r, \theta + \pi)$, $(r, \theta + 2\pi)$,

$(-r, \theta - \pi), (r, \theta - 2\pi)$, etc. all describe the same point.   a) $(2, 0)$ is also $(-2, \pi), (2, 2\pi), (-2, -\pi)$ and $(2, -2\pi)$.   b) $\left(-1, \dfrac{\pi}{2}\right)$ is also $\left(1, \dfrac{3\pi}{2}\right)$, $\left(-1, \dfrac{5\pi}{2}\right)$, $\left(1, -\dfrac{\pi}{2}\right)$ and $\left(-1, -\dfrac{3\pi}{2}\right)$.

7. Find the Cartesian coordinates of the points with polar coordinates   a) $\left(2, \dfrac{\pi}{4}\right)$ and   c) $\left(-1, \dfrac{\pi}{2}\right)$.

SOLUTION: The formulas for conversion from polar to Cartesian coordinates are $x = r \cos \theta$ and $y = r \sin \theta$.   a) Since $r = 2$ and $\theta = \pi/4$, then $x = 2 \cos \dfrac{\pi}{4} = \sqrt{2}$ and $y = 2 \sin \dfrac{\pi}{4} = \sqrt{2}$, so the point has Cartesian coordinates $(\sqrt{2}, \sqrt{2})$.   c) Since $r = -1$ and $\theta = \pi/2$, then $x = (-1) \cos \dfrac{\pi}{2} = 0$ and $y = (-1) \sin \dfrac{\pi}{2} = -1$, so the Cartesian coordinates are $(0, -1)$.

11. Show that $x^2 - y^2 = 1$ has polar equation $r^2 = \sec 2\theta$.

SOLUTION: Substitute $x = r \cos \theta$ and $y = r \sin \theta$ to obtain $(r \cos \theta)^2 - (r \sin \theta)^2 = 1$ or $r^2(\cos^2 \theta - \sin^2 \theta) = 1$.

Since $\cos^2 \theta - \sin^2 \theta = \cos 2\theta$ then the equation is equivalent to $r^2 \cos 2\theta = 1$ or $r^2 = \sec 2\theta$.

_____**9.2**

Graphing in Polar Coordinates

COMMENT: The use of periodicity, symmetries, the increasing and decreasing nature of r as a function of θ and point plotting are advocated in the text. In addition to these, you should also determine the values of θ where r is positive, negative and zero.

It is also useful to determine the smallest interval of θ-values over which the graph is sketched exactly once. This interval (if one exists) has length $k\pi$, called the θ-range, where k is the smallest positive integer for which replacement of (r, θ) by $\left((-1)^k, \theta + k\pi\right)$ in the equation gives an equivalent equation. Since each point (r, θ) can also be expressed as $(-r, \theta + \pi)$, $\left((-1)^2 r, \theta + 2\pi\right)$, $\left((-1)^3 r, \theta + 3\pi\right)$, etc., this test determines when the equation first describes a point (r, θ) in one of its other forms.

Consider the θ-range for the case of EXAMPLE 1 of the text where $r = 2 \sin \theta$. Here choose $k > 0$ to be the smallest integer so that $(-1)^k r = 2 \sin(\theta + k\pi)$ is equivalent to $r = 2 \sin \theta$. Since $k = 1$ works, this is the smallest such value so the θ-range in this case is π. Thus over any interval of length π the graph of $r = 2 \sin \theta$ is sketched exactly once.

5. Sketch the graph of $r = 3 \cos \theta$.

SOLUTION: If (r, θ) is replaced by $(r, -\theta)$ then the equation, $r = 3 \cos(-\theta)$ or $r = 3 \cos \theta$, is unchanged. Thus the graph is symmetric about the x-axis. Other tests for symmetry fail.

The values of r change sign at odd multiples of $\pi/2$; in particular, $0 \leq r \leq 3$ if $-\dfrac{\pi}{2} \leq \theta \leq \dfrac{\pi}{2}$ and $-3 \leq r \leq 0$ if $\dfrac{\pi}{2} \leq \theta \leq \dfrac{3\pi}{2}$.

Apply the test to determine the θ-extent of this graph; replace (r, θ) by $((-1)^k r, \theta + k\pi)$ in the equation to obtain $(-1)^k r = 3\cos(\theta + k\pi)$. Since for $k = 1$, $-r = 3(-\cos\theta)$ (an equivalent equation), the smallest interval over which this curve is described exactly once is of length π. Since the sign of r is nonnegative over the interval $\left[-\dfrac{\pi}{2}, \dfrac{\pi}{2}\right]$, plot points for this interval.

Notice further that r increases from $r = 0$ at $\theta = -\pi/2$ to a maximum of $r = 3$ at $\theta = 0$, then decreases to $r = 0$ at $\theta = \pi/2$.

θ	$-\dfrac{\pi}{2}$	$-\dfrac{\pi}{3}$	$-\dfrac{\pi}{4}$	$-\dfrac{\pi}{6}$	0	$\dfrac{\pi}{6}$	$\dfrac{\pi}{4}$	$\dfrac{\pi}{3}$	$\dfrac{\pi}{2}$
$r = 3\cos\theta$	0	$\dfrac{3}{2}$	$\dfrac{3\sqrt{2}}{2}$	$\dfrac{3\sqrt{3}}{2}$	3	$\dfrac{3\sqrt{3}}{2}$	$\dfrac{3\sqrt{2}}{2}$	$\dfrac{3}{2}$	0

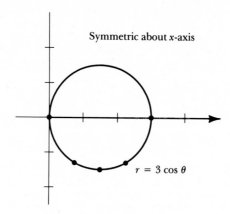

Symmetric about x-axis

$r = 3\cos\theta$

Notice that due to symmetry about the x-axis you need only plot points for $-\dfrac{\pi}{2} \leq \theta \leq 0$, and then use symmetry to sketch the rest of the graph.

11. Sketch the graph of $r = 2 + \sin\theta$.

SOLUTION: Since $\sin(\pi - \theta) = \sin\theta$, the equation is unchanged if (r, θ) is replaced by $(r, \pi - \theta)$, so the graph is symmetric about the y-axis. Other symmetry tests fail.

Since $-1 \leq \sin\theta \leq 1$ then $1 \leq r(= 2 + \sin\theta) \leq 3$ so r is everywhere positive.

Replace (r, θ) by $((-1)^k r, \theta + k\pi)$ to obtain

$$(-1)^k r = 2 + \sin(\theta + k\pi) = 2 + \sin\theta\cos(k\pi).$$

If $k = 1$, then this equation is $-r = 2 - \sin\theta$, which is not equivalent. For $k = 2$ the equation is $r = 2 + \sin\theta$, which implies that the θ-range is 2π. For convenience, choose $-\dfrac{\pi}{2} \leq \theta \leq \dfrac{3\pi}{2}$.

The values of r increase from $r = 1$ at $\theta = -\dfrac{\pi}{2}$ to $r = 3$ at $\theta = \dfrac{\pi}{2}$, then decrease to $r = 0$ at $\theta = \dfrac{3\pi}{2}$. Some typical values are

θ	$-\dfrac{\pi}{2}$	$-\dfrac{\pi}{6}$	0	$\dfrac{\pi}{3}$	$\dfrac{\pi}{2}$	$\dfrac{5\pi}{6}$	π	$\dfrac{7\pi}{6}$	$\dfrac{3\pi}{2}$
r	1	$\dfrac{3}{2}$	2	$2 + \dfrac{\sqrt{3}}{2}$	3	$2 + \dfrac{\sqrt{3}}{2}$	2	$\dfrac{3}{2}$	1

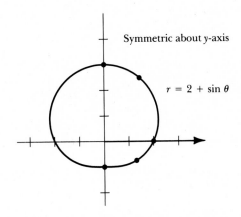

Symmetric about y-axis

$r = 2 + \sin\theta$

Due to symmetry about the y-axis, you only need to plot points for θ between $-\pi/2$ and $\pi/2$.

15. Sketch the graph of $r = 3\sin 3\theta$.

SOLUTION: According to Table 9.5, this graph is a 3-leaved rose since $n = 3$ is odd.

If (r, θ) is replaced by $(-r, -\theta)$, the equation $-r = 3\sin(-3\theta)$ is equivalent to the original, so the graph is symmetric about the y-axis.

Since $\sin 3\theta = 0$ whenever 3θ is a multiple of π, then r changes sign at $-\dfrac{\pi}{3}, 0, \dfrac{\pi}{3}, \dfrac{2\pi}{3}, \pi$, etc.

To determine the θ-range of this graph, replace (r, θ) by $\big((-1)^k r, \theta + k\pi\big)$ to obtain the equation

$$(-1)^k r = 3\sin(3\theta + 3k\pi) = 3\big(\sin 3\theta \cos(3k\pi) + \cos 3\theta \sin(3k\pi)\big).$$

When $k = 1$, this is $-r = -3\sin 3\theta$, so the equation is unchanged and the graph is described exactly once for θ in an interval of length π. Because of the symmetry, consider the interval $\theta \in [0, \pi]$ which is itself symmetric about $\theta = \dfrac{\pi}{2}$.

The values of r increase from $r = 0$ at $\theta = 0$ to $r = 3$ at $\theta = \pi/6$, then decrease through $r = 0$ at $\theta = \pi/3$ to $r = -3$ at $\theta = \pi/2$. Symmetry may be used to complete the graph.

θ	0	$\dfrac{\pi}{12}$	$\dfrac{\pi}{6}$	$\dfrac{\pi}{3}$	$\dfrac{5\pi}{12}$	$\dfrac{\pi}{2}$
r	0	$\dfrac{3\sqrt{2}}{2}$	3	0	$-\dfrac{3\sqrt{2}}{2}$	-3

Use symmetry about the y-axis for the rest of the graph.

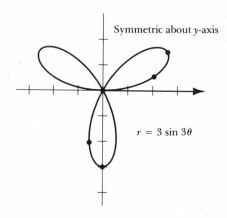

Symmetric about y-axis

$r = 3\sin 3\theta$

21. Sketch the graph of $r^2 = -9\cos 2\theta$.

SOLUTION: According to Table 9.5, this graph is a lemniscate.

If (r,θ) is replaced by any of $(r,-\theta)$, $(-r,-\theta)$, or $(-r,\theta)$, then the equation is unchanged, so the graph is symmetric about the x-axis, the y-axis and also the pole. Only the positive values of r will be plotted; symmetry about the pole will account for the corresponding negative values.

The values of θ are restricted to the intervals where $\cos 2\theta$ is non-positive, i.e., $\dfrac{\pi}{2} \le 2\theta \le \dfrac{3\pi}{2}$, $\dfrac{5\pi}{2} \le 2\theta \le \dfrac{7\pi}{2}$, etc. or $\dfrac{\pi}{4} \le \theta \le \dfrac{3\pi}{4}$, $\dfrac{5\pi}{4} \le \theta \le \dfrac{7\pi}{4}$, etc.

The θ-range is determined by finding the smallest k for which $\left[(-1)^k r\right]^2 = -9\cos(2\theta + 2k\pi)$ is equivalent to $r^2 = -9\cos 2\theta$. Since $k = 1$ works, then the graph is determined by any θ-interval of length π. Because of the symmetry about the y-axis, choose $0 \le \theta \le \pi$; actually the restriction on θ requires that only $\dfrac{\pi}{4} \le \theta \le \dfrac{3\pi}{4}$ be used.

The values of r increase from $r = 0$ at $\theta = \pi/4$ to $r = 3$ at $\theta = \pi/2$, then decrease to $r = 0$ at $\theta = 3\pi/4$. Symmetry with respect to the y and x axes suggests that only values of $\theta \in \left[\dfrac{\pi}{4}, \dfrac{\pi}{2}\right]$ be plotted.

θ	$\dfrac{\pi}{4}$	$\dfrac{3\pi}{8}$	$\dfrac{\pi}{2}$
r	0	$\dfrac{3}{2^{1/4}}$	3

Use symmetry about the y-axis for $\dfrac{\pi}{2} \leq \theta \leq \dfrac{3\pi}{4}$ and symmetry about the pole or the x-axis for $\dfrac{5\pi}{4} \leq \theta \leq \dfrac{7\pi}{4}$.

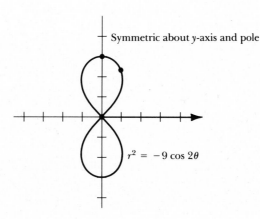

Symmetric about y-axis and pole

$r^2 = -9 \cos 2\theta$

29. Sketch the graph of $r = \dfrac{1}{\theta}$.

SOLUTION: According to Table 9.5, this graph is a spiral.

Since (r, θ) can be replaced by $(-r, -\theta)$ to obtain an equivalent equation, then the graph is symmetric about the y-axis. The points for $\theta > 0$ and $r > 0$ are graphed, then symmetry is used to complete the graph.

Clearly there is no periodicity which would lead to a finite θ-range so the entire graph can be sketched only for $-\infty < \theta < 0,\ 0 < \theta < \infty$.

The limit $\lim\limits_{\theta \to 0^+} \dfrac{1}{\theta} = \infty$ implies that the graph has a horizontal asymptote along the polar axis.

As θ increases from zero, $\dfrac{1}{\theta}$ decreases to a limit of 0 as θ approaches ∞. It is useful to plot a few points, especially for small values of θ and also where the curve crosses the axes.

θ	0^+	$\dfrac{\pi}{6}$	$\dfrac{\pi}{4}$	$\dfrac{\pi}{3}$	$\dfrac{\pi}{2}$	π	2π
r	$r \to \infty$	$\dfrac{6}{\pi}$	$\dfrac{4}{\pi}$	$\dfrac{3}{\pi}$	$\dfrac{2}{\pi}$	$\dfrac{1}{\pi}$	$\dfrac{1}{2\pi}$

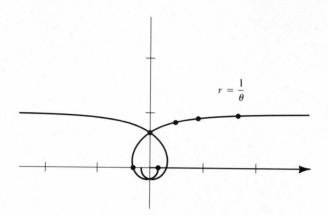

$$r = \frac{1}{\theta}$$

COMMENT: The next problem may be solved by at least two different techniques. The first is to "add the graphs" of $r = 2\sin\theta$ and $r = 2\cos\theta$ by drawing these two circles then for any value of θ graphically add the r-displacements along the fixed ray.

The second technique is to rewrite the sum as a sine with phase shift and then apply the following observation about "phase shifted graphs".

The graph of $r = f(\theta - \phi_0)$, where ϕ_0 is a constant "phase shift" is the same as the graph of $r = f(\theta)$ rotated about the pole through an angle of ϕ_0. The technique for drawing this graph is to treat the ray $\theta = \phi_0$ as the "polar axis" for the phase shifted graph.

31. Sketch the graph of $r = 2(\sin\theta + \cos\theta)$.

SOLUTION: First write the sum of trigonometric functions as

$$(\sin\theta + \cos\theta) = \sqrt{2}\left(\frac{\sqrt{2}}{2}\sin\theta + \frac{\sqrt{2}}{2}\cos\theta\right) = \sqrt{2}\left(\cos\frac{\pi}{4}\sin\theta + \sin\frac{\pi}{4}\cos\theta\right)$$

$$= \sqrt{2}\sin\left(\theta - \left(-\frac{\pi}{4}\right)\right).$$

The equation is thus $r = 2\sqrt{2}\sin\left(\theta - \left(-\frac{\pi}{4}\right)\right)$ so its graph is the same as that of $r = 2\sqrt{2}\sin\theta$ rotated through an angle of $\phi_0 = -\frac{\pi}{4}$.

The graph of $r = 2\sqrt{2}\sin\theta$ is analysed in the same way as the graph of $r = 2\sin\theta$ from Example 1 in the text; i.e., it is a circle of radius $\sqrt{2}$ tangent to the pole and with diameter along the ray $\theta = \frac{\pi}{2}$.

This graph is rotated through $-\frac{\pi}{4}$ to obtain the graph of $r = 2\sqrt{2}\sin\left(\theta - \left(-\frac{\pi}{4}\right)\right)$, a circle of radius $\sqrt{2}$ tangent to the pole with diameter along the ray $\theta = \frac{\pi}{2} - \frac{\pi}{4} = \frac{\pi}{4}$.

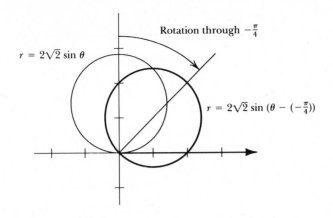

35. Compare the graphs of   a) $r = 1 + \cos\theta$,   b) $r = 1 - \cos\theta$,   c) $r = \cos\theta - 1$,   d) $r = -\cos\theta - 1$.

SOLUTION: According to Table 9.5, these four graphs are all cardioids. Before sketching the four graphs and comparing them, consider the effect of the following transformations.

If (r, θ) is replaced by $(-r, \theta)$ then the graph which results is obtained by reflecting each point on the original graph in the pole. With this observation, the graphs of equations a) and d) are reflections of each other through the pole since d) can be written as $-r = 1 + \cos\theta$. Similarly the graphs of b) and c) are reflections of each other through the pole.

As was observed in the comment preceding the solution to EXERCISE 31, the graph of a "phase shifted" equation is the same as the graph of the original equation rotated through the phase shift angle. Since $-\cos\theta = \cos(\theta - \pi)$, then equation b) is $r = 1 + \cos(\theta - \pi)$, so its graph is the same as the graph of a) rotated through π. Similarly, d) is $r = \cos(\theta - \pi) - 1$, so its graph is the same as that of c) rotated through π.

The graph of a), $r = 1 + \cos\theta$, has symmetry about the x-axis, has θ-range 2π, has $r \geq 0$ for all θ with $r = 0$ only at $\theta = \pi$, 3π, etc. Values of $\theta = [0, 2\pi]$ are considered with only those between 0 and π plotted due to symmetry.

θ	0	$\dfrac{\pi}{4}$	$\dfrac{\pi}{2}$	$\dfrac{3\pi}{4}$	π
r	2	$1 + \dfrac{\sqrt{2}}{2}$	1	$1 - \dfrac{\sqrt{2}}{2}$	0

Values for $\pi \leq \theta \leq 2\pi$ are obtained by symmetry about the x-axis.

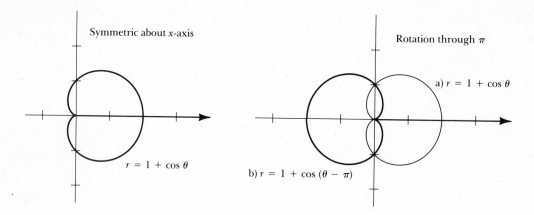

The transformations mentioned above can be applied to generate all the graphs from that of a) as follows: the graph of b) is obtained by rotating the graph of a) by π; the graph of c) is obtained by reflecting the graph of b) in the pole; the graph of d) is obtained by rotating the graph of c) by π.

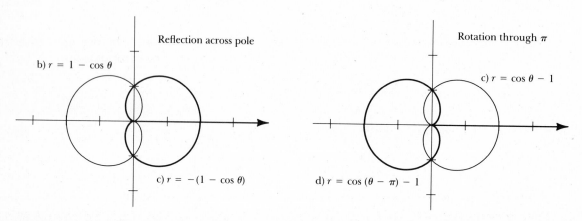

It should also be noticed that the graphs of a) and c) are identical as are the graphs of b) and d). This follows because the symmetry of a graph about the x-axis also implies that its rotation by π and its reflection through the pole are the same.

41. Compare the graphs of   a) $r = 2^\theta$,   b) $r = 2^{-\theta}$,   c) $r = -2^\theta$,   d) $r = -2^{-\theta}$.

SOLUTION: From the discussion in the previous solution concerning the replacement of (r, θ) by $(-r, \theta)$ and its effect on graphs, it should be clear that a) and c) are reflections of each other through the pole as are b) and d).

Along the same lines, if (r, θ) are replaced by $(r, -\theta)$ then the resulting graph is obtained by reflection of the original graph in the x-axis. This implies that b) can be obtained by a reflection of a) in the x-axis and d) can be obtained by a reflection of c) in the x-axis.

The graph of a), $r = 2^\theta$, is a spiral which has none of the standard symmetries. Its θ-range is infinite and r is positive for all θ. The limits $\lim_{\theta \to -\infty} 2^\theta = 0$ and $\lim_{\theta \to \infty} 2^\theta = \infty$ imply that the spiral approaches the pole as θ approaches 0 and that r increases without bound as θ increases. Values of (r, θ) are plotted for some typical values of $\theta \in [-\pi, \pi]$.

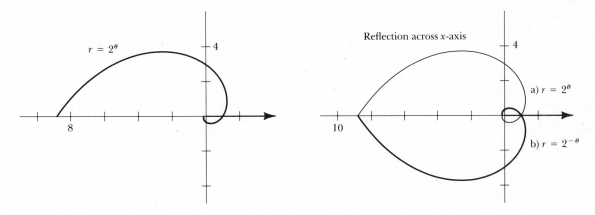

The graphs of b), c) and d) can be obtained by applying the transformations mentioned above: b) is obtained by reflection of a) across the x-axis; c) is obtained by reflection of a) through the pole; d) is obtained by the reflection of c) across the x-axis.

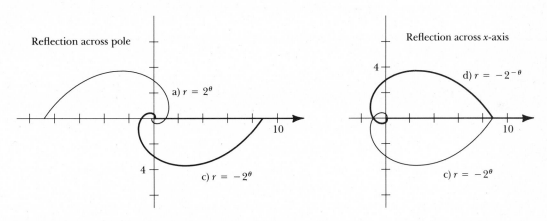

9.3
Areas of Regions Using
Polar Coordinates

3. a) Sketch the graph of $r = 2\sin\theta$; b) Find the area bounded by this graph.

SOLUTION: a) This graph was analyzed in EXAMPLE 1 of SECTION 9.2 of the text. It is a circle of radius 1 tangent to the pole with diameter on the ray $\theta = \pi/2$.

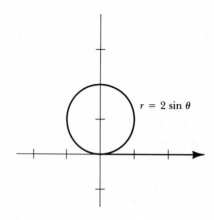

$r = 2 \sin \theta$

b) To determine the area inside this curve, integrate $\frac{1}{2}r^2\theta$ over an interval of θ-values for which the curve is described exactly once. The issue of calculating such an interval was addressed in the comment preceding the solutions to the exercises from SECTION 9.2 in this manual. It was shown there that for this particular graph the θ-range is π, so any interval of length π will work as the interval of integration, say $\theta \in [0, \pi]$. The area is thus

$$A = \int_0^\pi \frac{1}{2}r^2\,d\theta = \frac{1}{2}\int_0^\pi (2\sin\theta)^2\,d\theta = \int_0^\pi (1 - \cos 2\theta)\,d\theta = \left[\theta - \frac{1}{2}\sin 2\theta\right]\Big|_0^\pi = \pi.$$

9. a) Sketch the graph of $r = 4 - 2\sin\theta$.   b) Find the area of the region bounded by this graph.

SOLUTION: a)   The graph of this limaçon is symmetric about the y-axis. The r-values lie between 2 and 6 with r decreasing from a value of 6 at $\theta = -\pi/2$ to a value of $r = 2$ at $\theta = \pi/2$, then increasing to 6 at $\theta = 3\pi/2$. The θ-range is 2π since $k = 2$ is the smallest $k > 0$ for which the equation $(-1)^k r = 4 - 2\sin(\theta + k\pi)$ is equivalent to $r = 4 - 2\sin\theta$. Points are plotted for values of $\theta \in \left[-\frac{\pi}{2}, \frac{\pi}{2}\right]$, then symmetry about the y-axis is used to complete the graph.

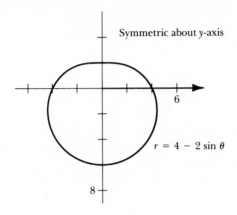

Symmetric about y-axis

$r = 4 - 2\sin\theta$

b) Since the graph is described exactly once for $\theta \in \left[-\dfrac{\pi}{2}, \dfrac{3\pi}{2}\right]$ (any interval of length 2π will do), then its area is

$$A = \int_{-\pi/2}^{3\pi/2} \frac{1}{2} r^2 \, d\theta = \frac{1}{2} \int_{-\pi/2}^{3\pi/2} (4 - 2\cos\theta)^2 \, d\theta$$

$$= \int_{-\pi/2}^{3\pi/2} (8 - 8\cos\theta + 2\cos^2\theta) \, d\theta = \int_{-\pi/2}^{3\pi/2} (9 - 8\cos\theta + \cos 2\theta) \, d\theta$$

$$= \left[9\theta - 8\sin\theta + \frac{1}{2}\sin 2\theta\right]\Bigg|_{-\pi/2}^{3\pi/2} = 18\pi.$$

13. a) Sketch the graph of $r^2 = 4\cos 2\theta$.   b) Find the area of the region bounded by the graph.

SOLUTION: a) This lemniscate is symmetric about both the x- and y-axes as well as the pole. The θ-range is π since $k = 1$ is the smallest k for which $\left[(-1)^k r\right]^2 = 4\cos\left(2(\theta + k\pi)\right)$ is equivalent to the original equation. The values of θ are further restricted by the requirement that $\cos 2\theta \geq 0$. One leaf of the lemniscate is described by $-\dfrac{\pi}{4} \leq \theta \leq \dfrac{\pi}{4}$; the other leaf is obtained by reflection through the pole. For this one leaf values of $\theta \in \left[-\dfrac{\pi}{4}, 0\right]$ are plotted; the other values are determined by symmetry.

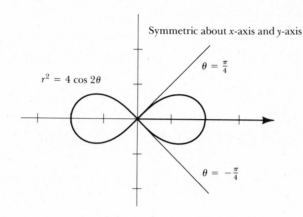

Symmetric about x-axis and y-axis

$\theta = \frac{\pi}{4}$

$r^2 = 4\cos 2\theta$

$\theta = -\frac{\pi}{4}$

b) The area is twice that inside one leaf or

$$A = 2\int_{-\pi/4}^{\pi/4} \frac{1}{2}r^2\, d\theta = \int_{-\pi/4}^{\pi/4} 4\cos 2\theta\, d\theta = \left[2\sin 2\theta\right]\bigg|_{-\pi/4}^{\pi/4} = 4.$$

23. a)   Sketch the graphs of $r = 1 + \cos\theta$ and $r = 1 + \sin\theta$.   **b)**   Find the area inside the graph of $r = 1 + \cos\theta$ and outside the graph of $r = 1 + \sin\theta$.

SOLUTION: a)   Both graphs are cardioids. Since $\sin\theta = \cos\left(\theta - \frac{\pi}{2}\right)$, then the graph of $r = 1 + \sin\theta$ or $r = 1 + \cos\left(\theta - \frac{\pi}{2}\right)$ is the same as the graph of $r = 1 + \cos\theta$ revolved by $\pi/2$ as was discussed in the comment preceding EXERCISE 31 of SECTION 9.2 in this manual.
The graph of $r = 1 + \cos\theta$ is discussed and sketched in the solution to EXERCISE 35 of SECTION 9.2. It is redrawn below along with its rotation by $\pi/2$ (the graph of $r = 1 + \sin\theta$).

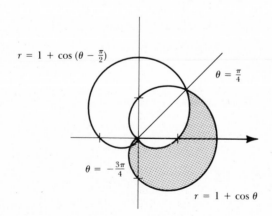

$r = 1 + \cos\left(\theta - \frac{\pi}{2}\right)$

$\theta = \frac{\pi}{4}$

$\theta = -\frac{3\pi}{4}$

$r = 1 + \cos\theta$

b) The region described above is shaded.
The θ-values at the points of intersection (other than the pole) satisfy the equation $1 + \sin\theta = 1 + \cos\theta$ or $\sin\theta = \cos\theta$, so $\theta = -\frac{3\pi}{4}, \frac{\pi}{4}, \frac{7\pi}{4}$, etc. Since each of these graphs have θ-range 2π,

choose a single θ-interval which includes both points of intersection and such that the θ-values lying in the shaded region are a subset of this interval, say $-\pi \leq \theta \leq \pi$.

The shaded region may be described as $-\dfrac{3\pi}{4} \leq \theta \leq \dfrac{\pi}{4}$ and for each θ; $1 + \sin\theta \leq r \leq 1 + \cos\theta$, so the area lying inside $r = 1 + \cos\theta$ and outside $r = 1 + \sin\theta$ between $\theta = -\dfrac{3\pi}{4}$ and $\theta = \dfrac{\pi}{4}$ is

$$A = \int_{-3\pi/4}^{\pi/4} \left(\frac{1}{2}(1 + \cos\theta)^2 - \frac{1}{2}(1 + \sin\theta)^2 \right) d\theta$$

$$= \int_{-3\pi/4}^{\pi/4} \left(\cos\theta - \sin\theta + \frac{1}{2}(\cos^2\theta - \sin^2\theta) \right) d\theta$$

$$= \int_{-3\pi/4}^{\pi/4} \left(\cos\theta - \sin\theta + \frac{1}{2}\cos 2\theta \right) d\theta$$

$$= \left[\sin\theta + \cos\theta + \frac{1}{4}\sin 2\theta \right] \Bigg|_{-3\pi/4}^{\pi/4} = 2\sqrt{2}.$$

29. a) Sketch the graphs of $r = \sin 2\theta$ and $r = \cos 2\theta$.   b)   Find the area of the region inside the graphs of both equations.

SOLUTION: a)   Both graphs are 4-leaved roses. The graph of $r = \cos 2\theta$ was analyzed and sketched in EXAMPLE 3 of SECTION 9.2 of the text. Since $\sin 2\theta = \cos\left(2\theta - \dfrac{\pi}{2}\right) = \cos\left(2\left(\theta - \dfrac{\pi}{4}\right)\right)$, then the graph of $r = \sin 2\theta$ is the same as the graph of $r = \cos 2\theta$ rotated by $\pi/4$. These are graphed below.

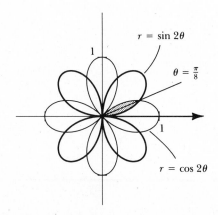

b) The areas inside the eight regions of intersection are all equal, so only one of these is calculated; the area lying inside the leaf of $r = \cos 2\theta$ for $-\dfrac{\pi}{4} \leq \theta \leq \dfrac{\pi}{4}$ and inside $r = \sin 2\theta$, $0 \leq \theta \leq \dfrac{\pi}{2}$. The point of intersection satisfies $\cos 2\theta = \sin 2\theta$ with $0 \leq \theta \leq \dfrac{\pi}{4}$, so $2\theta = \dfrac{\pi}{4}$ or $\theta = \dfrac{\pi}{8}$. This region of intersection can be described as $0 \leq \theta \leq \dfrac{\pi}{4}$ where if $0 \leq \theta \leq \dfrac{\pi}{8}$, then $0 \leq r \leq \sin 2\theta$ while if $\dfrac{\pi}{8} \leq \theta \leq \dfrac{\pi}{4}$, then $0 \leq r \leq \cos 2\theta$.

The area of one-eighth of the intersection is thus

$$
A_{1/8} = \int_0^{\pi/8} \frac{1}{2}(\sin 2\theta)^2 \, d\theta + \int_{\pi/8}^{\pi/4} \frac{1}{2}(\cos 2\theta)^2 \, d\theta
$$

$$
= \frac{1}{4} \left(\int_0^{\pi/8} (1 - \cos 4\theta) \, d\theta + \int_{\pi/8}^{\pi/4} (1 + \cos 4\theta) \, d\theta \right)
$$

$$
= \frac{1}{4} \left(\left[\theta - \frac{1}{4}\sin 4\theta \right] \Big|_0^{\pi/8} + \left[\theta + \frac{1}{4}\sin 4\theta \right] \Big|_{\pi/8}^{\pi/4} \right) = \frac{1}{4} \left(\frac{\pi}{4} - \frac{1}{2} \right).
$$

The total area is thus $A = 8A_{1/8} = \dfrac{\pi}{2} - 1$.

_____9.4

Parametric Equations
_____

COMMENT: A strategy for graphing curves described by parametric equations is to: i) Eliminate the parameter so as to obtain an equation involving only x and y (this may not always be possible); ii) Sketch the graph of the curve obtained in part i);   iii) This curve only contains the parametric curve, so determine which if any restrictions on x and/or y are imposed by the parametric functions and graph only points satisfying these restrictions. It is useful to plot several points corresponding to typical parameter values.

3. a) Sketch the graph of the curve described by $x = \sqrt{t}$, $y = t + 1$.   b) Find a cartesian equation describing this curve.

SOLUTION: a) Eliminate t between the two equations by noticing that $t = x^2$ so $y = x^2 + 1$. The curve $y - 1 = x^2$ is a parabola with vertex at $(0, 1)$ which opens upward. This parabola contains the curve but, since $x = \sqrt{t} \geq 0$, only those points for which $x \geq 0$ are graphed.

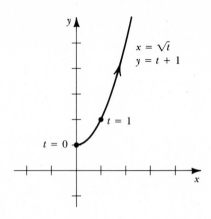

b) The cartesian equation is $y = 1 + x^2$, $x \geq 0$.

7. a) Sketch the curve with parametric equations $x = 3 \sin t$, $y = 4 \cos t$.   b) Find a cartesian equation describing this curve.

SOLUTION: a) Write the parametric equations as $\dfrac{x}{3} = \sin t$, $\dfrac{y}{4} = \cos t$, then use the trigonometric identity $\sin^2 t + \cos^2 t = 1$ to eliminate t, $\left(\dfrac{x}{3}\right)^2 + \left(\dfrac{y}{4}\right)^2 = 1$. This ellipse contains the curve; in fact as t varies from $-\infty$ to ∞, x oscillates between -3 and 3 and y oscillates between -4 and 4 both acheiving the extreme values infinitely often. The ellipse is retraced infinitely many times.

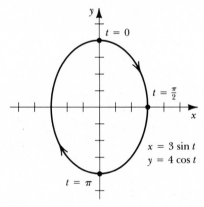

b) A cartesian equation is $\dfrac{x^2}{9} + \dfrac{y^2}{16} = 1$.

17. Sketch the graphs of   a) $x = t$, $y = t^2$;   b) $x = t^2$, $y = t$;   c) $x = t^2$, $y = t^4$.

SOLUTION: a) Eliminate t to obtain $y = x^2$, a parabola with vertex at $(0,0)$ which opens upward. The values of x are unrestricted so the entire parabola is the graph of this curve.

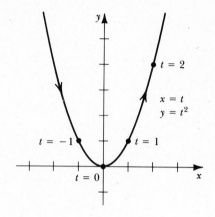

b) Eliminate t to obtain $x = y^2$, a parabola with vertex at $(0,0)$ which opens to the right. Since y is unrestricted, the entire parabola is the graph of this curve.

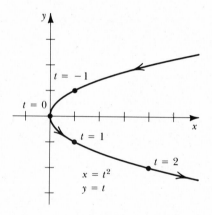

c) Eliminate t to obtain $y = x^2$, the same parabola as in a). Here, $x = t^2 \geq 0$ so only the part of the parabola lying in the first quadrant is on the graph.

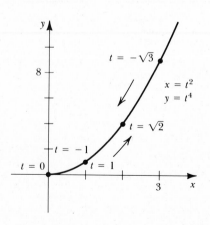

21. The graphs of the parametric values represent a portion of the same curve. Sketch the graphs of the parametric equations and label representative values of the parameter.   a) $x = \cos t,\ y = \sin t;\ 0 \le t \le 2\pi$,   d) $x = -t,\ y = \sqrt{1 - t^2};\ -1 \le t \le 1.$

SOLUTION: All of the pairs of parametric equations satisfy $x^2 + y^2 = 1$ so all the curves are contained on the circle of radius 1 centered at the origin.

a)

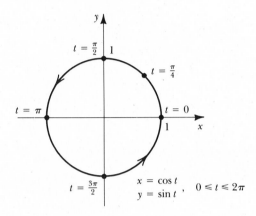

d)

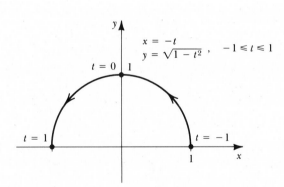

The upper semicircle is traversed in a counter-clockwise fashion.

27. Does the curve given parametrically by $x = \dfrac{\sin t}{t},\ y = \dfrac{\cos t}{t}$ have a horizontal or vertical asymptote?

SOLUTION: There is no horizontal asymptote since $-1 < x \le 1$ because $\dfrac{\sin t}{t}$ satisfies these inequalities. Thus, the curve does not extend to infinity in the x-direction.

The limits $\displaystyle\lim_{t \to 0^+} \frac{\cos t}{t} = \infty$ and $\displaystyle\lim_{t \to 0^-} \frac{\cos t}{t} = -\infty$ imply that there is a vertical asymptote as t approaches zero, that is, as $x = \dfrac{\sin t}{t}$ approaches 1.

31. An epicycloid is a curve traced by a fixed point P on a circle of radius b as it rotates around a stationary circle of radius a (see the accompanying figure). Suppose the fixed point was originally located at $A(a,0)$ and that the circle has rotated as shown in the figure. a) Show that the point C has coordinates $((a+b)\cos t,(a+b)\sin t)$. b) Show that the arc length $\overset{\frown}{PB}$ on the circle of radius b is at. c) Show that the angle $\angle BCP$ is $(a/b)t$. d) Show that the angle $\angle DCP$ is $\pi - \left(\dfrac{a+b}{b}\right)t$. e) Derive the parametric equations for the epicycloid:

$$x = (a+b)\cos t - b\cos\left(\frac{a+b}{b}\right)t \quad \text{and} \quad y = (a+b)\sin t - b\sin\left(\frac{a+b}{b}\right)t.$$

SOLUTION:

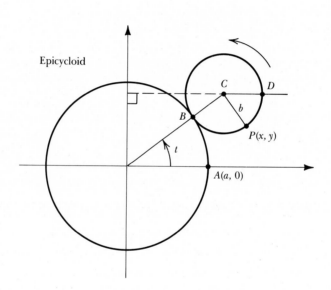

a) Since the two circles are tangent at B, then their radii OB and CB have a common direction, so the ray OC is a radius of the circle with radius $a+b$. Thus, since this radius makes an angle t with the positive x-axis, then the coordinates of C are $((a+b)\cos t,(a+b)\sin t)$.

b) The arc length $\overset{\frown}{AB}$ equals the radius a times the angle measure t; $\overset{\frown}{AB}=at$. Since the smaller circle rolls on the larger without slipping, then $\overset{\frown}{BP}=\overset{\frown}{AB}=at$.

c) The angle $\angle BCP$ subtends the arc $\overset{\frown}{BP}$ on the circle of radius b. Therefore its angle measure is arc length/radius, or $\angle BCP = \dfrac{at}{b}$.

d) Since the line through D and C is parallel to the x-axis, then $\angle TCO = t$, where T is the point where this line intersects the y-axis and O is the origin. Thus $\angle DCP = \pi-(\angle TCO)-(\angle BCP) = \pi-t-\left(\dfrac{a}{b}\right)t = \pi - \dfrac{(a+b)}{b}t.$

e) If the point (x, y) were plotted on a coordinate system with origin C then these coordinates would satisfy $x = b\cos(-\angle DCP)$, $y = b\sin(-\angle DCP)$ since this angle is negative relative to such a coordinate system. The coordinates of C relative to the point O were given in a) so the coordinates of (x, y) relative to O are

$$x = (a+b)\cos t + b\cos(-\angle DCP) = (a+b)\cos t + b\left[\cos\left(-\pi + \left(\frac{a+b}{b}\right)t\right)\right]$$

$$= (a+b)\cos t - b\cos\left[\left(\frac{a+b}{b}\right)t\right]$$

$$y = (a+b)\sin t + b\sin(-\angle DCP) = (a+b)\sin t + b\left[\sin\left(-\pi + \left(\frac{a+b}{b}\right)t\right)\right]$$

$$= (a+b)\sin t - b\sin\left[\left(\frac{a+b}{b}\right)t\right].$$

_____9.5

Tangent Lines
to Curves

_____

3. Find the slope, if it exists, of the tangent line to the curve $x = \sqrt{t}$, $y = t + 1$ at the point $t = 4$.

SOLUTION: Since $\dfrac{dx}{dt} = \dfrac{1}{2\sqrt{t}}$ and $\dfrac{dy}{dt} = 1$, then $\dfrac{dy}{dx} = \dfrac{dy/dt}{dx/dt} = 2\sqrt{t}$, and at $t = 4$ the slope is $\dfrac{dy}{dx} = 2\sqrt{4} = 4$.

19. a) Find the slope, if it exists, of the tangent line to the polar curve $r = 2\sin\theta$ at $\theta = \pi/4$.
    b) Find the cartesian equation of the tangent line.

SOLUTION: a) Since $\dfrac{dr}{d\theta} = 2\cos\theta$, then by Formula 9.8 the slope is

$$\frac{dy}{dx} = \frac{\dfrac{dr}{d\theta}\tan\theta + r}{\dfrac{dr}{d\theta} - r\tan\theta} = \frac{(2\cos\theta)\tan\theta + (2\sin\theta)}{(2\cos\theta) - (2\sin\theta)\tan\theta} = \frac{2\sin\theta\cos\theta}{\cos^2\theta - \sin^2\theta} = \tan 2\theta.$$

At $\theta = \pi/4$, the slope is undefined since $\tan\left(2\cdot\dfrac{\pi}{4}\right)$ is undefined; thus since the tangent line (to this circle) exists, then it must be a vertical line.

b) The cartesian coordinates of the point $\left(\sqrt{2}, \dfrac{\pi}{2}\right)$ on the curve $r = 2\sin\theta$ are $(1,1)$ so the equation of the (vertical) tangent line is $x = 1$.

33. Find $D_x^2 y$ for $x = 3\sin t$, $y = 4\cos t$.

SOLUTION: First calculate $\dfrac{dy}{dx}$ through the formula $\dfrac{dy}{dx} = \dfrac{dy/dt}{dx/dt} = \dfrac{-4\sin t}{3\cos t} = -\dfrac{4}{3}\tan t$. Following the procedure from the text,

$$D_x^2 y = \frac{D_t\left[\dfrac{dy}{dx}\right]}{\dfrac{dx}{dt}} = \frac{D_t\left[-\dfrac{4}{3}\tan t\right]}{3\cos t} = \frac{-\dfrac{4}{3}\sec^2 t}{3\cos t} = -\frac{4}{9}\sec^3 t.$$

37. Find $D_x^2 y$ for $r = \sin\theta$.

SOLUTION: This curve can be written in terms of the parameter θ as $x = r\cos\theta = \sin\theta\cos\theta$ and $y = r\sin\theta = \sin^2\theta$. The derivatives with respect to the parameter θ are

$$\frac{dx}{d\theta} = D_\theta\left[\sin\theta\cos\theta\right] = \cos^2\theta - \sin^2\theta = \cos 2\theta$$

$$\frac{dy}{d\theta} = D_\theta\left[\sin^2\theta\right] = 2\sin\theta\cos\theta = \sin 2\theta. \quad \text{Thus,}$$

$$\frac{dy}{dx} = \frac{dy/d\theta}{dx/d\theta} = \frac{\sin 2\theta}{\cos 2\theta} = \tan 2\theta.$$

Follow the procedure of the text, treating θ as the parameter, to calculate

$$D_x^2 y = \frac{D_\theta\left[\dfrac{dy}{dx}\right]}{\dfrac{dx}{d\theta}} = \frac{D_\theta\left[\tan 2\theta\right]}{\cos 2\theta} = \frac{2\sec^2 2\theta}{\cos 2\theta} = 2\sec^3 2\theta.$$

41. Find the equations of the tangent lines to $r = 1$ and $r = 1 + \cos\theta$ at the points of intersection.

SOLUTION: The graphs of the circle $r = 1$ and the cardioid $r = 1 + \cos\theta$ are sketched below.

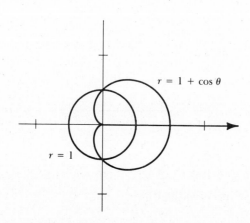

The θ-coordinate of the points of intersection satisfy $1 = 1 + \cos\theta$ or $\cos\theta = 0$. The curves intersect at the points where $\theta = -\dfrac{\pi}{2}$ and $\dfrac{\pi}{2}$; $\left(1, \dfrac{\pi}{2}\right)$, $\left(1, -\dfrac{\pi}{2}\right)$.

The slope of the tangent line to the circle is (using Formula 9.8 with $r = 1$, $\dfrac{dr}{d\theta} = 0$) $\dfrac{dy}{dx} = \dfrac{0 \cdot \tan\theta + 1}{0 - 1\tan\theta} = -\cot\theta$. Thus at both points $\left(1, \dfrac{\pi}{2}\right)$ and $\left(1, -\dfrac{\pi}{2}\right)$, the slope is $\dfrac{dy}{dx} = -\cot\left(\pm\dfrac{\pi}{2}\right) = 0$. The Cartesian coordinates of these two points are $(0, 1)$ and $(0, -1)$ respectively, so the tangent lines to the circle at these points have equations $y = 1$ and $y = -1$ respectively.

The slope of the tangent line to the cardioid (using $r = 1 + \cos\theta$ with $\dfrac{dr}{d\theta} = -\sin\theta$) is

$$\frac{dy}{dx} = \frac{(-\sin\theta)\tan\theta + (1 + \cos\theta)}{(-\sin\theta) - (1 + \cos\theta)\tan\theta} = \frac{\cos\theta + \cos 2\theta}{-(\sin\theta + \sin 2\theta)}.$$

At the intersection point $\left(1, \dfrac{\pi}{2}\right)$, the slope is $\dfrac{dy}{dx} = \dfrac{0 - 1}{-(1)} = 1$; so the equation of the tangent line at this point with cartesian coordinates $(0, 1)$ is $\dfrac{y - 1}{x} = 1$ or $y = 1 + x$.

At the intersection point $\left(1, -\dfrac{\pi}{2}\right)$ the slope is $\dfrac{dy}{dx} = \dfrac{-1}{-(-1)} = -1$. The tangent line at this point has cartesian equation $\dfrac{y + 1}{x} = -1$ or $y = -1 - x$.

9.6
Lengths of Curves

---

5. Find the length of the curve with parametric equations $x = t^2 + 1$, $y = 2t - 3$; $0 \le t \le 1$.

SOLUTION: With $f(t) = t^2 + 1$, $g(t) = 2t - 3$, $f'(t) = 2t$ and $g'(t) = 2$, DEFINITION 9.9 gives the length of this curve as

$$L = \int_0^1 \sqrt{(2t)^2 + (2)^2}\, dt = 2\int_0^1 \sqrt{1 + t^2}\, dt.$$

Use the trigonometric substitution $t = \tan\theta$ with $dt = \sec^2\theta\, d\theta$, $\sqrt{1 + t^2} = \sec\theta$ and $\theta = 0$ when $t = 0$, $\theta = \pi/4$ when $t = 1$.
The integral is

$$L = 2\int_0^{\pi/4} \sec^3\theta\, d\theta = 2\int_0^{\pi/4} \sec\theta(1 + \tan^2\theta)\, d\theta$$

$$= 2 \left(\int_0^{\pi/4} \sec \theta \, d\theta + \int_0^{\pi/4} \sec \theta \tan \theta \cdot \tan \theta \, d\theta \right).$$

Integrate the second integral by parts with $u = \tan \theta$, $dv = \sec \theta \tan \theta \, d\theta$ so that $du = \sec^2 \theta \, d\theta$ and $v = \sec \theta$.

$$\int \sec \theta \tan \theta \cdot \tan \theta \, d\theta = \sec \theta \tan \theta - \int \sec \theta \cdot \sec^2 \theta \, d\theta.$$

An identity for L is now possible.

$$(L =) \ 2 \int_0^{\pi/4} \sec^3 \theta \, d\theta = 2 \left(\ln |\sec \theta + \tan \theta| + \sec \theta \tan \theta \right) \Big|_0^{\pi/4} - 2 \int_0^{\pi/4} \sec^3 \theta \, d\theta.$$

Solve this last equation for $2 \displaystyle\int_0^{\pi/4} \sec^3 \theta \, d\theta$ to obtain

$$L = 2 \int_0^{\pi/4} \sec^3 \theta \, d\theta = \frac{1}{2} \cdot 2 \left(\ln |\sec \theta + \tan \theta| + \sec \theta \tan \theta \right) \Big|_0^{\pi/4} = \ln(\sqrt{2} + 1) + \sqrt{2}.$$

13. Find the length of the curve with polar equation $r = e^{2\theta}$, $0 \le \theta \le 1$.

SOLUTION: With $r = e^{2\theta}$ then $\dfrac{dr}{d\theta} = 2e^{2\theta}$, so by Formula 9.10 the length of this curve is

$$L = \int_0^1 \sqrt{(2e^{2\theta})^2 + (e^{2\theta})^2} \, d\theta = \sqrt{5} \int_0^1 e^{2\theta} \, d\theta = \frac{\sqrt{5}}{2} \left[e^{2\theta} \right] \Big|_0^1 = \frac{\sqrt{5}}{2} (e^2 - 1).$$

17. Sketch the graphs of the parametric equations given below for $0 \le t \le \dfrac{\pi}{2}$ and find the length of each curve.   a) $x = \cos t$, $y = \sin t$
   b) $x = \cos^2 t$, $y = \sin^2 t$ c) $x = \cos^3 t$, $y = \sin^3 t$.

SOLUTION: The three curves are all contained in the graphs of a) $x^2 + y^2 = 1$, b) $x + y = 1$ and c) $x^{2/3} + y^{2/3} = 1$ respectively. They each are that portion of the curve which lies in the first quadrant since $0 \le x \le 1$ and $0 \le y \le 1$ in each case.

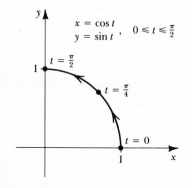

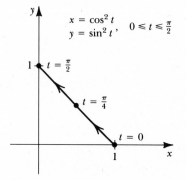

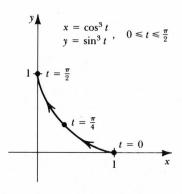

Their lengths are: a) $x = \cos t$, $y = \sin t$, $x' = -\sin t$, $y' = \cos t$,

$$L_a = \int_0^{\pi/2} \sqrt{(-\sin t)^2 + (\cos t)^2}\, dt = \int_0^{\pi/2} dt = \frac{\pi}{2},$$

b) $x = \cos^2 t$, $y = \sin^2 t$, $x' = -2\cos t \sin t$, $y' = 2\sin t \cos t$,

$$L_b = \int_0^{\pi/2} \sqrt{(-2\cos t \sin t)^2 + (2\sin t \cos t)^2}\, dt$$

$$= 2\sqrt{2} \int_0^{\pi/2} \sin t \cos t\, dt = 2\sqrt{2} \left[\frac{\sin^2 t}{2}\right]\Big|_0^{\pi/2} = \sqrt{2},$$

and c) $x = \cos^3 t$, $y = \sin^3 t$, $x' = -3\cos^2 t \sin t$, $y' = 3\sin^2 t \cos t$,

$$L_c = \int_0^{\pi/2} \sqrt{(-3\cos^2 t \sin t)^2 + (3\sin^2 t \cos t)^2}\, dt = 3\int_0^{\pi/2} \sin t \cos t\, dt$$

$$= 3\left[\frac{\sin^2 t}{2}\right]\Big|_0^{\pi/2} = \frac{3}{2}.$$

_____Chapter 9

Review Exercises

1. Find the rectangular coordinates for the point with polar coordinates $\left(3, \dfrac{\pi}{6}\right)$.

SOLUTION: Since $r = 3$, $\theta = \pi/6$ then $x = r\cos\theta = 3\cos\dfrac{\pi}{6} = \dfrac{3\sqrt{3}}{2}$, and $y = r\sin\theta =$

$3\sin\dfrac{\pi}{6} = \dfrac{3}{2}$ so the rectangular coordinates are $\left(\dfrac{3\sqrt{3}}{2}, \dfrac{3}{2}\right)$.

5. Find two different sets of polar coordinates for the points with Cartesian coordinates $(1, 1)$.

SOLUTION: This point lies in the first quadrant with $x = 1$, $y = 1$, so r and θ satisfy $1^2 + 1^2 = r^2$, $\tan\theta = \dfrac{1}{1}$; i.e., $r^2 = 2$, $\tan\theta = 1$.

Two solutions which correspond to points in the first quadrant are $r = \sqrt{2}$, $\theta = \pi/4$ and $r = -\sqrt{2}$, $\theta = 5\pi/4$.

15. Sketch the graph of the curve described by $r = 1 + 2\cos\theta$.

SOLUTION: This curve is symmetric about the x-axis. The values of r change sign at θ such that $\cos\theta = -\frac{1}{2}$; i.e., $\theta = \frac{2\pi}{3}, \frac{5\pi}{3}, \frac{8\pi}{3}, \frac{11\pi}{3}$, etc. The θ-range of this graph is 2π since $k = 2$ is the smallest integer for which $(-1)^k r = 1 + 2\cos(\theta + k\pi)$ is equivalent to $r = 1 + 2\cos\theta$. Choose the interval $0 \le \theta \le 2\pi$ to describe this curve.

Plot $\theta \in [0, \pi]$ paying particular attention to the sign change at $\theta = 2\pi/3$, then use symmetry to complete the graph.

θ	0	$\dfrac{\pi}{3}$	$\dfrac{\pi}{2}$	$\dfrac{2\pi}{3}$	$\dfrac{5\pi}{6}$	π
r	3	2	1	0	$1 - \sqrt{3}$	-2

Plot the rest using symmetry about the x-axis.

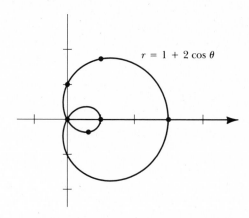

$r = 1 + 2\cos\theta$

23. Sketch the graphs of the curves described by $r = 1 + \ln\theta$.

SOLUTION: This curve has no standard symmetries. The value of r changes from negative to positive at $\theta = \frac{1}{e}$; as θ approaches 0, r approaches $-\infty$, and as θ grows without bound, so does r. This graph has a horizontal asymptote along the negative y-axis ($\theta \to 0$, $r \to -\infty$). The θ-range is infinite so the entire graph is described by $\theta \in (0, \infty)$. Furthermore r increases as θ increases. Some typical values of (r, θ) are plotted.

θ	0	$\left(\dfrac{1}{e}\right)^2 \approx 8°$	$\dfrac{1}{e} \approx 21°$	$1 \approx 57°$	$e \approx 156°$	$e^2 \approx 63°$
r	$-\infty$	-1	0	1	2	3

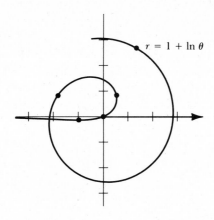

$r = 1 + \ln \theta$

29. a) Sketch the graph of the curve $x = \sin^2 t + 1$, $y = \cos^2 t$.   **b)** Find the slope of the tangent line at $t = \pi/4$.

SOLUTION: a) Rewrite the parametric equations as $\sin^2 t = x - 1$, $\cos^2 t = y$ and eliminate t, $\sin^2 t + \cos^2 t = x - 1 + y = 1$. This curve is contained in the line $x + y = 2$. Since $0 \le x - 1 \le 1$ and $0 \le y \le 1$, the "curve" lies on the segment connecting $(1,1)$ and $(2,0)$.

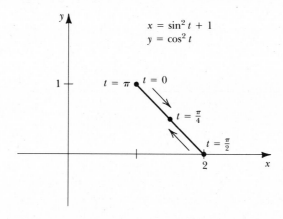

$x = \sin^2 t + 1$
$y = \cos^2 t$

b) The slope of the "tangent line" is given by

$$\frac{dy}{dx} = \frac{dy/dt}{dx/dt} = \frac{(2\cos t)(-\sin t)}{(2\sin t)(\cos t)} = -1$$

everywhere except at multiples of π or $\dfrac{\pi}{2}$, where it is undefined. In particular at $t = \dfrac{\pi}{4}$ the slope of the tangent line is -1.

39. a) Sketch the graph of the region inside $r = 3\cos 2\theta$.   **b)** Determine the area of this region.

SOLUTION: a) This is a 4-leaved rose similar to that which was analyzed and sketched in EXAMPLE 2 of SECTION 9.3 of the text, the only difference being that the leaves extend to a maximum distance of $r = 3$ rather than the $r = 1$ of the example.

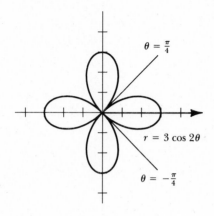

b) The four leaves of this rose are identical in shape, so it is only necessary to compute the area of the one leaf lying between the rays $\theta = -\dfrac{\pi}{4}$ and $\theta = \dfrac{\pi}{4}$. Its area is

$$A_{1/4} = \int_{-\pi/4}^{\pi/4} \frac{1}{2}(3\cos 2\theta)^2 \, d\theta = \frac{9}{4}\int_{-\pi/4}^{\pi/4}(1+\cos 4\theta)\,d\theta$$

$$= \frac{9}{4}\left[\theta + \frac{1}{4}\sin 4\theta\right]\bigg|_{-\pi/4}^{\pi/4} = \frac{9\pi}{8}.$$

Thus the total area bounded by the rose is $A = 4A_{1/4} = \dfrac{9\pi}{2}$.

45. a) Sketch the graph of the region inside $r = 1 + \sin\theta$ and outside $r = 1$. b) Determine the area of this region.

SOLUTION: a)   The cardioid $r = 1 + \sin\theta$ was analyzed and sketched in the solution to EXERCISE 23 of SECTION 9.3 in this manual. The circle $r = 1$ of radius 1 centered at the pole is sketched on the same graph as the cardioid, and the region is shaded.

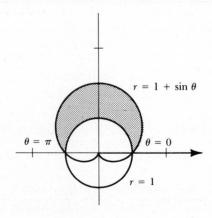

b) The points of intersection of these curves occur at θ such that $1 = 1 + \sin\theta$ or $\theta = 0, \pi$. The shaded region lies between the rays $\theta = 0$ and $\theta = \pi$ and can be described as $0 \le \theta \le \pi$ and $1 \le r \le 1 + \sin\theta$, thus its area is

$$A = \int_0^\pi \left(\frac{1}{2}(1 + \sin\theta)^2 - \frac{1}{2}(1)^2\right) d\theta = \int_0^\pi \left(\sin\theta + \frac{1}{2}\sin^2\theta\right) d\theta$$

$$= \int_0^\pi \left(\sin\theta + \frac{1}{4} - \frac{1}{4}\cos 2\theta\right) d\theta = \left[-\cos\theta + \frac{1}{4}\theta - \frac{1}{8}\sin 2\theta\right]\Big|_0^\pi = 2 + \frac{\pi}{4}.$$

49. a) Sketch the graph of the curve $r = 2 - 2\cos\theta$. b) Find the length of this curve.

SOLUTION: a) The cardioid $r = 2 - 2\cos\theta$ is symmetric about the x-axis. The values of r are positive everywhere except at $\theta = \pi, 2\pi$, etc. where they are 0. The θ-range is easily seen to be 2π, so the graph is described by $\theta \in [0, 2\pi]$. Plot points for $\theta \in [0, \pi]$ and use symmetry about the x-axis to complete the graph.

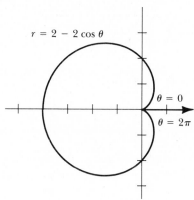

b) Since $r = 2 - 2\cos\theta$ with $\dfrac{dr}{d\theta} = 2\sin\theta$ describes this curve exactly once if $\theta \in [0, 2\pi]$, then the length is

$$L = \int_0^{2\pi} \sqrt{(2\sin\theta)^2 + (2 - 2\cos\theta)^2}\, d\theta = 2\int_0^{2\pi} \sqrt{2 - 2\cos\theta}\, d\theta = 4\int_0^{2\pi} \sqrt{\sin^2\frac{\theta}{2}}\, d\theta$$

$$= 4\int_0^{2\pi} \left|\sin\frac{\theta}{2}\right| d\theta = 4\int_0^{2\pi} \sin\frac{\theta}{2}\, d\theta = 4\left[-2\cos\frac{\theta}{2}\right]\Big|_0^{2\pi} = 16.$$

61. a) Sketch the graph of $r(4\cos\theta - 2\sin\theta) = 6$.
b) Find the corresponding cartesian equation.

SOLUTION: Use the fact that $\sqrt{4^2 + 2^2} = 2\sqrt{5}$ to rewrite the equation as

$$2r\sqrt{5}\left(\frac{4}{2\sqrt{5}}\cos\theta - \frac{2}{2\sqrt{5}}\sin\theta\right) = 6 \qquad \text{or}$$

$$r\left(\cos\alpha\cos\theta - \sin\alpha\sin\theta\right) = \frac{3}{\sqrt{5}},$$

where $0 \leq \alpha \leq \frac{\pi}{2}$, $\cos\alpha = 2/\sqrt{5}$ and $\sin\alpha = 1/\sqrt{5}$; that is, $\alpha = \arctan\frac{1}{2}$.

The equation is thus $r\cos(\theta + \alpha) = \frac{3}{\sqrt{5}}$, so its graph is the same as the line $r\cos\theta = \frac{3}{\sqrt{5}}$ rotated by an angle $-\alpha$. This latter graph, the angle $-\alpha$ whose tangent is $-\frac{1}{2}$, and the graph of the given line are sketched.

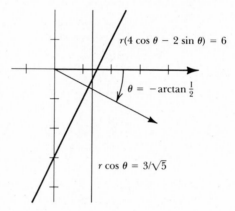

b) Rewrite the equation as $4r\cos\theta - 2r\sin\theta = 6$ to obtain the cartesian equation $4x - 2y = 6$. Notice that this line has x-intercept $3/2$ and y-intercept -3.

10
Conic Sections

Sharpening your skills

You should review material about the Cartesian coordinate system and graphing from APPEN-
DIX A and CHAPTERS 1 and 2, and about polar coordinates graphing from CHAPTER 9. You
must also use the technique of completing squares on several equations.

These tools and a few others are needed in the practice problems below. The section numbers of
the text refer to places where the tool is presented.

Practice Problems

1. Complete the squares and graph the equations
   a) $x^2 + y^2 + 2x - 4y - 4 = 0$
   b) $y = 2x^2 - 12x$.   (See SECTIONS 1.2–1.4)

2. Find $\cos\theta$ and $\sin\theta$ if $\cot\theta = \frac{1}{2}$. (See APPENDIX A.3)

3. Write the Cartesian equation for the curve whose polar coordinate equation is $r\cos\theta - 2r = 3$.
   (See SECTION 9.1)

4. Graph the curve with polar coordinate equation $r = 2 + \sin\theta$.   (See SECTION 9.2)

————————————————————————————10.1

Parabolas

3. a) Sketch the graph of the parabola with equation $y = -2x^2$.   b) Find the vertex, focal
   point and equation of the directrix.

SOLUTION: a) This parabola is in standard position with equation of the form $y = \dfrac{1}{4c}x^2$
with $\dfrac{1}{4c} = -2$ or $c = -\dfrac{1}{8}$. Thus the vertex is $V(0,0)$, the focal point is $F\left(0, -\dfrac{1}{8}\right)$, and the
directrix is $y = -\left(-\dfrac{1}{8}\right)$ or $y = \dfrac{1}{8}$.

The parabola has vertex $V(0,0)$, opens downward (around the focus $F\left(0, -\dfrac{1}{8}\right)$) and is symmetric
about the axis $x = 0$. Plot the vertex, another point, e.g., $(1, -2)$, and sketch the graph to show
the above-mentioned properties.

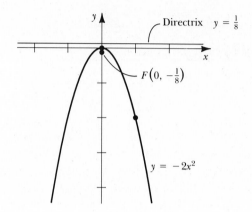

b) The vertex is $V(0,0)$, the focus is $F\left(0,-\dfrac{1}{8}\right)$, and the directrix has equation $y = \dfrac{1}{8}$.

11. a) Sketch the graph of the parabola with equation $y^2 - 8y + 12 = 2x$. b) Find the vertex, the focal point and equation of the directrix.

SOLUTION: a) Completing the square in the equation yields $y^2 - 8y + 16 = 2x + 4$ or $(y-4)^2 = 2(x+2)$. The corresponding standard position parabola has equation $y^2 = 2x$.

The standard position parabola with equation $x = \dfrac{1}{2}y^2$ has focal length c with $4c = 2$ or $c = \dfrac{1}{2}$.

Its vertex is $\hat{V}(0,0)$, its focus is $\hat{F}\left(\dfrac{1}{2},0\right)$, its directrix has equation $x = -\dfrac{1}{2}$ and its axis of symmetry has equation $y = 0$. The standard position parabola along with its vertex, focus and directrix is graphed below using a dotted line. The parabola with given equation along with its vertex, focus and directrix are obtained by translating the standard position data to the left by 2 and upward by 4.

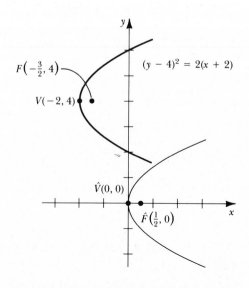

b) Translation of the standard position vertex $\hat{V}(0,0)$ by -2 in the x-direction and by 4 in the y-direction gives the vertex $V(-2,4)$. Similarly, the focus is $F\left(\frac{1}{2}-2,4\right)$ or $F(-\frac{3}{2},4)$. The standard position directrix, $x = -\frac{1}{2}$, is translated by -2 in the x-direction to become the line with equation $x = -\frac{1}{2}-2$ or $x = -\frac{5}{2}$.

17. Find an equation of the parabola with focus $(-2,2)$ and directrix $y = -2$.

SOLUTION: The parabola opens upward (around the focus) along the axis of symmetry $x = -2$ (the line perpendicular to the directrix and through the focus). Its vertex lies on the axis of symmetry midway between the focus and the directrix at the point $V(-2,0)$. The distance from the vertex to the focus is $c = 2$. The parabola obtained by translating this so that its vertex is at the origin also has focal length $c = 2$ and opens upward. This translate is the parabola in standard position with equation $y = \dfrac{1}{(4)(2)}x^2$ or $8y = x^2$. Since the given parabola is obtained by translating this parabola to the left by 2, then its equation is $8y = (x-(-2))^2$ or $8y = (x+2)^2$.

21. Find an equation of a parabola with vertex $V(-2,2)$ and directrix $x = 4$.

SOLUTION: The focal distance is $c = -6$ since the vertex is six units to the left of the directrix. The axis of symmetry is the horizontal line $y = 2$ and the focus lies six units along this line to the left of the vertex, $F(-8,2)$. The parabola opens to the left (around the focus) so the corresponding standard position parabola has equation $x = \dfrac{1}{4(-6)}y^2$ or $-24x = y^2$. This standard position parabola is translated by 2 units to the left and 2 units up to obtain the given parabola with equation $-24(x+2) = (y-2)^2$.

27. Find an equation of the parabola with axis parallel to the y-axis and vertex $V(0,2)$ which passes through the point $P(4,8)$.

SOLUTION: The standard position parabola with axis parallel to the y-axis has equation $y = \dfrac{1}{4c}x^2$. The translation of this with vertex at $V(0,2)$ has equation $(y-2) = \dfrac{1}{4c}x^2$. The point $P(4,8)$ is on the parabola if its coordinates satisfy the equation $(8-2) = \dfrac{1}{4c}(4)^2$; thus $c = \dfrac{2}{3}$ and the equation of the given parabola is $y - 2 = \dfrac{3}{8}x^2$.

43. The world's largest hanger is the Goodyear Airdock, built in 1929 in Akron, Ohio to house and service the rigid airships USS Akron and USS Macon. The main structure of this hangar is a 1175-foot long cylinder whose cross section is parabolic with height 211 feet and width 325 feet. What is the volume enclosed by this structure?

SOLUTION:

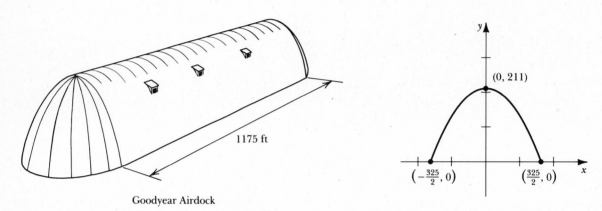

Goodyear Airdock

Since the Airdock is a cylinder, its volume is $V = l \times A$ where $l = 1175$ ft, its length, and where A is its cross-sectional area.

The parabola with vertex $V(0, 211)$ and which opens downward has equation $(y - 211) = \dfrac{1}{4c}x^2$. In order for this parabola to contain the points $\left(\pm\dfrac{325}{2}, 0\right)$, it is necessary that $(0 - 211) = \dfrac{1}{4c}\left(\dfrac{325}{2}\right)^2$ or $\dfrac{1}{4c} = -\dfrac{844}{(325)^2}$. The parabola which represents the cross section of the airdock is thus $y = 211 - \dfrac{4(211)}{(325)^2}x^2$. The area beneath this parabola, above the x-axis between $x = -\dfrac{325}{2}$ and $x = \dfrac{325}{2}$ is then

$$A = \int_{-325/2}^{325/2} \left(211 - \frac{4 \cdot 211}{(325)^2}x^2\right) dx = 211\left[x - \frac{4}{(325)^2} \cdot \frac{x^3}{3}\right]\Bigg|_{x=-325/2}^{325/2}$$

$$= 211\left(\left(\frac{325}{2} - \left(-\frac{325}{2}\right)\right) - \frac{4}{(325)^2}\left(\frac{(325/2)^3}{3} - \frac{(-325/2)^3}{3}\right)\right)$$

$$= 211\left(325 - \frac{325}{3}\right) = \frac{137,150}{3} \text{ square ft.}$$

The volume is thus

$$V = 1175 \times \frac{137,150}{3} = 53,717,083\frac{1}{3} \text{ cu ft.}$$

_____**10.2**

Ellipses

3. a) Sketch the graph of the ellipse $\dfrac{x^2}{25} + \dfrac{y^2}{16} = 1$. b) Find the vertices and focal points.

SOLUTION: a) This standard position ellipse has equation in the form of equation 10.7 with $a^2 = 25$ and $b^2 = 16$; thus the major axis lies between the vertices $(-5,0)$ and $(5,0)$ and the minor axis lies between $(0,-4)$ and $(0,4)$.

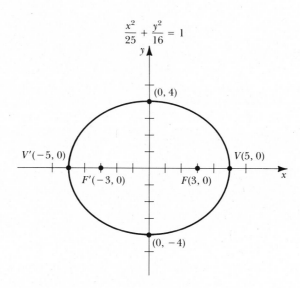

b) Since $c^2 = a^2 - b^2$, then $c^2 = 25 - 16 = 9$, so $c = 3$ and thus the focal points lie along the major axis at a distance of 3 units either side of the midpoint of this segment, $(-3,0)$ and $(3,0)$. The vertices are $(-5,0)$ and $(5,0)$.

13. a) Sketch the graph of the ellipse $3x^2 + 2y^2 - 18x + 4y + 28 = 0$. b) Find the vertices and focal point.

SOLUTION: a) Complete the square in both x and y. $3(x^2 - 6x + 9) + 2(y^2 + 2y + 1) = -28 + 27 + 2$ or $\dfrac{(x-3)^2}{1/3} + \dfrac{(y+1)^2}{1/2} = 1$. The standard position ellipse, $\dfrac{x^2}{1/3} + \dfrac{y^2}{1/2} = 1$, has vertices at $\left(0, -\sqrt{2}/2\right)$ and $\left(0, \sqrt{2}/2\right)$ since this equation is of the form of 10.8 with $a^2 = \dfrac{1}{2}$ and $b^2 = \dfrac{1}{3}$. The focal length is $c = \sqrt{(1/2) - (1/3)} = \sqrt{6}/6$, so the focal points lie on the major axis $\sqrt{6}/6$ units on each side of the center, at $(0, -\sqrt{6}/6)$ and $(0, \sqrt{6}/6)$. This standard position ellipse is translated by 3 to the right and by 1 downward to obtain the ellipse with given equation.

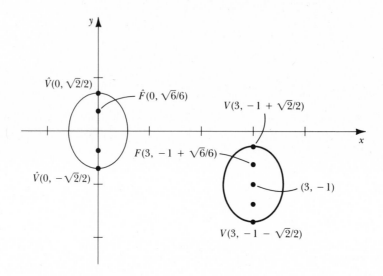

b) Translation of the vertices, $(0, -\sqrt{2}/2)$ and $(0, \sqrt{2}/2)$, and the focal points, $(0, -\sqrt{6}/6)$ and $(0, \sqrt{6}/6)$, of the standard position ellipse by 3 units to the right and by 1 unit downward result in the vertices, $\left(3, -1 - \dfrac{\sqrt{2}}{2}\right)$ and $\left(3, -1 + \dfrac{\sqrt{2}}{2}\right)$, and the focal points, $\left(3, -1 - \dfrac{\sqrt{6}}{6}\right)$ and $\left(3, -1 + \dfrac{\sqrt{6}}{6}\right)$ for the given ellipse.

19. Find an equation of the ellipse with vertices at $(2,2)$ and $(6,2)$ and with a focal point at $(5,2)$.

SOLUTION: The midpoint of the major axis is at $(4,2)$; so the distance from this point to the vertices is $a = 2$, and its distance from the focal point is $c = 1$. The parameter b satisfies $b = \sqrt{a^2 - c^2} = \sqrt{3}$. Since the vertices are on an axis parallel to the x-axis, then the standard position ellipse which is the translate of the given ellipse has equation $\dfrac{x^2}{(2)^2} + \dfrac{y^2}{(\sqrt{3})^2} = 1$. To obtain the equation of the given ellipse, translate this standard ellipse by 4 to the right and 2 upward. The equation is then $\dfrac{(x-4)^2}{4} + \dfrac{(y-2)^2}{3} = 1$.

25. Find an equation of a tangent line to the ellipse $4x^2 + y^2 = 4$ that passes through the point $(3,0)$.

SOLUTION: This standard position ellipse has equation $x^2 + \dfrac{y^2}{4} = 1$, so its vertices are $(0, \pm 2)$ and its x-intercepts are $(\pm 1, 0)$. This ellipse and the point $P(3,0)$ are sketched.

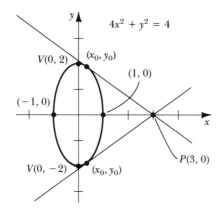

Notice that there are two tangent lines which satisfy the stated conditions.

Use implicit differentiation to determine an equation for the slope of a tangent line at the point (x_0, y_0), $y'(x_0)$, as $8x_0 + 2y_0 y'(x_0) = 0$ or $y'(x_0) = -\dfrac{4x_0}{y_0}$. The fact that a tangent line passes through $P(3,0)$ as well as (x_0, y_0) implies that its slope also is $\dfrac{y_0 - 0}{x_0 - 3}$. Equate this to the value of $y'(x_0)$ to obtain $-\dfrac{4x_0}{y_0} = \dfrac{y_0}{x_0 - 3}$ or, provided that neither $x_0 = 3$ nor $y_0 = 0$, i) $12x_0 = 4x_0^2 + y_0^2$. A second equation, ii) $4x_0^2 + y_0^2 = 4$, follows from the fact that the point (x_0, y_0) lies on the ellipse. Substitute the value, 4, for $4x_0^2 + y_0^2$ from the second equation into the first equation to obtain $12x_0 = 4$ or $x_0 = \dfrac{1}{3}$. The second equation then implies that $4(1/3)^2 + y_0^2 = 4$; i.e. $y_0^2 = \dfrac{32}{9}$ or $y_0 = \pm\dfrac{4}{3}\sqrt{2}$. The two points at which tangency occurs are $\left(1/3, 4\sqrt{2}/3\right)$ and $\left(1/3, -4\sqrt{2}/3\right)$, at these points the slopes of the tangent lines are $-\left(\dfrac{4 \cdot \frac{1}{3}}{\frac{4\sqrt{2}}{3}}\right) = -\dfrac{1}{\sqrt{2}}$, $-\left(\dfrac{4 \cdot \frac{1}{3}}{-\frac{4\sqrt{2}}{3}}\right) = \dfrac{1}{\sqrt{2}}$ respectively. Since both tangent lines pass through $(3,0)$ their equations are $\dfrac{y - 0}{x - 3} = \pm\dfrac{1}{\sqrt{2}}$.

35. Describe the curve traced by a point 2 feet from the top of a ladder 8 feet long as the bottom of the ladder moves away from a vertical wall.

SOLUTION: Set up a coordinate system so that x measures the horizontal distance from the point to the wall and y measures the vertical distance above the ground.

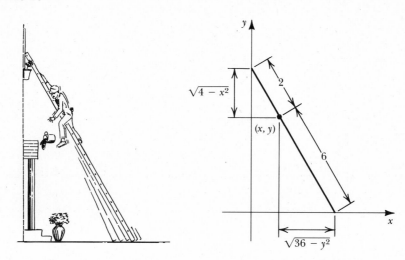

Consider the two right triangles with sides of lengths $\{2, x, \sqrt{4 - x^2}\}$ and $\left\{6, \sqrt{36 - y^2}, y\right\}$. Since these triangles are similar, then $\sqrt{36 - y^2}/6 = x/2$. Thus an equation for the point on the ladder is $\sqrt{36 - y^2} = 3x$ or $9x^2 + y^2 = 36$. The point moves through the first quadrant along this ellipse from the point $(0, 6)$ to the point $(0, 2)$.

39. The Goodyear airships *Columbia*, *America*, and *Europa* are each 192 feet long and 50 feet wide. A brochure available from Goodyear Aerospace in Akron, Ohio states that the volume contained in one of the blimps is 202,700 cubic feet. Is this figure reasonable?

SOLUTION: Assume that an airship is in the shape of a surface of revolution obtained by revolving the upper half of an ellipse around its major axis. From the given data this ellipse would have $a = 192/2 = 96$ and $b = 50/2 = 25$.

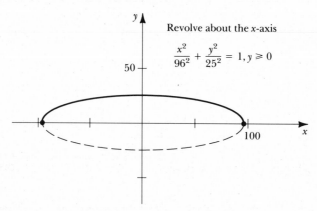

The equation of the ellipse is $\dfrac{x^2}{(96)^2} + \dfrac{y^2}{(25)^2} = 1$. Use the method of disks formula (5.7) to calculate the volume of this solid

$$V = \pi \int_{-96}^{96} y^2 \, dx = \pi \int_{-96}^{96} (25)^2 \left(1 - \frac{x^2}{(96)^2}\right) dx = (25)^2 \pi \left[x - \frac{x^3}{3(96)^2}\right]\Big|_{-96}^{96}$$

$$= (25)^2 \pi \frac{4}{3}(96) \approx 251,327 \text{ cubic feet.}$$

The figure in the advertising brochure is reasonable.

_____10.3

Hyperbolas

1. a) Sketch the graph of the hyperbola with equation $\dfrac{x^2}{4} - \dfrac{y^2}{9} = 1$. b) Find the coordinates of the vertices and focal points and write equations of the asymptotes.

SOLUTION: This standard position hyperbola has its equation of the form 10.10 with $a = 2$ and $b = 3$ so its axis is the x-axis with vertices at $(-2, 0)$ and $(2, 0)$ and with slant asymptotes $y = \pm\dfrac{3}{2}x$.

a) To sketch the graph, draw the slant asymptotes, locate the vertices, and sketch the two branches as passing through the vertices and asymptotic to the lines.

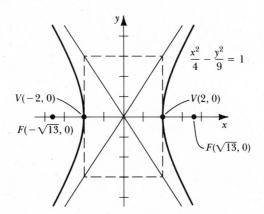

b) As was observed above, the vertices are $(\pm 2, 0)$, the slant asymptotes have equations $y = \pm\dfrac{3}{2}x$. Since $a = 2$ and $b = 3$, then the focal length is $c = \sqrt{a^2 + b^2} = \sqrt{13}$, so the focal points lie on the axis at $(\pm\sqrt{13}, 0)$.

9. a) Sketch the graph of the hyperbola $y^2 - 2x^2 = 8$. b) Find the coordinates of the vertices and focal points and write equations of the asymptotes.

SOLUTION: This standard position hyperbola has its equation of the form 10.12 with $a = 2\sqrt{2}$ and $b = 2$ so the axis is the y-axis, the vertices are $(0, \pm 2\sqrt{2})$, and the slant asymptotes have equations $y = \pm\sqrt{2}\, x$.

a) Sketch the two branches of the hyperbola so as to pass through the vertices $(0, \pm\sqrt{2})$ and to be asymptotic to the lines $y = \pm\sqrt{2}x$.

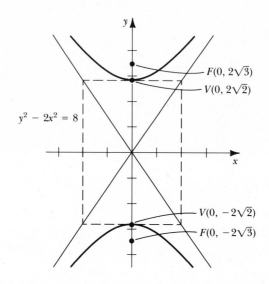

b) The vertices are $(0, \pm\sqrt{2})$, the asymptotes have equations $y = \pm\sqrt{2}x$ and, since $a = 2\sqrt{2}$ and $b = 2$, then the focal length is $c = \sqrt{a^2 + b^2} = \sqrt{12}$ so the focal points lie on the axis at $(0, \pm 2\sqrt{3})$.

17. a) Sketch the graph of the hyperbola with equation $4x^2 - 3y^2 + 8x + 18y = 11$. **b)** Find the coordinates of the vertices and focal points and write the equations of the asymptotes.

SOLUTION: Complete the squares on the x and y terms to obtain $4(x^2 + 2x + 1) - 3(y^2 - 6y + 9) = 11 + 4 - 27$ or $4(x + 1)^2 - 3(y - 3)^2 = -12$. This is rewritten as $\dfrac{(y - 3)^2}{4} - \dfrac{(x + 1)^2}{3} = 1$, so its graph is the translate of the standard position hyperbola whose equation is of the form 10.12 with $a = 2$ and $b = \sqrt{3}$. This standard position hyperbola has vertices at $(0, \pm 2)$ and asymptotes $y = \pm\dfrac{2}{\sqrt{3}}x$.

a) The standard position hyperbola is sketched so that its branches pass through the vertices $(0, \pm 2)$ and are asymptotic to the lines $y = \pm\dfrac{2}{\sqrt{3}}x$. The graph and asymptotes are translated by 3 units upward and 1 unit to the left to give the graph of the hyperbola with the given equation.

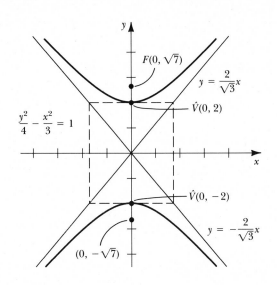

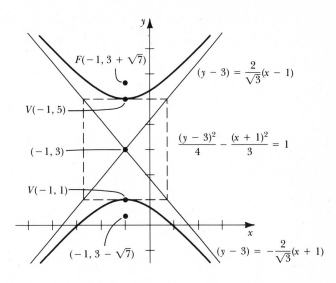

b) Since $a = 2$ and $b = 3$, the focal length is $c = \sqrt{2^2 + (\sqrt{3})^2} = \sqrt{7}$ so the focal points for the standard position hyperbola are at $(0, \pm\sqrt{7})$. These points along with the standard position vertices $(0, \pm 2)$ and asymptotes $y = \pm\dfrac{2}{\sqrt{3}}x$ are translated by 3 units in the y-direction and -1 in the x-direction to obtain focal points $(-1, 3 \pm \sqrt{7})$, vertices $(-1, 3 \pm 2)$ and asymptotes $(y - 3) = \pm\dfrac{2}{\sqrt{3}}(x + 1)$.

21. Find an equation of the hyperbola with foci at $(0, \pm 5)$ and vertices at $(0, \pm 4)$.

SOLUTION: Since the axis is the y-axis and since the vertices are distance 4 from the origin, then this hyperbola has equation of the form 10.12 with $a = 4$. Since the focal length is $c = 5$, then $b = \sqrt{c^2 - a^2} = \sqrt{25 - 16} = 3$. Thus the equation is $\dfrac{y^2}{4^2} - \dfrac{x^2}{3^2} = 1$.

29. Find an equation of the hyperbola with vertices at $(6, 1)$ and $(-2, 1)$ and equations of slant asymptotes $y = \dfrac{3}{4}x - \dfrac{1}{2}$ and $y = -\dfrac{3}{4}x + \dfrac{5}{2}$.

SOLUTION: The vertices lie on the line $y = 1$, parallel to the x-axis at a distance $a = 4$ from the midpoint of the major axis $(2, 1)$. The corresponding standard position hyperbola has equation $\dfrac{x^2}{4^2} - \dfrac{y^2}{b^2} = 1$, where b is yet to be determined. The asymptotes both pass through $(2, 1)$; their equations can be written as $(y - 1) = \pm\dfrac{3}{4}(x - 2)$. From this equation along with the fact that $a = 4$, conclude that $\dfrac{b}{a} = \dfrac{3}{4}$ or $b = 3$. With this value of b, the standard position equation above is translated by 2 in the x-direction and 1 in the y-direction to obtain

$$\frac{(x - 2)^2}{4^2} - \frac{(y - 1)^2}{3^2} = 1.$$

33. Find an equation for the tangent line to the hyperbola $9x^2 - 4y^2 = 36$ that passes through $(1,0)$.

SOLUTION: This standard position hyperbola and the point are graphed below.

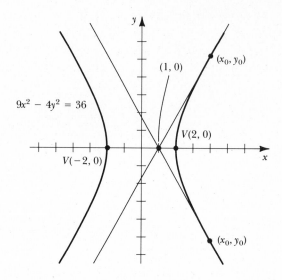

There are two such tangent lines. The slope of the tangent line at (x_0, y_0), $y'(x_0)$ is computed by implicit differentiation: $18x_0 - 8y_0 y'(x_0) = 0$ or $y'(x_0) = \dfrac{9x_0}{4y_0}$. The tangent line passes through $(1,0)$, so its slope also satisfies $y'(x_0) = \dfrac{y_0 - 0}{x_0 - 1}$ or $\dfrac{9x_0}{4y_0} = \dfrac{y_0}{x_0 - 1}$. Rewrite this as $9x_0^2 - 4y_0^2 = 9x_0$ and replace the value of $9x_0^2 - 4y_0^2$ by 36 since (x_0, y_0) lies on the hyperbola. This gives $36 = 9x_0$ or $x_0 = 4$ from which it follows that $9(4)^2 - 4(y_0)^2 = 36$ or $y_0 = \pm 3\sqrt{3}$. At the points $(4, \pm 3\sqrt{3})$ the slopes of the tangent lines are $\dfrac{9(4)}{4(\pm 3\sqrt{3})} = \pm\sqrt{3}$ respectively. Since the tangent lines both pass through $(1,0)$, their equations are $\dfrac{y - 0}{x - 1} = \pm\sqrt{3}$.

37. Consider the equation $Ax^2 - Cy^2 + Dx + Ey + F = 0$ where A and C are positive constants. Find conditions on the constants A, C, D, E and F that ensure that this equation describes
a) a hyperbola with axis parallel to the x-axis;
b) two lines;
c) a hyperbola with axis parallel to the y-axis.

SOLUTION: Complete the squares on the x and y terms separately to obtain

$$A\left(x^2 + \frac{D}{A}x + \left(\frac{D}{2A}\right)^2\right) - C\left(y^2 - \frac{E}{C}y + \left(\frac{E}{2C}\right)^2\right) = \frac{D^2}{4A} - \frac{E^2}{4C} - F \quad \text{or}$$

$$A\left(x + \frac{D}{2A}\right)^2 - C\left(y - \frac{E}{2C}\right)^2 = \frac{(D^2 C - E^2 A) - 4ACF}{4AC}.$$

The nature and orientation of the hyperbola depends entirely on the sign of the right-hand side of this equation. If it is positive, then division by this constant results in a hyperbola with axis parallel to the x-axis. If the right-hand side is negative, then division by this constant changes the signs of the quadratic terms resulting in a hyperbola with axis parallel to the y-axis. If the right-hand side is zero, then the equation is equivalent to

$$\left(\sqrt{A}\left(x+\frac{D}{2A}\right)-\sqrt{C}\left(y-\frac{E}{2C}\right)\right)\cdot\left(\sqrt{A}\left(x+\frac{D}{2A}\right)+\sqrt{C}\left(y-\frac{E}{2C}\right)\right)=0,$$

or the equations of two lines

$$\frac{\left(y-\frac{E}{2C}\right)}{\left(x+\frac{D}{2A}\right)}=\pm\sqrt{\frac{C}{A}}.$$

Since $4AC > 0$, then the nature of the graph is determined entirely by the sign of $D^2C - E^2A - 4ACF$;

a) the hyperbola has axis parallel to the x-axis if this expression is positive,

b) the graph is two lines if this expression is zero, and

c) the hyperbola has axis parallel to the y-axis if this expression is negative.

———————————————————————————————————10.4

Rotation of Axes

1. a) Use Formula 10.17 to determine if the conic with equation $x^2 - xy + y^2 = 2$ is an ellipse, hyperbola or parabola. **b)** Perform a suitable rotation and/or translation and sketch the graph.

SOLUTION: a) $B = -1$, $A = C = 1$, so $B^2 - 4AC = (-1)^2 - 4(1)(1) = -3$; thus the conic is an ellipse.

b) The xy term is eliminated by rotating through an angle $\theta \in \left(0, \frac{\pi}{2}\right)$, where

$$\cot\theta = \frac{A-C}{B} + \frac{\sqrt{(A-C)^2 + B^2}}{|B|} = \frac{1-1}{(-1)} + \frac{\sqrt{(1-1)^2 + (-1)^2}}{|-1|} = 1.$$ The solution is $\theta = \pi/4$,

so the rotation is acheived by the change of variables

$$x = \cos\frac{\pi}{4}\hat{x} - \sin\frac{\pi}{4}\hat{y}, \quad y = \sin\frac{\pi}{4}\hat{x} + \cos\frac{\pi}{4}\hat{y}$$

or $x = \frac{\sqrt{2}}{2}\hat{x} - \frac{\sqrt{2}}{2}\hat{y}$, $y = \frac{\sqrt{2}}{2}\hat{x} + \frac{\sqrt{2}}{2}\hat{y}$. Substitute these into the equation of the conic to obtain

$$\left(\frac{\sqrt{2}}{2}\hat{x} - \frac{\sqrt{2}}{2}\hat{y}\right)^2 - \left(\frac{\sqrt{2}}{2}\hat{x} - \frac{\sqrt{2}}{2}\hat{y}\right)\left(\frac{\sqrt{2}}{2}\hat{x} + \frac{\sqrt{2}}{2}\hat{y}\right) + \left(\frac{\sqrt{2}}{2}\hat{x} + \frac{\sqrt{2}}{2}\hat{y}\right)^2 = 2.$$

Notice that if the "$\frac{\sqrt{2}}{2}$" factors are factored out of the terms and the resulting equation is multiplied by 2 that the equation becomes

$$(\hat{x} - \hat{y})^2 - (\hat{x} - \hat{y})(\hat{x} + \hat{y}) + (\hat{x} + \hat{y})^2 = 4.$$

After expansion and simplification, this becomes $\hat{x}^2 + 3\hat{y}^2 = 4$, the equation of a standard position ellipse with the x-axis as axis and with $a = 2$ and $b = 2/\sqrt{3}$.

Graph this on a coordinate system which has been rotated by $\pi/4$. The graph will be that of the given conic in terms of the original coordinates.

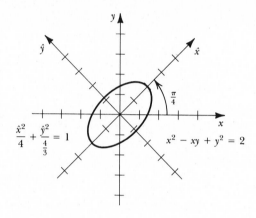

5. a) Use Formula 10.17 to determine if the conic with equation $14x^2 - 24xy + 7y^2 = 1$ is an ellipse, hyperbola, or parabola. b) Perform a suitable rotation and/or translation and sketch the graph.

SOLUTION: a) $B = -24$, $A = 14$ and $C = 7$, so $B^2 - 4AC = (-24)^2 - 4(14)(7) = 184 > 0$. The conic is a hyperbola.

b) The xy term is eliminated by rotating through an angle $\theta \in (0, \frac{\pi}{2})$, where
$$\cot\theta = \frac{14 - 7}{-24} + \frac{\sqrt{(14 - 7)^2 + (-24)^2}}{|-24|} = \frac{-7 + \sqrt{625}}{24} = \frac{3}{4}.$$ If $\cos\theta = a$ and $\sin\theta = b$, then
$a^2 + b^2 = 1$ and $\cot\theta = a/b = 3/4$; thus, $\left(\frac{3}{4}b\right)^2 + b^2 = 1$ or $b = \frac{4}{5}$ and $a = \frac{3}{5}$.
With $\cos\theta = \frac{3}{5}$ and $\sin\theta = \frac{4}{5}$, the change of coordinates which brings about this rotation is $x = \frac{3}{5}\hat{x} - \frac{4}{5}\hat{y}$, $y = \frac{4}{5}\hat{x} + \frac{3}{5}\hat{y}$. Substitute this into the given equation to obtain

$$14\left(\frac{3}{5}\hat{x} - \frac{4}{5}\hat{y}\right)^2 - 24\left(\frac{3}{5}\hat{x} - \frac{4}{5}\hat{y}\right)\left(\frac{4}{5}\hat{x} + \frac{3}{5}\hat{y}\right) + 7\left(\frac{4}{5}\hat{x} + \frac{3}{5}\hat{y}\right)^2 = 1.$$

Multiply both sides of the equation by 25 to cancel all the factors of 1/5 inside the squared terms and expand the quadratics to obtain

$$14\left[9\hat{x}^2 - 24\hat{x}\hat{y} + 16\hat{y}^2\right] - 24\left[12\hat{x}^2 - 7\hat{x}\hat{y} - 12\hat{y}^2\right] + 7\left[16\hat{x}^2 + 24\hat{x}\hat{y} + 9\hat{y}^2\right] = 25.$$

Simplify this (the $\hat{x}\hat{y}$ terms drop out). $(9 \cdot 14 - 12 \cdot 24 + 7 \cdot 16)\hat{x}^2 + (14 \cdot 16 + 24 \cdot 12 + 7 \cdot 9)\hat{y}^2 = 25$
or $\dfrac{\hat{y}^2}{1/23} - \dfrac{\hat{x}^2}{1/2} = 1$. This standard position hyperbola has vertices at the points with $(\hat{x}, \hat{y})$

coordinates $\left(0, \pm\dfrac{1}{\sqrt{23}}\right)$ and asymptotes with equations $\hat{y} = \pm\dfrac{1/\sqrt{23}}{1/\sqrt{2}}\hat{x}$ or $\hat{y} = \pm\sqrt{\dfrac{2}{23}}\hat{x}$.

This hyperbola is sketched onto an $(\hat{x}, \hat{y})$ coordinate system which is obtained by rotating the (x, y) coordinates through an angle of $\cot^{-1}\left(\frac{3}{4}\right) \approx 53.13°$.

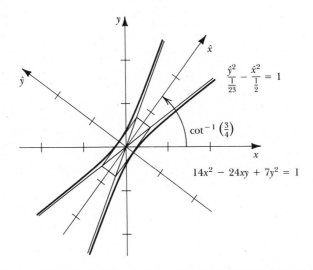

13. a) Use formula 10.17 to determine if the conic with equation $6x^2 + 4\sqrt{3}xy + 2y^2 - 9x + 9\sqrt{3}y - 63 = 0$ is an ellipse, hyperbola, or parabola. b) Perform a suitable rotation and/or translation and sketch the graph.

SOLUTION: a) $B = 4\sqrt{3}$, $A = 6$, $C = 2$ so $B^2 - 4AC = (4\sqrt{3})^2 - 4(6)(2) = 0$ and the conic is a parabola.

b) The rotation which eliminates the xy term is through an angle of $\theta \in \left(0, \frac{\pi}{2}\right)$ where $\cot\theta = \dfrac{6-2}{4\sqrt{3}} + \dfrac{\sqrt{(6-2)^2 + (4\sqrt{3})^2}}{|4\sqrt{3}|} = \sqrt{3}$. If $\cos\theta = a$ and $\sin\theta = b$, then $a^2 + b^2 = 1$ and $\cot\theta = a/b = \sqrt{3}$; thus $(\sqrt{3}b)^2 + b^2 = 1$ or $b = 1/2$ and $a = \sqrt{3}/2$.

Here $\cos\theta = \sqrt{3}/2$ and $\sin\theta = 1/2$, so the change of variables is $x = \frac{\sqrt{3}}{2}\hat{x} - \frac{1}{2}\hat{y}$, $y = \frac{1}{2}\hat{x} + \frac{\sqrt{3}}{2}\hat{y}$. With this change, the equation becomes

$$\left(\frac{\sqrt{3}}{2}\hat{x} - \frac{1}{2}\hat{y}\right)^2 + 4\sqrt{3}\left(\frac{\sqrt{3}}{2}\hat{x} - \frac{1}{2}\hat{y}\right)\left(\frac{1}{2}\hat{x} + \frac{\sqrt{3}}{2}\hat{y}\right)$$

$$+ \left(\frac{1}{2}\hat{x} + \frac{\sqrt{3}}{2}\hat{y}\right)^2 - 9\left(\frac{\sqrt{3}}{2}\hat{x} - \frac{1}{2}\hat{y}\right) + 9\sqrt{3}\left(\frac{1}{2}\hat{x} + \frac{\sqrt{3}}{2}\hat{y}\right) - 63 = 0.$$

Multiply the equation by 4 to cancel the factors of 1/4 which come from the quadratic terms and expand the result to obtain

$$6\left[3\hat{x}^2 - 2\sqrt{3}\hat{x}\hat{y} + \hat{y}^2\right] + 4\sqrt{3}\left[\sqrt{3}\hat{x}^2 + 2\hat{x}\hat{y} - \sqrt{3}\hat{y}^2\right] + 2\left[\hat{x}^2 + 2\sqrt{3}\hat{x}\hat{y} + 3\hat{y}^2\right]$$
$$- 18(\sqrt{3}\hat{x} - \hat{y}) + 18\sqrt{3}(\hat{x} + \sqrt{3}\hat{y}) - 252 = 0.$$

Both the $\hat{x}\hat{y}$ and $\hat{y}^2$ terms drop out to yield

$$32\hat{x}^2 + 72\hat{y} = 252 \quad \text{or} \quad \left(\hat{y} - \frac{7}{2}\right) = -\frac{4}{9}\hat{x}^2.$$

This parabola has vertex with $\hat{x}\hat{y}$-coordinates $\left(0, \frac{7}{2}\right)$ and opens down the $\hat{y}$-axis.

The graph is sketched on an $\hat{x}\hat{y}$-coordinate system which is obtained by a revolution of the x and y axes through $\theta = \cot^{-1}(\sqrt{3}) = \pi/6$.

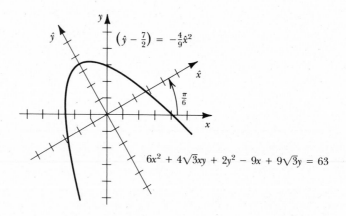

25. Find an equation of the ellipse with vertices $(0,0)$ and $(6,8)$ passing through the point $(0, 25/4)$.

SOLUTION: The ellipse is sketched and a rotated coordinate system is constructed so that the vertices lie on the $\hat{x}$-axis.

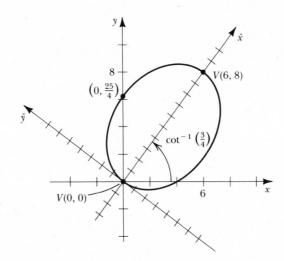

The distance between the vertices $(0,0)$ and $(6,8)$ is $2a = \sqrt{6^2 + 8^2} = 10$ so $a = 5$ and the $\hat{x}\hat{y}$-coordinates of the vertices are $(0,0)$ and $(10,0)$. The equation of the rotated ellipse is thus $\dfrac{(\hat{x} - 5)^2}{5^2} + \dfrac{\hat{y}^2}{b^2} = 1$, where b is to be determined.

Since the $\hat{x}$-axis passes through $(0,0)$ and $(6,8)$, then $\cot\theta = \frac{6}{8}$ so $\theta = \operatorname{arccot}\left(\frac{3}{4}\right)$ is the angle of rotation with $\cos\theta = \frac{3}{5}$ and $\sin\theta = \frac{4}{5}$. The xy-equation can be obtained from the $\hat{x}\hat{y}$-equation by a rotation through an angle of $-\theta$. This is acheived by the substitution $\hat{x} = \cos\left(-\theta\right)x - \sin\left(-\theta\right)y$, $\hat{y} = \sin\left(-\theta\right)x + \cos\left(-\theta\right)y$ or $\hat{x} = \frac{3}{5}x + \frac{4}{5}y$, $\hat{y} = -\frac{4}{5}x + \frac{3}{5}y$. Substituting these values into the equation $\hat{x}^2 - 10\hat{x} + \dfrac{25}{b^2}\hat{y}^2 = 0$ yields

$$\left(\frac{3}{5}x + \frac{4}{5}y\right)^2 + \frac{25}{b^2}\left(-\frac{4}{5}x + \frac{3}{5}y\right)^2 - 10\left(\frac{3}{5}x + \frac{4}{5}y\right) = 0.$$

Multiply through by 25, expand quadratics and simplify to obtain

$$\left(9 + \frac{25}{b^2}\cdot 16\right)x^2 + 24\left(1 - \frac{25}{b^2}\right)xy + \left(16 + \frac{25}{b^2}\cdot 9\right)y^2 - 150x - 200y = 0.$$

The point with xy-coordinates $(0, 25/4)$ lies on this ellipse only if b is chosen so that

$$\left(16 + \frac{25\cdot 9}{b^2}\right)\left(\frac{25}{4}\right)^2 - 200\left(\frac{25}{4}\right) = 0 \qquad \text{or} \qquad \left(\frac{25}{b^2}\right) = \frac{16}{9}.$$

The equation of the ellipse is thus

$$\left(9 + \frac{16}{9}\cdot 16\right)x^2 + 24\left(1 - \frac{16}{9}\right)xy + \left(16 + \frac{16}{9}\cdot 9\right)y^2 - 150x - 200y = 0,$$

or

$$337x^2 - 168xy + 288y^2 - 1350x - 1800y = 0.$$

_____**10.5**

Polar Equations of Conic Sections

COMMENT: A <u>stategy</u> for graphing polar equations of conics is i) to determine the proper form (10.19)–(10.22), ii) to determine the eccentricity e and the distance from focus to directrix d, iii) to determine the location of the directrix relative to the focus iv) to plot a few points; at least the vertex or vertices and two other points. Notice that for each conic, the curve "wraps around" the focus and "wraps away from" the directrix.

3. a) Sketch the graph of $r = \dfrac{3}{3 + 2\sin\theta}$. b) Determine a corresponding cartesian equation.

SOLUTION: a) Cancel a common factor of 3 in the numerator and denominator to write this in the form of equation 10.21, $r = \dfrac{1}{1 + \frac{2}{3}\sin\theta}$. With this form, $e = 2/3$, so the conic is an ellipse; $ed = 1$ so $d = 3/2$ is the distance of the directrix from the focus. Moreover, the directrix lies above the origin and is parallel to the polar axis; thus the axis of the conic corresponds to the angles $\theta = \pi/2$ and $\theta = 3\pi/2$. The vertices are at the points with polar coordinates $\left(\frac{3}{5}, \frac{\pi}{2}\right)$ and $\left(3, \frac{3\pi}{2}\right)$. Two other points on this ellipse corresponding to $\theta = 0$ and $\theta = \pi$ are $(1, 0)$ and $(1, \pi)$.

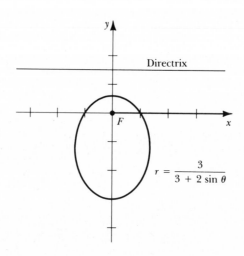

b) To determine a cartesian equation, first write the polar equation as $3r + 2r \sin\theta = 3$, so $3\sqrt{x^2 + y^2} + 2y = 3$.

Rearrange this equation and square to obtain

$$9(x^2 + y^2) = (3 - 2y)^2 \quad \text{or} \quad 9x^2 + 5y^2 + 12y = 9.$$

Complete squares on the y terms,

$$9x^2 + 5\left(y^2 + \frac{12}{5}y + \frac{36}{25}\right) = 9 + \frac{36}{5} \quad \text{or} \quad \frac{x^2}{9/5} + \frac{\left(y + \frac{6}{5}\right)^2}{(9/5)^2} = 1.$$

7. a) Sketch the graph of $r = \dfrac{5}{2 - 3\cos\theta}$. b) Determine a corresponding cartesian equation.

SOLUTION: a) This equation is of the form 10.19, $r = \dfrac{5/2}{1 - \frac{3}{2}\cos\theta}$, with $e = 3/2$ and $d = 5/3$. Since $e > 1$ the conic is a hyperbola and because of the form, the directrix is to the left a distance $d = 5/3$ from the focal point. The vertices occur on the rays $\theta = 0$ and $\theta = \pi$. The critical rays which determine the two branches of the hyperbola are $\theta_{\pm} = \cos^{-1}\left(\frac{2}{3}\right) \approx \pm 48.19°$; one branch lies in $\theta_- < \theta < \theta_+$ and the other branch lies in $\theta_+ < \theta < 2\pi - \theta_+$. An angle in each interval, say $\theta = \pi/6$ and $\theta = 2\pi/3$, gives a point on each branch $\left(\dfrac{5}{2 - \frac{3\sqrt{3}}{2}}, \dfrac{\pi}{6}\right)$ and $\left(\dfrac{5}{2 + \frac{3}{2}}, \dfrac{2\pi}{3}\right)$.

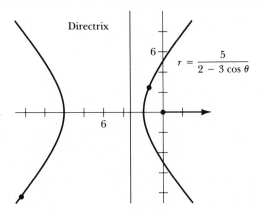

COMMENT: Notice that in graphing hyperbolas, one range of θ-values gives negative r-values where as the other range of θ-values gives positive r-values. It might be easier to graph the two vertices, graph the branch corresponding to positive r-values, locate the midpoint of the axis of the hyperbola and reflect the branch just drawn in the line perpendicular to the axis through this midpoint.

b) Write the equation as $2r - 3r\cos\theta = 5$ or $2\sqrt{x^2 + y^2} - 3x = 5$. Rearrange the equation and square to obtain $4(x^2 + y^2) = 25 + 30x + 9x^2$ or $5(x^2 + 6x + 9) - 4y^2 = -25 + 45$.

The cartesian equation is thus $\dfrac{(x+3)^2}{4} - \dfrac{y^2}{5} = 1$.

13. a) Sketch the graph of $r = \dfrac{2}{1 + \cos\left(\theta + \frac{\pi}{4}\right)}$.   b) Determine a cartesian equation for this conic.

SOLUTION: a) Recall the comment following EXERCISE 29 from SECTION 9.2 in this manual where it was shown that the graph of $r = f(\theta - \phi_0)$ is the same as the graph of $r = f(\theta)$ rotated through an angle of ϕ_0 about the pole. In this case the graph is the same as that of $r = \dfrac{2}{1 + \cos\theta}$ rotated by an angle of $-\dfrac{\pi}{4}$.

Since this latter equation is of the form of Formula 10.20 with $e = 1$ and $d = 2$, its graph is a parabola with focus at the origin and directrix to the right of the origin. Its vertex occurs when $\theta = 0$ at $(1, 0)$ and it opens to the left along the ray $\theta = \pi$.

The rotated graph will still be a parabola, but with vertex at $\theta = -\dfrac{\pi}{4}$, $(1, -\pi/4)$. This parabola opens along the ray $\theta = \pi - \dfrac{\pi}{4} = \dfrac{3\pi}{4}$. Plot two points in addition to the vertex, say for $\theta = 0$ and $\dfrac{\pi}{2}$, $\left(\dfrac{4}{2 + \sqrt{2}}, 0\right)$ and $\left(\dfrac{4}{2 - \sqrt{2}}, \dfrac{\pi}{2}\right)$, and use symmetry with respect to the axis $\theta = \dfrac{3\pi}{4}$ to complete the graph.

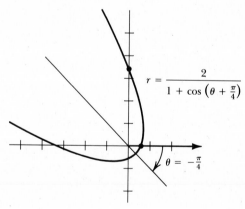

b) Rewrite the equation and expand $\cos\left(\theta + \frac{\pi}{4}\right)$;

$$r + r\left(\cos\theta\cos\frac{\pi}{4} - \sin\theta\sin\frac{\pi}{4}\right) = 2 \quad \text{or} \quad \sqrt{x^2 + y^2} + \frac{\sqrt{2}}{2}(x - y) = 2.$$

Rearrange and square to obtain

$$x^2 + y^2 = 4 - 2\sqrt{2}(x - y) + \frac{1}{2}(x^2 - 2xy + y^2) \quad \text{or}$$

$$x^2 + 2xy + y^2 + 4\sqrt{2}x - 4\sqrt{2}y - 8 = 0.$$

21. Find a polar equation of the conic with $e = 3$ and directrix having polar equation $r = 2 \csc \theta$.

SOLUTION: Assume that the focus is at the origin. The directrix is 2 units above the polar axis since its cartesian equation is $y = (r \sin \theta) = 2$. Thus with $e = 3$ and $ed = 2 \cdot 3 = 6$ the equation of this hyperbola is of the form of Formula 10.21

$$r = \frac{6}{1 + 3 \sin \theta}.$$

29. a) Express the cartesian equation $x^2 - y^2 - 2y = 4$ as a polar equation. b) State whether this conic is in a standard polar position.

SOLUTION: a) Substitute $x = r \cos \theta$ and $y = r \sin \theta$ to obtain

$$r^2 (\cos \theta)^2 - r^2 (\sin \theta)^2 - 2r \sin \theta = 4 \qquad \text{or} \qquad r^2 (\cos^2 \theta - \sin^2 \theta) - 2r \sin \theta - 4 = 0.$$

Use the quadratic formula to solve this equation for r,

$$r = \frac{2 \sin \theta \pm \sqrt{4 \sin^2 \theta + 16(\cos^2 \theta - \sin^2 \theta)}}{2(\cos^2 \theta - \sin^2 \theta)} = \frac{\sin \theta \pm \sqrt{3 + \cos^2 \theta}}{(\cos \theta - \sin \theta)(\cos \theta + \sin \theta)}.$$

b) Neither of these polar equations can be put into the standard polar form.

Chapter 10
Review Exercises

3. Identify and sketch the graph of $x^2 = -2(y - 5)$.

SOLUTION: This parabola is a translate of the standard position parabola $y = -\frac{1}{2}x^2$ by 5 upward. The latter parabola has focal length $c = 1/2$ and opens downward with focal point $1/2$ unit below the vertex and directrix $1/2$ unit above.

The given parabola has its vertex at $V(0, 5)$, its focal point at $F(0, 9/2)$ and its directrix with equation $y = 11/2$. The x-intercepts of this parabola are at $(-\sqrt{10}, 0)$ and $(\sqrt{10}, 0)$.

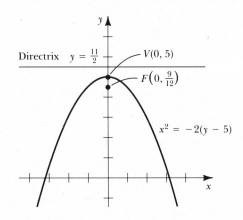

11. Identify and sketch the graph of $16(x-2)^2 - 25(y-3)^2 = 400$.

SOLUTION: This hyperbola is the translate by 2 to the right and 3 upward of the standard position hyperbola $\dfrac{x^2}{25} - \dfrac{y^2}{16} = 1$. This hyperbola has vertices on the x-axis at a distance of 5 units from the origin. Its slant asymptotes have slopes $\pm\dfrac{4}{5}$. Its focal length is $c = \sqrt{25+16} = \sqrt{41}$.

The given hyperbola has vertices at $V(2-5,3)$ and $V(2+5,3)$, and its slant asymptotes are the lines $\dfrac{y-3}{x-2} = \pm\dfrac{4}{5}$. Its focal points are at $F(2-\sqrt{41},3)$ and $F(2+\sqrt{41},3)$.

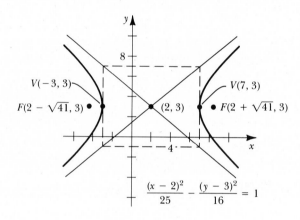

15. Identify and graph $9x^2 + 4y^2 - 90x - 16y + 205 = 0$.

SOLUTION: Complete the squares on both x and y to write this equation as

$$9(x^2 - 10x + 25) + 4(y^2 - 4y + 4) = -205 + 225 + 16$$

or $\dfrac{(x-5)^2}{4} + \dfrac{(y-2)^2}{9} = 1$. This ellipse is the translate by 5 to the right and 2 upward of the standard position ellipse with vertices on the y-axis a distance 3 from the origin. The x-intercepts are a distance 2 from the origin. The focal length is $c = \sqrt{9-4} = \sqrt{5}$.

The given ellipse has vertices at $V(5,2-3)$ and $V(5,2+3)$ and intercepts with the line $y = 2$ at $(5-2,2)$ and $(5+2,2)$. The focal points are at $F(5,2-\sqrt{5})$ and $F(5,2+\sqrt{5})$.

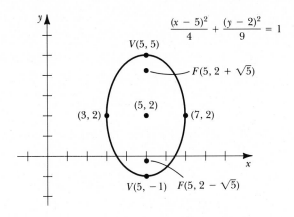

21. Identify and sketch the graph of $2xy - \sqrt{2}x + \sqrt{2}y - 5 = 0$.

SOLUTION: Since $B = 2$ and $A = C = 0$, then $B^2 - 4AC = 4 > 0$, so the conic is a hyperbola. Eliminate the xy term by a rotation through an angle $\theta \in \left(0, \dfrac{\pi}{2}\right)$, where $\cot\theta = \dfrac{0 - 0}{2} + \dfrac{\sqrt{(0 - 0)^2 + 2^2}}{|2|} = 1$, or $\theta = \dfrac{\pi}{4}$.

The change of variables which brings about this rotation is $x = \frac{\sqrt{2}}{2}\hat{x} - \frac{\sqrt{2}}{2}\hat{y}$, $y = \frac{\sqrt{2}}{2}\hat{x} + \frac{\sqrt{2}}{2}\hat{y}$. Substitution of these expressions into the equation results in

$$2\left(\frac{\sqrt{2}}{2}\hat{x} - \frac{\sqrt{2}}{2}\hat{y}\right)\left(\frac{\sqrt{2}}{2}\hat{x} + \frac{\sqrt{2}}{2}\hat{y}\right) - \sqrt{2}\left(\frac{\sqrt{2}}{2}\hat{x} - \frac{\sqrt{2}}{2}\hat{y}\right) + \sqrt{2}\left(\frac{\sqrt{2}}{2}\hat{x} + \frac{\sqrt{2}}{2}\hat{y}\right) - 5 = 0,$$

or after expanding and collecting common terms, $(\hat{x})^2 - (\hat{y})^2 + 2\hat{y} - 5 = 0$. Complete squares in the $\hat{y}$ term to write this equation as

$$\frac{(\hat{x})^2}{4} - \frac{(\hat{y} - 1)^2}{4} = 1.$$

This hyperbola has center at $\hat{x} = 0$, $\hat{y} = 1$ with vertices on the line parallel to the $\hat{x}$-axis a distance $a = 2$ from the center. The slant asymptotes have slope (relative to the $\hat{x}$- and $\hat{y}$-axes) $\pm\dfrac{2}{2} = \pm 1$. The focal points are on the major axis a distance $c = \sqrt{a^2 + b^2} = 2\sqrt{2}$ from the center. The graph is sketched on the $\hat{x}, \hat{y}$-coordinate system which was obtained as a $\pi/4$ rotation of the xy-coordinate axes.

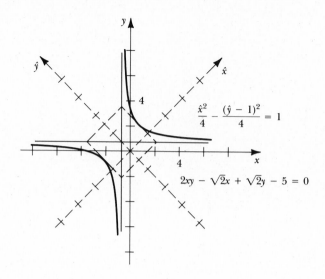

$$\frac{\hat{x}^2}{4} - \frac{(\hat{y}-1)^2}{4} = 1$$

$$2xy - \sqrt{2}x + \sqrt{2}y - 5 = 0$$

31. Identify and sketch the graph of $r = \dfrac{2}{3 + \sin\theta}$.

SOLUTION: Write this as $r = \dfrac{2/3}{1 + (1/3)\sin\theta}$ to identify this as an ellipse ($e = \frac{1}{3} < 1$) with focus at the pole and with a directrix at distance $d = 2$ units above the directrix. The vertices are at $\left(\dfrac{1}{2}, \dfrac{\pi}{2}\right)$ and $\left(1, \dfrac{3\pi}{2}\right)$ on the major axis.

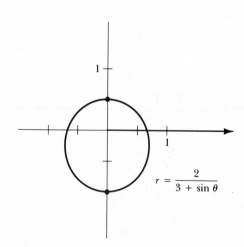

$$r = \frac{2}{3 + \sin\theta}$$

37. Find an equation of an ellipse with foci at $(0, \pm 1)$ and vertices at $(0, \pm 3)$.

SOLUTION: Since the foci and vertices are symmetrically situated relative to the origin, this ellipse is in standard position with axis along the y-axis. The distance from the vertices to the origin is $a = 3$ and since the focal length is $c = 1$, the distance from the x-intercepts to the origin is $b = \sqrt{a^2 - c^2} = \sqrt{3^2 - 1^2} = 2\sqrt{2}$.

The equation is thus $\dfrac{x^2}{(2\sqrt{2})^2} + \dfrac{y^2}{3^2} = 1$.

43. Find an equation of the conic with a focus at the origin, eccentricity 3, and directrix $y = -2$.

SOLUTION: This standard polar position hyperbola ($e = 3 > 1$) has its directrix $d = 2$ units below the focus and parallel to the polar axis, so its equation is $r = \dfrac{ed}{1 - e\sin\theta}$ or $r = \dfrac{6}{1 - 3\sin\theta}$.

11

Vectors

Sharpening your skills

You must review material from algebra such as the solution of systems of linear equations. You should also recall material on the Cartesian coordinate system, the distance and midpoint formulas, and the graphing of lines.

The practice problems below should help in this review. The section numbers refer to places in the text where the necessary tool is presented.

Practice Problems

1. a) Plot the points $(1, -2)$ and $(-3, 1)$ on an xy-plane. b) Find the distance between them. c) Determine the midpoint of the line segment through these points. (See APPENDIX A.2)

2. Graph the lines with equations   a) $2x - 3y = 6$,   b) $y = 1$,   c) $2x = 0$.   (See SECTION 1.2)

3. Find all solutions to the systems of linear equations (if any exist).
   a) $2x + 3y - z = 1,\ x + y + 3z = 4$;
   b) $\dfrac{x-1}{2} = y + 2,\ y + 2 = \dfrac{2-z}{3}$;
   c) $x + 1 = \dfrac{y-1}{2},\ \dfrac{y-1}{2} = 4z.$

The Rectangular Coordinate System in Space _____11.1

1. Plot each of the points and sketch the associated parallelepiped.
   a) $(1, 3, 4)$ b) $(1, -3, 4)$ c) $(2, 4, -3)$

SOLUTION: All three points and parallelepipeds are illustrated on the same graph.

a) $(1, 3, 4)$ lies in the first octant,   b) $(1, -3, 4)$ lies to the left of the xz-plane and   c) $(2, 4, -3)$ lies below the xy-plane.

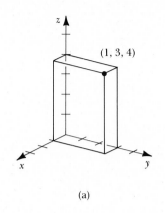

(a)

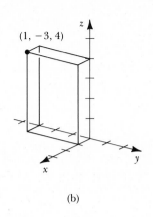

(b)

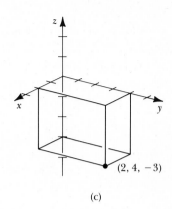

(c)

3. Plot the points $A(1,2,3)$ and $B(-1,3,4)$ and find the distance between them.

SOLUTION: $A(1,2,3)$ lies in the first octant and $B(-1,3,4)$ lies behind the yz-plane.

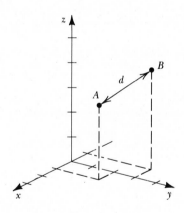

According to Formula 11.1, the distance between A and B is

$$d(A,B) = \sqrt{(-1-1)^2 + (3-2)^2 + (4-3)^2} = \sqrt{6}.$$

9. Find the midpoint of the line segment joining $A(1,2,3)$ and $B(-1,3,4)$.

SOLUTION: According to Formula 11.2, the midpoint is $M = \left(\frac{1+(-1)}{2}, \frac{2+3}{2}, \frac{3+4}{2}\right) = \left(0, \frac{5}{2}, \frac{7}{2}\right)$.

21. Find an equation of the sphere with center at $C(2,3,4)$ and radius $r = 1$.

SOLUTION: According to the solution of EXAMPLE 3 in the text, the standard equation of this sphere is $(x-2)^2 + (y-3)^2 + (z-4)^2 = 1^2$ or, upon expanding, $x^2 + y^2 + z^2 - 4x - 6y - 8z + 28 = 0$.

25. Find the center and radius of the sphere whose equation is $2x^2 + 2y^2 + 2z^2 + 8x - 8z = -7$.

SOLUTION: Complete squares for the terms involving x and z to write this equation as

$$2(x^2 + 4x + 4 - 4) + 2(y)^2 + 2(z^2 - 4z + 4 - 4) = -7 \quad \text{or} \quad 2(x+2)^2 + 2y^2 + 2(z-2)^2 = 9.$$

This is equivalent to $(x - (-2))^2 + (y - 0)^2 + (z - 2)^2 = \left(3/\sqrt{2}\right)^2$ which is the standard equation of the sphere with center $C(-2, 0, 2)$ and radius $r = 3\sqrt{2}/2$.

31. Sketch the points $(2, 4, 2)$, $(2, 1, 5)$, and $(5, 1, 2)$ and show that they are the vertices of an equilateral triangle.

SOLUTION: All three points lie in the first octant. Label them $A(2, 4, 2)$, $B(2, 1, 5)$ and $C(5, 1, 2)$.

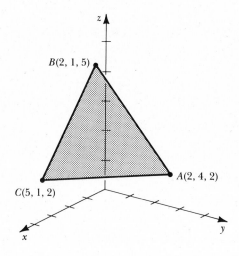

The lengths of the sides of the triangle ABC are

$$d(A, B) = \sqrt{(2-2)^2 + (1-4)^2 + (5-2)^2} = 3\sqrt{2},$$
$$d(B, C) = \sqrt{(5-2)^2 + (1-1)^2 + (2-5)^2} = 3\sqrt{2}, \quad \text{and}$$
$$d(C, A) = \sqrt{(5-2)^2 + (1-4)^2 + (2-2)^2} = 3\sqrt{2},$$

so the triangle is equilateral.

_____**11.2**

Vectors in Space

5. The initial point of a vector is $A\,(-2,2,1)$ and its terminal point is $B\,(0,5,0)$. Find a) the position-vector representation and   b) the length of this vector.

SOLUTION: a) The vector is $\overrightarrow{AB} = \langle 0-(-2), 5-2, 0-1 \rangle = \langle 2,3,-1 \rangle$.

b) Its length is $\left\| \overrightarrow{AB} \right\| = \| \langle 2,3,-1 \rangle \| = \sqrt{2^2 + 3^2 + (-1)^2} = \sqrt{14}.$

11. With $\mathbf{a} = \langle 1,1,0 \rangle$ and $\mathbf{b} = \langle -1,1,2 \rangle$ find $\mathbf{a} + \mathbf{b}$ and illustrate this sum geometrically.

SOLUTION: Add vectors component by component,

$$\mathbf{a} + \mathbf{b} = \langle 1,1,0 \rangle + \langle -1,1,2 \rangle = \langle 1+(-1), 1+1, 0+2 \rangle = \langle 0,2,2 \rangle.$$

In the graph below $\mathbf{a}$, $\mathbf{b}$, and $\mathbf{a} + \mathbf{b}$ are represented as displacements from $(0,0,0)$.

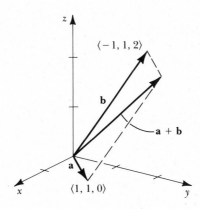

21. Find two vectors parallel to $\langle 3,4,-1 \rangle$ that have length 3.

SOLUTION: Construct two unit vectors with the same and opposite direction as $\langle 3,4,-1 \rangle$ respectively, then multiply these by the scalar 3. According to THEOREM 11.6 viii), the resulting vectors will have length 3.

The unit vector parallel to $\mathbf{v} = \langle 3,4,-1 \rangle$ is

$$\mathbf{u}_+ = \frac{1}{\| \mathbf{v} \|}\mathbf{v} = \frac{1}{\sqrt{3^2 + 4^2 + (-1)^2}} \langle 3,4,-1 \rangle = \left\langle \frac{3}{\sqrt{26}}, \frac{4}{\sqrt{26}}, -\frac{1}{\sqrt{26}} \right\rangle.$$

The unit vector with the direction opposite to $\mathbf{v}$ is $\mathbf{u}_- = -\mathbf{u}_+ = \langle -3/\sqrt{26}, -4/\sqrt{26}, 1/\sqrt{26} \rangle$. The required vectors are then

$$3\,\mathbf{u}_+ = \left\langle 9/\sqrt{26},\ 12/\sqrt{26},\ -3/\sqrt{26} \right\rangle \quad \text{and} \quad 3\,\mathbf{u}_- = \left\langle -9/\sqrt{26},\ -12/\sqrt{26},\ 3/\sqrt{26} \right\rangle.$$

27. Consider the accompanying figure where $\mathbf{c} = \frac{1}{2}(\mathbf{a} + \mathbf{b})$ a) Write $\mathbf{d}$ in terms of $\mathbf{b}$ and $\mathbf{c}$.
    b) Prove that the diagonals of a parallelogram bisect each other.

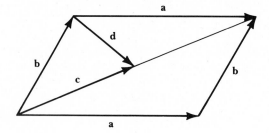

SOLUTION: a) Since $\mathbf{b} + \mathbf{d} = \mathbf{c}$ then $\mathbf{d} = \mathbf{c} - \mathbf{b}$.

b) The diagonals of the parallelogram are represented vectorially as $\vec{\gamma} = \mathbf{a} + \mathbf{b}$ and $\vec{\delta} = \mathbf{a} - \mathbf{b}$. Now $\mathbf{c} = \frac{1}{2}\vec{\gamma}$ by definition and $\mathbf{d} = \mathbf{c} - \mathbf{b}$ by the SOLUTION to part a). Substitute $\mathbf{c} = \frac{1}{2}(\mathbf{a} + \mathbf{b})$ into this last equation and simplify to get $\mathbf{d} = \frac{1}{2}(\mathbf{a} + \mathbf{b}) - \mathbf{b} = \frac{1}{2}(\mathbf{a} - \mathbf{b}) = \frac{1}{2}\vec{\delta}$. Thus both $\mathbf{c}$ and $\mathbf{d}$ terminate on the midpoints of the respective diagonals. Hence these diagonals bisect each other.

29. Three children are pulling on ropes attached to a common ring. The first child pulls in the direction of the positive x-axis with a force of 20 lb. The second child pulls in the direction of the positive y-axis with a force of 15 lb. If the ring does not move, in what direction and with what force must the third child be pulling?

SOLUTION: Consider the vector representation of the forces below.

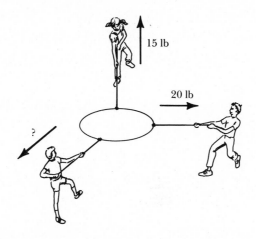

15 lb

20 lb

?

In order for the ring to remain in equilibrium, the sum of the three forces must be zero; otherwise, by Newton's Law of motion the ring would undergo an acceleration proportional to the force. Thus $\mathbf{F} + (20\ \mathbf{i}) + (15\ \mathbf{j}) = \overrightarrow{0}$ or $\mathbf{F} = -20\ \mathbf{i} - 15\ \mathbf{j}$.

—————————————————————————————————————11.3

The Dot Product
of Vectors

1. Find $\mathbf{a} \cdot \mathbf{b}$ for $\mathbf{a} = \langle 1, 3, 3 \rangle$ and $\mathbf{b} = \langle 2, 2, 4 \rangle$.

SOLUTION: By DEFINITION 11.9, $\mathbf{a} \cdot \mathbf{b} = \langle 1, 3, 3 \rangle \cdot \langle 2, 2, 4 \rangle = (1)(2) + (3)(2) + (3)(4) = 20$.

9. Find the angle between the vectors $\mathbf{a} = \langle 1, 3, 3 \rangle$ and $\mathbf{b} = \langle 2, 2, 4 \rangle$ and determine if they are orthogonal.

SOLUTION: By THEOREM 11.11, the cosine of the angle θ between $\mathbf{a}$ and $\mathbf{b}$ satisfies

$$\cos \theta = \frac{\mathbf{a} \cdot \mathbf{b}}{\|\mathbf{a}\| \|\mathbf{b}\|} = \frac{20}{\sqrt{1^2 + 3^2 + 3^2}\sqrt{2^2 + 2^2 + 4^2}} = \frac{20}{\sqrt{19}\sqrt{24}} = \frac{10}{\sqrt{114}}.$$

This angle is $\theta = \arccos\left(\frac{10}{\sqrt{114}}\right) \approx 0.358$ radians or approximately 20 degrees 31 minutes.

$\mathbf{a}$ and $\mathbf{b}$ are not orthogonal since this cosine was nonzero.

17. Find the component of **b** in the direction of **a** and the orthogonal projection of **b** onto **a** for $\mathbf{a} = \langle 1, 3, 3 \rangle$ and $\mathbf{b} = \langle 2, 2, 4 \rangle$.

SOLUTION: The component of **b** in the direction of **a** is given in Formula 11.18 as $\mathrm{comp}_{\mathbf{a}}\,\mathbf{b} = \dfrac{\mathbf{a} \cdot \mathbf{b}}{\|\mathbf{a}\|} = \dfrac{20}{\sqrt{19}}$. The projection of **b** on **a** is given in formula 11.19 as

$$\mathrm{proj}_{\mathbf{a}}\,\mathbf{b} = \frac{\mathbf{a} \cdot \mathbf{b}}{\|\mathbf{a}\|^2}\,\mathbf{a} = \frac{20}{19}\langle 1, 3, 3 \rangle = \left\langle \frac{20}{19}, \frac{60}{19}, \frac{60}{19} \right\rangle.$$

25. Find the direction cosines of the vector $\langle 2, 3, 4 \rangle$.

SOLUTION: The direction cosines of **v** are the components of the unit vector, **u**, with the same direction as **v**. Since

$$\mathbf{u} = \frac{1}{\|\mathbf{v}\|}\,\mathbf{v} = \frac{1}{\sqrt{2^2 + 3^2 + 4^2}}\langle 2, 3, 4 \rangle = \left\langle \frac{2}{\sqrt{29}}, \frac{3}{\sqrt{29}}, \frac{4}{\sqrt{29}} \right\rangle,$$

then the direction cosines are $\cos\alpha = 2/\sqrt{29}$, $\cos\beta = 3/\sqrt{29}$, and $\cos\gamma = 4/\sqrt{29}$.

31. Find a unit vector lying in the xy-plane orthogonal to $\langle 2, 4, 0 \rangle$. Is there more than one such vector?

SOLUTION: All vectors in the xy-plane can be written as $\langle a, b, 0 \rangle$. Those which are also orthogonal to $\langle 2, 4, 0 \rangle$ satisfy $\langle a, b, 0 \rangle \cdot \langle 2, 4, 0 \rangle = 0$ or $2a + 4b = 0$, so the vectors we seek must be of the form $\langle -2b, b, 0 \rangle$, where $\|\langle -2b, b, 0 \rangle\| = 1$. This condition is $\sqrt{(-2b)^2 + (b)^2} = \sqrt{5}\,|b| = 1$, so $b = \pm 1/\sqrt{5}$. There are two unit vectors in the xy-plane which are also orthogonal to $\langle 2, 4, 0 \rangle$; $\left\langle -\frac{2}{\sqrt{5}}, \frac{1}{\sqrt{5}}, 0 \right\rangle$ and $\left\langle \frac{2}{\sqrt{5}}, -\frac{1}{\sqrt{5}}, 0 \right\rangle$.

33. Express $\mathbf{b} = \langle -4, 1, -2 \rangle$ as $\mathbf{b} = \mathbf{b}_1 + \mathbf{b}_2$, where $\mathbf{b}_1$ is parallel to $\mathbf{a} = \langle 1, 3, -3 \rangle$ and $\mathbf{b}_2$ is orthogonal to **a**.

SOLUTION: According to THEOREM 11.20, the only solution to this problem is $\mathbf{b}_1 = \mathrm{proj}_{\mathbf{a}}\,\mathbf{b}$ and $\mathbf{b}_2 = \mathbf{b} - \mathrm{proj}_{\mathbf{a}}\,\mathbf{b}$. The projection is given by Formula 11.19,

$$\mathbf{b}_1 = \mathrm{proj}_{\mathbf{a}}\,\mathbf{b} = \frac{\mathbf{a} \cdot \mathbf{b}}{\|\mathbf{a}\|^2}\,\mathbf{a} = \frac{\langle 1, 3, -3 \rangle \cdot \langle -4, 1, -2 \rangle}{(1^2 + 3^2 + 3^2)}\langle 1, 3, -3 \rangle$$

$$= \frac{(-4 + 3 + 6)}{19}\langle 1, 3, -3 \rangle = \left\langle \frac{5}{19}, \frac{15}{19}, -\frac{15}{19} \right\rangle.$$

The complementary vector is

$$\mathbf{b}_2 = \mathbf{b} - \mathrm{proj}_{\mathbf{a}}\,\mathbf{b} = \langle -4, 1, -2 \rangle - \left\langle \frac{5}{19}, \frac{15}{19}, -\frac{15}{19} \right\rangle = \left\langle -\frac{81}{19}, \frac{4}{19}, -\frac{23}{19} \right\rangle.$$

39. Show that for any vector $\mathbf{a}$, $\mathbf{a} \cdot \mathbf{a} = \|\mathbf{a}\|^2$.

SOLUTION: For any $\mathbf{a} = \langle a_1, a_2, a_3 \rangle$,

$$\mathbf{a} \cdot \mathbf{a} = \langle a_1, a_2, a_3 \rangle \cdot \langle a_1, a_2, a_3 \rangle = (a_1)(a_1) + (a_2)(a_2) + (a_3)(a_3)$$

$$= \left(\sqrt{a_1^2 + a_2^2 + a_3^2} \right)^2 = \|\mathbf{a}\|^2.$$

49. A wagon loaded with groceries is pulled horizontally a half mile by a handle that makes an angle of $\pi/3$ with the horizontal. Find the work done if a force of 20 pounds is exerted on the handle.

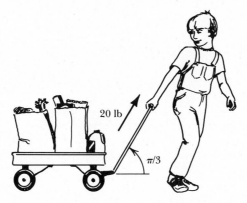

SOLUTION: Let $\overrightarrow{PQ} = 2640\,\mathbf{i}$ be the horizontal displacement of the wagon by the force $\mathbf{F}$. The force has magnitude 20 and makes an angle $\pi/3$ with $\mathbf{i}$, so its direction cosines are $\cos\alpha = \cos(\pi/3)$, $\cos\beta = \sin(\pi/3)$, $\cos\gamma = 0$, and $\mathbf{F} = 20\,[\cos(\pi/3)\,\mathbf{i} + \sin(\pi/3)\,\mathbf{j}] = 10\,\mathbf{i} + 10\sqrt{3}\,\mathbf{j}$. According to formula 11.21, the work done in applying the force $\mathbf{F}$ over the displacement $\overrightarrow{PQ}$ is $W = \mathbf{F} \cdot \overrightarrow{PQ} = (10\,\mathbf{i} + 10\sqrt{3}\,\mathbf{j}) \cdot (2640\,\mathbf{i}) = 26{,}400\,\text{ft-lb}$.

11.4

The Cross Product of Vectors

1. Find $\mathbf{a} \times \mathbf{b}$ for $\mathbf{a} = \langle -1, 3, 5 \rangle$, $\mathbf{b} = \langle 2, -1, 0 \rangle$.

SOLUTION: Use Formula 11.25 as a device to remember the cross product formula

$$\mathbf{a} \times \mathbf{b} = \langle -1, 3, 5 \rangle \times \langle 2, -1, 0 \rangle = \begin{vmatrix} \mathbf{i} & \mathbf{j} & \mathbf{k} \\ -1 & 3 & 5 \\ 2 & -1 & 0 \end{vmatrix}$$

$$= \begin{vmatrix} 3 & 5 \\ -1 & 0 \end{vmatrix} \mathbf{i} - \begin{vmatrix} -1 & 5 \\ 2 & 0 \end{vmatrix} \mathbf{j} + \begin{vmatrix} -1 & 3 \\ 2 & -1 \end{vmatrix} \mathbf{k}$$

$$= (3 \cdot 0 - (-1)5) \, \mathbf{i} - (-1 \cdot 0 - 2 \cdot 5) \, \mathbf{j} + ((-1)(-1) - 2 \cdot 3) \, \mathbf{k}$$

$$= 5 \, \mathbf{i} + 10 \, \mathbf{j} - 5 \, \mathbf{k} = \langle 5, 10, -5 \rangle .$$

5. Use $\mathbf{a} = \langle 1, 2, 0 \rangle$, $\mathbf{b} = \langle 1, 3, 1 \rangle$ and $\mathbf{c} = \langle 0, 1, 0 \rangle$ to find $\mathbf{a} \times \mathbf{b} + \mathbf{a} \times \mathbf{c}$ or state why the operation is impossible.

SOLUTION: Both $\mathbf{a} \times \mathbf{b}$ and $\mathbf{a} \times \mathbf{c}$ are vectors so their vector sum is defined. Rather than calculate two cross products and add them, it is simpler to calculate the cross product of $\mathbf{a}$ with $(\mathbf{b} + \mathbf{c})$, for by THEOREM 11.23 v) the cross product can be distributed over a vector sum. Thus,

$$\mathbf{a} \times \mathbf{b} + \mathbf{a} \times \mathbf{c} = \mathbf{a} \times (\mathbf{b} + \mathbf{c}) = \langle 1, 2, 0 \rangle \times (\langle 1, 3, 1 \rangle + \langle 0, 1, 0 \rangle)$$

$$= \langle 1, 2, 0 \rangle \times \langle 1, 4, 1 \rangle = \begin{vmatrix} \mathbf{i} & \mathbf{j} & \mathbf{k} \\ 1 & 2 & 0 \\ 1 & 4 & 1 \end{vmatrix}$$

$$= \begin{vmatrix} 2 & 0 \\ 4 & 1 \end{vmatrix} \mathbf{i} - \begin{vmatrix} 1 & 0 \\ 1 & 1 \end{vmatrix} \mathbf{j} + \begin{vmatrix} 1 & 2 \\ 1 & 4 \end{vmatrix} \mathbf{k} = 2 \, \mathbf{i} - \mathbf{j} + 2 \, \mathbf{k} = \langle 2, -1, 2 \rangle .$$

11. Use $\mathbf{a}$, $\mathbf{b}$, and $\mathbf{c}$ as in EXERCISE 5 to calculate $(\mathbf{a} \cdot \mathbf{b}) \times \mathbf{c}$ or state why this operation is impossible.

SOLUTION: $\mathbf{a} \cdot \mathbf{b}$ is a scalar while $\mathbf{c}$ is a vector so the cross product of a scalar and a vector is not defined.

17. Use the cross product to find a vector orthogonal to both $\mathbf{a} = \langle 1, 2, 4 \rangle$ and $\mathbf{b} = \langle 2, -2, 5 \rangle$.

SOLUTION: As was shown following DEFINITION 11.22, the cross product of $\mathbf{a}$ and $\mathbf{b}$ is orthogonal to both $\mathbf{a}$ and $\mathbf{b}$. The vector

$$\mathbf{a} \times \mathbf{b} = \langle 1, 2, 4 \rangle \times \langle 2, -2, 5 \rangle = \begin{vmatrix} \mathbf{i} & \mathbf{j} & \mathbf{k} \\ 1 & 2 & 4 \\ 2 & -2 & 5 \end{vmatrix}$$

$$= \begin{vmatrix} 2 & 4 \\ -2 & 5 \end{vmatrix} \mathbf{i} - \begin{vmatrix} 1 & 4 \\ 2 & 5 \end{vmatrix} \mathbf{j} + \begin{vmatrix} 1 & 2 \\ 2 & -2 \end{vmatrix} \mathbf{k} = 18 \, \mathbf{i} + 3 \, \mathbf{j} - 6 \, \mathbf{k}$$

$$= \langle 18, 3, -6 \rangle$$

is orthogonal to both $\mathbf{a}$ and $\mathbf{b}$.

21. Find the area of the triangle with vertices at $(2, 1, 0)$, $(0, 4, 2)$, and $(2, -3, 2)$.

SOLUTION: Label the points $A(2, 1, 0)$, $B(0, 4, 2)$, and $C(2, -3, 2)$. By Formula 11.30, the area of the parallelogram with two sides $\overrightarrow{AB}$ and $\overrightarrow{AC}$ is area $= \left\| \overrightarrow{AB} \times \overrightarrow{AC} \right\|$. The given triangle is bounded by these same two sides and the diagonal $\overrightarrow{BC} = \overrightarrow{AB} - \overrightarrow{AC}$ so its area is half that of the parallelogram.

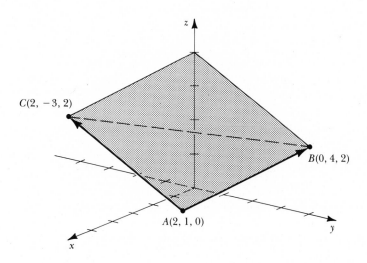

Since

$$\overrightarrow{AB} \times \overrightarrow{AC} = \langle -2, 3, 2 \rangle \times \langle 0, -4, 2 \rangle = \begin{vmatrix} \mathbf{i} & \mathbf{j} & \mathbf{k} \\ -2 & 3 & 2 \\ 0 & -4 & 2 \end{vmatrix}$$

$$= (6 + 8)\mathbf{i} - (-4 - 0)\mathbf{j} + (8 - 0)\mathbf{k} = \langle 14, 4, 8 \rangle,$$

then the area of the triangle is area$_{1/2} = \frac{1}{2} \left\| \overrightarrow{AB} \times \overrightarrow{AC} \right\| = \frac{1}{2}\sqrt{(14)^2 + 4^2 + 8^2} = \sqrt{69}.$

25. Use the scalar triple product to find the volume of the parallelepiped determined by the vectors $\mathbf{a} = \langle 3, -3, 2 \rangle$, $\mathbf{b} = \langle 0, 2, 2 \rangle$, $\mathbf{c} = \langle 2, 0, 0 \rangle$.

SOLUTION: By Formula 11.31, the volume of this parallelepiped is $V = |\mathbf{a} \cdot (\mathbf{b} \times \mathbf{c})|$. Use Formula 11.32 to calculate the triple scalar product as a determinant.

$$\mathbf{a} \cdot (\mathbf{b} \times \mathbf{c}) = \begin{vmatrix} 3 & -3 & 2 \\ 0 & 2 & 2 \\ 2 & 0 & 0 \end{vmatrix} = 3 \begin{vmatrix} 2 & 2 \\ 0 & 0 \end{vmatrix} - (-3) \begin{vmatrix} 0 & 2 \\ 2 & 0 \end{vmatrix} + 2 \begin{vmatrix} 0 & 2 \\ 2 & 0 \end{vmatrix}$$

$$= (3)(0) - (-3)(-4) + (2)(-4) = -20.$$

Thus the volume is $V = |-20| = 20.$

_____**11.5**
Planes

1. Find an equation of the plane that contains the point $(3, 3, 2)$ and has normal vector $\mathbf{n} = \langle 1, -1, 1 \rangle$.

SOLUTION: According to Formula 11.34, this equation is $(1)(x-3)+(-1)(y-3)+(1)(z-2) = 0$ or $x - y + z = 2$.

COMMENT: The graph of the equation $ax + by + cz = d$ is a plane, but other than to determine a normal, $\mathbf{N} = \langle a, b, c \rangle$, this equation is not in a convenient form for graphing. The following strategies are useful for plotting the graphs of linear equations:

case I) if $a, b, c, d \neq 0$,   i) Put the equation into the form $\frac{x}{A} + \frac{y}{B} + \frac{z}{C} = 1$ by dividing through by d.   ii) The x, y, and z intercepts are A, B and C respectively.   iii) Plot these three intercepts on the appropriate axes and sketch the graph.

case II) if any of a, b, c, and/or d are zero.   i) Successively, set $x = 0$, $y = 0$, $z = 0$ in the equation of the plane.   ii) Determine the equations of the lines of intersection with the yz-, xz-, and xy-planes respectively (if they exist).   iii) Plot these lines in the coordinate planes and use these traces to graph the plane. iv) In both cases, the normal $\mathbf{N} = \langle a, b, c \rangle$ should be orthogonal to the plane.

7. Sketch the graph of $2x + 3y + 4z = 12$.

SOLUTION: This equation is of the first type in the COMMENT above. Divide both sides of the equation by 12 and write the result as $\frac{x}{6} + \frac{y}{4} + \frac{z}{3} = 1$. The x-, y-, and z-intercepts are 6, 4, and 3 respectively. These points are plotted below, the plane is sketched, and the normal $\mathbf{N} = \langle 2, 3, 4 \rangle$ is indicated.

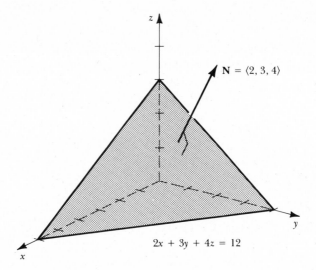

$$2x + 3y + 4z = 12$$

11. Sketch the graph of $2x + 3z = 4$.

SOLUTION: This equation is of the second type in the COMMENT above. Here the y-coordinate is missing, so the plane is parallel to the y-axis. The intersection with the xz-plane $(y = 0)$ is the line $2x + 3z = 4$ or $\dfrac{x}{2} + \dfrac{z}{4/3} = 1$; its x- and z-intercepts are 2 and 4/3 respectively. The intersection with the xy-plane $(z = 0)$ is the line $x = 2$ and that with the yz-plane $(x = 0)$ is the line $z = 4/3$. These lines are graphed below, and the plane containing them is sketched. The normal $\mathbf{N} = \langle 2, 0, 3 \rangle$ is indicated.

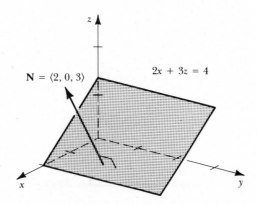

COMMENT: A <u>strategy</u> for finding an equation of a plane is to: i) Find a normal $\mathbf{N}$ to the plane. ii) Find a point in the plane. iii) Use Equation 11.34 to write an equation for the plane and simplify this equation.

17. Find an equation of the plane that contains the point $(1, 0, -1)$ and is parallel to $x+y-z = 4$.

SOLUTION: Since the plane is parallel to the plane with normal $\mathbf{N} = \langle 1, 1, -1 \rangle$, then according to DEFINITION 11.36 ii), the plane which is sought has the same normal. By DEFINITION 11.34 this plane has equation $(1)(x-1) + (1)(y-0) + (-1)(z-(-1)) = 0$ or $x + y - z = 2$.

23. Find an equation of the plane containing the points $(1, -1, 4)$, $(0, 2, 3)$, and $(2, 1, 0)$.

SOLUTION: Label the points $A(1, -1, 4)$, $B(0, 2, 3)$, and $C(2, 1, 0)$. The cross product $\overrightarrow{AB} \times \overrightarrow{AC}$ is orthogonal to $\overrightarrow{AB}$ and to $\overrightarrow{AC}$ and thus to any vector in the plane of these three points. A normal to this plane is thus

$$\mathbf{N} = \overrightarrow{AB} \times \overrightarrow{AC} = \langle -1, 3, -1 \rangle \times \langle 1, 2, -4 \rangle = \begin{vmatrix} \mathbf{i} & \mathbf{j} & \mathbf{k} \\ -1 & 3 & -1 \\ 1 & 2 & -4 \end{vmatrix} = -10\,\mathbf{i} - 5\,\mathbf{j} - 5\,\mathbf{k}.$$

Take the point A as lying in the plane; then an equation is
$(-10)(x-1) + (-5)(y-(-1)) + (-5)(z-4) = 0$ or $2x + y + z = 5$.

27. Find an equation of the plane that contains the point $(1, 2, 1)$ and is orthogonal to
$x + y + z = 1$ and $x + 2y + 3z = 6$.

SOLUTION: According to DEFINITION 11.36 i), the normal, $\mathbf{N}$, to the plane which is sought is orthogonal to both normals $\mathbf{N}_1 = \langle 1, 1, 1 \rangle$ and $\mathbf{N}_2 = \langle 1, 2, 3 \rangle$ of the given planes. A vector which is orthogonal to both these vectors is

$$\mathbf{N} = \mathbf{N}_1 \times \mathbf{N}_2 = \langle 1, 1, 1 \rangle \times \langle 1, 2, 3 \rangle = \begin{vmatrix} \mathbf{i} & \mathbf{j} & \mathbf{k} \\ 1 & 1 & 1 \\ 1 & 2 & 3 \end{vmatrix} = \mathbf{i} - 2\,\mathbf{j} + \mathbf{k}.$$

The plane with normal $\mathbf{N} = \langle 1, -2, 1 \rangle$ containing $P(1, 2, 1)$ has equation
$(1)(x-1) + (-2)(y-2) + (1)(z-1) = 0$ or $x - 2y + z = -2$.

31. Find the distance from the point $(1, -2, 3)$ to the plane $x + z = 1$.

SOLUTION: According to THEOREM 11.38 this distance is

$$d = \frac{|(1)(1) + (0)(-2) + (1)(3) - 1|}{\sqrt{1^2 + 0^2 + 1^2}} = \frac{3}{\sqrt{2}} = \frac{3\sqrt{2}}{2}.$$

35. Find the distance between the parallel planes $2x - 3y + z = 3$ and $4x - 6y + 2z = 9$.

SOLUTION: The point $(0, 0, 3)$ satisfies the equation $2x - 3y + z = 3$ and thus lies in this plane. The distance between this point and the second plane $4x - 6y + 2z = 9$ is given by THEOREM 11.38 as

$$d = \frac{|4(0) + (-6)(0) + 2(3) - 9|}{\sqrt{4^2 + (-6)^2 + 2^2}} = \frac{3}{\sqrt{56}} = \frac{3\sqrt{14}}{28}.$$

Lines in Space

1. Find parametric equations for the line passing through the point $(2, -1, 2)$ and having direction given by $\mathbf{v} = \langle 1, 1, 1 \rangle$.

SOLUTION: According to Equations 11.40 the parametric equations are
$x = 2 + (1)t$, $y = (-1) + (1)t$, and $z = 2 + (1)t$ or $x = 2 + t$, $y = -1 + t$, $z = 2 + t$.

7. Find parametric equations for the line passing through the points $P(3, 4, 4)$ and $Q(2, -3, 5)$.

SOLUTION: A direction for this line is given by $\mathbf{v} = \overrightarrow{PQ} = \langle -1, -7, 1 \rangle$, so by Equations 11.40 the parametric equations are $x = 3 + (-1)t$, $y = 4 + (-7)t$, and $z = 4 + (1)t$ or $x = 3 - t$, $y = 4 - 7t$, $z = 4 + t$.

15. Find symmetric equations for the line described in EXERCISE 7.

SOLUTION: From the SOLUTION to EXERCISE 7 this line has direction $\mathbf{v} = \langle -1, -7, 1 \rangle$ and contains the point $P(3, 4, 4)$. According to Equations 11.41, the symmetric equations for this line are $\dfrac{x - 3}{-1} = \dfrac{y - 4}{-7} = \dfrac{z - 4}{1}$. These can be rewritten as $3 - x = \dfrac{4 - y}{7} = z - 4$.

17. Find parametric equations for the line passing through the point $(1, 2, 3)$ and parallel to the line with parametric equations $x = t + 1$, $y = -t$, $z = 2 - t$.

SOLUTION: A direction for the given line is $\mathbf{v} = \langle 1, -1, -1 \rangle$. Since the line which is sought is parallel to the given line, then take $\mathbf{v} = \langle 1, -1, -1 \rangle$ as its direction and $P(1, 2, 3)$ as a given point. The parametric equations are $x = 1 + (1)t$, $y = 2 + (-1)t$, and $z = 3 + (-1)t$ or $x = 1 + t$, $y = 2 - t$, $z = 3 - t$.

23. Determine whether the pair of lines

$$l_1 : \quad \frac{x - 1}{2} = y + 2 = \frac{z - 3}{2} \quad \text{and} \quad l_2 : \quad \frac{x}{-2} = 1 - y = \frac{z + 2}{-2}$$

is a) parallel, or b) orthogonal. c) Find any points of intersection of l_1 and l_2.

SOLUTION: A direction of line l_1 is given by $\mathbf{v_1} = \langle 2, 1, 2 \rangle$. Rewrite the symmetric equations for l_2 as $\dfrac{x}{-2} = \dfrac{y - 1}{-1} = \dfrac{z + 2}{-2}$ to see that a direction for l_2 is $\mathbf{v_2} = \langle -2, -1, -2 \rangle$.
a) Since $\mathbf{v_1}$ and $\mathbf{v_2}$ are parallel, the lines are parallel.
b) The parallel lines are not orthogonal.

c) To determine possible point(s) of intersection, set up and solve the four equations for x, y, and z as was done in EXAMPLE 6 of the text. The point (x, y, z) lies on l_1 only if i) $(x-1) = 2(y+2)$ and ii) $2(y+2) = z-3$, while it lies on l_2 only if iii) $x = 2(y-1)$ and iv) $2(y-1) = (z+2)$. Substitute $x = 2y - 2$ from iii) into i) to obtain

$$2y - 3 = 2y + 4,$$

which is not satisfied for any y. Thus there are no points of intersection of l_1 and l_2.

33. Find parametric equations of the line that passes through the point $(1, -1, 1)$, is orthogonal to the line $3x = 2y = z$, and is parallel to the plane $x + y - z = 0$.

SOLUTION: The direction of the line which is sought must be orthogonal to a direction of the given line and orthogonal to a normal of the given plane. Since the symmetric equations of the given line can be written as

$$\frac{x - 0}{1/3} = \frac{y - 0}{1/2} = \frac{z - 0}{1},$$

then a direction for this given line is $\mathbf{v}_1 = \langle 1/3, 1/2, 1 \rangle$. A normal for the given plane is $\mathbf{N} = \langle 1, 1, -1 \rangle$. Thus a direction for the line which is sought is

$$\mathbf{v} = \mathbf{v}_1 \times \mathbf{N} = \left\langle \frac{1}{3}, \frac{1}{2}, 1 \right\rangle \times \langle 1, 1, -1 \rangle = \begin{vmatrix} \mathbf{i} & \mathbf{j} & \mathbf{k} \\ \frac{1}{3} & \frac{1}{2} & 1 \\ 1 & 1 & -1 \end{vmatrix} = -\frac{3}{2}\mathbf{i} + \frac{4}{3}\mathbf{j} - \frac{1}{6}\mathbf{k}.$$

The line with this direction through $(1, -1, 1)$ has parametric equations $x = 1 - \frac{3}{2}t$, $y = -1 + \frac{4}{3}t$ and $z = 1 - \frac{1}{6}t$.

37. Use the result in EXERCISE 36 to find the shortest distance between the lines given by l_1 : $x = 2t + 1$, $y = 3t - 2$, $z = t + 3$ and l_2 : $x = -t$, $y = 4t + 1$, $z = 2t - 3$.

SOLUTION: A point P_1 and direction $\mathbf{v}_1$ for line l_1 are $P_1(1, -2, 3)$ and $\mathbf{v}_1 = \langle 2, 3, 1 \rangle$ while a point P_2 and direction $\mathbf{v}_2$ for line l_2 are $P_2(0, 1, -3)$ and $\mathbf{v}_2 = \langle -1, 4, 2 \rangle$. According to the result of EXERCISE 36, the shortest distance between l_1 and l_2 is $\left\| \mathbf{proj}_{\mathbf{v}_1 \times \mathbf{v}_2} \overrightarrow{P_1 P_2} \right\|$, which by Formula 11.19 is equal to $\left| \mathrm{comp}_{\mathbf{v}_1 \times \mathbf{v}_2} \overrightarrow{P_1 P_2} \right|$. The cross product is

$$\mathbf{v}_1 \times \mathbf{v}_2 = \langle 2, 3, 1 \rangle \times \langle -1, 4, 2 \rangle = \begin{vmatrix} \mathbf{i} & \mathbf{j} & \mathbf{k} \\ 2 & 3 & 1 \\ -1 & 4 & 2 \end{vmatrix} = 2\mathbf{i} - 5\mathbf{j} + 11\mathbf{k}$$

with magnitude $\| \mathbf{v}_1 \times \mathbf{v}_2 \| = \sqrt{2^2 + (-5)^2 + 11^2} = 5\sqrt{6}$. The vector from line l_1 to line l_2 is $\overrightarrow{P_1 P_2} = \langle -1, 3, -6 \rangle$. The distance between the two lines is thus

$$d = \left| \mathrm{comp}_{\mathbf{v}_1 \times \mathbf{v}_2} \overrightarrow{P_1 P_2} \right| = \frac{\left| (\mathbf{v}_1 \times \mathbf{v}_2) \cdot \overrightarrow{P_1 P_2} \right|}{\| \mathbf{v}_1 \times \mathbf{v}_2 \|}$$

$$= \frac{|\langle 2, -5, 11 \rangle \cdot \langle -1, 3, -6 \rangle|}{5\sqrt{6}} = \frac{|-83|}{5\sqrt{6}} = \frac{83\sqrt{6}}{30}.$$

_____Chapter 11

Review Exercises

5. Use the vectors $\mathbf{a} = \langle 1, 2, -1 \rangle$, $\mathbf{b} = \langle 3, 5, 4 \rangle$ and $\mathbf{c} = \langle -2, 2, -3 \rangle$ to find $\mathbf{a} \cdot (\mathbf{b} \cdot \mathbf{c})$ or state why the operation is impossible.

SOLUTION: The dot product $\mathbf{b} \cdot \mathbf{c}$ is a scalar, and the dot product of the vector $\mathbf{a}$ with this scalar is undefined. Thus, the operation is impossible.

7. Use the vectors $\mathbf{a}$, $\mathbf{b}$ and $\mathbf{c}$ above to find $\mathbf{a} \times \mathbf{c} - \mathbf{b}$ or state why the operation is impossible.

SOLUTION: The cross product is a vector, so its difference with $\mathbf{b}$ is defined.

$$\mathbf{a} \times \mathbf{c} = \langle 1, 2, -1 \rangle \times \langle -2, 2, -3 \rangle = \begin{vmatrix} \mathbf{i} & \mathbf{j} & \mathbf{k} \\ 1 & 2 & -1 \\ -2 & 2 & -3 \end{vmatrix} = -4\mathbf{i} + 5\mathbf{j} + 6\mathbf{k}.$$

Thus $\mathbf{a} \times \mathbf{c} - \mathbf{b} = \langle -4, 5, 6 \rangle - \langle 3, 5, 4 \rangle = \langle -7, 0, 2 \rangle.$

15. a) Identify the set described by $y = 1 - x$, $z = 0$, as a plane, a line, or a sphere. b) Sketch the graph of this set on a rectangular coordinate system in space.

SOLUTION: a) The equations $y = 1 - x$ and $z = 0$ each describe planes whose intersection is the line with symmetric equations $\dfrac{x - 1}{-1} = \dfrac{y - 0}{1} = \dfrac{z - 0}{0}$. b) This line lies in the xy-plane ($z = 0$) with xy-equation $y = 1 - x$. It also can be described as passing through the point $(1, 0, 0)$ with direction $\mathbf{v} = \langle -1, 1, 0 \rangle$.

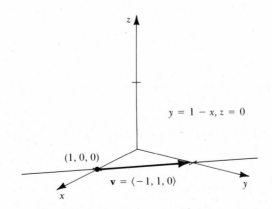

23. a) Identify the set described by $x + y + 2z = 4$. b) Sketch the graph of this equation.

SOLUTION: a) This set is a plane through the point $x = 0$, $y = 0$, $z = 2$ with normal $\mathbf{N} = \langle 1, 1, 2 \rangle$. b) To graph this plane, rewrite the equation as $\dfrac{x}{4} + \dfrac{y}{4} + \dfrac{z}{2} = 1$ to identify the x-, y-, and z-intercepts as 4, 4, and 2 respectively. These are plotted on the coordinate axes below, and the plane and its normal are sketched.

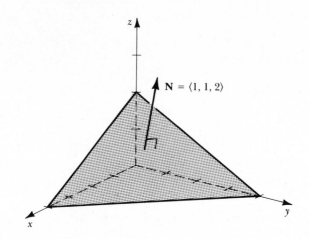

29. Find a vector that describes the direction of the line normal to $3x - 7y + z = 21$.

SOLUTION: A normal to this plane is $\mathbf{N} = \langle 3, -7, 1 \rangle$, so this suffices as the direction $\mathbf{v} = \langle 3, -7, 1 \rangle$.

35. Find a unit vector orthogonal to both $\mathbf{a} = \langle 2, 3, 0 \rangle$ and $\mathbf{b} = \langle -2, 1, 0 \rangle$.

SOLUTION: The vector

$$\mathbf{a} \times \mathbf{b} = \langle 2, 3, 0 \rangle \times \langle -2, 1, 0 \rangle = \begin{vmatrix} \mathbf{i} & \mathbf{j} & \mathbf{k} \\ 2 & 3 & 0 \\ -2 & 1 & 0 \end{vmatrix} = 0\,\mathbf{i} - 0\,\mathbf{j} + 8\,\mathbf{k}$$

is orthogonal to both $\mathbf{a}$ and $\mathbf{b}$. The unit vectors $\mathbf{u}_\pm = \pm \dfrac{8\,\mathbf{k}}{\|8\,\mathbf{k}\|} = \pm\mathbf{k}$ are both orthogonal to these vectors.

45. Find an equation of a plane that contains $(2, 0, 0)$, $(0, 3, 0)$, and $(0, 0, -3)$.

SOLUTION: Label points $A\,(2, 0, 0)$, $B\,(0, 3, 0)$, and $C\,(0, 0, -3)$. A normal to this plane is

$$\mathbf{N} = \overrightarrow{AB} \times \overrightarrow{BC} = \langle -2, 3, 0 \rangle \times \langle 0, -3, -3 \rangle = \begin{vmatrix} \mathbf{i} & \mathbf{j} & \mathbf{k} \\ -2 & 3 & 0 \\ 0 & -3 & -3 \end{vmatrix} = -9\,\mathbf{i} - 6\,\mathbf{j} + 6\,\mathbf{k}.$$

An equation for the plane with this normal and containing the point $A(2,0,0)$ is
$(-9)(x-2)+(-6)(y-0)+(6)(z-0)=0$ or $3x+2y-2z=6$.
Notice that the three given points A, B, and C are the x, y, and z-intercepts respectively of the
plane; so the equation of this plane could have been written immediately as $\dfrac{x}{2}+\dfrac{y}{3}+\dfrac{z}{-3}=1$.

51. Find equations of the line that passes through $(-2,1,2)$ and is parallel to the y-axis.

SOLUTION: A direction for the line is $\mathbf{v}=\mathbf{j}$ since this is the direction of the y-axis. Parametric
equations for the line are $x=-2+0t$, $y=1+t$, $z=2+0t$, or $x=-2$, $y=1+t$, $z=2$. The
symmetric equations are $\dfrac{x+2}{0}=\dfrac{y-1}{1}=\dfrac{z-2}{0}$ or, in more acceptable form, $x=-2$ and $z=2$.

55. Find the distance from $(2,4,6)$ to a) the xy-plane b) the plane $2x+y+z=3$.

SOLUTION: a) The equation of the xy-plane is $z=0$ so by THEOREM 11.38 the distance is

$$d=\frac{|(0)(2)+(0)(4)+(1)(6)-0|}{\sqrt{0^2+0^2+1^2}}=6.$$

Alternatively, you could reason that the distance from a point to one of the coordinate planes is
the appropriate coordinate value.
b) Use THEOREM 11.38 to obtain the distance

$$d=\frac{|(2)(2)+(1)(4)+(1)(6)-3|}{\sqrt{2^2+1^2+1^2}}=\frac{11}{\sqrt{6}}=\frac{11\sqrt{6}}{6}.$$

12
Vector-Valued
Functions

Sharpening your skills

You will need to recall material from Chapters 9 and 11 as well as to refresh your understanding of functions, differentiation and integration. The material on parametric curves, their tangents and their length from Chapter 9 is important. The material from Chapter 11 on three dimensional coordinate systems, vectors, dot and cross products, vector algebra and the parametric equations of a line will be used extensively in this chapter. You will also encounter ideas from the earlier chapters on domains of functions, limits of functions, derivatives and integrals. Prepare to differentiate and integrate again; in particular, review the product and quotient rules of differentiation and study integration by parts.

Perhaps the problems below will help you to review these ideas. The section numbers refer to the places in the text where these tools are presented.

Practice Problems

1. a) Sketch the curve with parametric equations

$$x = \frac{1}{t^2}, \quad y = 1 + \frac{1}{t^4}, \quad -\infty < t < \infty, \ t \neq 0.$$

(See SECTION 9.4)

b) Find an equation for the tangent line to this curve at the point $(1, 2)$. (See SECTION 9.5)

c) Find the length of this curve between the points $(1, 2)$ and $(2, 5)$. (See SECTION 9.6)

2. a) Sketch the graph of the sphere with equation $x^2 + y^2 + z^2 = 3$.

b) Plot the points with coordinates $(0, 1, -\sqrt{2})$, $(1, -1, 1)$, $(-1, 0, \sqrt{2})$ on the same graph. (See SECTION 11.1)

3. If $\mathbf{a} = \langle 2, -1, 1 \rangle$, and $\mathbf{b} = \langle 1, 0, -3 \rangle$, find   a) $\mathbf{a} + \mathbf{b}$ b) $\mathbf{a} - \mathbf{b}$ c) $2\mathbf{a}$ d) $\mathbf{a} \cdot \mathbf{b}$ e) $\cos\theta$, where θ is the angle between $\mathbf{a}$ and $\mathbf{b}$.   f) $\mathbf{a} \times \mathbf{b}$ g) $\mathbf{u}$, a unit vector in the direction of $\mathbf{a}$. (See SECTIONS 11.2, 11.3, 11.4)

4. If $\mathbf{a}$ and $\mathbf{b}$ are two vectors,

a) what condition on their dot product ensures that they are perpendicular? (See SECTION 11.3)

b) what condition on their cross product ensures that they are parallel?   (See SECTION 11.4)

5. Construct a vector whose magnitude is 40 and which makes an angle of 30° with the positive x-axis. (See SECTION 11.3)

6. Find the parametric equations of the line segment between $(1,-1,2)$ and $(2,3,1)$. (See SECTION 11.6)

7. For $f(t) = \sqrt{1 - \dfrac{1}{t^2}}$,

   a) find the domain of f. (See SECTION 1.1)
   b) find $\lim\limits_{t \to 1} f(t)$, $\lim\limits_{t \to 1^+} f(t)$, $\lim\limits_{t \to \infty} f(t)$. (See SECTIONS 1.6, 1.7, 1.8, 1.9)

8. Find $f'(t)$ and simplify where

   a) $f(t) = \dfrac{3t}{\sqrt{1 + t^2 + 2t^4}}$ (See SECTION 2.3),   b) $f(t) = te^t - e^t$ (See SECTION 6.3)

9. Evaluate the integrals

   a) $\displaystyle\int te^{2t}\, dt$ (See SECTION 7.1),

   b) $\displaystyle\int \sqrt{t^2 + 1}\, dt$ (See SECTION 7.3)

_____12.1

Definition of a Vector-Valued Function

3. Determine the domain of the vector-valued function $\mathbf{F}(t) = \sqrt{t}\,\mathbf{i} + (t^2 - 2)\mathbf{j} + t\,\mathbf{k}$

SOLUTION: The domain is the set on which all the functions $x(t) = \sqrt{t}$, $y(t) = t^2 - 2$ and $z(t) = t$ are all defined. Since $y(t)$ and $z(t)$ are defined for all real t, but $x(t)$ is defined only for $t \geq 0$, the domain is $\{t : t \geq 0\}$.

19. Sketch the curve given by $\mathbf{F}(t) = \cos t\,\mathbf{i} + \sin t\,\mathbf{j} + 2\,\mathbf{k}$ and indicate the direction of increasing t.

SOLUTION: The parametric equations for this curve are

$$x(t) = \cos t, \qquad y(t) = \sin t, \qquad z(t) = 2, \qquad -\infty < t < \infty.$$

This curve lies in the plane which has the equation $z = 2$. The variable t can be eliminated from the two equations for $x(t)$ and $y(t)$ by noticing that $x^2 + y^2 = 1$. Thus the curve given by this vector-valued function lies in a circle of radius 1 contained in the plane $z = 2$.

Because of the periodicity of the parametric functions $x(t) = \cos t$ and $y(t) = \sin t$, this circle is traced infinitely often.

Furthermore, as t increases, the point moves around the circle in a counter-clockwise fashion (if the plane is viewed from above).

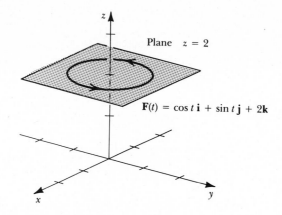

Plane $z = 2$

$\mathbf{F}(t) = \cos t \, \mathbf{i} + \sin t \, \mathbf{j} + 2\mathbf{k}$

COMMENT: This solution presents a <u>strategy</u> for graphing space curves; determine the parametric equations, eliminate the parameter t from among the parametric equations to obtain the equation of a surface which contains the given curve. For a more general study of surfaces, see CHAPTER 13. Notice that graphing a surface containing the curve adds to your understanding of the shape of the curve.

25. For the functions $\mathbf{F}(t) = t\,\mathbf{i} + t^{-2}\,\mathbf{j} + e^t\,\mathbf{k}$, $\mathbf{G}(t) = \sqrt{t}\,\mathbf{i} + \sin t\,\mathbf{k}$ and $f(t) = 2 - t$ determine the description and domain of the functions   a) $(\mathbf{F} \cdot \mathbf{G})$,   b) $(\mathbf{F} \circ f)(t)$,   c) $(f\,\mathbf{F})(t)$,   d) $(\mathbf{F} + \mathbf{G})(t)$,   e) $(\mathbf{F} - \mathbf{G})(t)$, and   f) $(\mathbf{F} \times \mathbf{G})(t)$.

SOLUTION:

a) The dot product of the two vector-valued functions is defined for $t > 0$ as

$$(\mathbf{F} \cdot \mathbf{G})(t) = (t\,\mathbf{i} + t^{-2}\,\mathbf{j} + e^t\,\mathbf{k}) \cdot (\sqrt{t}\,\mathbf{i} + \sin t\,\mathbf{k}) = t\sqrt{t} + t^{-2} \cdot 0 + e^t \sin t = t^{3/2} + e^t \sin t.$$

b) Evaluate $\mathbf{F}$ at the value of $f(t)$. For $t \neq 2$,

$$(\mathbf{F} \circ f)(t) = \mathbf{F}\big(f(t)\big) = f(t)\,\mathbf{i} + \big(f(t)\big)^{-2}\,\mathbf{j} + e^{f(t)}\,\mathbf{k} = (2 - t)\,\mathbf{i} + (2 - t)^{-2}\,\mathbf{j} + e^{2-t}\,\mathbf{k}.$$

c) Multiply each component of the vector-valued function by the scalar. For $t \neq 0, 2$,

$$(f\,\mathbf{F})(t) = \big(f(t) \cdot t\big)\,\mathbf{i} + \big(f(t) \cdot t^{-2}\big)\,\mathbf{j} + \big(f(t) \cdot e^t\big)\,\mathbf{k} = (2 - t)t\,\mathbf{i} + (2 - t)t^{-2}\,\mathbf{j} + (2 - t)e^t\,\mathbf{k}.$$

d) Add the vector-valued functions component-wise. For $t > 0$,

$$(\mathbf{F} + \mathbf{G})(t) = (t + \sqrt{t})\,\mathbf{i} + (t^{-2} + 0)\,\mathbf{j} + (e^t + \sin t)\,\mathbf{k}.$$

e) Subtract the components of $\mathbf{G}$ from those of $\mathbf{F}$. For $t > 0$,

$$(\mathbf{F} - \mathbf{G})(t) = (t - \sqrt{t})\,\mathbf{i} + (t^{-2} - 0)\,\mathbf{j} + (e^t - \sin t)\,\mathbf{k}.$$

f) Use the determinant-like device introduced in Chapter 11 to compute the cross product.

$$(\mathbf{F} \times \mathbf{G})(t) = \begin{vmatrix} \mathbf{i} & \mathbf{j} & \mathbf{k} \\ t & t^{-2} & e^t \\ \sqrt{t} & 0 & \sin t \end{vmatrix}$$

$$= \begin{vmatrix} t^{-2} & e^t \\ 0 & \sin t \end{vmatrix} \mathbf{i} - \begin{vmatrix} t & e^t \\ \sqrt{t} & \sin t \end{vmatrix} \mathbf{j} + \begin{vmatrix} t & t^{-2} \\ \sqrt{t} & 0 \end{vmatrix} \mathbf{k}$$

$$= (t^{-2} \cdot \sin t - e^t \cdot 0)\,\mathbf{i} - (t \cdot \sin t - \sqrt{t}\,e^t)\,\mathbf{j} + (t \cdot 0 - \sqrt{t}\,t^{-2})\,\mathbf{k}$$

$$= t^{-2} \sin t\,\mathbf{i} + \left(\sqrt{t}e^t - t \sin t\right)\mathbf{j} - t^{-3/2}\,\mathbf{k}, \qquad \text{for } t > 0.$$

_____12.2

The Calculus of Vector-Valued Functions

7. Find $\displaystyle\lim_{t \to 1} \mathbf{F}(t)$ where $\mathbf{F}(t) = \begin{cases} t^2\,\mathbf{i} - 2t\,\mathbf{j} + e^{t-1}\,\mathbf{k}, & t > 1 \\ \vec{0}, & t = 1 \\ (2t - 1)\,\mathbf{i} + 2\cos \pi t\,\mathbf{j} + t\,\mathbf{k}, & t < 1 \end{cases}$.

SOLUTION: First identify the component functions, then calculate their limits separately.

$$x(t) = \begin{cases} t^2, & t > 1 \\ 0, & t = 1 \\ (2t - 1), & t < 1 \end{cases} \qquad y(t) = \begin{cases} -2t, & t > 1 \\ 0, & t = 1 \\ 2\cos \pi t, & t < 1 \end{cases} \quad \text{and} \quad z(t) = \begin{cases} e^{t-1}, & t > 1 \\ 0, & t = 1 \\ t, & t < 1 \end{cases}$$

To calculate $\displaystyle\lim_{t \to 1} x(t)$ observe that the two one-sided limits are $\displaystyle\lim_{t \to 1^+} x(t) = \lim_{t \to 1^+} t^2 = 1$ and $\displaystyle\lim_{t \to 1^-} x(t) = \lim_{t \to 1^-} (2t - 1) = 1$. Since these limits are equal, they equal the desired limit. Similarly, $\displaystyle\lim_{t \to 1} y(t) = \lim_{t \to 1^+} (-2t) = -2 = \lim_{t \to 1^-} 2 \cos \pi t$, and $\displaystyle\lim_{t \to 1} z(t) = \lim_{t \to 1^+} e^{t-1} = 1 = \lim_{t \to 1^-} t$. Thus

$$\lim_{t \to 1} \mathbf{F}(t) = \left(\lim_{t \to 1} x(t)\right)\mathbf{i} + \left(\lim_{t \to 1} y(t)\right)\mathbf{j} + \left(\lim_{t \to 1} z(t)\right)\mathbf{k} = \mathbf{i} - 2\mathbf{j} + \mathbf{k}.$$

15. Find the values of t for which $\mathbf{F}(t)$ as given in EXERCISE 7 above is continuous.

SOLUTION: Part ii) of DEFINITION 12.4 says that $\mathbf{F}$ is continuous at all values of t where the component functions $x(t)$, $y(t)$, and $z(t)$ are continuous. By the definitions of these functions as in EXERCISE 7 above,

$$x(t) = \begin{cases} t^2, & t > 1 \\ 0, & t = 1, \\ (2t - 1), & t < 1 \end{cases} \quad y(t) = \begin{cases} -2t, & t > 1 \\ 0, & t = 1 \\ 2\cos \pi t, & t < 1 \end{cases} \text{ and } z(t) = \begin{cases} e^{t-1}, & t > 1 \\ 0, & t = 1 \\ t, & t < 1, \end{cases}$$

they are all continuous when $t > 1$ as well as $t < 1$. At $t = 1$, the limits all exist; $\lim_{t \to 1} x(t) = 1$, $\lim_{t \to 1} y(t) = -2$, and $\lim_{t \to 1} z(t) = 1$ and the component functions are all defined: $x(1) = 0 = y(1) = z(1)$. Since the limits don't equal the function values, all the component functions are *not* continuous at $t = 1$. Notice that had only one component been discontinuous at $t = 1$, the function would still have been discontinuous there.

The function is continuous for all $t > 1$ and $t < 1$ but is discontinuous at $t = 1$.

17. Find the derivative of $\mathbf{F}(t) = \ln t\, \mathbf{i} + t\mathbf{j} + \mathbf{k}$

SOLUTION: According to DEFINITION 12.4 iii),

$$D_t\, \mathbf{F}(t) = (D_t \ln t)\, \mathbf{i} + (D_t t)\, \mathbf{j} + (D_t \cdot 1)\, \mathbf{k} = \frac{1}{t}\mathbf{i} + 1\mathbf{j} + 0\mathbf{k} = \frac{1}{t}\mathbf{i} + \mathbf{j}.$$

25. For $\mathbf{F}(t) = \sin t\, \mathbf{i} + \cos t\, \mathbf{j} + t\mathbf{k}$ find $\mathbf{F}'(0)$, sketch the graph of $\mathbf{F}$ and sketch the vector $\mathbf{F}'(0)$.

SOLUTION: First calculate $\mathbf{F}'(t)$ and then evaluate this at $t = 0$.

$$\mathbf{F}'(t) = (D_t \sin t)\, \mathbf{i} + (D_t \cos t)\, \mathbf{j} + (D_t t)\, \mathbf{k} = \cos t\, \mathbf{i} - \sin t\, \mathbf{j} + \mathbf{k}.$$

So, $\mathbf{F}'(0) = \mathbf{i} - 0\mathbf{j} + \mathbf{k} = \mathbf{i} + \mathbf{k}.$

To sketch the graph of $\mathbf{F}$ use the strategy described after the solution to EXERCISE 19 of SECTION 12.1. Notice that the parametric equations are

$$x(t) = \sin t, \qquad y(t) = \cos t, \qquad \text{and} \quad z(t) = t.$$

One way to eliminate the parameter t from between these equations is to notice that

$$x^2 + y^2 = \sin^2 t + \cos^2 t = 1.$$

This curve is therefore contained in the surface which lies above and below the circle $x^2 + y^2 = 1$ in the xy-plane (this right circular cylinder is sketched).

Plot a few points, $\mathbf{F}(-\pi/2) = -\mathbf{i} - (\pi/2)\mathbf{k}$, $\mathbf{F}(0) = \mathbf{j}$, $\mathbf{F}(\pi/2) = \mathbf{i} + (\frac{\pi}{2})\mathbf{k}$, to see that as t increases, the point moves clockwise around the cylinder (as viewed from above) and the z-coordinate increases. The tangent vector $\mathbf{F}'(0) = \mathbf{i} + \mathbf{k}$ is illustrated.

$\mathbf{F}(t) = \sin t\,\mathbf{i} + \cos t\,\mathbf{j} + t\mathbf{k}$

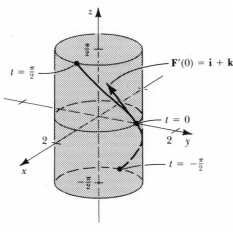

Cylinder over $x^2 + y^2 = 1$

29. Determine the derivative of the function $[(\mathbf{F} - 3\mathbf{G}) \circ f](t)$ where $\mathbf{F}(t) = t^2\,\mathbf{i} - 2t\,\mathbf{j} + \sin t\,\mathbf{k}$, $\mathbf{G}(t) = \ln t\,\mathbf{i} + 3e^t\,\mathbf{k}$, and $f(t) = \cos t$.

SOLUTION: First calculate the derivatives. $\mathbf{F}'(t) = 2t\,\mathbf{i} - 2\,\mathbf{j} + \cos t\,\mathbf{k}$, $\mathbf{G}'(t) = \dfrac{1}{t}\mathbf{i} + 3e^t\,\mathbf{k}$, and $f'(t) = -\sin t$. Next apply the chain rule as expressed in THEOREM 12.8 vi),

$$D_t\,[(\mathbf{F} - 3\mathbf{G}) \circ f]\,(t) = [\mathbf{F} - 3\mathbf{G}]'\,(f(t)) \cdot f'(t)$$

$$= \left((2(\cos t)\mathbf{i} - 2\,\mathbf{j} + \cos(\cos t)\,\mathbf{k}) - 3\left(\frac{1}{\cos t}\mathbf{i} + 3e^{\cos t}\,\mathbf{k}\right)\right)(-\sin t)$$

$$= \left(-2\cos t \sin t + 3\frac{\sin t}{\cos t}\right)\mathbf{i} + (2\sin t)\mathbf{j} + \left(9\sin t e^{\cos t} - \sin t \cos(\cos t)\right)\mathbf{k}.$$

41. Evaluate $\displaystyle\int (te^t\,\mathbf{i} + t\,\mathbf{j} + \mathbf{k})\,dt$.

SOLUTION: By DEFINITION 12.4 (iv),

$$\int (te^t\,\mathbf{i} + t\,\mathbf{j} + \mathbf{k})\,dt = \left(\int te^t\,dt\right)\mathbf{i} + \left(\int t\,dt\right)\mathbf{j} + \left(\int 1\,dt\right)\mathbf{k}.$$

The $\mathbf{i}$ component is integrated by parts with $u = t$, and $dv = e^t\,dt$ which implies $du = dt$ and $v = e^t\,dt$, so $\int te^t\,dt = te^t - \int e^t\,dt = te^t - e^t + c_1$. The $\mathbf{j}$ and $\mathbf{k}$ components are integrated directly: $\int t \, dt = \frac{1}{2}t^2 + c_2$ and $\int dt = t + c_3$, where c_1, c_2, and c_3 are arbitrary constants. The integral of the vector function is thus equal to

$$(te^t - e^t + c_1)\mathbf{i} + \left(\frac{t^2}{2} + c_2\right)\mathbf{j} + (t + c_3)\mathbf{k} = (te^t - e^t)\mathbf{i} + \left(\frac{t^2}{2}\right)\mathbf{j} + t\mathbf{k} + \mathbf{C},$$

where $\mathbf{C}$ is a vector with arbitrary components.

51. a) Show that the line segment joining the points $(1, 3, 1)$ and $(2, 5, 4)$ is described by each of the functions

$$\begin{aligned}
\mathbf{F}_1(t) &= (t + 1)\mathbf{i} + (2t + 3)\mathbf{j} + (3t + 1)\mathbf{k}, && 0 \le t \le 1 \\
\mathbf{F}_2(t) &= (t^2 + 1)\mathbf{i} + (2t^2 + 3)\mathbf{j} + (3t^2 + 1)\mathbf{k}, && 0 \le t \le 1 \\
\mathbf{F}_3(t) &= (\ln t + 1)\mathbf{i} + (\ln t^2 + 3)\mathbf{j} + (\ln t^3 + 1)\mathbf{k}, && 1 \le t \le e.
\end{aligned}$$

b) Find $\mathbf{F}_1(\frac{1}{2})$, $\mathbf{F}_2(\frac{1}{2})$, and $\mathbf{F}_3\left(\dfrac{1 + e}{2}\right)$.

SOLUTION: a) First show that the function $\mathbf{F}_1$ describes the line segment, then that $\mathbf{F}_2$ and $\mathbf{F}_3$ describe the same points as $\mathbf{F}_1$. The parametric equations for $\mathbf{F}_1$ are

$$x(t) = 1 + t, \qquad y(t) = 3 + 2t, \quad \text{and} \quad z(t) = 1 + 3t.$$

From SECTION 11.6 these are the parametric equations of the line through $(1, 3, 1)$ with direction given by $\langle 1, 2, 3 \rangle$. Since at $t = 0$, $(x(0), y(0), z(0)) = (1, 3, 1)$ and at $t = 1$, $(x(1), y(1), z(1)) = (2, 5, 4)$ we see that this curve is the desired line segment.

To show that $\mathbf{F}_2$ and $\mathbf{F}_3$ describe the same line segment, show that for every t_1 there is a t_2 such that $\mathbf{F}_1(t_1) = \mathbf{F}_2(t_2)$, that for any t_2 there is a t_3 such that $\mathbf{F}_2(t_2) = \mathbf{F}_3(t_3)$, and finally that for every t_3 there is a t_1 such that $\mathbf{F}_3(t_3) = \mathbf{F}_1(t_1)$. This implies that given any point on one of the curves, the same point lies on each of the other curves. In other words, the vector-valued functions all describe the same line segment.

Given $t_1 : 0 \le t_1 \le 1$, choose $t_2 = \sqrt{t_1}$. Now $0 \le t_2 \le 1$ and

$$\begin{aligned}
\mathbf{F}_2(t_2) &= \left((\sqrt{t_1})^2 + 1\right)\mathbf{i} + \left(2(\sqrt{t_1})^2 + 3\right)\mathbf{j} + \left(3(\sqrt{t_1})^2 + 1\right)\mathbf{k} \\
&= (t_1 + 1)\mathbf{i} + (2t_1 + 3)\mathbf{j} + (3t_1 + 1)\mathbf{k} = \mathbf{F}_1(t_1).
\end{aligned}$$

Given $t_2 : 0 \le t_2 \le 1$, choose $t_3 = e^{t_2^2}$. Here $e^{0^2} \le e^{t_2^2} \le e^{1^2}$ since the function $f(x) = e^{x^2}$ is increasing. Thus $1 \le t_3 \le e$. In addition

$$\begin{aligned}
\mathbf{F}_3(t_3) &= \left(\ln e^{t_2^2} + 1\right)\mathbf{i} + \left(\ln(e^{t_2^2})^2 + 3\right)\mathbf{j} + \left(\ln(e^{t_2^2})^3 + 1\right)\mathbf{k} \\
&= (t_2^2 + 1)\mathbf{i} + (2t_2^2 + 3)\mathbf{j} + (3t_2^2 + 1)\mathbf{k} && \text{(by rules for exponents)} \\
&= \mathbf{F}_2(t_2).
\end{aligned}$$

Finally, given $t_3 : 1 \leq t_3 \leq e$, choose $t_1 = \ln t_3$. Now since the logarithm function is increasing, $\ln 1 \leq \ln t_3 \leq \ln e$, so $\quad 0 \leq t_1 \leq 1$ and

$$
\begin{aligned}
\mathbf{F}_1(t_1) &= ((\ln t_3) + 1)\,\mathbf{i} + (2\ln t_3 + 3)\mathbf{j} + (3\ln t_3 + 1)\,\mathbf{k} \\
&= (\ln t_3 + 1)\,\mathbf{i} + (\ln t_3^2 + 3)\mathbf{j} + (\ln t_3^3 + 1)\,\mathbf{k} \qquad \text{(by the rules for logarithms)} \\
&= \mathbf{F}_3(t_3).
\end{aligned}
$$

b)

$$
\mathbf{F}_1\left(\frac{1}{2}\right) = \left(\frac{1}{2} + 1\right)\mathbf{i} + \left(2\cdot\frac{1}{2} + 3\right)\mathbf{j} + \left(3\cdot\frac{1}{2} + 1\right)\mathbf{k} = \frac{3}{2}\mathbf{i} + 4\mathbf{j} + \frac{5}{2}\mathbf{k},
$$

$$
\mathbf{F}_2\left(\frac{1}{2}\right) = \left(\left(\frac{1}{2}\right)^2 + 1\right)\mathbf{i} + \left(2\left(\frac{1}{2}\right)^2 + 3\right)\mathbf{j}\left(3\left(\frac{1}{2}\right)^2 + 1\right)\mathbf{k} = \frac{5}{4}\mathbf{i} + \frac{7}{2}\mathbf{j} + \frac{7}{4}\mathbf{k} \qquad \text{and}
$$

$$
\mathbf{F}_3\left(\frac{1+e}{2}\right) = \left(\ln\left(\frac{1+e}{2}\right) + 1\right)\mathbf{i} + \left(2\ln\left(\frac{1+e}{2}\right) + 3\right)\mathbf{j} + \left(3\ln\left(\frac{1+e}{2}\right) + 1\right)\mathbf{k}.
$$

COMMENT: This solution illustrates one way of proving that two (or more) vector functions describe the same curve. Notice that you must show that each point on the second curve lies on the first and vice-versa.

12.3

Unit Tangent and Unit
Normal Vectors

3. Find the principal unit tangent vector at $t = 1$ for $\mathbf{F}(t) = t^2\,\mathbf{i} + \ln t\,\mathbf{j} + t\,\mathbf{k}$.

SOLUTION: To find this unit tangent vector, $\mathbf{T}(1)$, compute $\mathbf{F}'(t)$, divide this vector by its magnitude to find $\mathbf{T}(t)$ and evaluate the result at $t = 1$. The derivative is, assuming $t > 0$,

$$
\mathbf{F}'(t) = 2t\,\mathbf{i} + \frac{1}{t}\mathbf{j} + \mathbf{k}.
$$

Its magnitude is

$$
\|\mathbf{F}'(t)\| = \sqrt{(2t)^2 + \left(\frac{1}{t}\right)^2 + 1^2} = \sqrt{4t^2 + \frac{1}{t^2} + 1} = \frac{1}{t}\sqrt{4t^4 + 1 + t^2}.
$$

The unit tangent vector is thus

$$T(t) = \frac{F'(t)}{\|F'(t)\|} = \frac{2t\,i + \frac{1}{t}\,j + k}{\frac{1}{t}\sqrt{4t^4 + 1 + t^2}}.$$

The factor of $\frac{1}{t}$ is the denominator becomes a factor of t in the numerator so

$$T(t) = \frac{2t^2\,i + j + t\,k}{\sqrt{4t^4 + 1 + t^2}} \qquad \text{and} \qquad T(1) = \frac{2i + j + k}{\sqrt{6}}.$$

COMMENT: When finding the principal unit tangent vector at a value of t_0 as in this example, there is the temptation to calculate $F'(t)$, evaluate this at t_0 to find a tangent vector, then divide this vector by its magnitude. While this yields the principal unit tangent vector, it is of little use in finding the principal unit normal vector. This latter vector is based on the derivative of $T(t)$ with respect to t so you must have an expression for the principal unit tangent vector at every t.

9. Find the principal unit normal vector at $t = 1$ for $F(t) = t^2\,i + \ln t\,j + t\,k$.

SOLUTION: The principal unit normal vector at an arbitrary t is

$$N(t) = \frac{T'(t)}{\|T'(t)\|}.$$

$T(t)$ was calculated in the solution to EXERCISE 3 of this section as

$$T(t) = \frac{2t^2\,i + j + t\,k}{\sqrt{4t^4 + 1 + t^2}}.$$

If this is viewed as the product of a scalar function and a vector function, then by THEO-REM 12.8 (ii),

$$T'(t) = D_t\left[\frac{1}{\sqrt{4t^4 + 1 + t^2}}(2t^2\,i + j + t\,k)\right]$$

$$= D_t\left[\frac{1}{\sqrt{4t^4 + 1 + t^2}}\right] \cdot (2t^2\,i + j + t\,k) + \frac{1}{\sqrt{4t^4 + 1 + t^2}} \cdot D_t\left[2t^2\,i + j + t\,k\right]$$

$$= \left(-\frac{1}{2} \cdot \frac{(16t^3 + 2t)}{(4t^4 + 1 + t^2)^{3/2}}\right)(2t^2\,i + j + t\,k) + \left(\frac{1}{\sqrt{4t^4 + 1 + t^2}}\right)(4t\,i + k).$$

No further use is made of the vector function $T'(t)$; instead, only $T'(1)$ is needed for the determination of $N(1)$ so evaluate $T'(1)$.

$$T'(1) = \left(\frac{-9}{6^{3/2}}\right)(2i + j + k) + \frac{1}{6^{1/2}}(4i + k) = \frac{1}{2\sqrt{6}}(2i - 3j - k).$$

The magnitude of this vector is

$$\| \mathbf{T}'(1)\| = \frac{1}{2\sqrt{6}}\sqrt{2^2 + (-3)^2 + (-1)^2} = \frac{\sqrt{14}}{2\sqrt{6}}$$

$$\text{so}\quad \mathbf{N}(1) = \frac{\mathbf{T}'(1)}{\|\mathbf{T}'(1)\|} = \frac{\frac{1}{2\sqrt{6}}(2\mathbf{i} - 3\mathbf{j} - \mathbf{k})}{\frac{\sqrt{14}}{2\sqrt{6}}} = \frac{1}{\sqrt{14}}(2\mathbf{i} - 3\mathbf{j} - \mathbf{k}).$$

COMMENT: In this solution the expression for $\mathbf{T}'(t)$ could have been simplifed further but to no apparent purpose, so the value of $\mathbf{T}'(1)$ was determined. It is a good tactic in any problem to look ahead at each step of the calculation to see whether a general expression or a specific value is called for in this problem or in later problems. If specific values are all that is required and if they are attainable from the current results, then they should be evaluated directly.

15. Determine the interval(s) on which $\mathbf{F}(t) = \mathbf{i} + t\mathbf{j} + \sqrt{t}\,\mathbf{k}$ is smooth.

SOLUTION: The curve is smooth at exactly those t where the component functions $x(t) = 1$, $y(t) = t$, and $z(t) = \sqrt{t}$ have continuous derivatives which do not simultaneously vanish. These derivatives are $x'(t) = 0$, $y'(t) = 1$, and $z'(t) = 1/(2\sqrt{t})$.

The derivatives of the first two components are defined everywhere. It is the derivative of $z(t)$ which must be restricted to the set where $t > 0$. Over this domain the derivatives don't vanish simultaneously anywhere. Thus, $\mathbf{F}(t)$ is smooth whenever $t > 0$.

21. Find a vector-valued function with arc length as parameter to describe the circle with radius 1 in the xy-plane with center at the origin.

SOLUTION: A parameterization which occurs naturally uses as parameter the angle θ between the ray $\overrightarrow{OA}$ and $\overrightarrow{OP}$ to describe the coordinates of P as $x = \cos\theta$ and $y = \sin\theta$. This follows from the definition of the trigonometric functions and is valid for $0 \le \theta < 2\pi$.

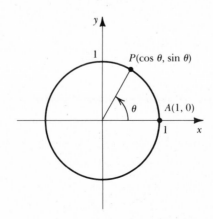

The circle is described by $\mathbf{R}(\theta) = \cos\theta\,\mathbf{i} + \sin\theta\,\mathbf{j}$, $0 \le \theta < 2\pi$.

For any value of θ, the length of the curve between points with parameter values 0 and θ is

$$s = \int_0^\theta \sqrt{(-\sin t)^2 + (\cos t)^2 + 0^2}\, dt = \int_0^\theta 1\, dt = \theta.$$

It is not surprising that $s = \theta$ since this recalls the fact that the arc of a unit circle subtended by an angle θ is $s = \theta$. Solving for θ in terms of s gives $\theta = s$, which can then be substituted into the expression for $\mathbf{R}(\theta)$ to yield the arc length parameterization

$$\mathbf{R}(s) = \cos s\,\mathbf{i} + \sin s\,\mathbf{j}, \qquad 0 \le s \le 2\pi.$$

COMMENT: The <u>strategy</u> for obtaining the arc length parameterization of a curve is illustrated here. Some parameterization, usually in terms of t although θ was used here, must be given with a point distinguished as corresponding to a special parameter value t_0 (frequently $t_0 = 0$). The length of curve $s(t)$ between points with paramter values t_0 and t is determined. The equation $s = s(t)$ is solved for t in terms of s: $t = t(s)$; this determines the parameter value t which corresponds to a length of arc s. The replacement of t by $t(s)$ in the parametric equations results in the arc length parameterization of the curve.

29. Find the binormal vector to the curve $\mathbf{F}(t) = 2t\,\mathbf{i} + e^t\,\mathbf{j} + t^3\,\mathbf{k}$, for $t = 0$.

SOLUTION: From the statement of EXERCISE 25, the binormal vector is $\mathbf{B} = \mathbf{T} \times \mathbf{N}$. From the SOLUTIONS to EXERCISES 4 and 10, the principal unit tangent and unit normal vectors at $t = 0$ are

$$\mathbf{T}(0) = \frac{2\mathbf{i} + \mathbf{j}}{\sqrt{5}} \quad \text{and} \quad \mathbf{N}(0) = \frac{-\mathbf{i} + 2\mathbf{j}}{\sqrt{5}}.$$

Thus

$$\mathbf{B} = \left(\frac{2\mathbf{i} + \mathbf{j}}{\sqrt{5}}\right) \times \left(\frac{-\mathbf{i} + 2\mathbf{j}}{\sqrt{5}}\right) = \frac{1}{\sqrt{5}\sqrt{5}} \begin{vmatrix} \mathbf{i} & \mathbf{j} & \mathbf{k} \\ 2 & 1 & 0 \\ -1 & 2 & 0 \end{vmatrix}$$

$$= \frac{1}{5}\left((1(0) - 2(0))\,\mathbf{i} - (2(0) + 1(0))\,\mathbf{j} + (2(2) + 1(1))\,\mathbf{k}\right) = \mathbf{k}.$$

_____12.4

Velocity and Acceleration
of Objects in Space

1. The motion of an object is described by $\mathbf{r}(t) = \sin t\,\mathbf{i} + \cos t\,\mathbf{j} + t\,\mathbf{k}$. Find   a) the velocity, b) the acceleration, and   c) the speed of the object.

SOLUTION: a) The velocity is $\mathbf{v}(t) = \mathbf{r}'(t) = \cos t\,\mathbf{k} - \sin t\,\mathbf{j} + \mathbf{k}$.

b) The acceleration is $\mathbf{a}(t) = \mathbf{v}'(t) = -\sin t\,\mathbf{i} - \cos t\,\mathbf{j}$.

c) The speed is $v(t) = \| \mathbf{v}(t) \| = \sqrt{(\cos t)^2 + (-\sin t)^2 + 1} = \sqrt{2}$, for all t.

13. The motion of an object is described by $\mathbf{r}(t) = t\mathbf{j} + (16t^2 - 10t)\mathbf{k}$. Determine the tangential and centripetal components of acceleration of the object.

SOLUTION: First find the velocity, speed $(v(t))$, and acceleration ($\mathbf{a}$), then use the facts that

$$a_T = \frac{dv}{dt} \quad \text{and} \quad a_N = \sqrt{\|\mathbf{a}\|^2 - a_T{}^2}$$

to compute the tangential and centripetal components of acceleration respectively.

The velocity is $\mathbf{v} = \mathbf{r}' = \mathbf{j} + (32t - 10)\mathbf{k}$, so the speed is $v(t) = \|\mathbf{v}\| = \sqrt{1 + (32t - 10)^2}$ and the acceleration is $\mathbf{a} = \mathbf{v}' = 32\,\mathbf{k}$ with magnitude $\|\mathbf{a}\| = 32$.

The tangential component of acceleration is

$$a_T = \frac{dv}{dt} = D_t\left[\sqrt{1 + (32t - 10)^2}\right] = \frac{32(32t - 10)}{\sqrt{1 + (32t - 10)^2}}.$$

The centripetal component is

$$a_N = \sqrt{\|\mathbf{a}\|^2 - a_T{}^2} = \sqrt{(32)^2 - \left(\frac{32(32t - 10)}{\sqrt{1 + (32t - 10)^2}}\right)^2} = \frac{32}{\sqrt{1 + (32t - 10)^2}}.$$

15. The path of a golf ball is described by

$$\mathbf{r}(t) = \begin{cases} 110t\,\mathbf{j} + 30t(2 - t)\,\mathbf{k}, & 0 \le t \le 2 \\ 220\sqrt{t - 1}\,\mathbf{j}, & 2 \le t \le 2.4, \end{cases}$$

where the time t is given in seconds and the distance in yards.
a) Sketch the curve that represents the path of the golf ball.
b) Find the maximum height of the golf ball.
c) Find the speed of the ball when it strikes the ground.

SOLUTION: a) The curve of motion lies in the yz-plane and consists of two segments. One has parametric equations

$$x = 0, \quad y = 110t, \quad \text{and} \quad z = 30t(2 - t), \qquad 0 \le t \le 2$$

which, on eliminating the parameter t, describes a parabolic arc

$$z = \frac{30}{110}y\left(2 - \frac{y}{110}\right) \text{ connecting } (0, 0, 0) \text{ to } (0, 220, 0).$$

The other segment consists of a portion of the y-axis

$$x = 0, \quad y = 220\sqrt{t-1}, \quad z = 0, \qquad 2 \le t \le 2.4$$

which connects $(0, 220, 0)$ to $(0, 220\sqrt{1.4}, 0)$.

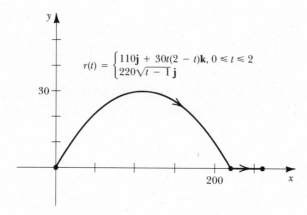

b) The maximum height occurs when the z-component of this motion is a maximum. Since

$$z(t) = \begin{cases} 30t(2-t), & 0 \le t \le 2 \\ 0, & 2 \le t \le 2.4 \end{cases}$$

the maximum must occur over the first time interval. A critical point of

$$z(t) = 30t(2-t), \qquad 0 \le t \le 2 \quad \text{occurs when} \quad z'(t) = 60 - 60t = 0$$

or when $t = 1$. At $t = 1$, $z''(t) = -60$, so $z(1) = 30(2-1) = 30$ is the maximum height since at the endpoints of this interval, $z(0) = 0 = z(2)$.

c) $z(t) = 30t(2-t) = 0$ if $t = 0$ or $t = 2$. Since $z(t) > 0$ for $0 < t < 2$, the ball strikes the ground when $t = 2$. The velocity at this instant is obtained by differentiating values of $\mathbf{r}(t)$ for $t < 2$:

$$\mathbf{v}(t) = 110\,\mathbf{i} + (60 - 60t)\,\mathbf{j}.$$

The instantaneous velocity at the time $t = 2$ is $\mathbf{v}(2) = 110\,\mathbf{i} - 60\,\mathbf{j}$, so the speed of the ball when it strikes the ground is

$$v(2) = \|\mathbf{v}(2)\| = \sqrt{(110)^2 + (-60)^2} = \sqrt{15,700}\ \frac{\text{yds}}{\text{sec}}.$$

COMMENT: This problem as well as later problems in this section are concerned with the motion of objects. A few terms should be clarified. The word *initial* refers to information when $t = 0$, e.g., *initial position* is $\mathbf{r}(0)$, *initial velocity* is $\mathbf{v}(0)$, *initial speed* is $v(0)$ and *initial angle of elevation* is the angle between $\mathbf{v}(0)$ and $\mathbf{i}$. *Horizontal* and *vertical* displacements are usually $x(t)$ and $y(t)$, the $\mathbf{i}$ and $\mathbf{j}$ components of position $\mathbf{r}(t)$, so if a problem asks the *maximum height* of an object you are to find the maximum value of $y(t)$. A special time to be determined in many problems is the time *when the object strikes the ground*, that is, the time t_0 when $y(t_0) = 0$. The speed at which the object strikes the ground is $v(t_0)$ while its velocity at this instant is $\mathbf{v}(t_0)$ and its horizontal displacement then is $x(t_0)$.

19. A quarterback throws a football downfield with an initial speed of 55 ft/sec and at an angle of elevation of $\pi/6$ radians.   a) How far from the quarterback should the receiver be to catch the ball?   b) How long from the time the ball is thrown does he have time to get into this position? (Assume that the ball is thrown and caught at the same height.)

SOLUTION: For convenience, set up the coordinate system so that the origin is at the point where the ball is released and the x-axis is parallel to the ground and lies under the path of the ball. The path of the ball is given by a vector function $\mathbf{r}(t)$ which must be determined from the information about the ball's initial trajectory. The problem is to determine the horizontal position of the ball when its vertical position is zero and to determine when this occurs. The initial position is $\mathbf{r}(0) = 0$. The initial velocity has magnitude 55 and has the same direction as a unit vector which makes an angle of $\pi/6$ with the vector $\mathbf{i}$,

$$\mathbf{v}(0) = 55 \left(\cos \frac{\pi}{6} \mathbf{i} + \sin \frac{\pi}{6} \mathbf{j} \right) = \frac{55}{2} (\sqrt{3}\,\mathbf{i} + \mathbf{j}).$$

Follow the procedure in the text to integrate the equation derived from the assumption that the only force acting on the ball is that due to gravity, $\mathbf{a} = -32\mathbf{j}$. Use the initial values $\mathbf{r}(0)$ and $\mathbf{v}(0)$ to obtain

$$\mathbf{r}(t) = -16t^2\,\mathbf{j} + \mathbf{v}(0)t + \mathbf{r}(0).$$

With the values of $\mathbf{v}(0)$ and $\mathbf{r}(0)$ given above, the position of the ball at time t is

$$\mathbf{r}(t) = -16t^2\,\mathbf{j} + \frac{55}{2}(\sqrt{3}\,\mathbf{i} + \mathbf{j})t + \overrightarrow{0} = \frac{55\sqrt{3}}{2}t\,\mathbf{i} + \left(\frac{55}{2}t - 16t^2\right)\mathbf{j}.$$

The horizontal and vertical displacements of the ball at time t are

$$x = \frac{55\sqrt{3}}{2}t \quad \text{and} \quad y = \frac{55}{2}t - 16t^2$$

respectively. The ball is in a position to be caught by the receiver when $y = 0$, that is when

$$\frac{55}{2}t - 16t^2 = 0$$

or $t = 55/32$.

a) At this instant the horizontal displacement of the ball is

$$x\left(\frac{55}{2}\right) = \frac{55\sqrt{3}}{2} \cdot \frac{55}{32} = \frac{(55)^2\sqrt{3}}{64}.$$

b) The receiver has $(55/32) \approx 1.72$ seconds after the ball is released to have covered the $\dfrac{(55)^2 \sqrt{3}}{64}$ ft (≈ 27.28 yards).

29. A Saab 37 Viggen multi-mission combat aircraft is capable of going from stationary on the ground to a speed of Mach 2 (approximately 1330 mph) and an altitude of 32,000 feet in 1 min 40 sec. Assuming the acceleration is a constant vector over this time period, derive the motion equations for this aircraft.

SOLUTION: The coordinate system is set up so that the origin is at the point where the aircraft begins its ascent, and the x-axis is along the ground directly beneath the path of the aircraft. The path is described by the vector-valued function $\mathbf{r}(t)$ to be determined. The initial position is $\mathbf{r}(0) = \vec{0}$, and since all the motion is due to the thrust, the initial velocity is zero, $\mathbf{v}(0) = \vec{0}$.

The acceleration is known to be a constant $\mathbf{a}_0 = a_x\,\mathbf{i} + a_y\,\mathbf{j}$. The equation describing acceleration along the path,

$$\frac{d^2\,\mathbf{r}}{dt^2} = \mathbf{a}_0,$$

can be integrated twice with respect to t to obtain

$$\mathbf{v}(t) = \mathbf{a}_0 t + \mathbf{v}(0) \qquad \text{and} \qquad \mathbf{r}(t) = \mathbf{a}_0 \frac{t^2}{2} + \mathbf{v}(0)t + \mathbf{r}(0).$$

Since $\mathbf{r}(0) = \vec{0}$ and $\mathbf{v}(0) = \vec{0}$ the position vector is

(i)
$$\mathbf{r}(t) = \frac{t^2}{2}\,\mathbf{a}_0 = \frac{t^2}{2}a_x\,\mathbf{i} + \frac{t^2}{2}\,a_y\,\mathbf{j}.$$

The velocity is given by

$$\mathbf{v}(t) = ta_x\,\mathbf{i} + ta_y\,\mathbf{j}.$$

Thus, the speed is

(ii)
$$v(t) = \sqrt{(ta_x)^2 + (ta_y)^2} = |t|\,\sqrt{a_x{}^2 + a_y{}^2}.$$

The given information is that when $t = 100$ sec, the speed is

(iii)
$$v(100) = 1330\left(\frac{\text{mi}}{\text{hr}}\right) \cdot \left(\frac{5280\,\text{ft}}{\text{mi}}\right) \cdot \left(\frac{1\,\text{hr}}{3600\,\text{sec}}\right)$$

and the altitude is

(iv)
$$y = 32,000\,\text{ft}.$$

The altitude given by the **j**-component of $\mathbf{r}(t)$ in formula (i) is

$$y(t) = \frac{t^2}{2}a_y$$

so equating this value at $t = 100$ with the value 32,000 ft gives

$$\frac{(100)^2}{2}\,a_y = 32,000 \qquad \text{or} \qquad a_y = \frac{6.4 \times 10^4}{10^4} = 6.4\,.$$

The speed in formula (ii) at $t = 100$ is equated to the value in (iii) to get

$$100\sqrt{a_x{}^2 + a_y{}^2} = \frac{1.33 \times 5.28}{3.6} \times 10^3 \qquad \text{or} \qquad a_x{}^2 + a_y{}^2 \approx (1.951 \times 10)^2.$$

The value $a_y = 6.4$ implies that

$$a_x \approx \sqrt{(1.951)^2 \times 10^2 - (6.4)^2} \approx 18.430.$$

Insert these values into formula (i) to obtain the position vector

$$\mathbf{r}(t) = \frac{18.430}{2}t^2\,\mathbf{i} + \frac{6.4}{2}t^2\,\mathbf{j} = 9.215t^2\,\mathbf{i} + 3.2t^2\,\mathbf{j}.$$

COMMENT: This problem is different from most others in the section in that the acceleration is not due to gravity but to the thrust provided by the jet engines. Nonetheless, the procedure of integrating the (unknown) acceleration twice with respect to t and of introducing the implied initial velocity and position results in a position vector for the motion whose exact value may be determined from the given data.

_____12.5

Curvature

5. Find the curvature at the point $(0,0,0)$ of the curve $\mathbf{r}(t) = 2t\,\mathbf{i} + t^2\,\mathbf{j} + 5t^3\,\mathbf{k}$.

SOLUTION: The simplest way to calculate the curvature in this problem is to use Formula 12.34 from the text.

$$K(t) = \|\mathbf{K}(t)\| = \frac{\|\mathbf{v}(t) \times \mathbf{a}(t)\|}{|v(t)|^3}.$$

The velocity, speed and acceleration are

$$\mathbf{v}(t) = 2\,\mathbf{i} + 2t\,\mathbf{j} + 15t^2\,\mathbf{k}$$

$$v(t) = \sqrt{2^2 + (2t)^2 + (15t^2)^2} = \sqrt{4 + 4t^2 + 225t^4}$$

and $$\mathbf{a}(t) = 2\,\mathbf{j} + 30t\,\mathbf{k}.$$

The point (0,0,0) at which curvature is desired occurs for $\mathbf{r}(t)$ when $t = 0$; from the above the velocity, speed and acceleration at $t = 0$ are

$$\mathbf{v}(0) = 2\,\mathbf{i}, \qquad v(0) = 2, \qquad \mathbf{a}(0) = 2\,\mathbf{j}.$$

The cross product is

$$\mathbf{v}(0) \times \mathbf{a}(0) = (2\,\mathbf{i}) \times (2\,\mathbf{j}) = 4\,\mathbf{k},$$

so the curvature at the point (0,0,0) is

$$K(0) = \frac{\|4\,\mathbf{k}\|}{|2|^3} = \frac{1}{2}.$$

13. For the curve with position vector given by $\mathbf{r}(t) = 3\cos t\,\mathbf{i} + 2\sin t\,\mathbf{j} + t\,\mathbf{k}$,
   a) find the curvature and radius of curvature at $\pi/2$, and
   b) sketch the curve.

SOLUTION: a)   Formula 12.34 from the text is again used for curvature.

Differentiate $\mathbf{r}(t) = 3\cos t\,\mathbf{i} + 2\sin t\,\mathbf{j} + t\,\mathbf{k}$ to obtain $\mathbf{v}(t) = -3\sin t\,\mathbf{i} + 2\cos t\,\mathbf{j} + \mathbf{k}$

and $\mathbf{a}(t) = -3\cos t\,\mathbf{i} - 2\sin t\,\mathbf{j}$ with

$$v(t) = \sqrt{(-3\sin t)^2 + (2\cos t)^2 + 1^2} = \sqrt{9\sin^2 t + 4\cos^2 t + 1}.$$

Evaluated at $t = \pi/2$, these become $\mathbf{v}(\pi/2) = -3\,\mathbf{i} + \mathbf{k}$, $\mathbf{a}(\pi/2) = -2\,\mathbf{j}$, and $v(\pi/2) = \sqrt{10}$. The cross product of $\mathbf{v}$ and $\mathbf{a}$,

$$\mathbf{v}\left(\frac{\pi}{2}\right) \times \mathbf{a}\left(\frac{\pi}{2}\right) = \begin{vmatrix} \mathbf{i} & \mathbf{j} & \mathbf{k} \\ -3 & 0 & 1 \\ 0 & -2 & 0 \end{vmatrix} = 2\,\mathbf{i} + 6\,\mathbf{k},$$

has magnitude $\left\| \mathbf{v}\left(\frac{\pi}{2}\right) \times \mathbf{a}\left(\frac{\pi}{2}\right) \right\| = \sqrt{2^2 + 6^2} = \sqrt{40}$, so the curvature at $t = \pi/2$ is

$$K\left(\frac{\pi}{2}\right) = \frac{\left\| \mathbf{v}\left(\frac{\pi}{2}\right) \times \mathbf{a}\left(\frac{\pi}{2}\right) \right\|}{\left(v\left(\frac{\pi}{2}\right)\right)^{3/2}} = \frac{\sqrt{40}}{(\sqrt{10})^3} = \frac{1}{5}.$$

Since the radius of curvature is the reciprocal of the curvature, $\rho(\pi/2) = 5$.

b)   To graph this curve, notice that the parametric equations

$$x(t) = 3\cos t, \quad y(t) = 2\sin t, \quad \text{and} \quad z = t$$

satisfy the equation

$$\frac{x^2}{9} + \frac{y^2}{4} = 1$$

so this curve lies above the ellipse with this equation in the xy-plane. As t increases, the z-coordinate also increases, so the curve is an elliptic spiral. The point where $t = \pi/2$ is plotted; notice that the curvature is slight at that point.

$$\mathbf{r}(t) = 3\cos t\,\mathbf{i} + 2\sin t\,\mathbf{j} + t\,\mathbf{k}$$

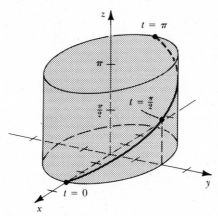

19. Determine the curvature vector for the curve $\mathbf{r}(t) = 3\cos t\,\mathbf{i} + 2\sin t\,\mathbf{j} + t\,\mathbf{k}$ at the point where $t = \pi/2$.

SOLUTION: As was shown in the SOLUTION to EXERCISE 13 above, $\mathbf{v}(t) = -3\sin t\,\mathbf{i} + 2\cos t\,\mathbf{j} + \mathbf{k}$ and $v(t) = \sqrt{9\sin^2 t + 4\cos^2 t + 1}$, so the unit tangent vector is

$$\mathbf{T}(t) = \frac{-3\sin t\,\mathbf{i} + 2\cos t\,\mathbf{j} + \mathbf{k}}{\sqrt{9\sin^2 t + 4\cos^2 t + 1}}.$$

Its derivative with respect to t is

$$\frac{d\mathbf{T}}{dt} = \frac{1}{\sqrt{9\sin^2 t + 4\cos^2 t + 1}}(-3\cos t\,\mathbf{i} - 2\sin t\,\mathbf{j})$$

$$- \frac{9\sin t\cos t - 4\cos t\sin t}{(9\sin^2 t + 4\cos^2 t + 1)^{3/2}}(-3\sin t\,\mathbf{i} + 2\cos t\,\mathbf{j} + \mathbf{k}),$$

which has the value at $t = \pi/2$ of $\dfrac{d\mathbf{T}}{dt}\left(\dfrac{\pi}{2}\right) = \dfrac{-2\mathbf{j}}{\sqrt{10}}$.

The curvature vector at $t = \pi/2$ is thus

$$\mathbf{K} = \frac{d\mathbf{T}}{ds} = \frac{1}{ds/dt} \cdot \frac{d\mathbf{T}}{dt} = \frac{1}{\sqrt{10}}\left(\frac{-2\mathbf{j}}{\sqrt{10}}\right) = -\frac{1}{5}\mathbf{j}.$$

23. Find the point(s) on the plane curve described by $\mathbf{r}(t) = 2\cos t\,\mathbf{i} + 3\sin t\,\mathbf{j}$ at which the curvature is zero.

SOLUTION: With $x(t) = 2\cos t$ and $y(t) = 3\sin t$, calculate the derivatives $x'(t) = -2\sin t$, $x''(t) = -2\cos t$, $y'(t) = 3\cos t$ and $y''(t) = -3\sin t$. Formula 12.35 for curvature gives

$$K(t) = \frac{|x'(t)y''(t) - x''(t)y'(t)|}{((x'(t))^2 + (y'(t))^2)^{3/2}} = \frac{|(-2\sin t)(-3\sin t) - (-2\cos t)(3\cos t)|}{((-2\sin t)^2 + (3\cos t)^2)^{3/2}}$$

$$= \frac{|6(\cos^2 t + \sin^2 t)|}{(4\sin^2 t + 9\cos^2 t)^{3/2}} = \frac{6}{(4\sin^2 t + 9\cos^2 t)^{3/2}}.$$

Since the numerator of $K(t)$ never vanishes, there is no point at which the curvature is zero.

25. For the curve in the xy-plane with cartesian equation $y = \ln x$,
   a)   write the curve in parametric form, and
   b)   find the curvature and radius of curvature at the point where $x = 1$.

SOLUTION: a)   One possible set of parametric equations is obtained by letting

$$x = t \quad\text{and}\quad y = \ln t \quad\text{for}\quad 0 < t.$$

b)   Apply Formula 12.35 from the text with

$$x'(t) = 1, \quad x''(t) = 0, \quad y'(t) = \frac{1}{t} \quad\text{and}\quad y''(t) = -\frac{1}{t^2}$$

to obtain the value for the curvature

$$K(t) = \frac{|x'(t)y''(t) - x''(t)y'(t)|}{\left((x'(t))^2 + (y'(t))^2\right)^{3/2}} = \frac{\left|1 \cdot \left(-\dfrac{1}{t^2}\right) - 0 \cdot \left(\dfrac{1}{t}\right)\right|}{\left((1)^2 + \left(\dfrac{1}{t}\right)^2\right)^{3/2}} = \frac{\dfrac{1}{t^2}}{\dfrac{1}{t^3}(t^2+1)^{3/2}} = \frac{t}{(1+t^2)^{3/2}}.$$

The point where $x = 1$ has parameter value $t = 1$, so the curvature at this point is

$$K(1) = \frac{1}{(1 + 1^2)^{3/2}} = \frac{\sqrt{2}}{4} \quad \text{and} \quad \rho(1) = \frac{1}{K(1)} = 2\sqrt{2}.$$

37. Use the result of EXERCISE 35 to find the curvature and radius of curvature for the curve with equation $y = \ln x$ at $x = 3$.

SOLUTION: If $y = \ln x$, then $\dfrac{dy}{dx} = \dfrac{1}{x}$, and $\dfrac{d^2y}{dx^2} = -\dfrac{1}{x^2}$ so the formula in EXERCISE 35 gives

$$K(x) = \frac{\left| -\dfrac{1}{x^2} \right|}{\left(1 + \left(\dfrac{1}{x} \right)^2 \right)^{3/2}}.$$

At $x = 3$ this is $K(3) = \dfrac{1/9}{(1 + \frac{1}{9})^{3/2}} = \dfrac{3\sqrt{10}}{100}$ and the radius of curvature is

$$\rho(3) = \frac{1}{K(3)} = \frac{10\sqrt{10}}{3}.$$

53. Use the formula in EXERCISE 50 to determine the curvature at $\theta = \pi/2$ of the curve with polar coordinates equation $r = \theta$.

SOLUTION: The formula for curvature in EXERCISE 50 requires the values $f(\theta) = \theta$, $f'(\theta) = 1$, and $f''(\theta) = 0$. Thus,

$$K(\theta) = \frac{\left| (f(\theta))^2 + 2\,(f'(\theta))^2 - f'(\theta) \cdot f''(\theta) \right|}{\left((f(\theta))^2 + (f'(\theta))^2 \right)^{3/2}}$$

$$= \frac{\left| (\theta)^2 + 2(1)^2 - (1)(0) \right|}{((\theta)^2 + (1)^2)^{3/2}} = \frac{2 + \theta^2}{(\theta^2 + 1)^{3/2}}.$$

At $\theta = \pi/2$ the curvature is

$$K\left(\frac{\pi}{2} \right) = \frac{2 + \left(\frac{\pi}{2} \right)^2}{\left(\left(\frac{\pi}{2} \right)^2 + 1 \right)^{3/2}} = \frac{\frac{1}{4}\left(8 + \pi^2 \right)}{\frac{1}{8}\left(\pi^2 + 4 \right)^{3/2}} = 2\frac{\left(\pi^2 + 8 \right)}{\left(\pi^2 + 4 \right)^{3/2}}.$$

_____12.6
Newton's and Kepler's Laws of Motion

3. Determine the magnitude of the acceleration due to the earth's gravity on an object that is above the earth's surface a distance of   a) 1000 km   b) 10,000 km   c) 50,000 km   d) 100,000 km.

SOLUTION: According to Formula 12.37, this magnitude is $a = |\mathbf{a}(t)| = \dfrac{GM}{(r+d)^2}$, where G is the universal gravitational constant, $G = 6.673 \times 10^{-11}$ m^3/kg · s^2; M is the mass of the earth, $M = 5.979 \times 10^{24}$ kg; r is the radius of the earth, $r = 6.371 \times 10^6$ m; and d is the distance above the earth's surface in 10^6 m. With these constants the magnitude of acceleration is

$$a = \frac{3.990}{(6.371 + d)^2} 10^2 \text{ m/sec}^2,$$

and the values for the given distances are as follows:

	(a)	(b)	(c)	(d)
d (10^6 m)	1	10^1	5×10^1	10^2
a (m/sec^2)	7.344	1.489	1.256×10^{-1}	3.526×10^{-2}

7. a) Use the data about the earth given in Table 12.1 to estimate the mass of the sun.
   b) Use the data about Mars to estimate the mass of the sun.

SOLUTION: Kepler's Third Law as stated in Formula 12.45 of the text relates the square of the period, T, of the planets orbit about the sun to the cube of the length, a, of half the major axis of the ellipse describing the orbit, and to the mass of the sun, M:

$$T^2 = \frac{4\pi^2}{GM} a^3.$$

Solve this equation for M to obtain

$$M = \frac{4\pi^2}{G} \frac{a^3}{T^2}.$$

a) The data for the earth from Table 12.1 are $a = 1.496 \times 10^{11}$ m and $T = 3.156 \times 10^7$ sec, so the sun's mass as determined by these data is

$$M = \frac{4(3.142)^2}{(6.673 \times 10^{-11})} \cdot \frac{(1.496 \times 10^{11})^3}{(3.156 \times 10^7)^2} = 1.989 \times 10^{30} \text{ kg}.$$

b) The data for Mars from Table 12.1 are $a = 2.279 \times 10^{11}$ m and $T = 5.936 \times 10^7$ sec, so the sun's mass as determined by these data is

$$M = \frac{4(3.142)^2}{(6.673 \times 10^{-11})} \cdot \frac{(2.279 \times 10^{11})^3}{(5.936 \times 10^7)^2} = 1.988 \times 10^{30} \text{ kg}.$$

17. Complete the steps in this alternative proof of Kepler's Second Law by considering the torque $\vec{\tau}$ and angular momentum **L** produced by the force given by Newton's Law of Gravitation.
a) Show that $\vec{\tau} = \vec{0}$.   b) Show that $\mathbf{L} = m(\mathbf{r} \times \mathbf{v})$ is constant.   c) Show that the area of the triangle in the figure that is generated by changing time by an amount dt is $dA = \frac{1}{2}|\mathbf{r} \times d\mathbf{r}|$, where $d\mathbf{r} = \mathbf{v}\, dt$.

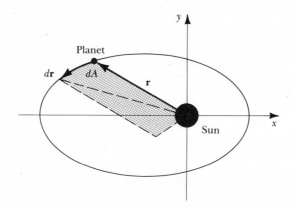

d) Show that $dA/dt = |\mathbf{L}|/2m$.

SOLUTION: a) According to EXERCISE 15, torque is $\vec{\tau} = m(\mathbf{r}(t) \times \mathbf{a}(t))$. Since the acceleration and position vectors are parallel (see Formula 12.37), then their cross product is zero; thus $\vec{\tau} = \vec{0}$.

b) According to EXERCISE 16, the angular momentum $\mathbf{L} = m(\mathbf{r} \times \mathbf{v})$ satisfies $\dfrac{d\mathbf{L}}{dt} = \vec{\tau}$. This implies by part a) that $\dfrac{d\mathbf{L}}{dt} = \vec{0}$ and thus that $\mathbf{L}(t) = \mathbf{c}$, a constant; thus $\mathbf{L} = m(\mathbf{r} \times \mathbf{v})$ is constant.

c) For small time increments the area swept out is approximately that of the indicated triangle with sides $\mathbf{r}$ and $d\mathbf{r}$. Recall from SECTION 11.4 that the area of this triangle is half the magnitude of the cross product of the sides

$$dA = \frac{1}{2}|\mathbf{r} \times d\mathbf{r}|.$$

d) Divide the increment of area by the increment of time and use the differential in part c) for the former. The increment of time can be divided into the magnitude of the cross product and then associated with the increment $d\mathbf{r}$ so that in the limit $\dfrac{dA}{dt} = \dfrac{1}{2}\left|\mathbf{r} \times \dfrac{d\mathbf{r}}{dt}\right|$. By EXERCISE 16, this right hand side is $\frac{1}{2}\left|\mathbf{r} \times \mathbf{v}\right| = \dfrac{1}{2}\left|\dfrac{\mathbf{L}}{m}\right|$ so $\dfrac{dA}{dt} = \dfrac{|\mathbf{L}|}{2m}$.

Since by part b) $\mathbf{L}$ is constant, then it follows that $\dfrac{dA}{dt}$ is constant as is claimed in Kepler's Second Law.

_____Chapter 12

Review Exercises

3. Determine the values of t for which the function $\mathbf{F}(t) = t\,\mathbf{i} + \dfrac{1}{t-1}\mathbf{j} + \mathbf{k}$ is continuous.

SOLUTION: According to DEFINITION 12.4 ii), this function is continuous at each t for which all of the component functions

$$f_1(t) = t, \quad f_2(t) = \frac{1}{t-1}, \quad \text{and} \quad f_3(t) = 1$$

are simultaneously continuous.

The first and last functions are continuous for all t and the second function, $f_2(t) = \dfrac{1}{t-1}$, is continuous for all t except $t = 1$, so the common domain of continuity is the set: $\{t \in \mathbb{R} : t \neq 1\}$.

5. Evaluate the integral $\displaystyle\int_0^\pi (\cos t\,\mathbf{i} + \sin t\,\mathbf{j} + e^t\,\mathbf{k})\,dt$.

SOLUTION: Integrate the vector function by integrating each of the components:

$$\int_0^\pi (\cos t\,\mathbf{i} + \sin t\,\mathbf{j} + e^t\,\mathbf{k})\,dt = \left(\int_0^\pi \cos t\,dt\right)\mathbf{i} + \left(\int_0^\pi \sin t\,dt\right)\mathbf{j} + \left(\int_0^\pi e^t\,dt\right)\mathbf{k}$$

$$= \left([\sin t]\Big|_0^\pi\right)\mathbf{i} + \left([-\cos t]\Big|_0^\pi\right)\mathbf{j} + \left([e^t]\Big|_0^\pi\right)\mathbf{k}$$

$$= (0-0)\,\mathbf{i} + (-(-1)+(1))\,\mathbf{j} + (e^\pi - e^0)\,\mathbf{k} = 2\,\mathbf{j} + (e^\pi - 1)\,\mathbf{k}.$$

9. Evaluate the integral $\displaystyle\int_0^1 (e^t\,\mathbf{i} + t^2\,\mathbf{j})\cdot(t\,\mathbf{i} + \sin t\,\mathbf{k})\,dt$.

SOLUTION: The integrand is a scalar function which must be simplified before the integration can proceed.

$$\int_0^1 (e^t\,\mathbf{i} + t^2\,\mathbf{j})\cdot(t\,\mathbf{i} + \sin t\,\mathbf{k})\,dt = \int_0^1 (te^t + t^2\cdot 0 + 0\cdot\sin t)\,dt = \int_0^1 te^t\,dt.$$

Integrate by parts, with the differentiation applied to the power of t. So

$$\int_0^1 (e^t\mathbf{i} + t^2\mathbf{j}) \cdot (t\mathbf{i} + \sin t\,\mathbf{k})\,dt = \left[te^t - \int e^t\,dt\right]\Bigg|_0^1 = [te^t - e^t]\,\Bigg|_0^1$$

$$= ((1e^1 - e^1) - (0e^0 - e^0)) = 1.$$

13. For the curve $\mathbf{F}(t) = \cos t\,\mathbf{i} + \sin t\,\mathbf{j} + 3\,\mathbf{k}$

  a)   sketch the graph and indicate the direction of increasing t;

  b)   find and sketch $D_t\,\mathbf{F}\left(\dfrac{\pi}{3}\right)$;

  c)   find the principal unit tangent and unit normal vectors at $t = \dfrac{\pi}{3}$ and sketch these vectors;

  d)   find the curvature at $t = \dfrac{\pi}{3}$.

SOLUTION: a)   Parametric equations for this curve are $x(t) = \cos t$, $y(t) = \sin t$, and $z(t) = 3$, so the curve lies in the plane $z = 3$ above the circle $x^2 + y^2 = 1$, $(\cos^2 t + \sin^2 t = 1)$. By plotting a few points, for $t = 0$, $\frac{\pi}{3}$, $\frac{\pi}{2}$, π, $\frac{3\pi}{2}$, one can see that the direction of increasing t is counterclockwise if the curve is viewed from above the plane $z = 3$.

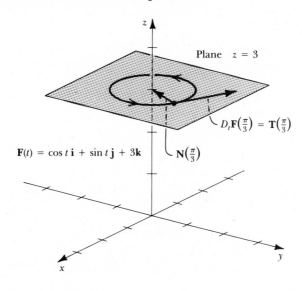

b)   The derivative of $\mathbf{F}(t) = \cos t\,\mathbf{i} + \sin t\,\mathbf{j} + 3\,\mathbf{k}$ is

$$D_t\,\mathbf{F}(t) = -\sin t\,\mathbf{i} + \cos t\,\mathbf{j}$$

which at $t = \pi/3$ is the vector

$$D_t\,\mathbf{F}\left(\frac{\pi}{3}\right) = -\sin\frac{\pi}{3}\mathbf{i} + \cos\frac{\pi}{3}\mathbf{j} = -\frac{\sqrt{3}}{2}\mathbf{i} + \frac{1}{2}\mathbf{j}.$$

This is illustrated on the graph of the curve at the point corresponding to $t = \dfrac{\pi}{3}$, $\left(\dfrac{1}{2}, \dfrac{\sqrt{3}}{2}, 3\right)$.

c)   From the solution to part b), the derivative of $\mathbf{F}(t)$ is

$$D_t \, \mathbf{F}(t) = -\sin t \, \mathbf{i} + \cos t \, \mathbf{j}.$$

This has magnitude $\|D_t \, \mathbf{F}(t)\| = \sqrt{(-\sin t)^2 + (\cos t)^2} = 1$, so $D_t \, \mathbf{F}(t)$ is the principal unit tangent vector for all t:

$$\mathbf{T}(t) = -\sin t \, \mathbf{i} + \cos t \, \mathbf{j},$$
$$\text{and} \quad D_t \, \mathbf{T}(t) = -\cos t \, \mathbf{i} - \sin t \, \mathbf{j},$$

which is also a unit vector; thus the principal unit normal vector is

$$\mathbf{N}(t) = \frac{D_t \, \mathbf{T}(t)}{\|D_t \, \mathbf{T}(t)\|} = -\cos t \, \mathbf{i} - \sin t \, \mathbf{j}.$$

At the point where $t = \pi/3$ these vectors are

$$\mathbf{T}\left(\frac{\pi}{3}\right) = -\frac{\sqrt{3}}{2}\mathbf{i} + \frac{1}{2}\mathbf{j} \quad \text{and } \mathbf{N}\left(\frac{\pi}{3}\right) = -\frac{1}{2}\mathbf{i} - \frac{\sqrt{3}}{2}\mathbf{j}.$$

These are illustrated above, but notice that $\mathbf{T}(\pi/3) = D_t \, \mathbf{F}(\pi/3)$.

d)   The curvature at any point is

$$K = \frac{\|D_t \, \mathbf{T}(t)\|}{\|D_t \, \mathbf{F}(t)\|} = \frac{\sqrt{(-\cos t)^2 + (-\sin t)^2}}{1} = 1.$$

Observe that since the curve is a circle of radius 1, its curvature is constant at each point and equal to the reciprocal of the radius, so the solution was particularly simple to obtain in this case.

21. Suppose the motion of an object is given by

$$\mathbf{F}(t) = \cos t \, \mathbf{i} + \sin t \, \mathbf{j} + 3 \, \mathbf{k}.$$

Determine the a) velocity, b) speed, and c) acceleration of this object at $a = \pi/3$.

SOLUTION: a)   The velocity of the motion is the derivative of the position vector,

$$\mathbf{v}(t) = D_t[\cos t \, \mathbf{i} + \sin t \, \mathbf{j} + 3 \, \mathbf{k}] = -\sin t \, \mathbf{i} + \cos t \, \mathbf{j} \qquad \mathbf{v}(\pi/3) = -(\sqrt{3}/2)\,\mathbf{i} + (1/2)\,\mathbf{j}.$$

b)   The speed is the magnitude of this velocity,

$$v(t) = \|\mathbf{v}(t)\| = \sqrt{\sin^2 t + \cos^2 t} = 1, \qquad v(\pi/3) = 1.$$

The object moves with unit speed along the circle.

c) The acceleration is the derivative of velocity,

$$\mathbf{a}(t) = D_t[-\sin t\,\mathbf{i} + \cos t\,\mathbf{j}] = -\cos t\,\mathbf{i} - \sin t\,\mathbf{j}, \qquad \mathbf{a}(\pi/3) = -(1/2)\mathbf{i} - (\sqrt{3}/2)\mathbf{j}.$$

27. If $\mathbf{F}(t) = t\,\mathbf{i} + (\ln t)\mathbf{j} + t\,\mathbf{k}$ and $f(t) = t^2$ find, if possible,

  a) $D_t[\mathbf{F} + f](t)$ b) $(D_t f(t))(D_t\,\mathbf{F}(t))$ c) $D_t[f\,\mathbf{F}](t)$ d) $D_t[f \circ \mathbf{F}](t)$
  e) $D_t[\mathbf{F} \circ f](t)$.

SOLUTION: a) The sum of the vector function $\mathbf{F}$ and the scalar function f is undefined so its derivative can't be computed.

b) The derivative $D_t f(t) = 2t$ is a scalar function and the derivative $D_t\,\mathbf{F}(t) = \mathbf{i} + \frac{1}{t}\mathbf{j} + \mathbf{k}$ is a vector function so their product is defined

$$(D_t f(t))(D_t\,\mathbf{F}(t)) = (2t)\cdot\left(\mathbf{i} + \frac{1}{t}\mathbf{j} + \mathbf{k}\right) = 2t\,\mathbf{i} + 2\mathbf{j} + 2t\,\mathbf{k}.$$

c) Use the rule for differentiating the product of scalar and vector functions, THEOREM 12.8 iii),

$$D_t[f\,\mathbf{F}](t) = (D_t f)(t)\,\mathbf{F}(t) + (f(t))\,D_t[\mathbf{F}(t)],$$

to obtain

$$D_t[f\,\mathbf{F}(t)] = (2t)(t\,\mathbf{i} + \ln t\,\mathbf{j} + t\,\mathbf{k}) + (t^2)\left(\mathbf{i} + \frac{1}{t}\mathbf{j} + \mathbf{k}\right).$$

The derivatives $D_t f$ and $D_t\,\mathbf{F}$ were calculated in part b) above. This can be simplified to

$$D_t[f\,\mathbf{F}](t) = 3t^2\,\mathbf{i} + t(2\ln t + 1)\mathbf{j} + 3t^2\,\mathbf{k}.$$

d) The composition of a scalar with a vector function is undefined since the domain of f is scalar not the vector values $\mathbf{F}(t)$. The derivative is undefined.

e) The chain rule, THEOREM 12.8 vi), can be applied to

$$D_t[\mathbf{F} \circ f](t) = (D_t f(t)) \cdot (D_t\,\mathbf{F})(f(t))$$

to obtain

$$D_t[\mathbf{F} \circ f](t) = (2t)\left(\mathbf{i} + \frac{1}{f(t)}\mathbf{j} + \mathbf{k}\right) = 2t\left(\mathbf{i} + \frac{1}{t^2}\mathbf{j} + \mathbf{k}\right) = 2t\,\mathbf{i} + \frac{2}{t}\mathbf{j} + 2t\,\mathbf{k}.$$

31. Find a vector-valued function with arc length as parameter that describes the straight line from $(3, 0, 0)$ to $(2, 7, 5)$.

SOLUTION: Use vector methods of CHAPTER 11 to write parametric equations for the line through the point $P(3, 0, 0)$ with direction $\mathbf{v} = \overrightarrow{PQ} = \langle 2 - 3, 7 - 0, 5 - 0 \rangle = \langle -1, 7, 5 \rangle$ as

$$x(t) = 3 - t, \qquad y(t) = 0 + 7t, \qquad z(t) = 0 + 5t.$$

Note that when $t = 0$, $(x(0), y(0), z(0)) = (3, 0, 0)$, that when $t = 1$, $(x(1), y(1), z(1)) = (2, 7, 5)$, and for $0 < t < 1$, $(x(t), y(t), z(t))$ lies on the desired line segment. A vector function which defines this segment is thus

$$\mathbf{r}(t) = (3 - t)\mathbf{i} + (7t)\mathbf{j} + (5t)\mathbf{k} \qquad 0 \le t \le 1,$$
$$\text{with} \qquad \mathbf{r}'(t) = -\mathbf{i} + 7\mathbf{j} + 5\mathbf{k}.$$

To determine an arc length parameterization of this curve, recall the strategy used to solve EXERCISE 21 of SECTION 12.3.

The arc length of the portion of this curve between points where $\tau = 0$ and t is

$$s(t) = \int_0^t \|\mathbf{r}'(\tau)\| \, d\tau = \int_0^t \sqrt{(-1)^2 + (7)^2 + (5)^2} \, d\tau = \int_0^t 5\sqrt{3} \, d\tau = 5\sqrt{3}\,t.$$

The total length of this curve between points where $t = 0$ and $t = 1$ is $s = 5\sqrt{3}$.

For any s such that $0 \le s \le 5\sqrt{3}$ the value of the parameter t for which s is the length of arc between the points $t = 0$ and t is obtained by solving $s = 5\sqrt{3}\,t$ for t in terms of s:

$$t = \frac{s}{5\sqrt{3}}.$$

If this expression is used in place of t in the formula for $\mathbf{r}$, you then have that the arc length parameterization of the line segment, $0 \le s \le 5\sqrt{3}$, is

$$\mathbf{r}(s) = \left(3 - \frac{s}{5\sqrt{3}}\right)\mathbf{i} + \left(7\frac{s}{5\sqrt{3}}\right)\mathbf{j} + \left(5\frac{s}{5\sqrt{3}}\right)\mathbf{k} = \left(\frac{15\sqrt{3} - s}{5\sqrt{3}}\right)\mathbf{i} + \left(\frac{7s}{5\sqrt{3}}\right)\mathbf{j} + \left(\frac{s}{\sqrt{3}}\right)\mathbf{k}.$$

33. Find the radius of curvature of the parabola $y = x^2$ at $(0, 0)$.

SOLUTION: Calculate the curvature by first parameterizing this plane curve by

$$x(t) = t, \qquad \text{and} \qquad y(t) = t^2$$

then applying Formula 12.35 from the text,

$$K(t) = \frac{|x'(t)y''(t) - x''(t)y'(t)|}{\left((x'(t))^2 + (y'(t))^2\right)^{3/2}}.$$

For this formula $x'(t) = 1$, $x''(t) = 0$, $y'(t) = 2t$, and $y''(t) = 2$ so

$$K(t) = \frac{|1 \cdot (2) - 0 \cdot (2t)|}{((1)^2 + (2t)^2)^{3/2}} = \frac{2}{(1 + 4t^2)^{3/2}}.$$

The point (0,0) occurs for this parameterization when $t = 0$ so the curvature at this point is

$$K = \frac{2}{(1 + 0)^{3/2}} = 2,$$

and the radius of curvature is its reciprocal $\rho = 1/2$.

39. A projectile is fired from a height of 200 feet with an initial speed of 400 feet/sec at an angle of elevation of $\pi/6$ radians. Describe the subsequent motion of the projectile and find:
a) the time in the air   b) the maximum height
c) the horizontal range   d) the speed at the instant of impact.

SOLUTION: Place a rectangular coordinate system with origin directly below the point of release and with x-axis along the ground directly under the path of motion of the object. The path of motion is given by

$$\mathbf{r}(t) = x(t)\,\mathbf{i} + y(t)\,\mathbf{j}$$

with $\mathbf{r}(0) = 200\,\mathbf{j}$, $\mathbf{v}(0) = 400(\cos(\pi/6)\,\mathbf{i} + \sin(\pi/6)\,\mathbf{j})$ and $\mathbf{a}(t) = -32$ (all measured in feet and seconds.)

Integrate the acceleration twice with respect to t and use the initial conditions to determine constants of integration to describe the motion of the object

$$\mathbf{r}(t) = -32\frac{t^2}{2}\,\mathbf{j} + \left(400\left(\frac{\sqrt{3}}{2}\,\mathbf{i} + \frac{1}{2}\,\mathbf{j}\right)\right)t + (200\,\mathbf{j}) = \left((200\sqrt{3})t\right)\,\mathbf{i} + \left(200 + 200t - 16t^2\right)\,\mathbf{j}.$$

Questions a), c), and d) involve determining when, where, and at what speed the projectile strikes the ground. Find the time, t_f, for which

$$y(t_f) = (200 + 200t_f - 16t_f^2) = 0.$$

Use the quadratic formula to solve for the positive root of this equation

$$t_f = \frac{-200 \pm \sqrt{(200)^2 + 4 \cdot 200 \cdot 16}}{-32} = \frac{-200 \pm 40\sqrt{33}}{-32}.$$

Take the negative sign above so that $t_f > 0$. The time when the projectile strikes the ground is

$$t_f = \frac{25 + 5\sqrt{33}}{4} \approx 13.4 \text{ seconds.}$$

c)   The horizontal range is

$$x(t_f) = 200\sqrt{3}\,t_f = 200\sqrt{3}\left(\frac{25 + 5\sqrt{33}}{4}\right) = 1250\sqrt{3} + 750\sqrt{11} \approx 4652.5\,\text{feet}.$$

d)   The velocity at each t is obtained by differentiating $\mathbf{r}(t)$ with respect to t

$$\mathbf{v}(t) = (200\sqrt{3})\,\mathbf{i} + (200 - 32t)\,\mathbf{j}$$

so the speed at each t is

$$v(t) = \sqrt{(200\sqrt{3})^2 + (200 - 32t)^2}\,.$$

At the instant t_f when the projectile strikes the ground,

$$v(t_f) = \sqrt{(200\sqrt{3})^2 + \left(200 - 32\left(\frac{25 + 5\sqrt{33}}{4}\right)\right)^2} = \sqrt{(200)^2 \cdot 3 + (40)^2 \cdot 33} = 240\sqrt{3}\,\text{ft/sec}.$$

b)   The maximum height is the maximum value of

$$y(t) = 200 + 200t - 16t^2.$$

The maximum occurs at a critical point t_0 where

$$y'(t) = 200 - 32t = 0.$$

That is, $t_0 = \dfrac{200}{32} = \dfrac{25}{4}$. Since $y''(t_0) = -32 < 0$, this is a maximum so the maximum height is

$$y\left(\frac{25}{4}\right) = 200 + 200 \cdot \frac{25}{4} - 16\left(\frac{25}{4}\right)^2 = 825\,\text{feet}.$$

13
Multivariable Functions

Sharpening your skills

You should review the graphing of equations in a Cartesian coordinate system; especially the graphing of conic sections from CHAPTER 10. You should recall the definition of polar coordinates and the graphs of polar equations from CHAPTER 9. Recall the definition of a three-dimensional Cartesian coordinate system and the material on graphing planes and lines from CHAPTER 11.

The section numbers in the practice problems below refer to places in the text where the tools are introduced.

Practice Problems

1. Identify the equation and sketch its graph.   a) $y - x^2 = 0$,   b) $9x^2 + 4y^2 = 36$,
   c) $9x^2 - y^2 + 4 = 0$. (See SECTIONS 10.1–10.4)

2. a) Plot the points with polar coordinates $(r, \theta) =$ i) $\left(1, \frac{\pi}{3}\right)$, ii) $\left(-2, \frac{5\pi}{4}\right)$, iii) $\left(\sqrt{2}, -\frac{47\pi}{6}\right)$.
   b) Find the Cartesian coordinates of these points.

3. Sketch the graphs of the polar equations   a) $r = 2$,   b) $\theta = \pi/3$,   c) $r = 3\cos\theta$.

4. Sketch the graph of the plane with equation $3x + 6y + 2z = 6$.

5. Sketch the graph of the line with symmetric equations $x - 1 = y - 2$, $z = 3$.

_____13.1

Functions of
Several Variables

1. If $f(x, y) = x^2 + y$, find
     a) $f(1, 0)$ b) $f(-1, -1)$ c) $f(\sqrt{3}, 2)$

SOLUTION: a) Replace x by 1 and y by 0 in the rule for $f(x, y)$ to get $f(1, 0) = (1)^2 + 0 = 1$.
b) Similarly, $f(-1, -1) = (-1)^2 + (-1) = 1 + (-1) = 0$ and   c) $f(\sqrt{3}, 2) = (\sqrt{3})^2 + 2 = 3 + 2 = 5$.

9. Find the domain of the function $f(x, y, z) = \sqrt{4 - x^2 - y^2 - z^2}$.

SOLUTION: The natural domain consists of all (x, y, z) for which the quantity under the radical is not negative; that is,

$$\{(x, y, z) : 4 - x^2 - y^2 - z^2 \geq 0\}.$$

Simplify this inequality to obtain

$$\text{Domain } (f) = \{(x, y, z) : x^2 + y^2 + z^2 \leq 4\}.$$

This is the ball of radius 2 centered at the origin.

13. For the function $f(x, y) = 4 - x^2 - y^2$ find $\dfrac{f(x + h, y) - f(x, y)}{h}$ and $\dfrac{f(x, y + k) - f(x, y)}{k}$ for constants h and k.

SOLUTION: Replace x by $x + h$ and y by $y + k$ in $f(x, y)$ successively to obtain

$$\begin{aligned}
f(x + h, y) &= 4 - (x + h)^2 - y^2 \\
&= 4 - x^2 - 2xh - h^2 - y^2 \qquad \text{and}
\end{aligned}$$

$$\begin{aligned}
f(x, y + k) &= 4 - x^2 - (y + k)^2 \\
&= 4 - x^2 - y^2 - 2ky - k^2.
\end{aligned}$$

The difference quotients are thus

$$\begin{aligned}
\frac{f(x + h, y) - f(x, y)}{h} &= \frac{(4 - x^2 - 2xh - h^2 - y^2) - (4 - x^2 - y^2)}{h} \\
&= \frac{-2xh - h^2}{h} = -2x - h \qquad \text{and}
\end{aligned}$$

$$\begin{aligned}
\frac{f(x, y + k) - f(x, y)}{k} &= \frac{(4 - x^2 - y^2 - 2ky - k^2) - (4 - x^2 - y^2)}{k} \\
&= \frac{-2ky - k^2}{k} = -2y - k.
\end{aligned}$$

15. Find $f \circ g$ if $g(x, y, z) = 2xy + 4xz + 6yz$ and $f(x) = 2x$.

SOLUTION: The domain of $f \circ g$ consists of all points in the domain of g whose values after being mapped by g lie in the domain of f. Since the domain of g is all of $\mathbb{R}^3$ and the domain of

f is all of $\mathbb{R}$, there is no restriction on the domain of $f \circ g$. For any $(x, y, z) \in \mathbb{R}^3$,

$$f \circ g(x, y, z) = f\left(g(x, y, z)\right) = 2 \cdot g(x, y, z) = 2(2xy + 4xz + 6yz) = 4xy + 8xz + 12yz.$$

_____**13.2**

Functions of Two Variables: Level Curves

7. Sketch the level curves of $f(x, y) = \ln(x + y)$ for $c = 0, 1$.

SOLUTION: The level curve is the set of those points whose coordinates satisfy the equation $\ln(x + y) = c$. Exponentiate both sides of this equation to obtain the equivalent equation $x + y = e^c$. The level curve is thus a line whose x and y intercepts are both e^c.

In particular, if $c = 0$ the level curve is $x + y = e^0 = 1$, and if $c = 1$ the level curve is $x + y = e^1 = e$.

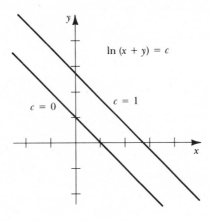

11. Sketch the graph of $f(x, y) = x + y - 2$.

SOLUTION: The graph of f is the set in $\mathbb{R}^3$ $\{(x, y, z) : z = x + y - 2\}$. Since the equation is linear, it can be put into the form for a plane as was described in CHAPTER 11, $x + y - z = 2$. This plane has x, y, and z intercepts at $(2, 0, 0)$, $(0, 2, 0)$ and $(0, 0, -2)$ respectively (see EXERCISE 38, SECTION 11.5); these intercepts and the triangle containing them are sketched.

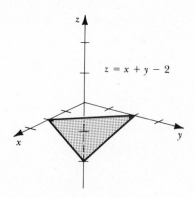

21. Sketch the graph of $f(x,y) = \begin{cases} x^2 + y^2, & \text{if } x^2 + y^2 \leq 9 \\ 0, & \text{if } x^2 + y^2 > 9. \end{cases}$

SOLUTION: The graph of f is the set in $\mathbb{R}^3$

$$\{(x,y,z) : z = x^2 + y^2 \text{ if } x^2 + y^2 \leq 9, \text{ and } z = 0 \text{ if } x^2 + y^2 > 9\}.$$

This set has two components,

i) the points where $z = x^2 + y^2$ when $x^2 + y^2 \leq 9$ and

ii) the points where $z = 0$ when $x^2 + y^2 > 9$.

The second component consists of the part of the xy-plane outside a circle of radius 3 centered at the origin.

The first component consists of the part of the circular paraboloid (see EXAMPLE 2 in SECTION 13.2 of the text) which lies over the inside of the circle of radius 3 mentioned above.

These two components are sketched.

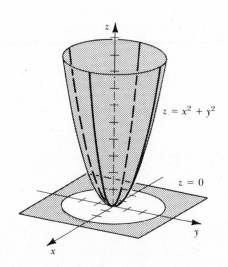

25. The elevation of a mountain above a point (x, y) in the base plane is described by $E(x, y) = 200 - x^2 - 4y^2$. Sketch the curves of constant elevation for $E = 0$, $E = 100$, $E = 150$, $E = 200$.

SOLUTION: The curves of constant elevation E have equations

$$200 - x^2 - 4y^2 = E \qquad \text{or equivalently}$$
$$x^2 + 4y^2 = 200 - E.$$

So long as $E < 200$, this graph is an ellipse with equation

$$\frac{x^2}{\left(\sqrt{200 - E}\right)^2} + \frac{y^2}{\left(\dfrac{\sqrt{200 - E}}{2}\right)^2} = 1.$$

This ellipse has center at $(0,0)$ and major and minor axes the x and y axes respectively. The major vertices are at $(\pm\sqrt{200 - E}, 0)$ and the minor vertices are at $\left(0, \pm(\sqrt{200 - E}/2)\right)$. Notice that these all have the same eccentricity. The ellipses corresponding to E-values 0, 100, and 150 are sketched below.

When $E = 200$ the "curve" has equation $x^2 + 4y^2 = 0$, so the level set consists of the single point $(0,0)$. This is also illustrated below corresponding to the E-value 200.

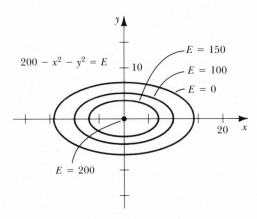

_____13.3

Functions of Three Variables:
Level Surfaces

3. Describe the level surfaces of the function $f(x, y, z) = z - x - y$.

SOLUTION: The level surfaces are the sets in $\mathbb{R}^3$

$$\{(x, y, z) : z - x - y = c\}.$$

Each is a plane with normal $\mathbf{N} = \langle -1, -1, 1 \rangle$ and with z-intercept $(0, 0, c)$. Several of these parallel planes are sketched.

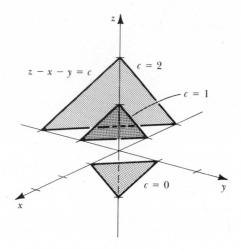

15. Sketch the graph of the right cylinder perpendicular to the xz-plane whose equation is $|z| = |x|$.

SOLUTION: Both sides of the equation $|z| = |x|$ are squared to yield the new equation $z^2 = x^2$ or $z^2 - x^2 = 0$. This can be simplified to the alternatives $z = x$ or $z = -x$ which are equivalent to the original set of equations. Each of these represents a line in the xz-plane which if extended along the y-axis yields a plane. These lines and the resulting planes are illustrated.

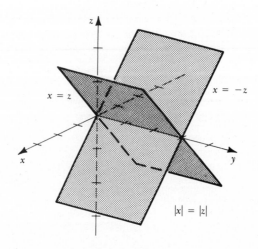

17. Suppose that C is a curve in the xy-plane described by $y = f(x)$, where $x \geq 0$, $y \geq 0$.

a) Show that (x, y, z) lies on the surface generated by revolving C about the y-axis precisely when $y = f(\sqrt{x^2 + z^2})$.

SOLUTION: a) The point with coordinates $(\tilde{x}, \tilde{y}, \tilde{z})$ lies on the surface only if the plane $y = \tilde{y}$ intersects the surface in a circle containing $(\tilde{x}, \tilde{y}, \tilde{z})$ which passes through the point in the xy-plane $(x_0, y_0, 0)$ with $y_0 = \tilde{y}$, so

(1) $$f(x_0) = \tilde{y} \quad \text{(see the figure below)}.$$

The radius of this circle is x_0, so if the circle is to contain $(\tilde{x}, \tilde{y}, \tilde{z})$ then

(2) $$\sqrt{(\tilde{x})^2 + (\tilde{y})^2} = x_0.$$

From (1) and (2), $(\tilde{x}, \tilde{y}, \tilde{z})$ must satisfy

$$f\left(\sqrt{(\tilde{x})^2 + (\tilde{z})^2}\right) = \tilde{y}.$$

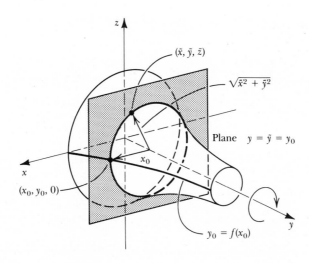

21. a) Use the results of EXERCISE 17 to find the equation of the surface $y = x^2$, $x \geq 0$ revolved about the y-axis.

SOLUTION: a) By the formula in part a) of EXERCISE 17, with $f(x) = x^2$, the equation of the surface of revolution is $y = \left(\sqrt{x^2 + z^2}\right)^2$ or $y = x^2 + z^2$. Its graph is a paraboloid which opens along the y-axis.

Equation	Traces: $\dfrac{\text{values of } k}{\text{curve}}$			Name	Graphical Example
	plane $x = k$	plane $y = k$	plane $z = k$		
$\dfrac{x^2}{a^2} + \dfrac{y^2}{b^2} + \dfrac{z^2}{c^2} = 1$	$\dfrac{\lvert k \rvert < a}{\text{ellipse}}$	$\dfrac{\lvert k \rvert < b}{\text{ellipse}}$	$\dfrac{\lvert k \rvert < c}{\text{ellipse}}$	ellipsoid	13.23
$\dfrac{x^2}{a^2} + \dfrac{y^2}{b^2} - \dfrac{z^2}{c^2} = 1$	$\dfrac{k \neq a}{\text{hyperbola}}$	$\dfrac{k \neq b}{\text{hyperbola}}$	$\dfrac{\text{all } k}{\text{ellipse}}$	hyperboloid of one sheet	13.24
$\dfrac{x^2}{a^2} - \dfrac{y^2}{b^2} + \dfrac{z^2}{c^2} = 1$	$\dfrac{k \neq a}{\text{hyperbola}}$	$\dfrac{\text{all } k}{\text{ellipse}}$	$\dfrac{k \neq c}{\text{hyperbola}}$		
$-\dfrac{x^2}{a^2} + \dfrac{y^2}{b^2} + \dfrac{z^2}{c^2} = 1$	$\dfrac{\text{all } k}{\text{ellipse}}$	$\dfrac{k \neq b}{\text{hyperbola}}$	$\dfrac{k \neq c}{\text{hyperbola}}$		
$\dfrac{x^2}{a^2} - \dfrac{y^2}{b^2} - \dfrac{z^2}{c^2} = 1$	$\dfrac{\lvert k \rvert > a}{\text{ellipse}}$	$\dfrac{\text{all } k}{\text{hyperbola}}$	$\dfrac{\text{all } k}{\text{hyperbola}}$	hyperboloid of two sheets	13.25
$-\dfrac{x^2}{a^2} - \dfrac{y^2}{b^2} + \dfrac{z^2}{c^2} = 1$	$\dfrac{\text{all } k}{\text{hyperbola}}$	$\dfrac{\text{all } k}{\text{hyperbola}}$	$\dfrac{\lvert k \rvert > c}{\text{ellipse}}$		
$-\dfrac{x^2}{a^2} + \dfrac{y^2}{b^2} - \dfrac{z^2}{c^2} = 1$	$\dfrac{\text{all } k}{\text{hyperbola}}$	$\dfrac{\lvert k \rvert > b}{\text{ellipse}}$	$\dfrac{\text{all } k}{\text{hyperbola}}$		
$\dfrac{x^2}{a^2} + \dfrac{y^2}{b^2} - \dfrac{z^2}{c^2} = 0$	$\dfrac{k = 0}{\text{lines}}$	$\dfrac{k = 0}{\text{lines}}$	$\dfrac{k \neq 0}{\text{ellipse}}$		
$\dfrac{x^2}{a^2} - \dfrac{y^2}{b^2} + \dfrac{z^2}{c^2} = 0$	$\dfrac{k = 0}{\text{lines}}$	$\dfrac{k \neq 0}{\text{ellipse}}$	$\dfrac{k = 0}{\text{lines}}$	elliptic cone	13.30 b)
$-\dfrac{x^2}{a^2} + \dfrac{y^2}{b^2} + \dfrac{z^2}{c^2} = 0$	$\dfrac{k \neq 0}{\text{ellipse}}$	$\dfrac{k = 0}{\text{lines}}$	$\dfrac{k = 0}{\text{lines}}$		
$\dfrac{x^2}{a^2} + \dfrac{y^2}{b^2} - cz = 0$	$\dfrac{\text{all } k}{\text{parabola}}$	$\dfrac{\text{all } k}{\text{parabola}}$	$\dfrac{ck > 0}{\text{ellipse}}$		
$\dfrac{x^2}{a^2} - by + \dfrac{z^2}{c^2} = 0$	$\dfrac{\text{all } k}{\text{parabola}}$	$\dfrac{bk > 0}{\text{ellipse}}$	$\dfrac{\text{all } k}{\text{parabola}}$	elliptic paraboloid	13.26
$-ax + \dfrac{y^2}{b^2} + \dfrac{z^2}{c^2} = 0$	$\dfrac{ak > 0}{\text{ellipse}}$	$\dfrac{\text{all } k}{\text{parabola}}$	$\dfrac{\text{all } k}{\text{parabola}}$		
$\dfrac{x^2}{a^2} - \dfrac{y^2}{b^2} - cz = 0$	$\dfrac{\text{all } k}{\text{parabola}}$	$\dfrac{\text{all } k}{\text{parabola}}$	$\dfrac{k \neq 0}{\text{hyperbola}}$		
$\dfrac{x^2}{a^2} - by - \dfrac{z^2}{c^2} = 0$	$\dfrac{\text{all } k}{\text{parabola}}$	$\dfrac{k \neq 0}{\text{hyperbola}}$	$\dfrac{\text{all } k}{\text{parabola}}$	hyperbolic paraboloid	13.27
$-ax + \dfrac{y^2}{b^2} - \dfrac{z^2}{c^2} = 0$	$\dfrac{k \neq 0}{\text{hyperbola}}$	$\dfrac{\text{all } k}{\text{parabola}}$	$\dfrac{\text{all } k}{\text{parabola}}$		

_____13.4

Quadric Surfaces
_____

COMMENT: To graph the quadric surfaces in EXERCISES 1–22 use the table on the preceding page based on the formulas given in SECTION 13.4 of the text to identify the name of the surface and to find an example of a graph of this type; then sketch the traces indicated to provide the outline of your graph.

1. Name and sketch the surface with equation $\dfrac{x^2}{9} + \dfrac{y^2}{4} + \dfrac{z^2}{16} = 1$.

SOLUTION: From the table this is an ellipsoid.

Its traces are sketched in the appropriate planes in Figure i below. For $x = 0$, the trace $\dfrac{y^2}{4} + \dfrac{z^2}{16} = 1$ is an ellipse. For $y = 0$, $\dfrac{x^2}{9} + \dfrac{z^2}{16} = 1$ is an ellipse, and for $z = 0$, $\dfrac{x^2}{9} + \dfrac{y^2}{4} = 1$ is also an ellipse.

Figure ii shows the outline of the ellipsoid with hidden lines dashed.

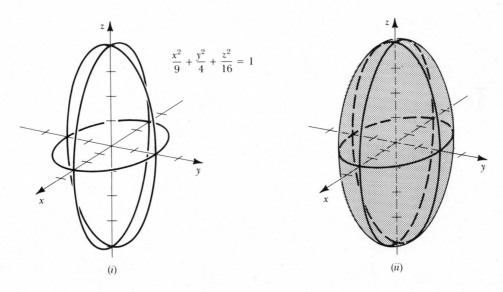

$$\frac{x^2}{9} + \frac{y^2}{4} + \frac{z^2}{16} = 1$$

(i)   (ii)

5. Name and sketch the surface with equation $x^2 - 4y^2 - 9z^2 = 36$.

SOLUTION: The equivalent equation in appropriate form for our table is

$$\frac{x^2}{36} - \frac{y^2}{9} - \frac{z^2}{4} = 1.$$

Here the two negative signs indicate that the surface is a hyperboloid of two sheets.

The traces $y = 0$ and $z = 0$ corresponding to the terms with negative coefficients are sketched below. Some traces corresponding to the term with positive coefficient can be traced, but they must correspond to fixing values of x with $|x| > 6$.

For $y = 0$ the trace $\dfrac{x^2}{36} - \dfrac{z^2}{4} = 1$ is a hyperbola, and for $z = 0$, $\dfrac{x^2}{36} - \dfrac{y^2}{9} = 1$ is also a hyperbola. For $x = \pm 8$ (arbitrarily chosen), the trace

$$\frac{64}{36} - \frac{y^2}{9} - \frac{z^2}{4} = 1 \qquad \text{or equivalently}$$

$$\frac{y^2}{7} + \frac{z^2}{28/9} = 1, \qquad \text{is an ellipse.}$$

These four traces are drawn in Figure i and the surface is completed in ii by the addition of outlines and dashed hidden lines.

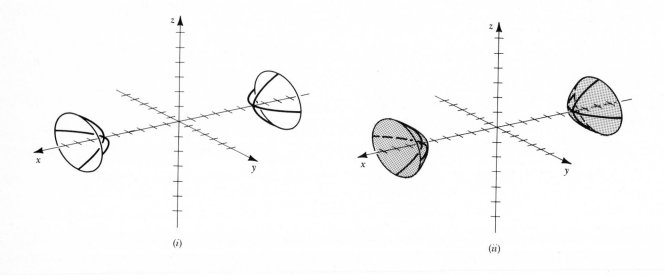

(i)   (ii)

9. Name and sketch the graph with equation $z = x^2 - 4y^2$.

SOLUTION: Since the only two quadratic terms involve x^2 and y^2 with opposite signs, and since z enters in linearly, this surface is a hyperbolic paraboloid.

The trace for $x = 0$ is $z = -4y^2$, a parabola which opens down in the yz-plane. The trace for $y = 0$ is $z = x^2$, a parabola which opens up in the xz-plane. These are illustrated in Figure i below.

The traces for nonzero values of z are hyperbolas; for $z = 1$ the curves are

$$x^2 - 4y^2 = 1$$

while for $z = -1$ they are

$$x^2 - 4y^2 = -1 \qquad \text{or}$$
$$4y^2 - x^2 = 1,$$

a hyperbola which is "complementary" to the one given earlier. These two hyperbolas are sketched in Figure ii.

The trick in drawing the saddle surface is to connect the "endpoints" of the hyperbolas lying in opposite planes. This is done in Figure iii and hidden lines are dashed.

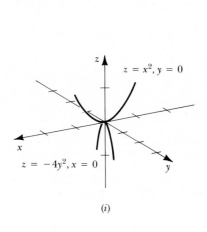

(i)

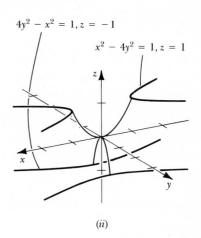

(ii)

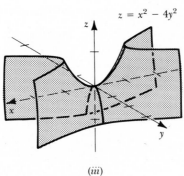

(iii)

13. Name and sketch the graph with equation $4x^2 + 9y^2 - z^2 = 0$.

SOLUTION: Since all terms appear as quadratics and there is the constant zero on the right hand side, the surface is an elliptic cone.

The trace for $x = 0$ is the pair of lines

$$z = 3y \quad \text{and} \quad z = -y,$$

while for $y = 0$ the trace is the pair of lines

$$z = 2x \quad \text{and} \quad z = -2x.$$

Typical traces for nonzero values of z are, for $z = \pm 6$, the ellipses

$$\frac{x^2}{3^2} + \frac{y^2}{4^2} = 1.$$

These traces are illustrated and the surface is sketched with hidden lines shown.

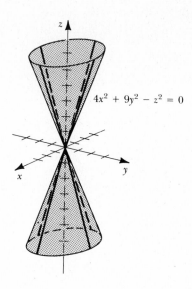

$4x^2 + 9y^2 - z^2 = 0$

17. Name and sketch the graph with equation $\dfrac{y^2}{16} + \dfrac{z^2}{9} - \dfrac{x^2}{25} = 1$.

SOLUTION: The two positive signs and one negative sign along with the constant 1 on the right-hand side imply that the surface is a hyperboloid of one sheet.

Traces in the plane $y = 0$ are hyperbolas

$$\frac{z^2}{9} - \frac{x^2}{25} = 1,$$

while traces in the plane $z = 0$ are hyperbolas

$$\frac{y^2}{16} - \frac{x^2}{25} = 1.$$

Traces in the planes $x = \pm 5$ are the ellipses

$$\frac{y^2}{2 \cdot 16} + \frac{z^2}{2 \cdot 9} = 1.$$

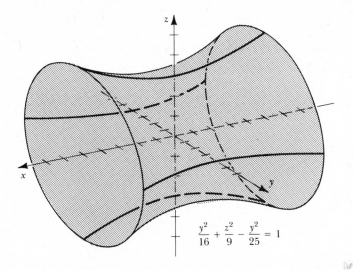

$$\frac{y^2}{16} + \frac{z^2}{9} - \frac{y^2}{25} = 1$$

25. Name and sketch the surface with equation $x^2 + y^2 - 6x - 8y - z + 20 = 0$.

SOLUTION: Complete the squares in the x and y terms:

$$(x^2 - 6x) + (y^2 - 8y) = z - 20$$
$$(x^2 - 6x + 3^2) + (y^2 - 8y + 4^2) = z - 20 + 3^2 + 4^2$$
$$(x - 3)^2 + (y - 4)^2 = (z + 5).$$

The graph is translated so the vertex is at $(3, 4, -5)$ rather than the origin. The equation involves the sum of two quadratic terms and a linear term in the third variable, so the surface is an elliptic paraboloid. The trace in the plane $x = 3$ is the parabola

$$(z + 5) = (y - 4)^2.$$

The trace in the plane $y = 4$ is the parabola

$$(z + 5) = (x - 3)^2.$$

The trace in the plane $z = -4$ (any value of $z > -5$ gives a trace) is the circle

$$(x - 3)^2 + (y - 4)^2 = 1.$$

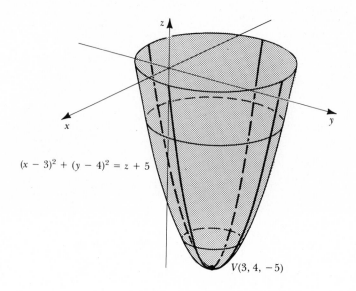

$$(x - 3)^2 + (y - 4)^2 = z + 5$$

$V(3, 4, -5)$

29. Sketch the graph of $z = x^2 + y^2$ and use the result to sketch the graph of each of the following:

a) $z = -(x^2 + y^2)$,   b) $z = x^2 + y^2 + 2$.

SOLUTION: The surface $z = x^2 + y^2$ is a circular paraboloid with traces given by

$$
\begin{aligned}
x = 0, && z = y^2, && \text{a parabola;} \\
y = 0, && z = x^2, && \text{a parabola;} \\
\text{and} \quad z = 1, && x^2 + y^2 = 1, && \text{a circle.}
\end{aligned}
$$

The surface is sketched below.

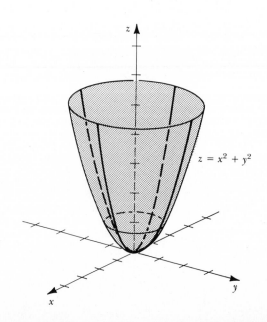

$z = x^2 + y^2$

a) $z = -(x^2 + y^2)$

Each point in the previous surface is represented by a point in this surface whose x and y coordinates are the same, but whose z coordinate is negative of the first. This surface is obtained by reflecting the original surface in the plane $z = 0$.

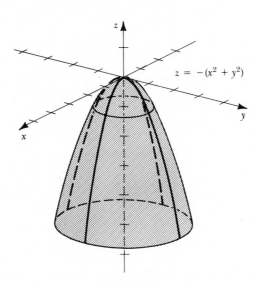

b) $z = x^2 + y^2 + 2$

Rewrite this equation as $(z-2) = x^2 + y^2$ and note that this surface can be obtained by translating the original surface by two units in the z direction.

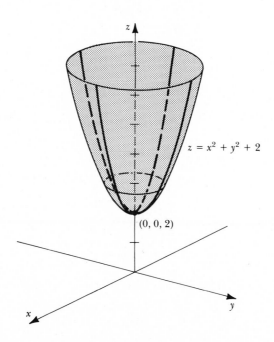

37. The line $y = x/3$ in the xy-plane is revolved about the x-axis. Sketch the surface of revolution.

SOLUTION: According to the SOLUTION to EXERCISE 17 b) of SECTION 13.3 the equation of this surface is $\sqrt{y^2 + z^2} = x/3$ or equivalently $x^2 = 9(y^2 + z^2)$. The line $y = x/3$ and the cone with the quadric equation above are sketched below.

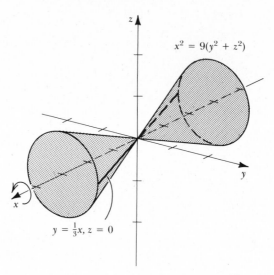

$x^2 = 9(y^2 + z^2)$

$y = \frac{1}{3}x, z = 0$

Cylindrical and Spherical Coordinates in Space
_____13.5

1. Rectangular coordinates of a point are $(1, 1, 3)$. Determine   a) cylindrical coordinates and
   b) spherical coordinates of the point.

SOLUTION: The point satisfies the equations $x = 1$, $y = 1$, $z = 3$.

a) Since $r^2 = x^2 + y^2$, $\tan \theta = y/x$ and $z = z$, the cylindrical coordinates satisfy the equations $r^2 = 1^2 + 1^2$, $\tan \theta = 1/1$, and $z = 3$. The point lies in the first octant so solve for r, θ with $\theta \in [0, \pi/2]$ and $r \geq 0$, that is, $r = \sqrt{2}$ and $\theta = \pi/4$, $z = 3$.

b) Since $\rho^2 = x^2 + y^2 + z^2$, $\tan \theta = y/x$, and $\cos \phi = z/\rho$, the spherical coordinates satisfy the equations

$$\rho^2 = 1^2 + 1^2 + 3^2, \qquad \tan \theta = 1, \quad \text{and} \quad \cos \phi = \frac{3}{\rho}.$$

As above, $0 \leq \rho$, $\theta \in [0, \pi/2]$ and $\phi \in [0, \pi/2]$ so

$$\rho = \sqrt{11}, \qquad \theta = \frac{\pi}{4}, \quad \text{and} \quad \phi = \arccos\left(\frac{3}{\sqrt{11}}\right).$$

9. Cylindrical coordinates of a point are $(4, \pi/4, -2)$. Determine   a) rectangular coordinates and   b) spherical coordinates of the point.

SOLUTION: The point satisfies $r = 4$, $\theta = \pi/4$, and $z = -2$.

a) Since $x = r\cos\theta$, $y = r\sin\theta$, and $z = z$, compute directly that the rectangular coordinates are:

$$x = 4\cos\frac{\pi}{4}, \qquad y = 4\sin\frac{\pi}{4} \quad \text{and} \quad z = -2$$
$$= 2\sqrt{2}. \qquad\qquad = 2\sqrt{2}.$$

b) The relations between cylindrical and spherical coordinates are

$$\rho^2 = r^2 + z^2, \qquad \theta = \theta, \quad \text{and} \quad z = \rho\cos\phi.$$

The spherical coordinates satisfy the equations

$$\rho^2 = 4^2 + 2^2, \qquad \theta = \frac{\pi}{4} \quad \text{and} \quad \cos\phi = -\frac{2}{\sqrt{20}},$$

and since $\phi \in [0, \pi]$ and $\rho > 0$, the coordinates are

$$\rho = \sqrt{20}, \qquad \theta = \frac{\pi}{4}, \quad \text{and} \quad \phi = \arccos\left(-\frac{1}{\sqrt{5}}\right).$$

15. Spherical coordinates of a point are $\left(2, \dfrac{5\pi}{6}, \dfrac{3\pi}{4}\right)$. Determine   a) rectangular coordinates and   b) cylindrical coordinates of the point.

SOLUTION: The spherical coordinates satisfy $\rho = 2$, $\theta = 5\pi/6$, and $\phi = 3\pi/4$.

a) Since the rectangular coordinates satisfy

$$x = \rho\sin\phi\cos\theta, \quad y = \rho\sin\phi\sin\theta \quad \text{and} \quad z = \rho\cos\phi,$$

this point has rectangular coordinates

$$x = 2\sin\frac{3\pi}{4}\cos\frac{5\pi}{6} \qquad y = 2\sin\frac{3\pi}{4}\sin\frac{5\pi}{6} \qquad z = 2\cos\frac{3\pi}{4}$$
$$= 2 \cdot \frac{\sqrt{2}}{2}\left(-\frac{\sqrt{3}}{2}\right) \qquad = 2 \cdot \frac{\sqrt{2}}{2} \cdot \frac{1}{2} \qquad = 2 \cdot \left(-\frac{\sqrt{2}}{2}\right)$$
$$= -\frac{\sqrt{6}}{2} \qquad\qquad = \frac{\sqrt{2}}{2} \qquad\qquad = -\sqrt{2}.$$

b) The cylindrical coordinates satisfy the equations

$$r = \rho \sin \phi, \qquad \theta = \theta, \quad \text{and} \quad z = \rho \cos \phi$$

so the spherical coordinates of this point are

$$r = 2 \sin \frac{3\pi}{4} \qquad \theta = \frac{5\pi}{6} \qquad z = 2 \cos \frac{3\pi}{4}$$

$$= 2 \cdot \left(\frac{\sqrt{2}}{2} \right) \qquad\qquad\qquad = 2 \cdot \left(-\frac{\sqrt{2}}{2} \right)$$

$$= \sqrt{2} \qquad\qquad\qquad\qquad = -\sqrt{2}.$$

23. Find the cylindrical equation corresponding to the rectangular equation $z = x^2 + y^2$.

SOLUTION: The equations for cylindrical coordinates are

$$r^2 = x^2 + y^2, \qquad \tan \theta = \frac{y}{x}, \quad \text{and} \quad z = z.$$

Substitute r^2 for $x^2 + y^2$ in the given equation to obtain $z = r^2$.

29. Sketch the graph of the cylindrical equation $\theta = \pi/2$.

SOLUTION: The points whose θ-coordinate is $\pi/2$ lie in a plane containing the z-axis which makes an angle of $\pi/2$ with the xz-plane. This plane is the yz-plane.

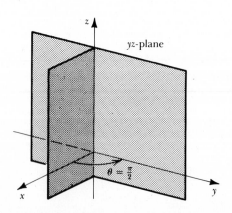

31. Sketch the graph of the cylindrical equation $z = 4r^2$.

SOLUTION: Use $r^2 = x^2 + y^2$ to write the rectangular equation

$$z = 4(x^2 + y^2).$$

This is an elliptic paraboloid with trace in $x = 0$ the parabola $z = 4y^2$ and with trace in $y = 0$ the parabola $z = 4x^2$. The trace in the plane $z = 4$ is the circle $x^2 + y^2 = 1$.

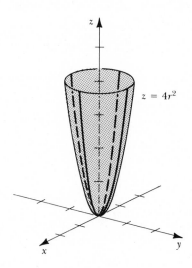

35. Sketch the graph of $r = \cos\theta$.

SOLUTION: Since the cylindrical equation is independent of z the surface must be a cylinder with directrix $r = \cos\theta$ in the (r, θ) plane. This curve is a circle of radius $1/2$ tangent to the pole and symmetric to the polar axis $(x = 0)$. The surface is sketched.

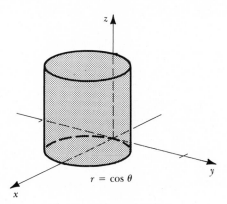

COMMENT: In the preceding solution it was noted that since z is missing in the cylindrical equation the surface is a right cylinder. Another observation about cylindrical or spherical equations is that if the equation is independent of θ then the graph is a surface of revolution obtained by revolving a curve in the yz plane around the z-axis. Each trace in a plane $\theta =$ constant, is the same curve and as θ varies, this curve revolves around the z-axis. Observe that the surface in EXERCISE 31 is such a surface of revolution.

43. Sketch the graph of the spherical equation $\rho = \cos\phi$.

SOLUTION: By the comment above, this is a surface of revolution obtained by revolving the curve $\rho = \cos\phi$ in the yz plane ($\theta = \pi/2$) about the z-axis. In this plane, ρ and ϕ provide a polar coordinate system where the polar axis is the positive z-axis and the pole is at the origin. The polar equation $\rho = \cos\phi$ is the same circle as described in the SOLUTION to EXERCISE 35 above placed in the yz plane.

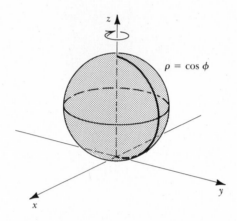

45. Sketch the graph of the spherical equations $\rho = 3$, and $\phi = \frac{\pi}{4}$.

SOLUTION: The graph of $\rho = 3$ is a sphere of radius 3 centered at the origin. The graph of $\phi = \pi/4$ is the cone which makes an interior angle with the positive z-axis of $\pi/4$. The graph of these two equations is the circle which results from the intersection of the sphere and the cone.

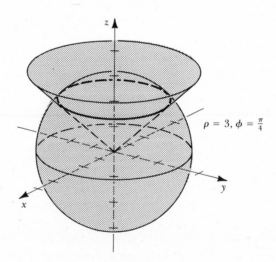

49. Sketch the region described by the inequalities $0 \le \theta \le \frac{\pi}{2}$, $0 \le r \le 1$, $0 \le z \le 3$.

SOLUTION: The solid region lies in the quarter-space between the planes $\theta = 0$ and $\theta = \pi/2$

(i.e., $x \geq 0$ and $y \geq 0$). The region contains the z-axis ($r \geq 0$) and all points out to and including the circular cylinder of radius 1 ($r \leq 1$). Finally, the region is bounded below by the plane $z = 0$ and above by $z = 3$.

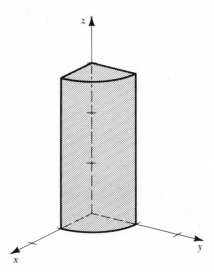

55. Sketch the region described by the inequalities $1 \leq \rho \leq 2$, $\frac{\pi}{4} \leq \phi \leq \frac{\pi}{3}$, $\frac{\pi}{6} \leq \theta \leq \frac{\pi}{3}$.

SOLUTION: The region lies outside the sphere of radius 1 and inside the sphere of radius 2 between cones with inner angles $\pi/4$ and $\pi/3$, respectively, and between planes making angles $\pi/6$ and $\pi/3$, respectively, with the xz-plane.

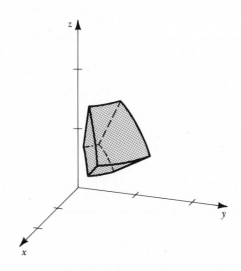

57. Use cylindrical coordinates to describe the region that is inside the sphere $x^2 + y^2 + z^2 = 4$

and outside the cylinder $x^2 + y^2 = 1$.

SOLUTION: The sphere $x^2 + y^2 + z^2 = 4$ has cylindrical equation $r^2 + z^2 = 4$ while the cylinder has equation $r = 1$. Since these equations are both independent of θ, their graphs are surfaces of revolution so the solid is a solid of revolution with $0 \leq \theta \leq 2\pi$. For each fixed θ, the trace in the constant θ plane is described by $1 \leq r \leq 2$ and $-\sqrt{4 - r^2} \leq z \leq \sqrt{4 - r^2}$.

59. Use spherical coordinates to describe the region that is inside the sphere $x^2 + y^2 + z^2 = 9$ and outside the sphere $x^2 + y^2 + z^2 = 4$.

SOLUTION: The region lies between the spheres of radius 2 and 3 respectively: $2 \leq \rho \leq 3$, $0 \leq \theta \leq 2\pi$ and $0 \leq \phi \leq \pi$.

63. An ice cream cone has the shape of a cone of height 3 inches topped with a hemisphere of diameter 2 inches. The vertex of the cone is at the origin, and the axis of the cone is the positive z-axis. Express the region on or within the ice cream cone using   a) rectangular coordinates b) cylindrical coordinates c) spherical coordinates.

SOLUTION:

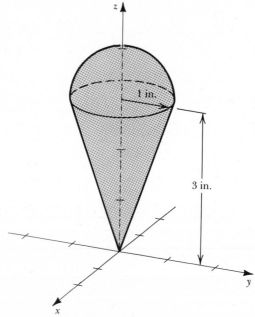

a) The cone is generated by revolving the line $z = 3y$ about the z-axis so, by the same reasoning as was applied in the SOLUTION to EXERCISE 17 of SECTION 13.3, its rectangular equation is $z = 3\sqrt{x^2 + y^2}$. The sphere of radius 1 with center at $(0, 0, 3)$ has equation $x^2 + y^2 + (z - 3)^2 = 1$, so the upper hemisphere is given by $z = 3 + \sqrt{1 - x^2 - y^2}$. The region lies above the cone $z = 3\sqrt{x^2 + y^2}$ and below the hemisphere $z = 3 + \sqrt{1 - x^2 - y^2}$.

b) The equation of the cone in cylindrical coordinates is $z = 3r$ and that of the hemisphere is $z = 3 + \sqrt{1 - r^2}$, where $0 \leq r \leq 1$, so the solid lies between the surfaces with equations $z = 3r$ and $z = 3 + \sqrt{1 - r^2}$, $0 \leq \theta \leq 2\pi$.

c) The spherical equation of the cone is derived from the cylindrical equation $\dfrac{r}{z} = \dfrac{1}{3}$ or, since $\tan \phi = r/z$, the spherical equation is $\phi = \arctan(1/3)$.

The cylindrical equation of the sphere can be written as $z^2 - 6z + 9 + r^2 = 1$. Replace $z^2 + r^2$ by ρ^2 and z by $\rho \cos \phi$ to obtain the spherical equation $\rho^2 - 6\rho \cos \phi + 8 = 0$. For each value of ϕ there are two values of ρ which solve this equation; take the larger value corresponding to points of the upper hemisphere

$$\rho = \frac{6 \cos \phi + \sqrt{36 \cos^2 \phi - 32}}{2} = 3 \cos \phi + \sqrt{(3 \cos \phi)^2 - 8}.$$

This region is described by requiring $0 \le \phi \le \arctan(1/3)$ and $0 \le \rho \le 3 \cos \phi + \sqrt{(3 \cos \phi)^2 - 8}$ for $0 \le \theta \le 2\pi$.

Chapter 13

Review Exercises

5. Find the domain of the function $f(x, y, z) = \ln(xyz)$.

SOLUTION: The domain consists of all points (x, y, z) such that $xyz > 0$. This is the union of four of the eight octants in three dimensional space:

$$\{z > 0, \; x > 0, \; y > 0\} \cup \{z > 0, \; x < 0, \; y < 0\} \cup \{z < 0, \; x > 0, \; y < 0\} \cup \{z < 0, \; x < 0, \; y > 0\}.$$

9. Sketch representative level curves for the function $f(x, y) = 9x^2 + 4y^2$.

SOLUTION: The level curves are the sets in the plane $\{(x, y) : 9x^2 + 4y^2 = c\}$ for various values of c. For $c < 0$ the level set is empty so no curves exist. For $c = 0$ the level curve is the point $(0, 0)$, while for $c > 0$ the level curves are ellipses with center at $(0, 0)$ and with major and minor axes the y and x axes respectively. These latter are sketched for several values of $c \ge 0$.

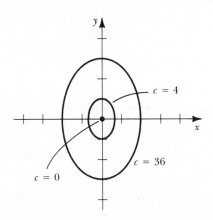

13. Sketch, in the first octant, representative level surfaces for the function
$f(x, y, z) = x^2 + y^2 + z^2$.

SOLUTION: The level surfaces are the sets $\{(x, y, z) : x^2 + y^2 + z^2 = c^2\}$. For $c < 0$ there are none; for $c = 0$ the level set is a point $(0, 0, 0)$, while for $c > 0$ the level sets are spheres of radius $\sqrt{c}$ centered at $(0, 0, 0)$.

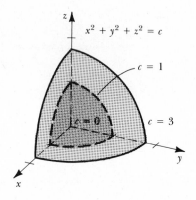

17. Name and sketch the surface described by $z = x^2 + y^2 - 2$.

SOLUTION: Rewrite the equation as $(z + 2) = x^2 + y^2$ to notice that this is the surface with equation $z = x^2 + y^2$ with $(0, 0, 0)$ translated to $(0, 0, -2)$. The latter surface is an elliptic paraboloid with vertex at $(0, 0, 0)$ which opens up (refer to the Table in SECTION 13.4), so the given surface is an elliptic paraboloid with vertex at $(0, 0, -2)$. To graph it, sketch the parabolic traces in the planes $x = 0$ and $y = 0$ then sketch some (circular) traces in the planes $z + 2 = k$. Alternatively, notice that this is a surface of revolution obtained by revolving the parabola $z + 2 = y^2$ about the z-axis.

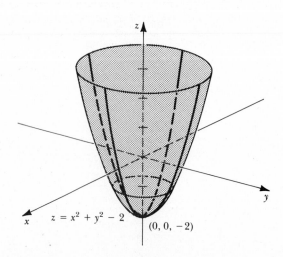

21. Name and sketch the surface with equation $\dfrac{x^2}{9} + \dfrac{y^2}{4} - \dfrac{z^2}{16} = 1$.

SOLUTION: Refer to the Table in SECTION 13.4 to see that this equation is that of a hyperboloid of one sheet. Traces in the planes $x = 0$ and $y = 0$ are hyperbolae while traces in the planes $z = k$ are ellipses. These are sketched below, and the surface is constructed.

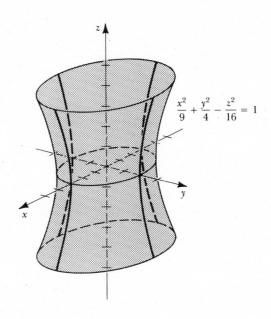

$$\frac{x^2}{9} + \frac{y^2}{4} - \frac{z^2}{16} = 1$$

25. Name and sketch the surface with equation $x^2 - y^2 = 1$.

SOLUTION: Since z is missing from this equation, the surface is a cylinder generated by the hyperbola with equation $x^2 - y^2 = 1$ in the (x, y) plane. The hyperbola and this cylinder are sketched below.

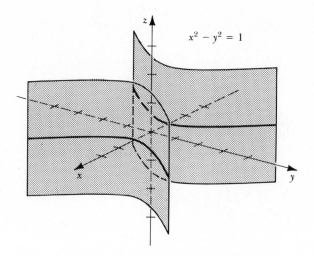

$$x^2 - y^2 = 1$$

31. Name and sketch the surface with equation $r = 2 \sin \theta$.

SOLUTION: Since z is missing from this equation in cylindrical coordinates, the surface is a cylinder generated by the curve $r = 2 \sin \theta$ in the (r, θ) plane. This curve is a circle of radius 1 tangent to the pole and symmetric to the ray $\theta = \pi/2$ (the y-axis). The circle and cylinder are sketched below.

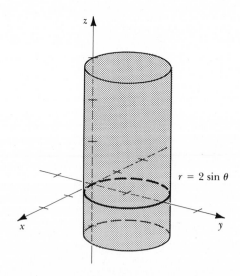

$$r = 2 \sin \theta$$

37. Determine cylindrical and spherical coordinates of the points with rectangular coordinates
   a) $(1, 0, 0)$ b) $(1, 1, 0)$ c) $(1, 1, 1)$.

SOLUTION: a) The rectangular coordinates are $x = 1$, $y = 0$, and $z = 0$, so the cylindrical coordinates are $r = \sqrt{1^2 + 0^2} = 1$, $\tan\theta = 0/1 = 0$, or $\theta = 0$, $z = 0$, and spherical coordinates are $\rho = \sqrt{r^2 + z^2} = \sqrt{1^2 + 0^2} = 1$, $\theta = 0$, and since $z = 0$, the point lies in the plane $\phi = \pi/2$.

b) With rectangular coordinates $x = 1$, $y = 1$, $z = 0$, the cylindrical coordinates are $r = \sqrt{1^2 + 1^2} = \sqrt{2}$, $\theta = \tan^{-1}(1/1) = \pi/4$ and $z = 0$. The spherical coordinates are $\rho = \sqrt{2 + 0^2} = \sqrt{2}$, $\theta = \pi/4$ and again $\phi = \pi/2$ since $z = 0$.

c) With rectangular coordinates $x = 1$, $y = 1$, $z = 1$ the cylindrical coordinates are $r = \sqrt{1^2 + 1^2} = \sqrt{2}$, $\theta = \arctan(1/1) = \pi/4$ and $z = 1$. The spherical coordinates are $\rho = \sqrt{r^2 + z^2} = \sqrt{2 + 1} = \sqrt{3}$, $\theta = \pi/4$ and $\phi = \arctan(r/z) = \arctan(\sqrt{2}/1) = \pi/3$.

41. a) Describe the surface obtained by revolving the curve $y = \sqrt{4 - x^2}$, $z = 0$ about the x-axis.   b) Determine an equation of the surface.

SOLUTION: a) The curve $y = \sqrt{4 - x^2}$, $z = 0$ is a semicircle of radius 2 with center at $(0,0)$ in the (x, y) plane. Revolving this around the x-axis generates a sphere.

b) Replace y by $\sqrt{y^2 + z^2}$ to obtain the equation of this sphere $\sqrt{y^2 + z^2} = \sqrt{4 - x^2}$ or $x^2 + y^2 + z^2 = 4$.

14

The Differential Calculus
of Multivariable Functions

Sharpening your skills

You should review limits and continuity in CHAPTER 1 as well as derivatives, their calculation, and applications in CHAPTERS 2, 3, and 6. Recall the material on vectors, especially unit vectors, dot products, and the equation of a plane from CHAPTER 11.

The problems below are followed by references to the sections in the text where the appropriate tools are presented.

Practice Problems

1. Use DEFINITION 1.28 in the text to show that $\lim_{t \to 1}(3t - 1) = 2$.

2. Calculate each limit or tell why it does not exist.

   a) $\lim_{x \to -1}(4x^2 - x^3 + 1)$,   b) $\lim_{x \to 0} \dfrac{3x^2 + x - 1}{x^2 - 2x}$,

   c) $\lim_{x \to 0} \dfrac{\sin 4x}{x}$.

3. Determine all points of continuity for the function

$$f(x) = \begin{cases} \dfrac{\tan x}{x}, & \text{if } x \neq 0, \pm\dfrac{\pi}{2}, \pm\dfrac{3\pi}{2}, \ldots \\ \\ 1, & \text{if } x = 0, \pm\dfrac{\pi}{2}, \pm\dfrac{3\pi}{2}, \ldots \end{cases}$$

4. Use DEFINITION 2.3 to calculate $f'(2)$ where $f(t) = 2t^2 - 3t + 1$.

5. Calculate the derivatives of the functions

   a) $f(x) = \sqrt{1 + x^2}$,   b) $g(x) = (x + 1)(x^2 - 2)$,   c) $h(x) = \dfrac{\sin(x^2)}{x}$,

   d) $f(x) = \arctan(4x)$,   e) $g(x) = e^{x^2}\sin x$.

6. Use the differential to approximate $\sqrt{3.98}$.

7. Find critical points and use the second derivative test to find maxima and minima for
   a) $f(x) = x^4 + 2x^2$ and   b) $f(x) = x^2 \log|x|$.

414

8. a) Find the unit vector, **u**, which points from $P(1,-1,-2)$ to $Q(-3,4,1)$.   b) Find the component of the vector $\mathbf{v} = \langle 2,1,-3 \rangle$ which is in the direction of **u**.

9. Find an equation for the plane through $(1,2,3)$ with normal $\mathbf{N} = \langle -2,-4,5 \rangle$.

_____14.1

Limits and Continuity

7. Determine the limit of $f(x,y) = \dfrac{x^3 - x^2 y + xy^2}{x+y}$ at $(1,1)$ if it exists.

SOLUTION: Since $\lim\limits_{(x,y)\to(1,1)} x+y \neq 0$, then THEOREM 14.5(iv) can be applied; other parts of this THEOREM are also applied below.

$$\lim_{(x,y)\to(1,1)} \frac{x^3 - x^2 y + xy^2}{x+y} = \frac{\lim\limits_{(x,y)\to(1,1)} \left(x^3 - x^2 y + xy^2\right)}{\lim\limits_{(x,y)\to(1,1)} x+y}$$

$$= \frac{\lim\limits_{(x,y)\to(1,1)} \left(x^3\right) - \lim\limits_{(x,y)\to(1,1)} \left(x^2 y\right) + \lim\limits_{(x,y)\to(1,1)} \left(xy^2\right)}{\lim\limits_{(x,y)\to(1,1)} x + \lim\limits_{(x,y)\to(1,1)} y}$$

$$= \frac{\left(\lim\limits_{(x,y)\to(1,1)} x\right)^3 - \left(\lim\limits_{(x,y)\to(1,1)} x\right)^2 \left(\lim\limits_{(x,y)\to(1,1)} y\right)}{\lim\limits_{(x,y)\to(1,1)} x + \lim\limits_{(x,y)\to(1,1)} y}$$

$$+ \frac{\left(\lim\limits_{(x,y)\to(1,1)} x\right)\left(\lim\limits_{(x,y)\to(1,1)} y\right)^2}{\lim\limits_{(x,y)\to(1,1)} x + \lim\limits_{(x,y)\to(1,1)} y}$$

$$= \frac{1^3 - 1^2 \cdot 1 + 1 \cdot 1^2}{1+1} = \frac{1}{2}.$$

11. Determine the limit of $f(x,y) = \dfrac{x^2 - y^2}{x-y}$ at $(1,1)$ if it exists.

SOLUTION: The function $f(x,y) = \dfrac{x^2 - y^2}{x-y}$ is undefined along the line $y = x$ which passes through $(1,1)$; thus f is undefined at points in every set of the form $\{(x,y) : 0 < \sqrt{(x-1)^2 + (y-1)^2} < \delta\}$ no matter how small δ is. The limit does not exist.

13. Determine the limit of $f(x,y) = \dfrac{\sin(x^2 + y^2)}{x^2 + y^2}$ at $(0,0)$ if it exists.

SOLUTION: This function is undefined only at the limit point $(0,0)$ so the discussion in the solution to EXERCISE 11 does not apply. Indeed, the limit exists. The function of a single variable

$$g(u) = \begin{cases} \dfrac{\sin u}{u}, & u \neq 0 \\ 1, & u = 0 \end{cases}$$

is continuous at $u = 0$. By THEOREM 14.6 the given limit can be written as

$$\lim_{(x,y)\to(0,0)} g(x^2 + y^2) = g\left(\lim_{(x,y)\to(0,0)} x^2 + y^2\right) = g(0) = 1$$

by THEOREM 14.6.

19. Determine the region where $f(x,y) = \dfrac{y - x}{x^2 + y^2}$ is continuous.

SOLUTION: The function is defined at each point (a,b) such that $a^2 + b^2 \neq 0$, that is, everywhere except at $(0,0)$. For any such point, the limit, $\lim\limits_{(x,y)\to(a,b)} f(x,y)$ is

$$\lim_{(x,y)\to(a,b)} \frac{y - x}{x^2 + y^2} = \frac{\lim\limits_{(x,y)\to(a,b)} y - \lim\limits_{(x,y)\to(a,b)} x}{\left(\lim\limits_{(x,y)\to(a,b)} x\right)^2 + \left(\lim\limits_{(x,y)\to(a,b)} y\right)^2} = \frac{b - a}{a^2 + b^2} = f(a,b).$$

Thus, f is continuous everywhere except at $(0,0)$.

25. Show that the limit $\lim\limits_{(x,y)\to(0,0)} \dfrac{y^2}{x^2 + y^2}$ does not exist.

SOLUTION: The function is defined everywhere except at $(0,0)$ so to show that the limit does not exist, use the observation (14.3) of the text. Here you find two curves through the limit point along which the function has distinct limits. As curves, take the lines $x = t$, $y = mt$ with slope m. Along them, $f(t, mt) = m^2 t^2 / (t^2 + m^2 t^2) = m^2 / (1 + m^2)$ for $t \neq 0$, so for any two lines, with different slopes, say $m = 0$ and $m = 1$, f has the distinct limiting values, for example 0 and 1/2 respectively. Thus the limit does not exist.

33. Sketch the region in the (x,y) plane described by

a) $0 < \sqrt{(x - 1)^2 + (y - 2)^2} < 0.5$.

SOLUTION: The region is a "punctured" disk of radius 1/2 centered at $(1,2)$. The region does not include either the center or the boundary.

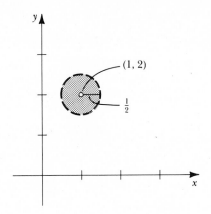

37. If $f(x,y,z) = x + y + z$ and $g(x) = \cos x$, find $\displaystyle\lim_{(x,y,z)\to(\pi/2,\pi/2,0)} g\left(f(x,y,z)\right)$.

SOLUTION: $g(x) = \cos x$ is continuous everywhere and $\displaystyle\lim_{(x,y,z)\to(\pi/2,\pi/2,0)} f(x,y,z)$ is calculated by THEOREM 14.5 as

$$\lim_{(x,y,z)\to(\pi/2,\pi/2,0)} f(x,y,z) = \lim_{(x,y,z)\to(\pi/2,\pi/2,0)} x + \lim_{(x,y,z)\to(\pi/2,\pi/2,0)} y + \lim_{(x,y,z)\to(\pi/2,\pi/2,0)} z$$

$$= \frac{\pi}{2} + \frac{\pi}{2} + 0 = \pi$$

Thus, by THEOREM 14.6,

$$\lim_{(x,y,z)\to(\pi/2,\pi/2,0)} g\left(f(x,y,z)\right) = g(\pi) = \cos \pi = -1.$$

43. Use DEFINITION 14.2 to prove $\displaystyle\lim_{(x,y,z)\to(1,2,3)} (2x - y + z) = 3$.

SOLUTION: For arbitrary $\epsilon > 0$, one must find $\delta > 0$ so that whenever $0 < \sqrt{(x-1)^2 + (y-2)^2 + (z-3)^2} < \delta$ then $|(2x - y + z) - 3| < \epsilon$. If such a δ exists, then if

(1) $0 < \sqrt{(x-1)^2 + (y-2)^2 + (z-3)^2} < \delta,$ it follows that

$$|x - 1| \leq \sqrt{(x-1)^2 + (y-2)^2 + (z-3)^2} < \delta$$
(2) $$|y - 2| \leq \sqrt{(x-1)^2 + (y-2)^2 + (z-3)^2} < \delta \quad \text{and}$$
$$|z - 3| \leq \sqrt{(x-1)^2 + (y-2)^2 + (z-3)^2} < \delta.$$

Thus

(3) $$|(2x - y + z) - 3| = |2(x-1) - (y-2) + (z-3)|$$
$$\leq 2\,|x-1| + |y-2| + |z-3|.$$

By the triangle inequality and inequalities (2) above,

$$|(2x - y + z) - 3| < (2\delta + \delta + \delta) = 4\delta.$$

To ensure that $|(2x - y + z) - 3| < \epsilon$, one should choose $\delta < \epsilon/4$. With this value of δ and the hypothesis that $0 < \sqrt{(x-1)^2 + (y-2)^2 + (z-3)^2} < \delta$, then inequalities (3) and (2) above can be invoked to conclude that $|(2x - y + z) - 3| < 4\delta < 4 \cdot (\epsilon/4) = \epsilon$. Thus

$$\lim_{(x,y,z)\to(1,2,3)} 2x - y + z = 3.$$

Partial Derivatives 14.2

COMMENT: The symbol D is used to indicate the differentiation operation; the variable with respect to which differentiation is applied is indicated by the subscript; so, for example D_x denotes differentiation with respect to x and $D^2_{xy} = D_y[D_x]$ denotes differentiation with respect to x followed by differentiation with respect to y.

7. Find the first partial derivatives of $f(x,y) = \dfrac{xy}{x^2 + y^2}$.

SOLUTION:

$$f_x = D_x\left[\frac{xy}{x^2 + y^2}\right] \qquad \text{(apply the quotient rule)}$$

$$= \frac{(x^2 + y^2)D_x[xy] - (xy)D_x[x^2 + y^2]}{(x^2 + y^2)^2}$$

$$= \frac{(x^2 + y^2)(y) - (xy)(2x + 0)}{(x^2 + y^2)^2} = \frac{y^3 - x^2 y}{(x^2 + y^2)^2}.$$

$$f_y = D_y\left[\frac{xy}{x^2 + y^2}\right] = \frac{(x^2 + y^2)D_y[xy] - (xy)D_y[x^2 + y^2]}{(x^2 + y^2)^2}$$

$$= \frac{(x^2 + y^2)x - (xy)(0 + 2y)}{(x^2 + y^2)^2} = \frac{x^3 - xy^2}{(x^2 + y^2)^2}.$$

19. Find the first partial derivatives of $f(x,y,z) = \cos(2x + 3y + 4z)$.

SOLUTION:

$$f_x = D_x[\cos(2x + 3y + 4z)]$$

(apply the chain rule to the cosine function)

$$= (-\sin(2x + 3y + 4z)) \cdot D_x\,[2x + 3y + 4z] = -2\sin(2x + 3y + 4z),$$
$$f_y = D_y\,[\cos(2x + 3y + 4z)]$$
$$= (-\sin(2x + 3y + 4z))\,D_y\,[2x + 3y + 4z] = -3\sin(2x + 3y + 4z) \qquad \text{and}$$
$$f_z = D_z\,[\cos(2x + 3y + 4z)]$$
$$= (-\sin(2x + 3y + 4z)) \cdot D_z\,[2x + 3y + 4z] = -4\sin(2x + 3y + 4z).$$

29. Show that $f_{xy} = f_{yx}$ for $f(x,y) = x^3 + 2x^2 y$.

SOLUTION:

$$f_{xy} = D_y\,\Big[D_x\,\big[x^3 + 2x^2 y\big]\Big]$$

(Differentiate the expression with respect to x.)

$$= D_y\,[3x^2 + 4xy] = 0 + 4x = 4x.$$
$$f_{yx} = D_x\,\Big[D_y\,\big[x^3 + 2x^2 y\big]\Big] = D_x\,\big[0 + 2x^2\big] = 4x.$$

Thus $f_{xy} = f_{yx}$ for all (x,y).

41. Find $\dfrac{\partial^3 w}{\partial x\, \partial y\, \partial z}$ if $w = \sin(xyz)$.

SOLUTION:

$$\frac{\partial^3 w}{\partial x\, \partial y\, \partial z} = D_x\,\Big[D_y\,\big[D_z\,[\sin(xyz)]\big]\Big] \qquad \text{(First differentiate with respect } z.)$$
$$= D_x\,\Big[D_y\,\big[\cos(xyz) \cdot D_z\,[(xyz)]\big]\Big]$$
$$= D_x\,\big[D_y\,[xy\cos(xyz)]\big]$$

(Use the product rule to differentiate with respect to y.)

$$= D_x\,\big[x\,(D_y\,[y]) \cdot \cos(xyz) + y \cdot D_y\,[\cos(xyz)]\big]$$
$$= D_x\,\big[x\,(\cos(xyz) + y\,(-\sin(xyz))\,D_y\,[(xyz)])\big]$$
$$= D_x\,\big[x\cos(xyz) - x^2 yz\sin(xyz)\big]$$

(Use the product rule twice.)

$$= (D_x\,[x]\,(\cos(xyz)) + x D_x\,[\cos(xyz)])$$
$$\qquad - (D_x\,[x^2 yz]\sin(xyz) + (x^2 yz)D_x\,[\sin(xyz)])$$

$$= (\cos(xyz) + x(yz)(-\sin(xyz)))$$
$$- (2xyz\sin(xyz) + (x^2yz)(yz)\cos(xyz))$$
$$= (1 - x^2y^2z^2)\cos(xyz) - 3(xyz)\sin(xyz).$$

43. Find an equation of the line in the plane $y = 1$ that is tangent to the curve of intersection of this plane and the surface $z = 4 - x^2 - y^2$ at $(1,1,2)$.

SOLUTION: The partial derivative is $D_x\left[4 - x^2 - y^2\right] = -2x$ which at $(1,1)$ gives slope equal to -2. The line in the plane $y = 1$ passing through the point $x = 1$, $z = 2$ with this slope satisfies $y = 1$ and $(z-2)/(x-1) = -2$ or, in symmetric form,

$$\frac{x-1}{1} = \frac{y-1}{0} = \frac{z-2}{-2}.$$

45. Let $f(x,y) = \sqrt{y^2 - x^2}\,\arctan(y/x)$. Show that $x\dfrac{\partial f}{\partial x} + y\dfrac{\partial f}{\partial y} = f(x,y)$.

SOLUTION:

$$f_x = D_x\left[\sqrt{y^2 - x^2}\,\arctan(y/x)\right] \qquad \text{(Use the product rule)}$$

$$= D_x\left[\sqrt{y^2 - x^2}\right]\arctan(y/x) + \sqrt{y^2 - x^2}\,D_x\left[\arctan(y/x)\right]$$

$$= \frac{1}{2\sqrt{y^2 - x^2}}(-2x)\arctan(y/x) + \sqrt{y^2 - x^2}\,\frac{1}{1 + \left(\frac{y}{x}\right)^2}\left(-\frac{y}{x^2}\right)$$

$$= \frac{-x}{\sqrt{y^2 - x^2}}\arctan(y/x) - \frac{y\sqrt{y^2 - x^2}}{x^2 + y^2}$$

$$f_y = D_y\left[\sqrt{y^2 - x^2}\,\arctan(y/x)\right] \qquad \text{(Use the product rule)}$$

$$= D_y\left[\sqrt{y^2 - x^2}\right]\arctan(y/x) + \sqrt{y^2 - x^2}\,D_y\left[\arctan(y/x)\right]$$

$$= \frac{y}{\sqrt{y^2 - x^2}}\arctan(y/x) + \sqrt{y^2 - x^2}\,\frac{1/x}{1 + (y/x)^2}.$$

Thus,

$$xf_x + yf_y = x\left(\left(\frac{-x}{\sqrt{y^2 - x^2}}\right)\arctan(y/x) - \frac{y\sqrt{y^2 - x^2}}{x^2 + y^2}\right)$$

$$+ y\left(\frac{y}{\sqrt{y^2 - x^2}}\arctan(y/x) + \frac{x\sqrt{y^2 - x^2}}{x^2 + y^2}\right)$$

$$= \frac{y^2 - x^2}{\sqrt{y^2 - x^2}} \arctan(y/x) + \frac{(-xy + yx)\sqrt{y^2 - x^2}}{x^2 + y^2}$$

$$= \sqrt{y^2 - x^2} \arctan(y/x) = f(x, y).$$

49. Find $f_x(0,0)$ and $f_y(0,0)$ if $f(x, y) = \begin{cases} \dfrac{xy^2}{x^2 + y^2}, & \text{if } (x, y) \neq (0,0) \\[2mm] 0, & \text{if } (x, y) = (0,0). \end{cases}$

SOLUTION: Use DEFINITION 14.9 to calculate the partial derivatives:

$$f_x(0,0) = \lim_{h \to 0} \frac{f(h,0) - f(0,0)}{h} = \lim_{h \to 0} \frac{\frac{h \cdot 0^2}{h^2 + 0^2} - 0}{h} = \lim_{h \to 0} 0 = 0 \quad \text{and}$$

$$f_y(0,0) = \lim_{h \to 0} \frac{f(0,h) - f(0,0)}{h} = \lim_{h \to 0} \frac{\frac{0 \cdot h^2}{0^2 + h^2} - 0}{h} = \lim_{h \to 0} 0 = 0.$$

53. A function f is said to be *harmonic* if it satisfies *Laplace's equation*. Show that the function

c) $f(x, y, z) = \dfrac{1}{\sqrt{x^2 + y^2 + z^2}}$ is harmonic.

SOLUTION:

$$\frac{\partial^2 f}{\partial x^2} = D_x \left[D_x \left[\frac{1}{\sqrt{x^2 + y^2 + z^2}} \right] \right]$$

$$= D_x \left[\frac{-x}{(x^2 + y^2 + z^2)^{3/2}} \right] \qquad \text{(Use the quotient rule)}$$

$$= \frac{-(x^2 + y^2 + z^2)^{3/2} + x \cdot 2x \cdot \frac{3}{2}(x^2 + y^2 + z^2)^{1/2}}{(x^2 + y^2 + z^2)^3}$$

$$= \frac{2x^2 - y^2 - z^2}{(x^2 + y^2 + z^2)^{5/2}}.$$

Similarly,

$$\frac{\partial^2 f}{\partial y^2} = \frac{2y^2 - x^2 - z^2}{(x^2 + y^2 + z^2)^{5/2}} \quad \text{and} \quad \frac{\partial^2 f}{\partial z^2} = \frac{2z^2 - x^2 - y^2}{(x^2 + y^2 + z^2)^{5/2}}, \quad \text{so}$$

$$\frac{\partial^2 f}{\partial x^2} + \frac{\partial^2 f}{\partial y^2} + \frac{\partial^2 f}{\partial z^2} = \frac{(2x^2 - y^2 - z^2) + (2y^2 - x^2 - z^2) + (2z^2 - x^2 - y^2)}{(x^2 + y^2 + z^2)^{5/2}} = 0.$$

_____14.3

Differentiability of
Multivariable Functions

---

3. Use THEOREM 14.19 to show that $f(x, y) = \ln(x^2 + y^2)$ is differentiable.

SOLUTION: The theorem says that if the partial derivatives f_x and f_y exist and are continuous, then f is differentiable. For the function $f(x, y) = \ln(x^2 + y^2)$,

$$f_x = \frac{2x}{x^2 + y^2} \quad \text{and} \quad f_y = \frac{2y}{x^2 + y^2}.$$

These partials satisfy the hypotheses of THEOREM 14.19 everywhere except $(0,0)$, so f is differentiable at all $(x, y) \neq (0, 0)$.

11. Find dz for $z = y^2 \cos x$.

SOLUTION: The differential of $z = f(x, y)$ is defined in Formula 14.23 of the text as $dz = f_x \, dx + f_y \, dy$. In this case, $f_x = y^2(-\sin x)$ and $f_y = (2y) \cos x$, so

$$dz = (-y^2 \sin x) \, dx + (2y \cos x) \, dy.$$

15. Use $z = f(x, y) = x/y$, $\Delta x = 0.2$ and $\Delta y = -0.1$ to calculate dz and then to approximate $f(0.2, 0.9)$.

SOLUTION: The partial derivatives of $f(x, y) = x/y$ are $f_x = 1/y$ and $f_y = (-x)/y^2$, so the differential is $dz = (1/y)(\Delta x) - (x/y^2)(\Delta y)$. Since $\Delta x = 0.2$, $\Delta y = -0.1$ and the point at which f is to be approximated is $(x + \Delta x, y + \Delta y) = (0.2, 0.9)$, conclude that $x = .2 - \Delta x = 0$ and $y = .9 - \Delta y = 1$. Evaluate f and dz at this point to obtain $f(0, 1) = 0/1 = 0$ and

$$dz = (1/1)(0.2) - (0/1^2)(-0.1) = 0.2.$$

The approximation to $f(0.2, 0.9)$ using the differential dz is thus

$$f(.2, .9) \approx f(0, 1) + dz \quad \text{or} \quad f(.2, .9) \approx 0.2.$$

21. Find dw, where $w = xye^z$.

SOLUTION: According to the extension of Formula 14.23 given in EXAMPLE 5 of the text, $dw = f_x \, dx + f_y \, dy + f_z \, dz$. Here $w = f(x, y, z) = xye^z$ so $f_x = ye^z$, $f_y = xe^z$, and $f_z = xye^z$. Thus,

$$dz = ye^z \, dx + xe^z \, dy + xye^z \, dz.$$

23. Use $w = f(x, y, z) = xyz$, $\Delta x = 0.1$, $\Delta y = 0.2$ and $\Delta z = 0.3$ to calculate dw and then to approximate $f(1.1, 2.2, 3.3)$.

SOLUTION: The partial derivatives of $f(x, y, z) = xyz$ are $f_x = yz$, $f_y = xz$ and $f_z = xy$, so

$$dw = yz \, \Delta x + xz \, \Delta y + xy \, \Delta z.$$

The point (x, y, z) at which these partials and f are evaluated is such that
$(x + \Delta x, y + \Delta y, z + \Delta z) = (1.1, 2.2, 3.3)$. Since $\Delta x = .1$, $\Delta y = .2$, and $\Delta z = .3$, conclude that
$x = 1.1 - 0.1$, $y = 2.2 - 0.2$, and $z = 3.3 - 0.3$. So $(x, y, z) = (1, 2, 3)$, $f(1, 2, 3) = 1 \cdot 2 \cdot 3 = 6$, and

$$dw = (2 \cdot 3)(0.1) + (1 \cdot 3)(0.2) + (1 \cdot 2)(0.3) = 1.8.$$

The approximation is thus

$$f(1.1, 2.2, 3.3) \approx f(1, 2, 3) + dw \quad \text{or} \quad f(1.1, 2.2, 3.3) \approx 7.8.$$

29. For $f(x, y) = x^2 - y^2$, find functions ϵ_1 and ϵ_2 that satisfy DEFINITION 14.17 and show that f is differentiable.

SOLUTION: Since the partial derivatives of $f(x, y) = x^2 - y^2$ are $f_x(x, y) = 2x$ and $f_y(x, y) = -2y$, write the expression in DEFINITION 14.17,

$$f(x + \Delta x, y + \Delta y) - f(x, y) = f_x(x, y) \, \Delta x + f_y(x, y) \, \Delta y + \epsilon_1(\Delta x, \Delta y) \, \Delta x + \epsilon_2(\Delta x, \Delta y) \, \Delta y,$$

as

$$\left((x + \Delta x)^2 - (y + \Delta y)^2 \right) - (x^2 - y^2) = \\ (2x)\Delta x + (-2y)\Delta y + \epsilon_1(\Delta x, \Delta y) \, \Delta x + \epsilon_2(\Delta x, \Delta y) \, \Delta y.$$

Expand the left hand side, simplify, group terms which involve the Δx and Δy factors to write the last equation as

$$(\epsilon_1(\Delta x, \Delta y) - \Delta x) \, \Delta x + (\epsilon_2(\Delta x, \Delta y) + \Delta y) \, \Delta y = 0.$$

In order for this equation to be valid for all choices of Δx and Δy it is necessary that

$$\epsilon_1(\Delta x, \Delta y) = \Delta x \quad \text{and} \quad \epsilon_2(\Delta x, \Delta y) = -\Delta y.$$

It is easy to verify the condition that $\lim_{(x,y) \to (0,0)} \epsilon_i(\Delta x, \Delta y) = 0$ for $i = 1, 2$.

$$\text{\underline{\hspace{8cm}}}14.4$$

The Chain Rule

3. Find $\dfrac{df}{dt}$ where $f(x,y) = 3x^3 - \sqrt{x+y}$ with $x(t) = \ln t$ and $y(t) = t^2$.

SOLUTION: The derivatives are

$$\frac{\partial f}{\partial x} = D_x \left[3x^3 - \sqrt{x+y}\right] = 9x^2 - \frac{1}{2\sqrt{x+y}},$$

$$\frac{\partial f}{\partial y} = D_y \left[3x^3 - \sqrt{x+y}\right] = -\frac{1}{2\sqrt{x+y}},$$

$$\frac{dx}{dt} = D_t \left[\ln t\right] = \frac{1}{t} \quad \text{and} \quad \frac{dy}{dt} = D_t \left[t^2\right] = 2t.$$

Thus, by the chain rule, $\dfrac{df}{dt} = \dfrac{\partial f}{\partial x} \cdot \dfrac{dx}{dt} + \dfrac{\partial f}{\partial y} \cdot \dfrac{dy}{dt}$

$$= \left(9x^2 - \frac{1}{2\sqrt{x+y}}\right)\left(\frac{1}{t}\right) + \left(-\frac{1}{2\sqrt{x+y}}\right)(2t)$$

or, since $x = \ln t$ and $y = t^2$,

$$\frac{df}{dt} = \left(9(\ln t)^2 - \frac{1}{2\sqrt{(\ln t)+t^2}}\right)\frac{1}{t} - \frac{2t}{2\sqrt{(\ln t)+t^2}} \ .$$

13. Find a) $\dfrac{\partial f}{\partial u}$ and b) $\dfrac{\partial f}{\partial v}$ where $f(x,y) = x^3 y^5$ with $x(u,v) = u+v$ and $y(u,v) = u^2 - v^2$.

SOLUTION: The partial derivatives are

$$\frac{\partial f}{\partial x} = 3x^2 y^5, \quad \frac{\partial f}{\partial y} = 5x^3 y^4; \quad \frac{\partial x}{\partial u} = 1 = \frac{\partial x}{\partial v};$$

$$\frac{\partial y}{\partial u} = 2u, \quad \text{and} \quad \frac{\partial y}{\partial v} = -2v.$$

Thus by the chain rule,

a) $\dfrac{\partial f}{\partial u} = \dfrac{\partial f}{\partial x} \cdot \dfrac{\partial x}{\partial u} + \dfrac{\partial f}{\partial y} \cdot \dfrac{\partial y}{\partial u} = (3x^2 y^5)(1) + (5x^3 y^4)(2u)$

$$= 3(u+v)^2 (u^2 - v^2)^5 + 10u(u+v)^3 (u^2 - v^2)^4$$

$$= (u + v)^7 (u - v)^4 \left(3(u - v) + 10u \right) = (u + v)^7 (u - v)^4 (13u - 3v)$$

and   b) $$\frac{\partial f}{\partial v} = \frac{\partial f}{\partial x} \cdot \frac{\partial x}{\partial v} + \frac{\partial f}{\partial y} \cdot \frac{\partial y}{\partial v} = (3x^2 y^5)(1) + (5x^3 y^4)(-2v)$$

$$= 3(u + v)^2 (u^2 - v^2)^5 - 10v(u + v)^3 (u^2 - v^2)^4$$

$$= (u + v)^7 (u - v)^4 \left(3(u - v) - 10v \right) = (u + v)^7 (u - v)^4 (3u - 13v).$$

21. Find   a) $\dfrac{\partial f}{\partial u}$ and   b) $\dfrac{\partial f}{\partial v}$ where $f(x, y, z) = \ln(x + y + z)$ with $x(u, v) = e^{u^2 + v^2}$, $y(u, v) = \ln(u^2 + v^2)$ and $z(u, v) = u - v$.

SOLUTION: The partial derivatives are

$$\frac{\partial f}{\partial x} = \frac{1}{x + y + z} = \frac{\partial f}{\partial y} = \frac{\partial f}{\partial z}; \qquad \frac{\partial x}{\partial u} = 2ue^{u^2 + v^2}, \quad \frac{\partial x}{\partial v} = 2ve^{u^2 + v^2};$$

$$\frac{\partial y}{\partial u} = \frac{2u}{u^2 + v^2}, \quad \frac{\partial y}{\partial v} = \frac{2v}{u^2 + v^2}; \qquad \text{and} \qquad \frac{\partial z}{\partial u} = 1, \quad \frac{\partial z}{\partial v} = -1.$$

By the chain rule,

a) $$\frac{\partial f}{\partial u} = \frac{\partial f}{\partial x} \cdot \frac{\partial x}{\partial u} + \frac{\partial f}{\partial y} \cdot \frac{\partial y}{\partial u} + \frac{\partial f}{\partial z} \cdot \frac{\partial z}{\partial u}$$

$$= \left(\frac{1}{x + y + z} \right) \left(2ue^{u^2 + v^2} \right) + \left(\frac{1}{x + y + z} \right) \left(\frac{2u}{u^2 + v^2} \right) + \left(\frac{1}{x + y + z} \right) (1) \quad (1)$$

$$= \left(\frac{1}{e^{u^2 + v^2} + \ln(u^2 + v^2) + u - v} \right) \left(2ue^{u^2 + v^2} + \frac{2u}{u^2 + v^2} + 1 \right)$$

and   b) $$\frac{\partial f}{\partial v} = \frac{\partial f}{\partial x} \cdot \frac{\partial x}{\partial v} + \frac{\partial f}{\partial y} \cdot \frac{\partial y}{\partial v} + \frac{\partial f}{\partial z} \cdot \frac{\partial z}{\partial v}$$

$$= \left(\frac{1}{x + y + z} \right) \left(2ve^{u^2 + v^2} \right) + \left(\frac{1}{x + y + z} \right) \left(\frac{2v}{u^2 + v^2} \right) + \left(\frac{1}{x + y + z} \right) (-1)$$

$$= \left(\frac{1}{e^{u^2 + v^2} + \ln(u^2 + v^2) + u - v} \right) \left(2ve^{u^2 + v^2} + \frac{2v}{u^2 + v^2} - 1 \right).$$

23. Find $\dfrac{df}{dt}$ where $f(x, y) = x^3 y^5$, $x = u + v$, $y = u^2 - v^2$ as in EXERCISE 13, and where $u = 2t$ and $v = 3t$.

SOLUTION: The only derivatives needed are $\dfrac{du}{dt} = 2$ and $\dfrac{dv}{dt} = 3$. Use the solution of EXER-

CISE 13 above for $\dfrac{\partial f}{\partial u}$ and $\dfrac{\partial f}{\partial v}$ in the chain rule,

$$\frac{df}{dt} = \frac{\partial f}{\partial u} \cdot \frac{du}{dt} + \frac{\partial f}{\partial v} \cdot \frac{dv}{dt}$$

$$= (u + v)^7(u - v)^4(13u - 3v)(2) + (u + v)^7(u - v)^4(3u - 13v)(3)$$

$$= (2t + 3t)^7(2t - 3t)^4(26t - 9t)(2) + (2t + 3t)^7(2t - 3t)^4(6t - 39t)(3)$$

$$= -5,078,125\, t^{12}.$$

31. Find $\dfrac{df}{dt}$ where $f(x, y, z) = \ln(x + y + z)$, $x = e^{u^2 + v^2}$, $y = \ln(u^2 + v^2)$ and $z = u - v$ as in EXERCISE 21, and where $u = 2t$ while $v = 3t$.

SOLUTION: Use the results of EXERCISE 21 above for $\dfrac{\partial f}{\partial u}$ and $\dfrac{\partial f}{\partial v}$ in the chain rule:

$$\frac{df}{dt} = \frac{\partial f}{\partial u} \cdot \frac{du}{dt} + \frac{\partial f}{\partial v} \cdot \frac{dv}{dt}$$

$$= \left(\frac{1}{e^{u^2 + v^2} + \ln(u^2 + v^2) + u - v} \right) \left(2u e^{u^2 + v^2} + \frac{2u}{u^2 + v^2} + 1 \right)(2)$$

$$+ \left(\frac{1}{e^{u^2 + v^2} + \ln(u^2 + v^2) + u - v} \right) \left(2v e^{u^2 + v^2} + \frac{2v}{u^2 + v^2} - 1 \right)(3)$$

$$= \left(\frac{1}{e^{[(2t)^2 + (3t)^2]} + \ln\left((2t)^2 + (3t)^2\right) + 2t - 3t} \right) \left(\left(2(2t)e^{(2t)^2 + (3t)^2} + \frac{2(2t)}{(2t)^2 + (3t)^2} + 1 \right)(2) \right.$$

$$\left. + \left(2(3t)e^{(2t)^2 + (3t)^2} + \frac{2(3t)}{(2t)^2 + (3t)^2} - 1 \right)(3) \right)$$

$$= \left(\frac{1}{e^{13t^2} + \ln(13t^2) - t} \right) \left(26t e^{13t^2} + \frac{2}{t} - 1 \right).$$

35. Use THEOREM 14.31 to find $\dfrac{dy}{dx}$ where $x^2 y + xy^2 = 6(x^2 + y^2)$.

SOLUTION: Here y is implicitly defined as a function of x by the equation

$$F(x, y) = x^2 y + xy^2 - 6(x^2 + y^2) = 0.$$

Since $F_x = 2xy + y^2 - 12x$ and $F_y = x^2 + 2xy - 12y$, then

$$\frac{dy}{dx} = -\frac{F_x(x, y)}{F_y(x, y)} = -\frac{2xy + y^2 - 12x}{x^2 + 2xy - 12y}.$$

39. Show that if $z = f(x, y)$, $x = r \cos\theta$, and $y = r \sin\theta$, then

$$\text{i)} \qquad \frac{\partial z}{\partial r} = \frac{\partial f}{\partial x} \cos\theta + \frac{\partial f}{\partial y} \sin\theta, \qquad \text{and}$$

$$\text{ii)} \qquad \frac{\partial z}{\partial \theta} = r \left[-\frac{\partial f}{\partial x} \sin\theta + \frac{\partial f}{\partial y} \cos\theta \right].$$

SOLUTION: The partial derivatives are

$$\frac{\partial x}{\partial r} = \cos\theta, \quad \frac{\partial x}{\partial \theta} = -r\sin\theta, \quad \frac{\partial y}{\partial r} = \sin\theta \quad \text{and} \quad \frac{\partial y}{\partial \theta} = r\cos\theta.$$

By the chain rule,

i) $\quad\dfrac{\partial f}{\partial r} = \dfrac{\partial f}{\partial x}\cdot\dfrac{\partial x}{\partial r} + \dfrac{\partial f}{\partial y}\cdot\dfrac{\partial y}{\partial r} = \dfrac{\partial f}{\partial x}(\cos\theta) + \dfrac{\partial f}{\partial y}(\sin\theta), \quad$ and

ii) $\quad\dfrac{\partial f}{\partial \theta} = \dfrac{\partial f}{\partial x}\cdot\dfrac{\partial x}{\partial \theta} + \dfrac{\partial f}{\partial y}\cdot\dfrac{\partial y}{\partial \theta} = \dfrac{\partial f}{\partial x}(-r\sin\theta) + \dfrac{\partial f}{\partial y}(r\cos\theta)$

$$= r\left(-\frac{\partial f}{\partial x}\sin\theta + \frac{\partial f}{\partial y}\cos\theta\right).$$

45. Suppose that $f(x, y) = 0$ implicitly defines y as a function of x and that y'' and the second partial derivatives of f exist. Express y'' in terms of the first and second partial derivatives of f.

SOLUTION: By THEOREM 14.31, $y' = -\dfrac{f_x(x,y)}{f_y(x,y)}$. Use the chain rule to calculate

$$y''(x) = \frac{d}{dx}[y'(x)] = D_x\left[-\frac{f_x(x,y)}{f_y(x,y)}\right]\cdot\frac{dx}{dx} + D_y\left[-\frac{f_x(x,y)}{f_y(x,y)}\right]\cdot\frac{dy}{dx}$$

$$= \left(-\frac{f_y(x,y)D_x[f_x(x,y)] - f_x(x,y)D_x[f_y(x,y)]}{(f_y(x,y))^2}\right)$$

$$+ \left(-\frac{f_y(x,y)D_y[f_x(x,y)] - f_x(x,y)D_y[f_y(x,y)]}{(f_y(x,y))^2}\right)\left(-\frac{f_x(x,y)}{f_y(x,y)}\right)$$

$$= -\frac{(f_y(x,y))^2 f_{xx}(x,y) - 2f_x(x,y)f_y(x,y)f_{xy}(x,y) + (f_x(x,y))^2 f_{yy}(x,y)}{(f_y(x,y))^3}.$$

——————————————————————————————**14.5**

Directional Derivatives and Gradients

3. Find the directional derivative of $f(x, y) = x^2 + y^2$ at $P(1, 1)$ in the direction of $\mathbf{v} = \mathbf{i} + \mathbf{j}$.

SOLUTION: To apply the formula in THEOREM 14.33, $D_{\mathbf{u}}f(x, y) = f_x(x, y)u_1 + f_y(x, y)u_2$, calculate the partial derivatives, evaluate them at $(1, 1)$, calculate the unit vector $\mathbf{u}$ with the same direction as **v** and form the expression above. The partial derivatives are $f_x = 2x$ and $f_y = 2y$; at $P(1,1)$ these are $f_x(1,1) = 2$ and $f_y(1,1) = 2$. The unit vector is $\mathbf{u} = \mathbf{v}/\|\mathbf{v}\| = (\mathbf{i} + \mathbf{j})/(\sqrt{1^2 + 1^2}) = (1/\sqrt{2})\mathbf{i} + (1/\sqrt{2})\mathbf{j}$. The directional derivative is thus

$$D_{\mathbf{u}}f(1,1) = 2 \cdot \frac{1}{\sqrt{2}} + 2 \cdot \frac{1}{\sqrt{2}} = 2\sqrt{2}.$$

9. Find the directional derivative of $f(x,y,z) = \cos(x + y + z)$ at $P\left(0, \frac{\pi}{4}, \frac{\pi}{2}\right)$ in the direction $\mathbf{v} = \mathbf{i} - 2\mathbf{j} + 2\mathbf{k}$.

SOLUTION: The partial derivatives of f are $f_x = -\sin(x + y + z) = f_y = f_z$; at $P\left(0, \frac{\pi}{4}, \frac{\pi}{2}\right)$ these have the same value: $f_x = f_y = f_z\left(0, \frac{\pi}{4}, \frac{\pi}{2}\right) = -\sin\left(0 + \frac{\pi}{4} + \frac{\pi}{2}\right) = -\frac{\sqrt{2}}{2}$. The unit vector is $\mathbf{u} = \dfrac{\mathbf{i} - 2\mathbf{j} + 2\mathbf{k}}{\sqrt{1^2 + 2^2 + 2^2}} = (1/3)\mathbf{i} - (2/3)\mathbf{j} + (2/3)\mathbf{k}$, so the directional derivative is

$$D_{\mathbf{u}}f\left(0, \frac{\pi}{4}, \frac{\pi}{2}\right) = \left(-\frac{\sqrt{2}}{2}\right)\left(\frac{1}{3}\right) + \left(-\frac{\sqrt{2}}{2}\right)\left(-\frac{2}{3}\right) + \left(-\frac{\sqrt{2}}{2}\right)\left(\frac{2}{3}\right) = -\frac{\sqrt{2}}{6}.$$

15. Find the gradient of $f(x,y) = \dfrac{xy}{x^2 + y^2}$.

SOLUTION: The gradient is $\nabla f(x,y) = f_x(x,y)\mathbf{i} + f_y(x,y)\mathbf{j}$ where

$$f_x(x,y) = D_x\left[\frac{xy}{x^2 + y^2}\right] = \frac{y(x^2 + y^2) - xy(2x)}{(x^2 + y^2)^2} = \frac{y(y^2 - x^2)}{(x^2 + y^2)^2}$$

and $$f_y(x,y) = D_y\left[\frac{xy}{x^2 + y^2}\right] = \frac{x(x^2 + y^2) - xy(2y)}{(x^2 + y^2)^2} = \frac{x(x^2 - y^2)}{(x^2 + y^2)^2}.$$

Thus, $$\nabla f(x,y) = \frac{y(y^2 - x^2)}{(x^2 + y^2)^2}\mathbf{i} + \frac{x(x^2 - y^2)}{(x^2 + y^2)^2}\mathbf{j}.$$

23. Find the gradient of $f(x,y,z) = \cos xyz$ at $P\left(1, 2, \frac{\pi}{4}\right)$.

SOLUTION: The partial derivatives of $f(x,y,z) = \cos xyz$ are $f_x = -yz\sin xyz$, $f_y = -xz\sin xyz$ and $f_z = -xy\sin xyz$. Their values at $P\left(1, 2, \frac{\pi}{4}\right)$ are $f_x\left(1, 2, \frac{\pi}{4}\right) = -\frac{\pi}{2}\sin\frac{\pi}{2} = -\frac{\pi}{2}$, $f_y\left(1, 2, \frac{\pi}{4}\right) = -\frac{\pi}{4}\sin\frac{\pi}{2} = -\frac{\pi}{4}$ and $f_z\left(1, 2, \frac{\pi}{4}\right) = -2\sin\frac{\pi}{2} = -2$, so the gradient is

$$\nabla f\left(1, 2, \frac{\pi}{4}\right) = -\frac{\pi}{2}\mathbf{i} - \frac{\pi}{4}\mathbf{j} - 2\mathbf{k}.$$

27. a) Find the direction in which $f(x,y) = 9x^2 + 4y^2$ increases most rapidly at $P(2,0)$.
b) Find this maximum rate of increase.

SOLUTION: Since f is differentiable then according to THEOREM 14.37, the direction of maximum increase of f is the same direction as the gradient, and the maximum rate of increase is the magnitude of the gradient. The gradient has components $f_x(2,0) = 18(2) = 36$ and $f_y(2,0) = 8(0) = 0$, so $\nabla f(2,0) = 36\,\mathbf{i} + 0\,\mathbf{j}$.
a) The unit direction of maximum increase of f at $(2,0)$ is $\mathbf{u} = (\nabla f)/(\|\nabla f\|) = (36\,\mathbf{i})/36 = \mathbf{i}$.
b) The maximum rate of increase is $\|\nabla f\| = 36$. At $(2,0)$ $f(x,y)$ increases most rapidly in the direction of the x-axis and this maximum directional derivative is 36.

31. a) Find the direction in which $f(x,y,z) = e^x(\cos y - \sin z)$ increases most rapidly at $P\left(1,\pi,\frac{\pi}{2}\right)$. b) What is this maximum rate of increase?

SOLUTION: As above, the gradient of f at P provides the solution. This gradient has components $f_x\left(1,\pi,\frac{\pi}{2}\right) = e^1\left(\cos\pi - \sin\frac{\pi}{2}\right) = -2e$, $f_y\left(1,\pi,\frac{\pi}{2}\right) = e^1(-\sin\pi) = 0$, and $f_z\left(1,\pi,\frac{\pi}{2}\right) = e^1\left(-\cos\frac{\pi}{2}\right) = 0$. The gradient is thus $\nabla f\left(1,\pi\frac{\pi}{2}\right) = -2e\,\mathbf{i} + 0\,\mathbf{j} + 0\,\mathbf{k}$.
a) The unit direction of maximum increase is $\mathbf{u} = (\nabla f)/(\|\nabla f\|) = (-2e\,\mathbf{i})/|2e| = -\mathbf{i}$.
b) The maximum rate of increase is $\|\nabla f\| = 2e$.

35. Find the directional derivative of $f(x,y) = x^2\ln xy$ at $P(e,1)$ in the direction $\mathbf{v}$ which makes an angle $\theta = -\pi/3$ with the positive x-axis.

SOLUTION: Formula 14.34 of the text gives the formula for this directional derivative as $D_{\mathbf{u}}f(x,y) = f_x(x,y)\cos\theta + f_y(x,y)\sin\theta$. The partial derivatives are $f_x = 2x\ln xy + x$ and $f_y = x^2/y$. Use the values $x = e$, $y = 1$, and $\theta = -\pi/3$ to obtain

$$D_{\mathbf{u}}f(e,1) = (2e\ln e + e)\cos\left(-\frac{\pi}{3}\right) + \left(\frac{e^2}{1}\right)\sin\left(-\frac{\pi}{3}\right) = \frac{3}{2}e - \frac{\sqrt{3}}{2}e^2.$$

41. Find the directional derivative of $f(x,y,z) = x^2 + y^2 + z^2$ at $P(0,1,1)$ in the direction from P to $Q(2,-1,3)$.

SOLUTION: The unit vector $\mathbf{u}$ with the same direction as the vector from P to Q is

$$\mathbf{u} = \frac{\overrightarrow{PQ}}{\|\overrightarrow{PQ}\|} = \frac{2\,\mathbf{i} - 2\,\mathbf{j} + 2\,\mathbf{k}}{\sqrt{2^2 + (-2)^2 + 2^2}} = \frac{1}{\sqrt{3}}\mathbf{i} - \frac{1}{\sqrt{3}}\mathbf{j} + \frac{1}{\sqrt{3}}\mathbf{k}.$$

The partial derivatives of f at P are $f_x(0,1,1) = 2\cdot 0 = 0$, $f_y(0,1,1) = 2(1) = 2$, and $f_z(0,1,1) = 2(1) = 2$. The directional derivative is

$$D_{\mathbf{u}}f(0,1,1) = 0\left(\frac{1}{\sqrt{3}}\right) + 2\left(-\frac{1}{\sqrt{3}}\right) + 2\left(\frac{1}{\sqrt{3}}\right) = 0.$$

_____**14.6**

Tangent Planes
and Normals

_____

5. Find a vector normal to the surface $z = f(x, y) = \ln xy$ at $(e, e^2, 3)$.

SOLUTION: Write the equation as $z - \ln xy = 0$ to view the surface as the 0-level surface of $F(x, y, z) = z - \ln xy$. A normal to this surface at a point (x, y, z) is $-(1/x)\mathbf{i} - (1/y)\mathbf{j} + 1\mathbf{k}$, so a normal at the point $(e, e^2, 3)$ is

$$\mathbf{N} = -(1/e)\mathbf{i} - (1/e^2)\mathbf{j} + \mathbf{k}.$$

11. Find an equation of the tangent plane to the surface with equation $z^2 = x^2 + y^2$ at the point $(3, -4, -5)$.

SOLUTION: This surface is the 0-level surface of the function $F(x, y, z) = z^2 - x^2 - y^2$ so a normal at (x, y, z) is $\nabla F(x, y, z) = (-2x)\mathbf{i} + (-2y)\mathbf{j} + (2z)\mathbf{k}$. A normal at $(3, -4, -5)$ is $\mathbf{N} = -6\mathbf{i} + 8\mathbf{j} - 10\mathbf{k}$, so the equation of the tangent plane at this point is $-6(x - 3) + 8(y - (-4)) - 10(z - (-5)) = 0$, or

$$6x - 8y + 10z = 0.$$

19. Find equations of the tangent line to the curve of intersection of the surfaces $x^2 + y^2 = 4$ and $z^2 = x^2 + y^2$ at the point $(0, 2, 2)$.

SOLUTION: Formula 14.48 in the text gives the vector $\nabla F_1 \times \nabla F_2$ as a direction of the tangent to the curve of intersection $F_1(x, y, z) = c_1$ and $F_2(x, y, z) = c_2$. With $F_1(x, y, z) = x^2 + y^2 - 4$ and $F_2(x, y, z) = z^2 - x^2 - y^2$, the gradients at the common point $(0, 2, 2)$ are $\nabla F_1(0, 2, 2) = 2(0)\mathbf{i} + 2(2)\mathbf{j} + 0\mathbf{k} = 4\mathbf{j}$ and $\nabla F_2(0, 2, 2) = -2(0)\mathbf{i} - 2(2)\mathbf{j} + 2(2)\mathbf{k} = -4\mathbf{j} + 4\mathbf{k}$. The cross product is

$$\nabla F_1 \times \nabla F_2 = \begin{vmatrix} \mathbf{i} & \mathbf{j} & \mathbf{k} \\ 0 & 4 & 0 \\ 0 & -4 & 4 \end{vmatrix} = 16\mathbf{i}$$

which is used as the direction vector for the tangent line. Parametric equations for the line through $(0, 2, 2)$ with direction $\mathbf{v} = 16\mathbf{i}$ are $x = 0 + 16t$, $y = 2 + 0t$, $z = 2 + 0t$, or

$$x = 16t, \qquad y = 2, \qquad z = 2.$$

25. Find the points on the paraboloid $z = 4x^2 + y^2$ at which the tangent plane is parallel to the plane $x + 2y + z = 6$.

SOLUTION: The tangent plane is parallel to the given plane at all points where the normal to the surface is parallel to the normal to the plane. The surface is the 0-level surface for $F(x, y, z) = z - 4x^2 - y^2$ so a normal at the point (x, y, z) in the surface $z = 4x^2 + y^2$ is $\nabla F(x, y, z) = (-8x)\mathbf{i} + (-2y)\mathbf{j} + \mathbf{k}$. A normal to the plane $x + 2y + z = 6$ is $\mathbf{N} = \mathbf{i} + 2\mathbf{j} + \mathbf{k}$. These normals are parallel at all points in the surface $z = 4x^2 + y^2$ at which a constant λ exists so that $\nabla F(x, y, z) = \lambda \mathbf{N}$. This vector equation, $-8x\,\mathbf{i} - 2y\mathbf{j} + \mathbf{k} = \lambda \mathbf{i} + 2\lambda\mathbf{j} + \lambda\mathbf{k}$, along with the requirement that the point lies in the surface, gives the set of equations

$$-8x = \lambda, \quad -2y = 2\lambda, \quad 1 = \lambda, \quad \text{and} \quad z = 4x^2 + y^2.$$

The third equation, $\lambda = 1$, implies that $x = -1/8$, $y = -1$, and thus by the fourth equation that $z = 4(-1/8)^2 + (-1)^2 = 17/16$.

The tangent plane at $(-1/8, -1, 17/16)$ to the surface $z = 4x^2 + y^2$ is parallel to the plane $x + 2y + z = 6$, and this is the only such point.

COMMENT: Notice that the multiplier, λ, is one in this problem. You would have obtained the correct result by seeking a point where the two normals were equal. This is a coincidence here and will not work for most problems.

_____14.7

Extrema of
Multivariable Functions

1. Show that if $f(x, y) = 4 - x^2 - y^2$, then f has an absolute maximum at $(0, 0)$.

SOLUTION: Since $x^2 + y^2 \geq 0$ then, for each (x, y), $f(x, y) = 4 - (x^2 + y^2) \leq 4 - 0 = 4 = f(0, 0)$; that is, $f(x, y) \leq f(0, 0)$ so f has an absolute maximum at $(0, 0)$.

5. Find all critical points of $f(x, y) = x^2 - xy + y^2$.

SOLUTION: Since $f_x = 2x - y$ and $f_y = -x + 2y$ are defined everywhere, the only critical points are where these partial derivatives are simultaneously zero. Solve the system of equations

$$\text{i) } (f_x =)\ 2x - y = 0 \qquad \text{ii) } (f_y =)\ -x + 2y = 0;$$

by solving i) for y in terms of x and substituting the result into ii),

$$\text{i)}'\ y = 2x \qquad \text{and} \qquad \text{ii)}'\ -x + 2(2x) = 0.$$

The solution to ii)$'$ is $x = 0$ and thus i)$'$ is solved by $y = 0$. The only critical point is $(0, 0)$.

11. Find all critical points of $f(x,y) = xy^2 + x^3 - 4y^2$.

SOLUTION: Since $f_x = y^2 + 3x^2$ and $f_y = 2xy - 8y$ exist everywhere then the critical points are solutions to the system of equations

$$\text{i) } (f_x =)\ y^2 + 3x^2 = 0 \qquad \text{ii) } (f_y =)\ 2xy - 8y = 0.$$

Since the left hand side of i) is a sum of squares, its only solution is $x = 0$, $y = 0$, which also solves ii), so the only critical point is $(0,0)$.

13. Use THEOREM 14.55 to determine whether the critical point $(0,0)$ is a relative maximum, relative minimum, or saddle point for $f(x,y) = x^2 - xy + y^2$.

SOLUTION: With values of f_x and f_y from the solution to EXERCISE 5 above, the second partial derivatives are $f_{xx} = 2$, $f_{yy} = 2$, and $f_{xy} = -1$ so the discriminant is $D(x,y) = (2)(2) - (-1)^2 = 1$. At the critical point $(0,0)$, $D(0,0) = 1 > 0$ and $f_{xx}(0,0) = 2 > 0$ so according to part (ii) of THEOREM 14.55, f has a relative minimum at $(0,0)$.

19. Use THEOREM 14.55 to determine whether the critical point $(0,0)$ is a relative maximum, relative minimum, or saddle point for $f(x,y) = xy^2 + x^3 - 4y^2$.

SOLUTION: With the values of f_x and f_y from the solution to EXERCISE 11 above, the second partial derivatives are $f_{xx} = 6x$, $f_{yy} = 2x - 8$, and $f_{xy} = 2y$ so the discriminant is $D(x,y) = (6x)(2x - 8) - (2y)^2$. At the critical point $(0,0)$, $D(0,0) = 0$ so THEOREM 14.55 does not apply.

COMMENT: The function $f(x,y) = xy^2 + x^3 - 4y^2$ has a saddle point at $(0,0)$ since $f(x,0) = x^3$ is both positive and negative inside each circle centered at $(0,0)$, and thus $f(x,y)$ has neither a relative minimum nor a relative maximum at $(0,0)$.

23. Find all critical points for $f(x,y) = x^2y - 5xy + 6y$ and use THEOREM 14.55 to determine any relative extrema for f.

SOLUTION: Since $f_x = 2xy - 5y$ and $f_y = x^2 - 5x + 6$ exist everywhere then the critical points are the solutions to the system of equations

$$\text{i) } (f_x =)\ 2xy - 5y = 0 \qquad \text{ii) } (f_y =)\ x^2 - 5x + 6 = 0.$$

Equation ii) can be solved by factoring the left hand side to give   ii) $(x - 3)(x - 2) = 0$ which has solutions $x = 3$ and $x = 2$. In either case the only solution to equation i) is $y = 0$. Thus, the two critical points are $(2,0)$ and $(3,0)$.

The second partial derivatives are $f_{xx} = 2y$, $f_{yy} = 0$, and $f_{xy} = 2x - 5$, so the discriminant is $D(x,y) = (2y)(0) - (2x - 5)^2 = -(2x - 5)^2$. The values of D at the critical points, $D(2,0) = -1$ and $D(3,0) = -1$, are both negative so each is a saddle point. There are no relative extrema.

31. Find all critical points for $f(x, y) = \cos x + \cos y$ and use THEOREM 14.55 to determine any relative extrema for f.

SOLUTION: Since $f_x = -\sin x$ and $f_y = -\sin y$ exist everywhere, then the only critical points are the solutions to the system of equations

$$\text{i) } (f_x =) \ -\sin x = 0 \qquad \text{ii) } (f_y =) \ -\sin y = 0.$$

The sine function vanishes only at multiples of π so the solutions to this system are all (x, y) such that $x = m\pi$ and $y = n\pi$ for any integers m and n. There are infinitely many critical points $(m\pi, n\pi)$ where $m, n = -\infty, \ldots, \infty$.

The second partial derivatives are $f_{xx} = -\cos x$, $f_{yy} = -\cos y$ and $f_{xy} = 0$ so the discriminant is $D(x, y) = (-\cos x)(-\cos y) - 0^2 = \cos x \cos y$. At the critical point of the form $(n\pi, m\pi)$, $D(n\pi, m\pi) = \cos(n\pi)\cos(m\pi) = (-1)^{n+m}$ so there are three cases:

i) if n and m are both even, then $D(n\pi, m\pi) = (-1)^{n+m} = 1 > 0$ and $f_{xx} = -\cos(n\pi) = -1 < 0$ so all points of this form are relative maxima for f.

ii) if n and m are both odd, then $D(n\pi, m\pi) = (-1)^{n+m} = 1 > 0$ and $f_{xx} = -\cos(n\pi) = 1 > 0$ so all points of this form are relative minima for f.

iii) if n and m are of opposite parity, then $D(n\pi, m\pi) = (-1)^{n+m} = -1 < 0$ so all points of this form are saddle points.

If even numbers are written as $2k$ and odd numbers as $2k + 1$, then we can classify the critical points as follows; for all n and m,

i) $(2n\pi, 2m\pi)$ are relative maxima for f.

ii) $((2n + 1)\pi, (2m + 1)\pi)$ are relative minima for f.

iii) $(2n\pi, (2m + 1)\pi)$ and $((2n + 1)\pi, 2m\pi)$ are saddle points for f.

37. Determine whether the relative minimum of $f(x, y) = e^{x^2 + y^2}$ found in EXERCISE 25 is an absolute minimum.

SOLUTION: The point $(0, 0)$ is a relative minimum of $f(x, y) = e^{x^2 + y^2}$. To see that it is an absolute minimum, observe that the exponential function is increasing since its derivative is everywhere positive. Thus for any (x, y), since $x^2 + y^2 \geq 0$ then $f(x, y) = e^{x^2 + y^2} \geq e^0 = f(0, 0)$. Hence, $(0, 0)$ is an absolute minimum.

43. Determine whether the relative extrema of $f(x, y) = \cos x + \cos y$ found in EXERCISE 31 are absolute extrema.

SOLUTION: The relative maxima of f are at the points $(2n\pi, 2m\pi)$, where $f(2n\pi, 2m\pi) = \cos(2n\pi) + \cos(2m\pi) = 2$. The relative minima are at the points $((2n + 1)\pi, (2m + 1)\pi)$, where

$$f((2n + 1)\pi, (2m + 1)\pi) = \cos(2n + 1)\pi + \cos(2m + 1)\pi = -2.$$

Since $-1 \leq \cos\theta \leq 1$ then $-2 \leq \cos x + \cos y \leq 2$ for all (x, y), so

$$f((2n + 1)\pi, (2m + 1)\pi) \leq f(x, y) \leq f(2n\pi, 2m\pi).$$

Hence, all points of the form $(2n\pi, 2m\pi)$ are absolute maxima of f, and those of the form $((2n + 1)\pi, (2m + 1)\pi)$ are absolute minima of f.

47. Find the absolute maximum and minimum values of $f(x, y) = xy$ on the region $x^2 + 2y^2 \le 4$.

SOLUTION: As was suggested in the text, first find any relative extrema in the interior of the region, then find the extrema of the function for values lying on the boundary. Select from among all these the absolute maximum and minimum.

Candidates for relative extrema in the interior are the critical points, (x, y) :

$$\text{i) } (f_x =) \; y = 0 \qquad \text{and} \qquad \text{ii) } (f_y =) \; x = 0.$$

The only critical point is $(0, 0)$. The discriminant is $D(x, y) = (f_{xx})(f_{yy}) - (f_{xy})^2 = (0)(0) - 1^2 < 0$, so, at the critical point, $D(0, 0) < 0$ and this point is a saddle point. The boundary of this region is an ellipse which can be described parametrically by $x(t) = 2 \cos t$, $y(t) = \sqrt{2} \sin t$, for $0 \le t \le 2\pi$. At a point $(x(t), y(t))$ on the boundary, the function f has the value $f(x(t), y(t)) = (2 \cos t)(\sqrt{2} \sin t) = \sqrt{2} \sin(2t)$, so the extrema of f on the boundary correspond to the extrema of the function $F(t) = \sqrt{2} \sin(2t)$ on the interval $0 \le t \le 2\pi$. The derivatives of this function are $F'(t) = 2\sqrt{2} \cos 2t$ and $F''(t) = -4\sqrt{2} \sin 2t$. F has critical points where $(F'(t) =) \; 2\sqrt{2} \cos(2t) = 0$, $0 \le t \le 2\pi$; that is, at $t = \pi/4, 3\pi/4, 5\pi/4$, and $7\pi/4$. At $t = \pi/4$ and $5\pi/4$, $F''(t) = -4\sqrt{2} < 0$ so these points are relative maxima of F. The value of f at these points is $-\sqrt{2}$. At $t = 3\pi/4$ and $t = 7\pi/4$, $F''(t) = 4\sqrt{2} > 0$ so these points are relative minima of F. The value of f here is $-\sqrt{2}$. At the endpoints of the t-interval $F(0) = F(2\pi) = 0$. The absolute maximum and minimum values of $\sqrt{2}$ and $-\sqrt{2}$ occur on the boundary of the region.

53. Find the absolute minimum of the function f described by $f(x, y, z) = 2x + 3y + z$ if x, y, and z satisfy $z = x^2 + y^2$.

SOLUTION: Reduce the number of variables by one by using the constraint equation $z = x^2 + y^2$ to construct the reduced function of x and y,

$$F(x, y) = 2x + 3y + (x^2 + y^2).$$

Find the absolute minimum of this reduced function where x and y are unconstrained. The critical points of F satisfy the system

$$\text{i) } (F_x =) \; 2 + 2x = 0 \qquad \text{ii) } (F_y =) \; 3 + 2y = 0.$$

The only solution to these equations is $x = -1$, $y = -3/2$. The second partials are $F_{xx} = 2$, $F_{yy} = 2$ and $F_{xy} = 0$ so the discriminant is $D(x, y) = (2)(2) - (0)^2$. Since $D(-1, -3/2) > 0$ and $F_{xx} > 0$, the point $(-1, -3/2)$ is a relative minimum of F. To see that this is an absolute minimum, rewrite the reduced function as $F(x, y) = (x + 1)^2 + (y + 3/2)^2 - 13/4$. Since the sum of squares is always nonnegative, it then follows that

$$F(x, y) \ge -\frac{13}{4} = F(-1, -3/2) \quad \text{for all } (x, y).$$

The absolute minimum of the original function $f(x, y, z) = 2x + 3y + z$ has x and y coordinates $x = -1$ and $y = -3/2$. Its z coordinate as determined by the constraint which was used to eliminate z is $z = (-1)^2 + (-3/2)^2 = 13/4$. The absolute minimum of f is at $(-1, -3/2, 13/4)$.

COMMENT: (1) One <u>strategy</u> for solving constrained extremization problems is to: (i) Reduce the number of variables by eliminating as many variables as there are constraint equations. This is done by solving the constraint equations for certain variables in terms of the remaining variables. (ii) Reformulate the problem as the extremization of the reduced function F obtained by substituting these certain variable value expressions where they occur in the expression for f. (iii) Minimize or maximize the reduced function F of fewer variables. The region over which the problem is to be solved may still be restricted by inequalities, so care should be taken to describe it carefully. (iv) Resubstitute the variable values which solve the reduced problem into the constraint equations to determine the values of the eliminated variables at the extremum. (v) Determine that you have solved the problem as posed and that your solution makes sense.

COMMENT: (2) The problem of determining absolute extrema is more difficult for unbounded regions than for bounded regions. In the latter case the minimum must occur on the boundary or at critical points in the interior. In the case of an unbounded region, there may be no extremum because of the behavior of the function at faraway points. Indeed, the *values of f at infinity* must be determined, either explicitly as is done in Example 8 of the text or implicitly as is done through the use of inequalities in the solutions above. These values are then compared to the relative extrema in the interior and the boundary extrema to determine the absolute extrema if they exist. Notice that the function $f(x, y, z) = 2x + 3y + z$ in Exercise 53 has no absolute maximum over the set $z = x^2 + y^2$ because the reduced function $F(x, y) = (x + 1)^2 + (y + 3/2)^2 - 13/4$ is unbounded above for arbitrarily large x and y.

59. Determine the three positive numbers whose product is 27 and whose sum is as small as possible.

SOLUTION: Formulate this problem as finding the absolute minimum of $f(x, y, z) = x + y + z$ subject to the constraints $xyz = 27$ and $x > 0$, $y > 0$, $z > 0$.

Solve the equality constraint for z, $z = 27/(xy)$ to obtain the reduced function

$$F(x, y) = x + y + \frac{27}{xy}.$$

The reduced problem is to find the absolute minimum of F over the set where $x > 0$, $y > 0$, and $(27/xy) > 0$. (This last inequality is redundant since it is a consequence of the first two. It may be removed here, but in general, inequalities that involve the eliminated variable(s) must not be ignored.)

The critical points of F interior to the region satisfy

i) $(F_x =) 1 - \dfrac{27}{x^2 y} = 0$ ii) $(F_y =) 1 - \dfrac{27}{xy^2} = 0$,   for $x > 0$, $y > 0$.

Since x and y are both positive, these equations can be written as i)' $x^2 y = 27$, and ii)' $xy^2 = 27$. From i)' conclude that $y = (27)/(x^2)$ which, when substituted into ii)' yields $x\left(27/x^2\right)^2 = 27$ or $x^3 = 27$. Thus $x = 3$, $y = 3$ is the only critical point of the reduced function F for which $x > 0$, $y > 0$. The discriminant is

$$D(x,y) = \left(2\frac{27}{x^3 y}\right)\left(2\frac{27}{xy^3}\right) - \left(\frac{27}{x^2 y^2}\right)^2 = \frac{3(27)^2}{x^4 y^4}.$$

Since $D(3,3) > 0$ and $F_{xx}(3,3) = 2\dfrac{27}{3^3 3} > 0$ then $(3,3)$ is a relative minimum of F. Indeed, this is the only relative extremum of F in the region where x and y are positive.

Since x and y are positive, $F(x,y) = x + y + (27/xy) > (27/xy)$ so as x or y approaches zero F becomes infinite. Similarly, $F(x,y) = x + y + (27/xy) > x + y$ so as x or y becomes infinite so does F. Thus the reduced function F has an absolute minimum at $(3,3)$.

The original function has an absolute minimum at $x = 3$, $y = 3$, $z = 27/(3 \cdot 3) = 3$, so of all sets of three positive numbers with product 27, the smallest sum occurs when all three numbers are 3.

63. U.S. postal regulations require that in post offices serving more than 600 units the length plus the girth of a package to be mailed cannot exceed 84 inches. Find the dimensions of the rectangular package of greatest volume that can be mailed. (Girth = 2(width) + 2(height)).

SOLUTION:

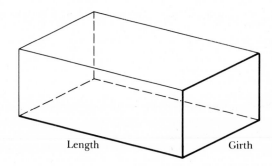

Length   Girth

Let variables l, h, and w represent length, height, and width of the package respectively. The girth is $2w + 2h$ so the postal regulation is that $l + 2w + 2h \le 84$; of course, $l \ge 0$, $w \ge 0$, and $h \ge 0$ are required by common sense. The volume is $V = lwh$.

The problem here is to maximize $f(l,w,h) = lwh$ where $l + 2w + 2h \le 84$ and $l \ge 0$, $w \ge 0$, $h \ge 0$. The region for this problem is bounded (it is the tetrahedron bounded by the planes $l + 2w + 2h = 84$, $l = 0$, $w = 0$, and $h = 0$) so an absolute maximum exists. The function $f(l,w,h) = lwh$ has no critical points in the interior of this region. On the boundaries where one of the variables is zero, $f = 0$. This leaves the boundary $l + 2w + 2h = 84$, $l > 0$, $w > 0$, $h > 0$

for consideration. Use this constraint equation to reduce the number of variables by one, solving for l, $l = 84 - 2w - 2h$. The reduced problem is thus to maximize $F(w, h) = (84 - 2w - 2h)wh$ where $w > 0$, $h > 0$, and $84 - 2w - 2h > 0$ or $w + h < 42$.

The critical points of the reduced function satisfy

$$\text{i)} \ (F_w =) \ 84h - 4wh - 2h^2 = 0 \qquad \text{ii)} \ (F_h =) \ 84w - 2w^2 - 4wh = 0.$$

Since both w and h are positive, divide both sides of i) by $2h$ and both sides of ii) by $2w$ to obtain the linear system $\begin{cases} 2w + h = 42 \\ w + 2h = 42 \end{cases}$, the solution to which is $w = 14$, $h = 14$. The critical point $(14, 14)$ satisfies all the inequalities. The discriminant is $D(w, h) = (-4h)(-4w) - (84 - 4h - 4w)^2$. Since $D(14, 14) = 4^2 \left((14)^2 - (21 - 14 - 14)^2 \right) > 0$ and $F_{ww}(14, 14) = -56 < 0$, then $(14, 14)$ is a relative maximum for the reduced function F, whose value is $F(14, 14) = 5488$. This value is greater than zero, the constant value of F on the boundary of the reduced region, $w = 0$, $h = 0$, $w + h = 42$.

Thus the absolute maximum of the reduced function is at $w = h = 14$. The corresponding value of l which satisfies the constraint is $l = 84 - 28 - 28 = 28$. The function value is $f(l, w, h) = 5488$ which is certainly greater than the value of f, zero, on the other three boundaries $l = 0$, $w = 0$, $h = 0$.

The maximum value of the volume occurs when the length is 28 and both width and height are 14. This situation occurs when the bound on the sum of length and girth is met exactly.

67. *The Method of Least Squares.* Given n points (x_1, y_1), $\ldots$, (x_n, y_n) in the xy-plane, it is usually impossible to find a straight line that passes through all the points. The Method of Least Squares finds a best approximating straight line, $y = ax + b$, for the points by finding values of a and b that minimize the sum of the squares of the differences between the y-values on the approximating line and the given y-values:

$$E(a, b) = \sum_{i=1}^{n} \left(y_i - (ax_i + b) \right)^2 .$$

Show that these values of a and b are

$$a = \frac{n(XY) - (X)(Y)}{n(X_2) - (X)^2}, \qquad b = \frac{(X_2)(Y) - (X)(XY)}{n(X_2) - (X)^2}$$

where n = number of data points (x_i, y_i), $X = \sum_{i=1}^{n} x_i$, $Y = \sum_{i=1}^{n} y_i$, $XY = \sum_{i=1}^{n} x_i y_i$, and

$$X_2 = \sum_{i=1}^{n} x_i^2 .$$

SOLUTION: The first partials of $E(a, b)$ are

$$\frac{\partial E}{\partial a} = D_a \left[\sum_{i=1}^{n} (y_i - (ax_i + b))^2 \right] = \sum_{i=1}^{n} D_a \left[(y_i - (ax_i + b))^2 \right]$$

$$= \sum_{i=1}^{n} 2\left(y_i - (ax_i + b)\right) D_a\left[-(ax_i - b)\right] = \sum_{i=1}^{n} 2\left(y_i - (ax_i + b)\right)(-x_i)$$

$$= -2\sum_{i=1}^{n}(x_i y_i - ax_i^2 - bx_i) = -2\left(\left(\sum_{i=1}^{n} x_i y_i\right) - a\left(\sum_{i=1}^{n} x_i^2\right) - b\left(\sum_{i=1}^{n} x_i\right)\right)$$

$$\frac{\partial E}{\partial b} = \sum_{i=1}^{n} D_b\left[\left(y_i - (ax_i + b)\right)^2\right] = \sum_{i=1}^{n} 2\left(y_i - (ax_i + b)\right)(1)$$

$$= 2\left(\left(\sum_{i=1}^{n} y_i\right) - a\left(\sum_{i=1}^{n} x_i\right) - b\left(\sum_{i=1}^{n} 1\right)\right).$$

Use the notation above, $X = \sum_{i=1}^{n} x_i$, etc., to write the system of equations for the critical points:

i) $\left(\dfrac{\partial E}{\partial a} =\right) \; -2(XY - aX_2 - bX) = 0$

ii) $\left(\dfrac{\partial E}{\partial b} =\right) \; 2(Y - aX - bn) = 0.$

These equations can be rearranged and written as the linear system

$$\begin{cases} (X_2)a + (X)b = (XY) \\ (X)a + nb = (Y) \end{cases}$$

which has the solution

$$a = \frac{n(XY) - (X)(Y)}{n(X_2) - (X)^2}, \qquad b = \frac{(X_2)(Y) - (X)(XY)}{n(X_2) - (X)^2}.$$

The least squares best-approximating line for a set of points $(x_1, y_1), \ldots, (x_n, y_n)$ is $y = ax + b$ where a and b are as above.

71. Use the Method of Least Squares to find the best approximating line for the collection of points $(-1, 6)$ $(1, 5)$ $(2, 3)$ $(5, 3)$ $(7, -1)$.

SOLUTION: Use the x and y coordinates of the given five points to compute: $n = 5$,

$$X = \sum_{i=1}^{5} x_i = -1 + 1 + 2 + 5 + 7 = 14,$$

$$X_2 = \sum_{i=1}^{5} x_i^2 = (-1)^2 + 1^2 + 2^2 + 5^2 + 7^2 = 80,$$

$$Y = \sum_{i=1}^{5} y_i = 6 + 5 + 3 + 3 + (-1) = 16, \quad \text{and}$$

$$XY = \sum_{i=1}^{5} x_i y_i = (-1)(6) + (1)(5) + (2)(3) + (5)(3) + (7)(-1) = 13.$$

Use the formulae given in the solution to EXERCISE 67 to compute

$$a = \frac{5(13) - (14)(16)}{5(80) - (14)^2} = -\frac{53}{68} \quad \text{and} \quad b = \frac{(80)(16) - (14)(13)}{5(80) - (14)^2} = \frac{183}{34},$$

so the line is $y = -(53/68)x + (183/34)$.

_____14.8
Lagrange Multipliers

COMMENT: The strategy for solving constrained extremization problems by the method of Lagrange multipliers is to:

I) Identify the objective f to be minimized or maximized and the constraint equation(s) $g(x, y, z) = 0$ $(h(x, y, z) = 0)$, and calculate their gradients.

II) Determine the equations satisfied by constrained critical points: $\nabla f = \lambda \nabla g$ and $g = 0$ (or $\nabla f = \lambda \nabla g + \mu \nabla h$ and $g = 0$, $h = 0$).

III) Solve the system of equations in II). Be sure to find all solutions (x, y, z, λ, μ).

This strategy will be followed with only the numerals I), II), etc. and key words used to indicate the main steps of the strategy. Some emphasis will be placed on explaining how step III), the solution to the system, is obtained in each case.

1. Find the local extrema of $f(x, y) = x^2 + y^2$ subject to $x + y = 2$.

SOLUTION: I) Here $f(x, y) = x^2 + y^2$ and $g(x, y) = x + y - 2$, so their gradients are $\nabla f = 2x\,\mathbf{i} + 2y\,\mathbf{j}$ and $\nabla g = \mathbf{i} + \mathbf{j}$.

II) The constrained critical points satisfy $\nabla f = \lambda \nabla g$ or $(2x\,\mathbf{i} + 2y\,\mathbf{j}) = \lambda(\mathbf{i} + \mathbf{j})$ with $x + y - 2 = 0$, or equivalently,

$$\text{i)}\ \ 2x = \lambda, \quad \text{ii)}\ \ 2y = \lambda, \quad \text{iii)}\ \ x + y = 2.$$

III)   Solve i) and ii) for $x = \lambda/2$ and $y = \lambda/2$ respectively, then substitute these into iii), $\lambda/2 + \lambda/2 = 2$ to obtain $\lambda = 2$ whereby $x = 1$ and $y = 1$.

The only possible local extremum of f is at $(1, 1)$.

COMMENT: One strategy to use in solving the system of equations in III is to solve the equations involving the Lagrange multipliers for x, y, and z in terms of the multipliers, to substitute these values into the constraint equation to obtain equations for the multipliers, then to use the solution(s) to these equations to determine x, y, and z. This procedure is used throughout.

Care must be taken not to "lose" solutions which might correspond to zero divisors. This possibility occurs in the solution to Exercise 11.

7. Find the local extrema of $f(x, y, z) = 2xy + 4xz + 6yz$ subject to $xyz = 48$.

SOLUTION: I) Here $f(x, y, z) = 2xy + 4xz + 6yz$ and $g(x, y, z) = xyz - 48$ so the gradients are $\nabla f = (2y + 4z)\mathbf{i} + (2x + 6z)\mathbf{j} + (4x + 6y)\mathbf{k}$ and $\nabla g = (yz)\mathbf{i} + (xz)\mathbf{j} + (xy)\mathbf{k}$.
II)   The constrained critical points satisfy $(2y + 4z)\mathbf{i} + (2x + 6z)\mathbf{j} + (4x + 6y)\mathbf{k} = \lambda((yz)\mathbf{i} + (xz)\mathbf{j} + (xy)\mathbf{k})$ and $xyz - 48 = 0$, or equivalently,

$$\text{i) } 2y + 4z = \lambda yz, \quad \text{ii) } 2x + 6z = \lambda xz, \quad \text{iii) } 4x + 6y = \lambda xy, \quad \text{and} \quad \text{iv) } xyz = 48.$$

III) By iv), none of x, y, or z can be zero so divide both sides of i), ii), and iii) by yz, xz, and xy respectively to obtain i) $2(1/z) + 4(1/y) = \lambda$, ii) $2(1/z) + 6(1/x) = \lambda$, and iii) $4(1/y) + 6(1/x) = \lambda$. Equation i) plus equation ii) minus equation iii) gives $4(1/z) = \lambda$ or $z = 4/\lambda$. Similarly, equation i) minus equation ii) plus equation iii) gives $8(1/y) = \lambda$ or $y = 8/\lambda$ and equation ii) plus equation iii) minus equation i) gives $12(1/x) = \lambda$ or $x = 12/\lambda$. Substitute these values for x, y and z into equation iv), $(12/\lambda)(8/\lambda)(4/\lambda) = 48$ or $\lambda^3 = 8$. Since $\lambda = 2$, the solution to this system is $x = 12/2 = 6$, $y = 8/2 = 4$, $z = 4/2 = 2$.
The only possible local extremum is $(6, 4, 2)$.

11. Find the local extrema for $f(x, y, z) = x^2 + y^2 + z^2$ subject to $x^2 + 4y^2 + 4z^2 = 4$ and $x - 4y - z = 0$.

SOLUTION: I) Here $f(x, y, z) = x^2 + y^2 + z^2$ and there are two constraints, $g(x, y, z) = x^2 + 4y^2 + 4z^2 - 4$ and $h(x, y, z) = x - 4y - z = 0$. The gradients are $\nabla f = (2x)\mathbf{i} + (2y)\mathbf{j} + (2z)\mathbf{k}$, $\nabla g = (2x)\mathbf{i} + (8y)\mathbf{j} + (8z)\mathbf{k}$ and $\nabla h = \mathbf{i} - 4\mathbf{j} - \mathbf{k}$.
II) The equations for the critical points are $\nabla f = \lambda \nabla g + \mu \nabla h$ or

$$(2x)\mathbf{i} + (2y)\mathbf{j} + (2z)\mathbf{k} = \lambda((2x)\mathbf{i} + (8y)\mathbf{j} + (8z)\mathbf{k}) + \mu(\mathbf{i} - 4\mathbf{j} - \mathbf{k})$$

and $x^2 + 4y^2 + 4z^2 - 4 = 0$ and $x - 4y - z = 0$, or equivalently,

$$\text{i) } 2x = \lambda(2x) + \mu(1), \quad \text{ii) } 2y = \lambda(8y) + \mu(-4), \quad \text{iii) } 2z = \lambda(8z) + \mu(-1),$$
$$\text{iv) } x^2 + 4y^2 + 4z^2 = 4, \quad \text{and} \quad \text{v) } x - 4y - z = 0.$$

III) Solve equations i)–iii) for x, y, and z respectively in terms of λ and μ: i) $(2 - 2\lambda)x = \mu$ or $x = \mu/(2(1 - \lambda))$ if $\lambda \neq 1$, ii) $(2 - 8\lambda)y = -4\mu$ or $y = (-2\mu)/(1 - 4\lambda)$ if $\lambda \neq 1/4$, and iii) $(2 - 8\lambda)z = -\mu$ or $z = (-\mu)/(2(1 - 4\lambda))$ if $\lambda \neq 1/4$. Consider the cases $\lambda = 1$ and $\lambda = 1/4$ later. Substitute the values of x, y, and z into equations iv) and v) to obtain

$$\text{iv)}' \qquad \frac{\mu^2}{4(1 - \lambda)^2} + \frac{16\mu^2}{(1 - 4\lambda)^2} + \frac{\mu^2}{(1 - 4\lambda)^2} = 4$$

and   v)′ $\dfrac{\mu}{2(1-\lambda)} + \dfrac{8\mu}{(1-4\lambda)} + \dfrac{\mu}{2(1-4\lambda)} = 0.$

Because of equation iv)′, $\mu \neq 0$ so equation v)′ can be divided by μ to get

$$(18 - 21\lambda)/\left(2(1-\lambda)(1-4\lambda)\right) = 0.$$

Substitute the solution $\lambda = 6/7$ into iv)′ to obtain $(11081/1156)\mu^2 = 4$. The solutions $\mu = \pm\dfrac{4}{7}\sqrt{\dfrac{17}{21}}$, $\lambda = 6/7$ give values

$$x = \pm 2\sqrt{\dfrac{17}{21}}, \qquad y = \pm\dfrac{8}{17}\sqrt{\dfrac{17}{21}}, \quad \text{and} \quad z = \pm\dfrac{2}{17}\sqrt{\dfrac{17}{21}}.$$

If $\lambda = 1$ is used in equation i), then it follows that $\mu = 0$. Equations ii) and iii) then imply that $y = z = 0$. These values give a contradiction between equations iv) and v) so $\lambda \neq 1$. If $\lambda = 1/4$ is used in equations ii) and iii), then both give that $\mu = 0$. Equation i) with $\lambda = 1/4$ and $\mu = 0$ has the solution $x = 0$. Equations iv) and v) with $x = 0$ become iv)″ $y^2 + z^2 = 1$ and v)″ $4y + z = 0$ respectively. Substitute $z = -4y$ from v)″ into iv)″ to get $y^2 + (-4y)^2 = 1$. This has solution $y = \pm 1/\sqrt{17}$ which implies that $z = \mp 4/17$ and $x = 0$.

The objective function values at the four constrained critical points are

$$f\left(0, \dfrac{1}{\sqrt{17}}, -\dfrac{4}{\sqrt{17}}\right) = 1, \quad f\left(0, -\dfrac{1}{\sqrt{17}}, \dfrac{4}{\sqrt{17}}\right) = 1,$$

$$f\left(2\sqrt{\dfrac{17}{21}}, \dfrac{8}{17}\sqrt{\dfrac{17}{21}}, \dfrac{2}{17}\sqrt{\dfrac{17}{21}}\right) = 24/7, \quad \text{and} \quad f\left(-2\sqrt{\dfrac{17}{21}}, -\dfrac{8}{17}\sqrt{\dfrac{17}{21}}, -\dfrac{2}{17}\sqrt{\dfrac{17}{21}}\right) = 24/7.$$

The points $(0, \pm 1/\sqrt{17}, \mp 4/\sqrt{17})$ are relative minima and $\left(\pm 2\sqrt{\dfrac{17}{21}}, \pm\dfrac{8}{17}\sqrt{\dfrac{17}{21}}, \pm\dfrac{2}{17}\sqrt{\dfrac{17}{21}}\right)$ are relative maxima.

13. Find the point on the sphere $x^2 + y^2 + z^2 - 4x - 6y - 8z + 28 = 0$ that is closest to the origin.

SOLUTION: I) Here, minimize the square of the distance from the origin, $f(x, y, z) = x^2 + y^2 + z^2$, subject to the constraint that $g(x, y, z) = x^2 + y^2 + z^2 - 4x - 6y - 8z + 28 = 0$. The gradients are $\nabla f = (2x)\mathbf{i} + (2y)\mathbf{j} + (2z)\mathbf{k}$ and $\nabla g = (2x - 4)\mathbf{i} + (2y - 6)\mathbf{j} + (2z - 8)\mathbf{k}$.
II)   The extrema satisfy $(2x)\mathbf{i} + (2y)\mathbf{j} + (2z)\mathbf{k} = \lambda((2x - 4)\mathbf{i} + (2y - 6)\mathbf{j} + (2z - 8)\mathbf{k})$ and $x^2 + y^2 + z^2 - 4x - 6y - 8z + 28 = 0$ or, equivalently, the system

$$\text{i) } 2x = \lambda(2x - 4), \quad \text{ii) } 2y = \lambda(2y - 6), \quad \text{iii) } 2z = \lambda(2z - 8),$$
$$\text{and } \text{iv) } (x - 2)^2 + (y - 3)^2 + (z - 4)^2 = 1.$$

III) Solve equations i), ii), and iii) for x, y, and z in terms of λ: $x = (2\lambda)/(\lambda - 1)$ if $\lambda \neq 1$; $y = (3\lambda)/(\lambda - 1)$, if $\lambda \neq 1$ and $z = (4\lambda)/(\lambda - 1)$, $\lambda \neq 1$. Notice that for $\lambda = 1$, equation i) has no solution; so this case is to be ignored.

Substitute these values into iv) to obtain

$$\left(\frac{2\lambda}{\lambda - 1} - 2\right)^2 + \left(\frac{3\lambda}{\lambda - 1} - 3\right)^2 + \left(\frac{4\lambda}{\lambda - 1} - 4\right)^2 = 1,$$

or $2^2 + 3^2 + 4^2 = (\lambda - 1)^2$ which has solutions $\lambda = 1 \pm \sqrt{29}$. The points corresponding to these values of λ have coordinates

$$x = \frac{2(1 \pm \sqrt{29})}{\pm\sqrt{29}}, \quad y = \frac{3(1 \pm \sqrt{29})}{\pm\sqrt{29}}, \quad z = \frac{4(1 \pm \sqrt{29})}{\pm\sqrt{29}}.$$

The distance from the origin to the point $(1.63, 2.44, 3.26)$ (determined by using the "$-$" sign and approximating) is approximately 4.39 while the distance to the other point $(2.37, 3.56, 4.74)$ is 6.39. Thus the point $\left(2(1 - \sqrt{29}/29), 3(1 - \sqrt{29}/29), 4(1 - \sqrt{29}/29)\right)$ is closest to the origin.

21. Suppose a rectangular room is to be built inside a recreation shelter in the shape of the upper half of an ellipsoid with equation $\dfrac{x^2}{400} + \dfrac{y^2}{2500} + \dfrac{z^2}{100} = 1$. Find the dimensions of the room with maximum volume if the corners of the ceiling are to lie on the ellipsoid.

SOLUTION: I) Assume that the base of the room lies in the xy-plane and that the four corners of the ceiling lie on the ellipsoid. For a point (x, y, z) on the ellipsoid, the height of the rectangle is z, the width is $2y$ and the length is $2x$.

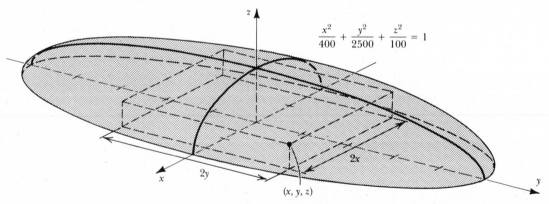

The volume to be maximized is $f(x, y, z) = (2x)(2y)z$ subject to the constraint $g(x, y, z) = x^2/400 + y^2/2500 + z^2/100 - 1 = 0$. The gradients are $\nabla f(4yz)\,\mathbf{i} + (4xz)\,\mathbf{j} + (4xy)\,\mathbf{k}$ and $\nabla g = (x/200)\,\mathbf{i} + (y/1250)\,\mathbf{j} + (z/50)\,\mathbf{k}$.

II) The extrema satisfy the equations

i) $4yz = \lambda\dfrac{x}{200}$,   ii) $4xz = \lambda\dfrac{y}{1250}$,   iii) $4xy = \lambda\dfrac{z}{50}$,   and   iv) $\dfrac{x^2}{400} + \dfrac{y^2}{2500} + \dfrac{z^2}{100} = 1$.

III) Check that none of x, y, z, or λ can be zero, else there is a contradiction in the system above. Equate the quotients of left and right sides of equations i) and ii) to get $y/x = (x/y)(1250/200)$. Do the same with equations ii) and iii) to get $z/y = (y/z)(50/1250)$. Rewrite these as $x^2/400 = y^2/2500 = z^2/100$. By equation iv), this common value is $1/3$, thus $x = \pm 20/\sqrt{3}$, $y = \pm 50/\sqrt{3}$, and $z = 10/\sqrt{3}$. By symmetry, take the point as $(20/\sqrt{3}, 50/\sqrt{3}, 10/\sqrt{3})$.

The dimensions of the largest room are length $= 40/\sqrt{3}$, width $= 100/\sqrt{3}$, and height $= 10/\sqrt{3}$.

_____Chapter 14

Review Exercises

3. a) Determine any points of discontinuity of the function described by

$$f(x,y) = \begin{cases} x^2 + y^2, & \text{if } x^2 + y^2 \le 1 \\ 0, & \text{if } x^2 + y^2 > 1. \end{cases}$$

b) Sketch the graph of f.

SOLUTION: a) At each (x_0, y_0) such that $x_0^2 + y_0^2 < 1$, the limit

$$\lim_{(x,y)\to(x_0,y_0)} f(x,y) = \lim_{(x,y)\to(x_0,y_0)} x^2 + y^2 = x_0^2 + y_0^2 = f(x_0, y_0)$$

so f is continuous at all such points. At each (x_0, y_0) such that $x_0^2 + y_0^2 > 1$, the limit

$$\lim_{(x,y)\to(x_0,y_0)} f(x,y) = \lim_{(x,y)\to(x_0,y_0)} 0 = 0 = f(x_0, y_0),$$

so f is again continuous there. Let the point (x_0, y_0) be on the circle $x_0^2 + y_0^2 = 1$. The limit of f along any curve approaching (x_0, y_0) from inside the circle is 1 while the limit of f along any curve approaching (x_0, y_0) from outside the circle is 0. Thus the limit $\lim_{(x,y)\to(x_0,y_0)} f(x,y)$ does not exist on $x_0^2 + y_0^2 = 1$ and the function is discontinuous there.

b) The graph of f is $\{(x,y,z) : z = x^2 + y^2,\ \text{if } x^2 + y^2 \le 1\ \text{ and } z = 0\ \text{if } x^2 + y^2 > 1\}$. This graph consists of the portion of the paraboloid $z = x^2 + y^2$ lying above the disk $x^2 + y^2 \le 1$ and the portion of the xy-plane outside this disk.

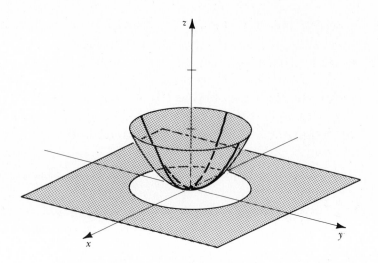

7. Find the first partial derivatives of $f(x, y) = x^2 y + 2xe^{1/y}$.

SOLUTION:

$$f_x = D_x \left[x^2 y + 2xe^{1/y} \right] = 2xy + 2e^{1/y} \quad \text{and} \quad f_y = D_y \left[x^2 y + 2xe^{1/y} \right] = x^2 + 2xe^{1/y} \left(-\frac{1}{y^2} \right).$$

13. For the function described by $z = f(x, y) = y\sqrt{x} + x\sqrt[3]{y}$, together with values $\Delta x = 0.1$ and $\Delta y = -0.1$: a) determine dz and   b) use dz to approximate $f(1.1, 0.9)$.

SOLUTION: a) Since $x + \Delta x = 1.1$ and $y + \Delta y = 0.9$, then $x = 1$ and $y = 1$, so $dz = f_x(1, 1)\, dx + f_y(1, 1)\, dy$. Now

$$f_x = \frac{y}{2\sqrt{x}} + \sqrt[3]{y} \quad \text{and} \quad f_y = \sqrt{x} + \frac{x}{3\sqrt[3]{y^2}},$$

so $dz = (3/2)\, dx + (4/3)\, dy$ or with $dx = 0.1$ and $dy = -0.1$, $dz = 1/60$.

b) An approximation to $f(1.1, 0.9)$ is $f(1.1, .9) \approx f(1, 1) + dz$ where $f(1, 1) = 2$ and $dz = 1/60$. Thus, $f(1.1, .9) \approx 121/60$.

19. Find all critical points of $f(x, y) = x^2 e^{x+y}$ and determine whether each critical point is a relative maximum, relative minimum, or a saddle point.

SOLUTION: First, $f_x = e^{x+y}(x^2 + 2x)$ and $f_y = x^2 e^{x+y}$, so the equations for critical points are

$$\text{i) } (x^2 + 2x)e^{x+y} = 0 \quad \text{and} \quad \text{ii) } x^2 e^{x+y} = 0.$$

Since e^{x+y} never vanishes, the only solution to both these equations is $x = 0$. Thus all points $(0, y)$ are critical points.

Also, $f_{xx} = e^{x+y}(x^2 + 4x + 2)$, $f_{yy} = x^2 e^{x+y}$, and $f_{xy} = e^{x+y}(x^2 + 2x)$ so the discriminant is $D(x, y) = e^{2(x+y)}\left((x^2 + 4x + 2)(x^2) - (x^2 + 2x)^2\right)$. When $x = 0$, $D(0, y) = 0$ so nothing can be concluded from THEOREM 14.54.

Notice that for $x \neq 0$, $f(x, y) = x^2 e^{x+y} > 0 = f(0, y)$ so each point $(0, y)$ is a relative minimum for f.

33. Find the directional derivative of $f(x, y, z) = 5x^2 - 2y^2 + z$ at $P(1, 1, 1)$ in the direction $\mathbf{v} = 3\mathbf{i} - 4\mathbf{k}$.

SOLUTION: Since $\|\mathbf{v}\| = \sqrt{(3)^2 + (-4)^2} = 5$, the unit vector with the direction of $\mathbf{v}$ is $\mathbf{u} = \frac{3}{5}\mathbf{i} - \frac{4}{5}\mathbf{k}$. The gradient of f is $\nabla f = (10x)\mathbf{i} - (4y)\mathbf{j} + \mathbf{k}$, so the directional derivative is

$$D_{\mathbf{u}} f(1, 1, 1) = \nabla f(1, 1, 1) \cdot \mathbf{u} = (10\mathbf{i} - 4\mathbf{j} + \mathbf{k}) \cdot \left(\frac{3}{5}\mathbf{i} - \frac{4}{5}\mathbf{k}\right) = (10)\left(\frac{3}{5}\right) + (1)\left(-\frac{4}{5}\right) = \frac{26}{5}.$$

35. a) Find the direction in which $f(x, y) = x^2 + xy$ is increasing most rapidly at $P(1, -1)$.
b) Find the maximum rate of increase.

SOLUTION: a) The direction of most rapid increase is the unit vector with the same direction as the gradient. Since $\nabla f = (2x + y)\mathbf{i} + x\mathbf{j}$, then $\nabla f(1, -1) = \mathbf{i} + \mathbf{j}$ so this unit direction is

$$\mathbf{u} = \frac{\nabla f(1, -1)}{\|\nabla f(1, -1)\|} = \frac{\mathbf{i} + \mathbf{j}}{\sqrt{1^2 + 1^2}} = \frac{1}{\sqrt{2}}\mathbf{i} + \frac{1}{\sqrt{2}}\mathbf{j}.$$

b) The maximum rate of increase is $\|\nabla f(1, -1)\| = \sqrt{2}$.

41. Find an equation of the tangent plane to the surface $z = xy \sin(xy)$ at $P(1, \pi/2, \pi/2)$.

SOLUTION: Describe the surface as $f(x, y, z) = z - xy \sin(xy) = 0$. A normal to the tangent plane is given by the gradient

$$\nabla f = (-y \sin xy - xy^2 \cos xy)\mathbf{i} + (-x \sin xy - x^2 y \cos xy)\mathbf{j} + \mathbf{k}.$$

At $P(1, \pi/2, \pi/2)$ this normal is $\mathbf{N} = \nabla f(1, \pi/2, \pi/2) = (-\pi/2)\mathbf{i} + (-1)\mathbf{j} + \mathbf{k}$ so an equation for the tangent plane at this point is

$$-\frac{\pi}{2}(x - 1) - 1\left(y - \frac{\pi}{2}\right) + \left(z - \frac{\pi}{2}\right) = 0 \qquad \text{or} \qquad \pi x + 2y - 2z = \pi.$$

49. Find the slope of the curve at the point $(1, 2, 4)$ formed by the intersection of the surface $z = xy^2$ with a plane perpendicular to the y-axis.

SOLUTION: Within this plane, $y = 2$, the slope of the line is given by the partial derivative $\frac{\partial z}{\partial x}$ evaluated at $(1, 2, 4)$. Now $\frac{\partial z}{\partial x} = D_x[xy^2] = y^2$ so the slope is $2^2 = 4$.

53. Find $\dfrac{\partial f}{\partial r}$ and $\dfrac{\partial f}{\partial \theta}$ if $f(x,y) = xy$, where $x = e^{2r}\cos\theta$, $y = e^r \sin\theta$.

SOLUTION: Use the chain rule $\dfrac{\partial f}{\partial r} = \dfrac{\partial f}{\partial x} \cdot \dfrac{\partial x}{\partial r} + \dfrac{\partial f}{\partial y} \cdot \dfrac{\partial y}{\partial r}$ and $\dfrac{\partial f}{\partial \theta} = \dfrac{\partial f}{\partial x} \cdot \dfrac{\partial x}{\partial \theta} + \dfrac{\partial f}{\partial y} \cdot \dfrac{\partial y}{\partial \theta}$ with $\dfrac{\partial f}{\partial x} = y$, $\dfrac{\partial f}{\partial y} = x$, $\dfrac{\partial x}{\partial r} = 2e^{2r}\cos\theta$, $\dfrac{\partial y}{\partial r} = e^r \sin\theta$, $\dfrac{\partial x}{\partial \theta} = -e^{2r}\sin\theta$, and $\dfrac{\partial y}{\partial \theta} = e^r \cos\theta$. Thus,

$$\frac{\partial f}{\partial r} = y(2e^{2r}\cos\theta) + x(e^r \sin\theta)$$

$$= (e^r \sin\theta)(2e^{2r}\cos\theta) + (e^{2r}\cos\theta)(e^r \sin\theta) = 3e^{3r}\sin\theta\cos\theta,$$

and $\quad \dfrac{\partial f}{\partial \theta} = y(-e^{2r}\sin\theta) + x(e^r \cos\theta)$

$$= (e^r \sin\theta)(-e^{2r}\sin\theta) + (e^{2r}\cos\theta)(e^r \cos\theta) = e^{3r}(\cos^2\theta - \sin^2\theta).$$

59. Show that $\displaystyle\lim_{(x,y)\to(1,1)} \frac{(y-1)^2}{(x-1)^2 + (y-1)^2}$ does not exist.

SOLUTION: Consider the line through $(1,1)$ with slope m: $x = 1+t$, $y = 1+mt$. The limit along this line is

$$\lim_{(1+t,1+mt)\to(1,1)} \frac{(1+mt-1)^2}{(1+t-1)^2 + (1+mt-1)^2} = \lim_{t\to 0} \frac{m^2 t^2}{t^2 + m^2 t^2} = \frac{m^2}{1+m^2}.$$

Since for different slopes, m, the limit is different, the original limit does not exist.

69. A silo is to be constructed in the shape of a right circular cylinder topped with a cone of equal height and radius. The volume of the silo must be $8000\,\text{ft}^3$. Use Lagrange multipliers to determine the height and radius of the silo that will minimize the surface area of the silo, assuming that it needs a bottom.

SOLUTION: Denote the height and radius of the cylinder as h and r respectively. The lateral surface area of the cylinder is $2\pi rh$ and its volume is $\pi r^2 h$. The cone with equal height and radius r has lateral surface area $\sqrt{2}\pi r^2$ since if the cone were cut along a line from the vertex to the base and flattened, the area would be that of the sector of a circle of radius $\sqrt{2}r$ subtended by an arc of the circle of length $2\pi r$. The volume of this cone is $\pi r^3/3$. The area of the base is πr^2. The total surface area of the silo is thus $f(r,h) = 2\pi rh + \sqrt{2}\pi r^2 + \pi r^2$, which is to be minimized subject to the (volume $= 8000$) constraint $g(r,h) = \pi r^2 h + \pi r^3/3 - 8000 = 0$. The gradients are $\nabla f = \langle f_r, f_h \rangle = \langle 2\pi h + 2(1+\sqrt{2})\pi r, 2\pi r \rangle$ and $\nabla g = \langle g_r, g_h \rangle = \langle 2\pi rh + \pi r^2, \pi r^2 \rangle$. The constrained critical points satisfy the equations $\langle 2\pi h + 2(1+\sqrt{2})\pi r, 2\pi r \rangle = \lambda \langle 2\pi rh + \pi r^2, \pi r^2 \rangle$ and $\pi r^2 h + \pi r^3/3 = 8000$ or equivalently

i) $2\pi h + 2(1+\sqrt{2})\pi r = \lambda(2\pi rh + \pi r^2)$,   ii) $2\pi r = \lambda \pi r^2$,

and   iii) $\pi r^2 h + \dfrac{\pi r^3}{3} = 8000$.

Note that if $\lambda = 0$ then by ii) $r = 0$ and by i) $h = 0$ which violates iii), so $\lambda \neq 0$. By similar reasoning $h \neq 0$ and $r \neq 0$. Equation ii) implies that $r = 2/\lambda$. Substitute this for r in i) to get

$$2\pi h + 2(1 + \sqrt{2})\pi \left(\frac{2}{\lambda}\right) = \lambda \left(2\pi \left(\frac{2}{\lambda}\right) h + \pi \left(\frac{2}{\lambda}\right)^2\right),$$

which is solved for h, $h = 2\sqrt{2}/\lambda$. Notice that $h = r\sqrt{2}$, so from equation iii),

$$\pi r^2 \sqrt{2} r + \frac{\pi}{3} r^3 = 8000 \qquad \text{or} \qquad r^3 = \frac{8000}{\pi(\sqrt{2} + (1/3))}.$$

Thus,

$$r = 20 \left(\pi \left(\sqrt{2} + \frac{1}{3}\right)\right)^{-1/3} \approx 11.337$$

$$\text{and} \qquad h = \sqrt{2} 20 \left(\pi \left(\sqrt{2} + \frac{1}{3}\right)\right)^{-1/3} \approx 16.033.$$

The height of the silo is thus $r + h \approx 27.370$, and the radius is $r \approx 11.337$.

15
Integral Calculus of Multivariable Functions

Sharpening your skills

You should recall the definition of the definite integral from CHAPTER 4 as well as the techniques for integration presented in CHAPTER 7. It will also be necessary to visualize and graph planar and solid regions described in terms of Cartesian, polar or cylindrical, and spherical coordinates.

The practice problems below are followed by the numbers of the sections where the material may be found.

Practice Problems

1. Use DEFINITION 4.7 of the definite integral to evaluate $\int_0^1 (2x+1)\,dx$.   (See SECTION 4.2)

2. Evaluate the integrals

   a) $\int_0^1 x^2 e^{2x}\,dx$ (See SECTION 7.1)   b) $\int_{-1}^0 t\sqrt{1-2t}\,dt$ (See SECTION 4.5)

   c) $\int_0^{\pi/2} \sin^4 x \cos^3 x\,dx$ (See SECTION 7.2)   d) $\int \frac{1}{x^3-1}\,dx$ (See SECTION 7.4)

   e) $\int_1^{\sqrt{2}} \frac{\sqrt{x^2-1}}{x^2}\,dx$ (See SECTION 7.3)   f) $\int_1^\infty \frac{1}{x(x^2+1)}\,dx$ (See SECTION 7.4).

3. Sketch the graph of the planar region
   a) in the xy-plane between $y = 1 - x^2$ and $y = 0$.   (See SECTION 5.1)
   b) in the $r\theta$-plane inside $r = 3 - 2\cos\theta$.   (See SECTION 9.2)

4. Sketch the graph of the solid region
   a) lying in the first octant beneath the plane $3x + 2y + z = 6$.   (See SECTION 11.5)

   b) in the first octant lying inside the sphere with cylindrical equation $r^2 + z^2 = 8$ and above the cone $z = r$.   (See SECTION 13.5)

   c) lying between the spheres with spherical coordinates equation $\rho = 2$; $\rho = 3$ and above the cone $\phi = \pi/4$.   (See SECTION 13.5)

_____15.1
Double Integrals

3. Suppose $f(x, y) = y^2 - x^2$, R is the triangle in the xy-plane with vertices $(1, 1)$, $(5, 4)$ and $(7, 0)$, and $\wp$ is the partition defined by the lines at integer values of x and y. Find the value of the Riemann sum if (x_i, y_i) is chosen to be
a) the lower left corner of R_i;   b) The upper right corner of R_i;
c) the midpoint of R_i.

SOLUTION: The region R consists of points (x, y) such that $3x - 4y \geq -1$, $x + 6y \geq 7$ and $2x + y \leq 14$. The partition is illustrated below.

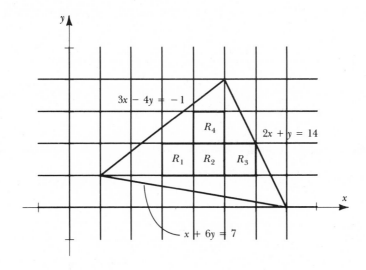

In order to determine which rectangles lie inside R, test the coordinates of the points of intersection of the lines $x = 1, 2, 3, 4, 5, 6, 7$ and $y = 0, 1, 2, 3, 4$. Those which satisfy all three inequalities are $(1, 1)$, $(2, 1)$, $(3, 1)$, $(4, 1)$, $(5, 1)$, $(6, 1)$, $(3, 2)$, $(4, 2)$, $(5, 2)$, $(6, 2)$, $(4, 3)$, $(5, 3)$, $(5, 4)$. The only rectangles which lie entirely inside R are those labeled R_1, R_2, R_3, R_4 on the graph. These each have area $\Delta A_i = 1$ for each R_i.

a) With evaluation at the lower left hand corner of R_i, the Riemann sum is

$$f(3, 1)\Delta A_1 + f(4, 1)\Delta A_2 + f(5, 1)\Delta A_3 + f(4, 2)\Delta A_4$$
$$= (1^2 - 3^2)(1) + (1^2 - 4^2)(1) + (1^2 - 5^2)(1) + (2^2 - 4^2)(1) = -59.$$

b) With evaluation at the upper right hand corner of R_i, the Riemann sum is

$$f(4, 2)\Delta A_1 + f(5, 2)\Delta A_2 + f(6, 2)\Delta A_3 + f(5, 3)\Delta A_4$$

$$= (2^2 - 4^2)(1) + (2^2 - 5^2)(1) + (2^2 - 6^2)(1) + (3^2 - 5^2)(1) = -81.$$

c) With evaluation at the midpoints of each R_i, the Riemann sum is

$$f\left(\frac{7}{2}, \frac{3}{2}\right) \Delta A_1 + f\left(\frac{9}{2}, \frac{3}{2}\right) \Delta A_2 + f\left(\frac{11}{2}, \frac{3}{2}\right) \Delta A_3 + f\left(\frac{9}{2}, \frac{5}{2}\right) \Delta A_4$$

$$= \left(\left(\frac{3}{2}\right)^2 - \left(\frac{7}{2}\right)^2\right)(1) + \left(\left(\frac{3}{2}\right)^2 - \left(\frac{9}{2}\right)^2\right)(1)$$

$$+ \left(\left(\frac{3}{2}\right)^2 - \left(\frac{11}{2}\right)^2\right)(1) + \left(\left(\frac{5}{2}\right)^2 - \left(\frac{9}{2}\right)^2\right)(1) = -70.$$

9. Use the method in EXAMPLE 3 to evaluate $\displaystyle\iint_R \sqrt{9 - x^2 - y^2}\, dA$ where R is the disk $x^2 + y^2 \leq 9$ in the xy-plane.

SOLUTION: Since the integrand is positive, this represents the volume under the surface $z = \sqrt{9 - x^2 - y^2}$ lying above the disk $x^2 + y^2 \leq 9$ in the xy-plane. The solid described is the upper hemisphere of radius 3 with center at the origin. Its volume is $V = (1/2)(4\pi/3)(3)^3 = 18\pi$, so this is the value of the double integral.

_____15.2

Iterated Integrals

3. Evaluate $\displaystyle\int_{-1}^{1} \int_{-2}^{4} (x^2 + y)\, dy\, dx.$

SOLUTION: Integrate with respect to y treating x as constant:

$$\int_{-1}^{1} \int_{-2}^{4} (x^2 + y)\, dy\, dx = \int_{-1}^{1} \left[x^2 y + \frac{y^2}{2}\right]\Bigg|_{y=-2}^{4} dx$$

$$= \int_{-1}^{1} (6x^2 + 6)\, dx = [2x^3 + 6x]\Big|_{-1}^{1} = 16.$$

COMMENT: It is useful practice to indicate the variable of integration when evaluating the antiderivative of the inner integral. This is denoted above by the expression $\Big|_{y=-2}^{4}$ in the second integral.

9. Evaluate $\displaystyle\int_0^2 \int_x^{2x} (x^2 + y^3)\, dy\, dx.$

SOLUTION: Integrate with respect to y treating x as constant.

$$\int_0^2 \int_x^{2x} (x^2 + y^3)\, dy\, dx = \int_0^2 \left[x^2 y + \frac{y^4}{4} \right] \Bigg|_{y=x}^{2x} dx$$

$$= \int_0^2 \left(x^3 + \frac{15}{4} x^4 \right) dx = \left[\frac{x^4}{4} + \frac{3x^5}{4} \right] \Bigg|_0^2 = 28.$$

19. a) Sketch the graph of the region of integration for $\displaystyle\int_{-1}^1 \int_{-2}^4 (x^2 + y)\, dy\, dx$ and express the integral as a double integral which reverses the order of integration.   **b)** Evaluate the double integral obtained.

SOLUTION: The x-simple region $R = \{(x,y) : -1 \le x \le 1; \text{for each } x, \ -2 \le y \le 4\}$ is a rectangle whose points have x values between -1 and 1 and which is bounded below and above by the lines $y = -2$ and $y = 4$ respectively.

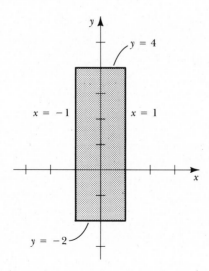

This is also a y-simple region where for each y between -2 and 4, x varies from $x = -1$ on the left to $x = 1$ on the right; that is, $R = \{(x,y) : -2 \le y \le 4; \ \text{for each } y, \ -1 \le x \le 1\}$. The double integral with the limits reversed is

$$\int_{-2}^4 \int_{-1}^1 (x^2 + y)\, dx\, dy.$$

b) Integrate first with respect to x, treating y as constant.

$$\int_{-2}^{4} \int_{-1}^{1} (x^2 + y)\, dx\, dy = \int_{-2}^{4} \left[\frac{x^3}{3} + yx \right] \Big|_{x=-1}^{1} dy = \int_{-2}^{4} \left(\frac{2}{3} + 2y \right) dy$$

$$= \left[\frac{2}{3}y + y^2 \right] \Big|_{-2}^{4} = 16.$$

COMMENT: 1) A <u>strategy</u> for reversing the order of integration in $\int_a^b \int_{g_1(x)}^{g_2(x)} f(x,y)\, dy\, dx$ is to
I) Describe the x-simple region $\{(x,y) : a \le x \le b; \text{ for each } x, \quad g_1(x) \le y \le g_2(x)\}$.   II) Sketch the region lying between the lines $x = a$ and $x = b$ bounded below by $y = g_1(x)$ and above by $y = g_2(x)$.
III) Determine if the region can be described as one (or more) y- simple region(s); a second sketch is useful here.   IV) For each y-simple region, determine the smallest and largest y-values in the region, c and d, and determine the left and right boundaries, $x = h_1(y)$ and $x = h_2(y)$ respectively. Describe the region as $\{(x,y) : c \le y \le d; \text{ for each } y, \quad h_1(y) \le x \le h_2(y)\}$.   V) Write the integral as the sum over all y-simple regions (if there is more than one) of the integrals $\int_c^d \int_{h_1(y)}^{h_2(y)} f(x,y)\, dx\, dy$.

2) This strategy can be easily adapted to reversing the order of integration in $\int_c^d \int_{h_1(y)}^{h_2(y)} f(x,y)\, dx\, dy$.

3) To determine whether a region is y-simple, first sketch the graph; solve the equation of the left boundary curve for x in terms of y; do the same for the right boundary curve. If the same formula holds for the left and the same formula holds for the right for all values of y between the smallest and largest in the region, then the region is y-simple. If either formula changes, then sub-divide the region by horizontal lines at all y-values where such changes occur.

4) It is good practice to write the set description of the region as in steps I) or IV) above. Notice that the limits and order of integration are intimately related to this description. Indeed, given the set description of R and the integrand f, the integral can be written down directly and conversely, the set description can be determined from the integral.

25. a) Sketch the graph of the region of integration for $\int_0^2 \int_x^{2x} (x^2 + y^3)\, dy\, dx$ and express the integral as a double integral which reverses the order of integration.   b) Evaluate the double integral obtained.

SOLUTION: The region is $\{(x,y) : 0 \le x \le 2; \text{ for each } x, \quad x \le y \le 2x\}$. The x-simple region has smallest and largest x values 0 and 2 respectively and each vertical line (x fixed) runs from $y = x$ on the bottom to $y = 2x$ on top.

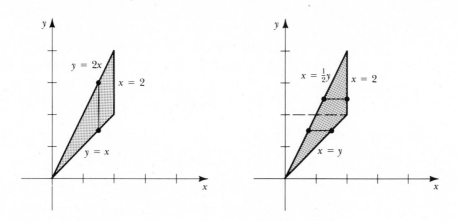

When the boundaries are written for x in terms of y, the left boundary is always given by $x = (1/2)y$, but the formula for the right boundary changes from $x = y$ to $x = 2$ at $y = 2$. Thus this region may be described as the union of two y-simple regions: $\{(x,y) : 0 \le y \le 2; \text{ for each } y, \quad y/2 \le x \le y\}$ and $\{(x,y) : 2 \le y \le 4; \text{ for each } y, \quad y/2 \le x \le 2\}$.

The double integral is thus the sum

$$b) \quad \int_0^2 \int_{y/2}^y (x^2 + y^3)\, dx\, dy + \int_2^4 \int_{y/2}^2 (x^2 + y^3)\, dx\, dy$$

$$= \int_0^2 \left[\frac{x^3}{3} + y^3 x\right]\Bigg|_{x=y/2}^{y} dy + \int_2^4 \left[\frac{x^3}{3} + y^3 x\right]\Bigg|_{x=y/2}^{2} dy$$

$$= \int_0^2 \left(\frac{7y^3}{24} + \frac{y^4}{2}\right) dy + \int_2^4 \left(-\frac{y^4}{2} + \frac{47y^3}{24} + \frac{8}{3}\right) dy$$

$$= \left[\frac{7y^4}{96} + \frac{y^5}{10}\right]\Bigg|_0^2 + \left[-\frac{y^5}{10} + \frac{47y^4}{96} + \frac{8}{3}y\right]\Bigg|_2^4 = 28.$$

37. Consider the solid bounded by $x = -1$, $x = 1$, $y = 2x + 2$, $y = 3 + 2x - x^2$, $z = 0$, and $z = x + y + 1$.   a) Sketch the region. Use double integrals to compute   b) the area of the base of the solid in the xy-plane and   c) the volume of the solid.

SOLUTION: a) The solid is bounded laterally by the (vertical) plane $y = 2x + 2$ and the cylinder $(y - 4)^2 = -(x - 1)^2$, on top by the plane $z = x + y + 1$, and below by the plane $z = 0$.

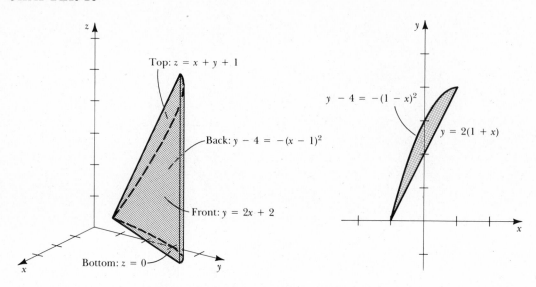

The projection of the solid onto the xy-plane is the region of integration. This is an x-simple region because each vertical line for a fixed x between -1 and 1 runs from the line $y = 2x + 2$ on the bottom to the parabola $y = 4 - (x - 1)^2$ on the top. The region is described by $R = \{(x, y) : -1 \le x \le 1; \text{ for each } x, \quad 2x + 2 \le y \le 4 - (x - 1)^2\}$. The order and limits of integration are the same for both the area of the base and the volume calculations.

b) The area, $A = \displaystyle\iint_R 1 \, dA$ is calculated by the iterated integral

$$A = \int_{-1}^{1} \int_{2(x+1)}^{4-(x-1)^2} dy \, dx = \int_{-1}^{1} [y] \Big|_{y=2(x+1)}^{4-(x-1)^2} dy$$

$$= \int_{-1}^{1} \left(4 - (x - 1)^2 - 2(x + 1)\right) dx = \left[4x - \frac{(x - 1)^3}{3} - (x + 1)^2\right]\Big|_{-1}^{1} = \frac{4}{3}.$$

c) Since the solid is bounded by $z = x + y + 1$ on top and $z = 0$ on bottom, the volume is the double integral $\displaystyle\iint_R (x + y + 1) \, dA$ which is calculated as the iterated integral

$$V = \int_{-1}^{1} \int_{2(x+1)}^{4-(x-1)^2} (y + (x + 1)) \, dy \, dx = \int_{-1}^{1} \left[\frac{y^2}{2} + (x + 1)y\right]\Big|_{y=2(x+1)}^{4-(x-1)^2} dx$$

$$= \int_{-1}^{1} \left(\frac{1}{2}\left(4 - (x - 1)^2\right)^2 + \left(4 - (x - 1)^2\right)(x + 1) - 4(x + 1)^2\right) dx$$

$$= \int_{-1}^{1} \left(8 - 4(x - 1)^2 + \frac{1}{2}(x - 1)^4 + 4(x + 1) - (x - 1)^3 - 2(x - 1)^2 - 4(x + 1)^2\right) dx$$

$$= \left[8x - 2(x-1)^3 - \frac{(x-1)^4}{4} + \frac{(x-1)^5}{10} + 2(x+1)^2 - \frac{4(x+1)^3}{3} \right] \Big|_{-1}^{1} = \frac{68}{15}.$$

COMMENT: 1)   A <u>strategy</u> for calculating the volume of a solid is to I) Sketch the solid on a 3-dimensional rectangular coordinate system.   II) Project the solid onto the xy-plane to determine the region of integration R, sketch R and describe it as x-simple or y-simple as appropriate. III) Identify the top and bottom surfaces $z = f_{top}(x,y)$ and $z = f_{bottom}(x,y)$, from your sketch in part I). IV) Use the description of R in step II) to write the double integral for volume

$$\iint\limits_{R} (f_{top}(x,y) - f_{bottom}(x,y))\, dA$$

as an (or a sum of) iterated integral. V) Evaluate this.

2) Notice that a special effort was made to write the limits of integration and the integrand in terms of $(x+1)$ or $(x-1)$. This was done because these terms vanish at the endpoints $x = -1$ and $x = 1$ respectively. They also occurred naturally in the computation. A final reason for looking for "natural groupings" like these is that they save effort and possible errors which both result from algebraic expansion.

39. Find the volume of the solid in the first octant bounded by the plane $z = 4 - x - y$.

SOLUTION: The solid is bounded laterally by the planes $x = 0$ and $y = 0$, on top by $z = 4 - x - y$ and below by $z = 0$.

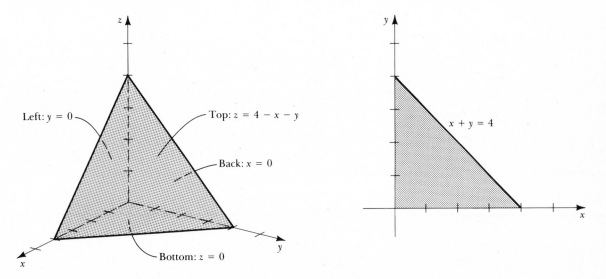

The projection of this solid is bounded by the lines $x = 0$, $y = 0$ and the intersection of the plane $z = 4 - x - y$ with the plane $z = 0$, that is the line $4 - x - y = 0$ or $y = 4 - x$ in the xy-plane.

This is an x-simple region since each vertical line for x between 0 and 4 runs from the bottom $y = 0$ to the top $y = 4 - x$. The region is $R = \{(x, y) : \text{for } x, \quad 0 \le x \le 4; 0 \le y \le 4 - x\}$.

The top and bottom surfaces are $z = 4 - x - y$ and $z = 0$, so the volume is the double integral $V = \iint_R (4 - x - y)\, dA$ which is evaluated as the iterated integral $\int_0^4 \int_0^{4-x} (4 - x - y)\, dy\, dx$. It's natural to group the $4 - x$ terms to evaluate this as

$$V = \int_0^4 \left[(4 - x)y - \frac{y^2}{2} \right]\bigg|_{y=0}^{4-x} dx = \int_0^4 \frac{(4 - x)^2}{2}\, dx = \left[-\frac{(4 - x)^3}{6} \right]\bigg|_0^4 = \frac{32}{3}.$$

45. Find the volume of the solid bounded by the cylinder $9x^2 + 4y^2 = 36$ and the planes $z = 0$ and $x + y + 2z = 6$.

SOLUTION: The solid is bounded laterally by the elliptic cylinder, above by the plane $z = (6 - x - y)/2$ and below by $z = 0$.

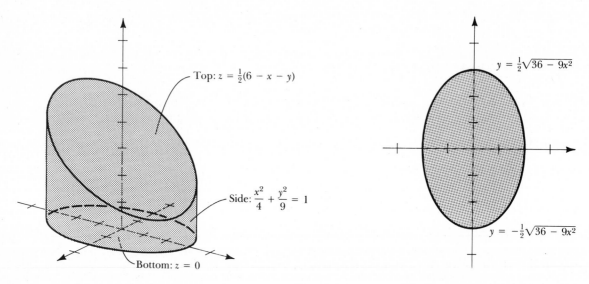

The projection of the solid onto the xy-plane is the region inside the ellipse $9x^2 + 4y^2 = 36$. Solve for the y-coordinates on the top and bottom respectively for each value of x between -2 and 2 to get $y = \sqrt{36 - 9x^2}/2$ and $y = -\sqrt{36 - 9x^2}/2$. This x-simple region can be described as

$$R = \left\{ (x, y) : -2 \le x \le 2 : \text{for each } x, \quad \frac{-\sqrt{36 - 9x^2}}{2} \le y \le \frac{\sqrt{36 - 9x^2}}{2} \right\}.$$

The volume is thus the iterated integral

$$V = \int_{-2}^2 \int_{-\sqrt{36-9x^2}/2}^{\sqrt{36-9x^2}/2} \frac{6 - x - y}{2}\, dy\, dx$$

$$= \frac{1}{2} \int_{-2}^{2} \left[(6-x)y - \frac{y^2}{2} \right] \Bigg|_{-\sqrt{36-9x^2}/2}^{\sqrt{36-9x^2}/2} dx = \frac{1}{2} \int_{-2}^{2} (6-x)\sqrt{36-9x^2}\, dx.$$

Use the trigonometric substitution $x = 2\sin\theta$, $dx = 2\cos\theta\, d\theta$ and $\sqrt{36-9x^2} = 6\cos\theta$ with limits of $\theta = -\pi/2$ and $\pi/2$ in place of limits $x = -2$ and 2 to rewrite this integral as

$$V = \frac{1}{2} \int_{-\pi/2}^{\pi/2} (6 - 2\sin\theta)(6\cos\theta)(2\cos\theta)\, d\theta = 12 \int_{-\pi/2}^{\pi/2} (3 - \sin\theta)\cos^2\theta\, d\theta$$

$$= 12 \left(\int_{-\pi/2}^{\pi/2} \left(\frac{3}{2}(1 + \cos 2\theta) - \cos^2\theta\sin\theta \right) d\theta \right)$$

$$= 12 \left[\frac{3}{2}\theta + \frac{3}{4}\sin 2\theta + \frac{\cos^3\theta}{3} \right] \Bigg|_{-\pi/2}^{\pi/2} = 18\pi.$$

15.3

Double Integrals in Polar Coordinates

5. Use double integrals in polar coordinates to find the volume of the solid inside both the sphere $x^2 + y^2 + z^2 = 4$ and the cylinder $x^2 + y^2 = 1$.

SOLUTION: The sphere has polar equation $r^2 + z^2 = 4$ and the cylinder has polar equation $r = 1$. The intersection of their interiors is sketched.

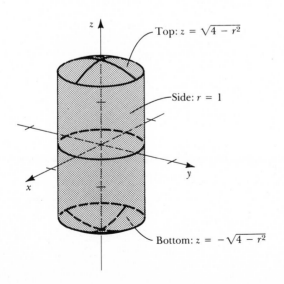

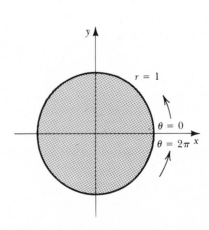

The projection of the solid into the xy-plane lies inside the circle $r = 1$. This is the θ-simple region $R = \{(r, \theta) : 0 \leq \theta \leq 2\pi; \text{for each } \theta, \quad 0 \leq r \leq 1\}$.

The top and bottom of the solid are given by $z = \sqrt{4 - r^2}$ and $z = -\sqrt{4 - r^2}$ respectively, so the volume is

$$V = \int_0^{2\pi} \int_0^1 \left(\sqrt{4 - r^2} - (-\sqrt{4 - r^2})\right) r \, dr \, d\theta = \int_0^{2\pi} \int_0^1 \sqrt{4 - r^2} \, 2r \, dr \, d\theta$$

$$= \int_0^{2\pi} \left[-\frac{2}{3}(4 - r^2)^{3/2}\right]\Big|_{r=0}^1 d\theta = \int_0^{2\pi} \frac{16 - 6\sqrt{3}}{3} \, d\theta = \left(\frac{16 - 6\sqrt{3}}{3}\right) [\theta]\Big|_0^{2\pi}$$

$$= \frac{4\pi(8 - 3\sqrt{3})}{3}.$$

COMMENT: A <u>strategy</u> for solving volume or area problems described in polar coordinates is to   I) Sketch the solid or region.   II) Describe the region of integration as θ-simple (or occasionally r-simple, if appropriate).   III) Write the appropriate double integral with area element $dA = r \, dr \, d\theta$.   IV) Evaluate this integral.

11. Use double integrals in polar coordinates to find the volume inside the cylinder formed by the intersection of $r = \sin \theta$ and $r = \cos \theta$ and bounded above by the paraboloid $z = x^2 + y^2$ and below by $z = 0$.

SOLUTION: The solid is sketched; its top has polar equation $z = r^2$.

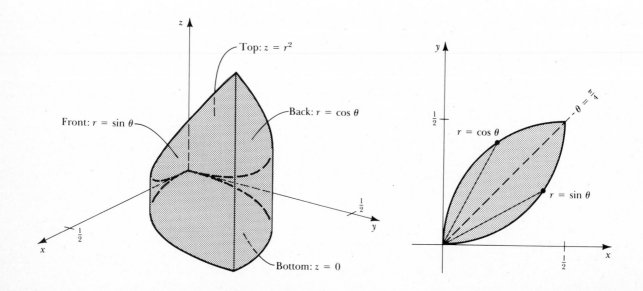

The projection on the xy-plane is the region of intersection of the insides of the circles $r = \sin \theta$ and $r = \cos \theta$. This region is not θ-simple since for θ, $0 \leq \theta \leq \pi/4$, $0 \leq r \leq \sin \theta$ while for θ, $\pi/4 \leq \theta \leq \pi/2$, $0 \leq r \leq \cos \theta$. Thus the volume is computed as the sum of two iterated integrals.

$$V = \int_0^{\pi/4} \int_0^{\sin \theta} r^2 r \, dr \, d\theta + \int_{\pi/4}^{\pi/2} \int_0^{\cos \theta} r^2 r \, dr \, d\theta$$

$$= \int_0^{\pi/4} \frac{(\sin \theta)^4}{4} \, d\theta + \int_{\pi/4}^{\pi/2} \frac{(\cos \theta)^4}{4} \, d\theta.$$

First use the identity $\cos \theta = \sin(\pi/2 - \theta)$, then the change of variables $\phi = \pi/2 - \theta$ to see that the second integral is identical to the first. Thus,

$$V = \frac{1}{2} \int_0^{\pi/4} (\sin \theta)^4 \, d\theta.$$

Use the identity

$$(\sin^2 \theta)^2 = \left(\frac{1 - \cos 2\theta}{2} \right)^2 = \frac{1 - 2 \cos 2\theta + \cos^2 2\theta}{4}$$

$$= \frac{1 - 2 \cos 2\theta + 1/2 + (1/2) \cos 4\theta}{4} = \frac{3}{8} - \frac{1}{2} \cos 2\theta + \frac{1}{8} \cos 4\theta$$

to write this integral as

$$V = \frac{1}{16} \int_0^{\pi/4} (3 - 4 \cos 2\theta + \cos 4\theta) \, d\theta = \frac{1}{16} \left[3\theta - 2 \sin 2\theta + \frac{1}{4} \sin 4\theta \right] \Big|_0^{\pi/4} = \frac{3\pi}{64} - \frac{1}{8}.$$

15. Use a double integral to find the area inside the curve $r = 3 - 2 \cos \theta$.

SOLUTION: This curve, a limaçon, is traced out exactly once as θ varies from 0 to 2π.

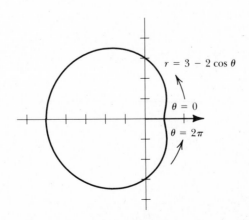

This θ-simple region is described by $R = \{(r,\theta) : 0 \le \theta \le 2\pi;$ for each $\theta, \quad 0 \le r < 3 - 2\theta\}$. The area is

$$A = \int_0^{2\pi} \int_0^{3-2\cos\theta} r\, dr\, d\theta = \int_0^{2\pi} \left[\frac{r^2}{2}\right]\Bigg|_{r=0}^{3-2\cos\theta} d\theta$$

$$= \frac{1}{2}\int_0^{2\pi} (3 - 2\cos\theta)^2\, d\theta = \frac{1}{2}\int_0^{2\pi}(9 - 12\cos\theta + 4\cos^2\theta)\, d\theta$$

$$= \frac{1}{2}\int_0^{2\pi}(11 - 12\cos\theta + 2\cos 2\theta)\, d\theta = \frac{1}{2}[11(\theta) - 12\sin\theta + \sin 2\theta]\Bigg|_0^{2\pi} = 11\pi.$$

19. Use a double integral to find the area inside $r = \sin\theta$ and outside $r^2 = (\sin 2\theta)/2$.

SOLUTION: The intersection of the region inside both the circle $r = \sin\theta$ and the lemniscate $r^2 = (\sin 2\theta)/2$ is sketched.

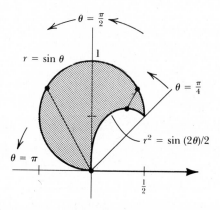

The θ value of the point of intersection solves $\sin^2\theta = (\sin 2\theta)/2$ or $\sin^2\theta = \sin\theta\cos\theta$, so the intersection occurs at $\theta = \pi/4$ and π. The region is neither θ-simple nor r-simple. The outside boundary is given by $r = \sin\theta$ for all θ, but the inside boundary changes formula at $\theta = \pi/2$ from $r = \sqrt{(\sin 2\theta)/2}$ to $r = 0$. The region is thus the union of
$\{(r,\theta) : \pi/4 \le \theta \le \pi/2;$ for each $\theta, \quad \sqrt{(\sin 2\theta)/2} \le r \le \sin\theta\}$ and
$\{(r,\theta) : \pi/2 \le \theta \le \pi;$ for each $\theta, \quad 0 \le r \le \sin\theta\}$.

The area is then the sum

$$A = \int_{\pi/4}^{\pi/2} \int_{\sqrt{(\sin 2\theta)/2}}^{\sin\theta} r\, dr\, d\theta + \int_{\pi/2}^{\pi} \int_0^{\sin\theta} r\, dr\, d\theta$$

$$= \int_{\pi/4}^{\pi/2} \left[\frac{r^2}{2}\right]\Bigg|_{r=\sqrt{(\sin 2\theta)/2}}^{\sin\theta} d\theta + \int_{\pi/2}^{\pi} \left[\frac{r^2}{2}\right]\Bigg|_{r=0}^{\sin\theta} d\theta$$

$$= \frac{1}{2} \left(\int_{\pi/4}^{\pi/2} \left(\sin^2 \theta - \frac{\sin 2\theta}{2} \right) d\theta + \int_{\pi/2}^{\pi} \sin^2 \theta \, d\theta \right)$$

$$= \frac{1}{4} \left(\int_{\pi/4}^{\pi/2} (1 - \cos 2\theta - \sin 2\theta) \, d\theta + \int_{\pi/2}^{\pi} (1 - \cos 2\theta) \, d\theta \right)$$

$$= \frac{1}{4} \left(\left[\theta - \frac{1}{2} \sin 2\theta + \frac{1}{2} \cos 2\theta \right] \Big|_{\pi/4}^{\pi/2} + \left[\theta - \frac{1}{2} \sin 2\theta \right] \Big|_{\pi/2}^{\pi} \right) = \frac{3\pi}{16}.$$

25. Change $\int_0^1 \int_{\sqrt{3}x/3}^{x} \frac{1}{\sqrt{x^2 + y^2}} \, dy \, dx$ to a double integral in polar coordinates and evaluate.

SOLUTION: The region of integration $\{(x, y) : 0 \le x \le 1, \text{for each } x, \quad \sqrt{3}x/3 \le y \le x\}$ is bounded above and below by the lines $y = x$ and $y = x\sqrt{3}/3$ for x between 0 and 1.

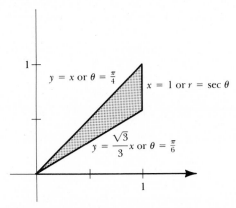

The boundaries of this triangle are converted to polar equations as follows: The line $y = \sqrt{3}x/3$ becomes $y/x = \sqrt{3}/3$ or $\tan \theta = 1/\sqrt{3}$, so $\theta = \pi/6$; the line $y = x$ becomes $(y/x) = 1$ or $\tan \theta = 1$; so $\theta = \pi/4$, and the line $x = 1$ becomes $r \cos \theta = 1$ or $r = \sec \theta$. This θ-simple region is described as $R = \{(r, \theta) : \pi/6 \le \theta \le \pi/4, \text{for each } \theta, \quad 0 \le r \le \sec \theta\}$. The integrand is $\frac{1}{\sqrt{x^2 + y^2}} = \frac{1}{r}$ and the area form $dy \, dx$ becomes $r \, dr \, d\theta$ so the integral is

$$\int_0^1 \int_{\sqrt{3}x/3}^{x} \frac{1}{\sqrt{x^2 + y^2}} \, dy \, dx = \int_{\pi/6}^{\pi/4} \int_0^{\sec \theta} \frac{1}{r} r \, dr \, d\theta.$$

This integral is evaluated.

$$\int_{\pi/6}^{\pi/4} \int_0^{\sec \theta} dr \, d\theta = \int_{\pi/6}^{\pi/4} [r] \Big|_{r=0}^{\sec \theta} d\theta$$

$$= \int_{\pi/6}^{\pi/4} \sec\theta \, d\theta = \left[\ln|\sec\theta + \tan\theta|\right]\Big|_{\pi/6}^{\pi/4} = \ln\left(\frac{\sqrt{2}+1}{\sqrt{3}}\right).$$

29. Evaluate $\displaystyle\int_{\pi/4}^{3\pi/4} \int_{0}^{3\csc\theta} re^{r^2\sin^2\theta} \, dr \, d\theta$ by changing to a double integral in cartesian coordinates.

SOLUTION: The region $R = \{(r,\theta) : \pi/4 \le \theta \le 3\pi/4, \text{for each } \theta, \quad 0 \le r \le 3\csc\theta\}$ lies between the rays $\theta = \pi/4$ and $\theta = 3\pi/4$ and is bounded inside by $r = 0$ and outside by $r = 3\csc\theta$. The cartesian equations are: for $\theta = \pi/4$, $y/x = \tan(\pi/4) = 1$ or $y = x$; for $\theta = 3\pi/4$, $y/x = \tan(3\pi/4) = -1$ or $y = -x$; and for $r = 3\csc\theta$, $y = r\sin\theta = 3$. The region is the triangle sketched below.

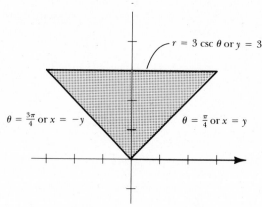

This y-simple region may be described as $R = \{(x,y) : 0 \le y \le 3, \text{for each } y, \quad -y \le x \le y\}$. The area form $r \, dr \, d\theta$ becomes $dx \, dy$ and the integrand (with an r term factored out) becomes $e^{r^2\sin^2\theta} = e^{y^2}$.

$$\int_{\pi/4}^{3\pi/4} \int_{0}^{3\csc\theta} e^{r^2\sin^2\theta} r \, dr \, d\theta = \int_{0}^{3} \int_{-y}^{y} e^{y^2} \, dx \, dy.$$

This is evaluated as

$$\int_{0}^{3} \int_{-y}^{y} e^{y^2} \, dx \, dy = \int_{0}^{3} e^{y^2}[x]\Big|_{x=-y}^{y} \, dy$$

$$= \int_{0}^{3} e^{y^2} 2y \, dy = \left[e^{y^2}\right]\Big|_{0}^{3} = e^9 - 1.$$

_____**15.4**

Center of Mass and
Moments of Inertia

COMMENT: A <u>strategy</u> for determining mass and moments of a planar region is to: I) Describe the region as a simple region (if possible) in an appropriate coordinate system. II) Use this description to express each of the integrals required with the same limits and order of integration but with integrand as required. III) Evaluate the integrals.

3. Find a) the mass, b) the moments about the axes, and c) the center of mass of the lamina bounded by $y = 1 - x$, $y = 0$, and $x = 0$ and having density $\sigma(x,y) = x$.

SOLUTION: This planar region is a triangle.

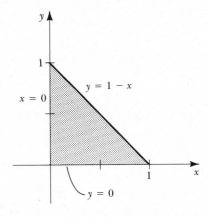

It is an x-simple region which may be described as
$R = \{(x,y) : 0 \le x \le 1; \text{for each } x, \quad 0 \le y \le 1 - x\}$.
a) With $\sigma(x,y) = x$, its mass is

$$M = \iint\limits_{R} \sigma(x,y)\,dA = \int_0^1 \int_0^{1-x} x\,dy\,dx = \int_0^1 x[y]\Big|_{y=0}^{1-x} dx$$

$$= \int_0^1 x(1-x)\,dx = \left[\frac{x^2}{2} - \frac{x^3}{3}\right]\Big|_0^1 = \frac{1}{6}.$$

b) Its moments about the axes are

$$M_x = \iint\limits_{R} y\sigma(x,y)\,dA = \int_0^1 \int_0^{1-x} yx\,dy\,dx$$

$$= \int_0^1 x \left[\frac{y^2}{2} \right] \Big|_{y=0}^{1-x} dx = \frac{1}{2} \int_0^1 x(1-x)^2 \, dx = \frac{1}{2} \int_0^1 (x - 2x^2 + x^3) \, dx$$

$$= \frac{1}{2} \left[\frac{x^2}{2} - \frac{2x^3}{3} + \frac{x^4}{4} \right] \Big|_0^1 = \frac{1}{24} \qquad \text{and}$$

$$M_y = \iint\limits_R x\sigma(x,y) \, dA = \int_0^1 \int_0^{1-x} x^2 \, dy \, dx$$

$$= \int_0^1 x^2 [y] \Big|_{y=0}^{1-x} dx = \int_0^1 x^2(1-x) \, dx = \left[\frac{x^3}{3} - \frac{x^4}{4} \right] \Big|_0^1 = \frac{1}{12}.$$

c) The center of mass is $(\bar{x}, \bar{y})$ where

$$\bar{x} = \frac{M_y}{M} = \frac{1/12}{1/6} = \frac{1}{2} \quad \text{and} \quad \bar{y} = \frac{M_x}{M} = \frac{1/24}{1/6} = \frac{1}{4}.$$

13. Find the moments of inertia about the axis and the origin, and the radius of gyration of the lamina bounded by $y = 1 - x^2$ and $y = 0$ having density $\sigma(x,y) = x^2$.

SOLUTION: The region lies beneath the parabola $y = 1 - x^2$ and above the x-axis.

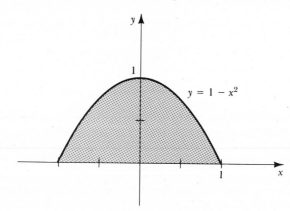

Its x-simple description is $R = \{(x,y) : -1 \le x \le 1; \text{for each } x, \quad 0 \le y \le 1 - x^2\}$. Its moments of inertia are

$$I_x = \iint\limits_R y^2 \sigma(x,y) \, dA = \int_{-1}^1 \int_0^{1-x^2} y^2 x^2 \, dy \, dx$$

$$= \int_{-1}^1 x^2 \left[\frac{y^3}{3} \right] \Big|_{y=0}^{1-x^2} dx = \frac{1}{3} \int_{-1}^1 x^2(1-x^2)^3 \, dx$$

$$= \frac{1}{3} \int_{-1}^{1} (x^2 - 3x^4 + 3x^6 - x^8)\, dx = \frac{1}{3} \left[\frac{x^3}{3} - \frac{3x^5}{5} + \frac{3x^7}{7} - \frac{x^9}{9} \right] \Big|_{-1}^{1} = \frac{32}{945}$$

$$I_y = \iint_R x^2 \sigma(x,y)\, dA = \int_{-1}^{1} \int_{0}^{1-x^2} x^2 x^2\, dy\, dx$$

$$= \int_{-1}^{1} x^4 (1 - x^2)\, dx = \left[\frac{x^5}{5} - \frac{x^7}{7} \right] \Big|_{-1}^{1} = \frac{4}{35}$$

$$I_o = \iint_R (x^2 + y^2)\sigma(x,y)\, dA = I_y + I_x = \frac{4}{27}.$$

From the SOLUTION to EXERCISE 5, its mass is $M = 4/15$, so its radius of gyration about the x-axis is

$$\hat{x} = \sqrt{\frac{I_y}{M}} = \sqrt{\frac{4/35}{4/15}} = \sqrt{\frac{3}{7}},$$

and its radius of gyration about the y-axis is

$$\hat{y} = \sqrt{\frac{I_x}{M}} = \sqrt{\frac{32/945}{4/15}} = \sqrt{\frac{8}{63}}.$$

21. Use the formulas in EXERCISES 17 and 18 to find   a) the mass,   b) the moments about the axis, and   c) the moments of inertia for the plane lamina whose boundary is $r = \sin\theta$ and whose density is $\sigma(r,\theta) = r$.

SOLUTION: The region is the circle $\{(r,\theta) : 0 \le \theta \le \pi; \text{for each } \theta, \quad 0 \le r \le \sin\theta\}$. The mass is

$$M = \iint_R \sigma r\, dr\, d\theta = \int_0^\pi \int_0^{\sin\theta} r^2\, dr\, d\theta$$

$$= \int_0^\pi \frac{1}{3} \sin^3\theta\, d\theta = \frac{1}{3} \int_0^\pi (1 - \cos^2\theta)\sin\theta\, d\theta = \frac{1}{3} \left[-\cos\theta + \frac{(\cos^3\theta)}{3} \right] \Big|_0^\pi = \frac{4}{9}.$$

The moments are

$$M_x = \iint_R r^2 \sin\theta\, \sigma(r,\theta)\, dr\, d\theta = \int_0^\pi \int_0^{\sin\theta} r^3 \sin\theta\, dr\, d\theta$$

$$= \int_0^\pi \frac{1}{4} (\sin\theta)^4 \sin\theta\, d\theta = \frac{1}{4} \int_0^\pi (1 - 2\cos^2\theta + \cos^4\theta)\sin\theta\, d\theta$$

$$= \frac{1}{4}\left[-\cos\theta + \frac{2}{3}\cos^3\theta - \frac{1}{5}\cos^5\theta\right]\Big|_0^\pi = \frac{4}{15} \quad \text{and}$$

$$M_y = \iint\limits_R r^2\cos\theta\,\sigma(r,\theta)\,dr\,d\theta = \int_0^\pi\int_0^{\sin\theta} r^3\cos\theta\,dr\,d\theta$$

$$= \int_0^\pi \frac{1}{4}(\sin\theta)^4\cos\theta\,d\theta = \left[\frac{\sin^5\theta}{20}\right]\Big|_0^\pi = 0.$$

The moments of inertia are

$$I_x = \iint\limits_R r^3\sin^2\theta\,\sigma(r,\theta)\,dr\,d\theta$$

$$= \int_0^\pi\int_0^{\sin\theta} r^4\sin^2\theta\,dr\,d\theta = \int_0^\pi \frac{(\sin\theta)^5}{5}\sin^2\theta\,d\theta$$

$$= \frac{1}{5}\int_0^\pi (1 - 3\cos^2\theta + 3\cos^4\theta - \cos^6\theta)\sin\theta\,d\theta$$

$$= \frac{1}{5}\left[-\cos\theta + \cos^3\theta - \frac{3}{5}\cos^5\theta + \frac{1}{7}\cos^7\theta\right]\Big|_0^\pi = \frac{32}{175},$$

$$I_y = \iint\limits_R r^3\cos^2\theta\,\sigma(r,\theta)\,dr\,d\theta = \int_0^\pi\int_0^{\sin\theta} r^4\cos^2\theta\,dr\,d\theta$$

$$= \int_0^\pi \frac{(\sin\theta)^5}{5}\cos^2\theta\,d\theta = \frac{1}{5}\int_0^\pi \cos^2\theta(1 - 2\cos^2\theta + \cos^4\theta)\sin\theta\,d\theta$$

$$= \frac{1}{5}\left[-\frac{1}{3}\cos^3\theta + \frac{2}{5}\cos^5\theta - \frac{1}{7}\cos^7\theta\right]\Big|_0^\pi = \frac{16}{525}, \quad \text{and}$$

$$I_o = \iint\limits_R r^3\sigma(r,\theta)\,dr\,d\theta = \int_0^\pi\int_0^{\sin\theta} r^4\,dr\,d\theta$$

$$= \int_0^\pi \frac{(\sin\theta)^5}{5}\,d\theta = \frac{1}{5}\int_0^\pi (1 - 2\cos^2\theta + \cos^4\theta)\sin\theta\,d\theta$$

$$= \frac{1}{5}\left[-\cos\theta + \frac{2}{3}\cos^3\theta - \frac{1}{5}\cos^5\theta\right]\Big|_0^\pi = \frac{16}{75}.$$

23. Use the formulas in EXERCISE 17 to find the center of mass of the plane lamina whose boundary is $r = 1 - \sin\theta$ and density is $\sigma(r,\theta) = r$.

SOLUTION: The region inside the cardioid is described as
$R = \{(r,\theta) : 0 \le \theta \le 2\pi, \text{ for each } \theta, \quad 0 \le r \le 1 - \sin\theta\}$.

To compute $\bar{r}$ and $\bar{\theta}$, first find M, M_x, and M_y:

$$M = \iint\limits_R r\sigma(r,\theta)\,dr\,d\theta = \int_0^{2\pi} \int_0^{1-\sin\theta} r^2\,dr\,d\theta$$

$$= \int_0^{2\pi} \frac{(1-\sin\theta)^3}{3}\,d\theta = \frac{1}{3}\int_0^{2\pi}(1 - 3\sin\theta + 3\sin^2\theta - \sin^3\theta)\,d\theta$$

$$= \frac{1}{3}\left(\int_0^{2\pi}(1 + 3\sin^2\theta)\,d\theta - \int_0^{2\pi}(3 + \sin^2\theta)\sin\theta\,d\theta\right)$$

$$= \frac{1}{3}\left(\int_0^{2\pi}\left(\frac{5}{2} - \frac{3}{2}\cos 2\theta\right)\,d\theta - \int_0^{2\pi}(4 - \cos^2\theta)\sin\theta\,d\theta\right)$$

$$= \frac{1}{3}\left[\frac{5}{2}\theta - \frac{3}{4}\sin 2\theta + 4\cos\theta - \frac{\cos^3\theta}{3}\right]\Bigg|_0^{2\pi} = \frac{5\pi}{3},$$

$$M_x = \iint\limits_R r^2\sin\theta\,\sigma(r,\theta)\,dr\,d\theta = \int_0^{2\pi}\int_0^{1-\sin\theta} r^3\sin\theta\,dr\,d\theta = \int_0^{2\pi}\frac{(1-\sin\theta)^4}{4}\sin\theta\,d\theta$$

$$= \frac{1}{4}\int_0^{2\pi}(1 - 4\sin\theta + 6\sin^2\theta - 4\sin^3\theta + \sin^4\theta)\sin\theta\,d\theta$$

$$= \frac{1}{4}\int_0^{2\pi}(1 + 6\sin^2\theta + \sin^4\theta)\sin\theta\,d\theta - \int_0^{2\pi}(\sin^2\theta + \sin^4\theta)\,d\theta$$

$$= \frac{1}{4}\int_0^{2\pi}(8 - 8\cos^2\theta + \cos^4\theta)\sin\theta\,d\theta - \int_0^{2\pi}\left(\frac{7}{8} - \cos 2\theta + \frac{1}{8}\cos 4\theta\right)\,d\theta$$

$$= \frac{1}{4}\left[\left(-3\cos\theta + \frac{8}{3}\cos^3\theta - \frac{1}{5}\cos^5\theta\right) - \left(\frac{7}{8}\theta - \frac{1}{2}\sin 2\theta + \frac{1}{32}\sin 4\theta\right)\right]\Bigg|_0^{2\pi}$$

$$= -\frac{7\pi}{4}, \quad\text{and}$$

$$M_y = \iint\limits_R r^2\cos\theta\,\sigma(r,\theta)\,dr\,d\theta = \int_0^{2\pi}\int_0^{1-\sin\theta} r^3\cos\theta\,dr\,d\theta$$

$$= \int_0^{2\pi}\frac{(1-\sin\theta)^4}{4}\cos\theta\,d\theta = \left[-\frac{(1-\sin\theta)^5}{20}\right]\Bigg|_0^{2\pi} = 0.$$

Thus,

$$\bar{r}^2 = \frac{(M_x)^2 + (M_y)^2}{M^2} = \frac{\left(-\frac{7\pi}{4}\right)^2 + (0)^2}{\left(\frac{5\pi}{3}\right)^2} = \left(\frac{21}{20}\right)^2,$$

and $\tan \bar{\theta} = \dfrac{M_x}{M_y}$ is undefined so $\bar{r} = 21/20$ and $\bar{\theta} = 3\pi/2$.

Surface Area

---

5. Find the surface area of the part of the paraboloid $z = x^2 + y^2$ that lies inside the cylinder $x^2 + y^2 = 4$.

SOLUTION: The surface is the portion of the graph of $f(x, y) = x^2 + y^2$ which lies over the region R inside the circle $x^2 + y^2 = 4$.

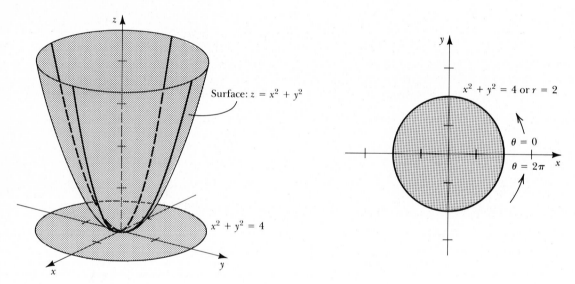

With the surface given by $z = f(x, y) = x^2 + y^2$ with $f_x = 2x$ and $f_y = 2y$, the surface area is

$$SA = \iint_R \sqrt{1 + (f_x)^2 + (f_y)^2}\, dA = \iint_R \sqrt{1 + 4(x^2 + y^2)}\, dA.$$

Since the term "$x^2 + y^2$" appears in the integrand and since the region of integration is a circular disk, use polar coordinates to describe $R = \{(r, \theta) : 0 \le \theta \le 2\pi; \text{for each } \theta, \quad 0 \le r \le 2\}$. Thus the surface area is

$$SA = \int_0^{2\pi} \int_0^2 \sqrt{1 + 4r^2}\, r\, dr\, d\theta = \int_0^{2\pi} \left[\frac{1}{12}(1 + 4r^2)^{3/2} \right] \Bigg|_{r=0}^{2} d\theta$$

$$= \left(\frac{17\sqrt{17} - 1}{12} \right) [\theta] \Bigg|_0^{2\pi} = \frac{(17\sqrt{17} - 1)\pi}{6}.$$

7. Find the surface area of the portion of the cylinder $y^2 + z^2 = 4$ that lies above the xy-plane between $x = 0$ and $x = 3$.

SOLUTION: The surface and region over which it lies are sketched.

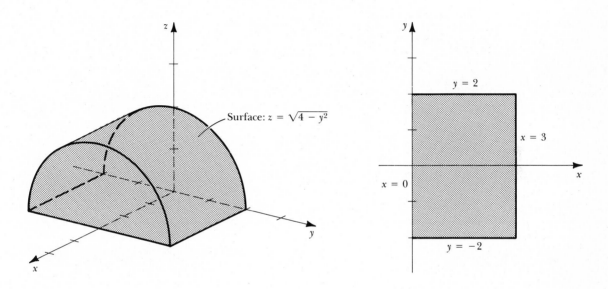

The surface is given by $z = f(x,y) = \sqrt{4 - y^2}$, with $f_x = 0$ and $f_y = -y/\sqrt{4 - y^2}$, over the rectangle $R = \{(x,y) : 0 \le x \le 3; \text{ for each } x, \quad -2 \le y \le 2\}$. The surface area is thus

$$SA = \iint\limits_R \sqrt{1 + 0^2 + \frac{y^2}{4 - y^2}} \, dA = \int_0^3 \int_{-2}^2 \frac{2}{\sqrt{4 - y^2}} \, dy \, dx$$

$$= \int_0^3 \left[2\arccos\left(\frac{y}{2}\right) \right] \Big|_{y=-2}^2 dx = \int_0^3 2\pi \, dx = 6\pi.$$

15. Suppose $ax + by + cz = 1$ is an equation of a plane with a, b, and c all positive. Determine the surface area of the portion of this plane that is bounded by the coordinate planes.

SOLUTION: The surface lies over the region in the xy-plane bounded by $x = 0$, $y = 0$, and $ax + by = 1$.

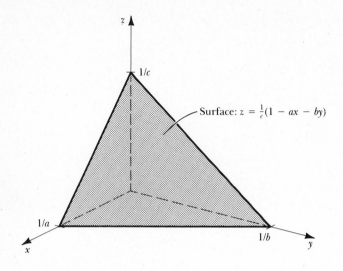

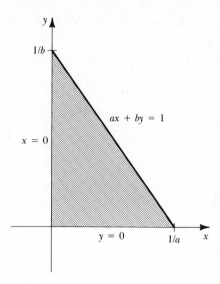

The region may be described by $R = \{(x, y) : 0 \le x \le 1/a; \text{for each } x, \quad 0 \le y \le (1/b)(1 - ax)\}$. With the surface described by $z = f(x, y) = (1/c)(1 - ax - by)$, with $f_x = -a/c$ and $f_y = -b/c$, the surface area is

$$SA = \iint\limits_{R} \sqrt{1 + \left(-\frac{a}{c}\right)^2 + \left(-\frac{b}{c}\right)^2}\, dA = \frac{\sqrt{a^2 + b^2 + c^2}}{c} \int_0^{1/a} \int_0^{(1/b)(1-ax)} dy\, dx$$

$$= \frac{\sqrt{a^2 + b^2 + c^2}}{c} \int_0^{1/a} \frac{1}{b}(1 - ax)\, dx = \frac{\sqrt{a^2 + b^2 + c^2}}{c} \frac{1}{b}\left[\left(-\frac{1}{a}\right) \frac{(1 - ax)^2}{2}\right]\Big|_0^{1/a}$$

$$= \frac{\sqrt{a^2 + b^2 + c^2}}{2abc}.$$

_____15.6

Triple Integrals

5. Evaluate $\displaystyle\int_0^\pi \int_1^z \int_0^{xz} \frac{1}{x} \sin\left(\frac{y}{x}\right) dy\, dx\, dz.$

SOLUTION: Integrate first with respect to y treating x and z as constants.

$$\int_0^\pi \int_1^z \int_0^{xz} \sin\left(\frac{y}{x}\right) \frac{1}{x}\, dy\, dx\, dz = \int_0^\pi \int_1^z \left[-\cos\left(\frac{y}{x}\right)\right]\Big|_{y=0}^{xz} dx\, dz$$

$$= \int_0^\pi \int_1^z (1 - \cos z)\, dx\, dz = \int_0^\pi (1 - \cos z)[x] \Big|_{x=1}^z dz$$

$$= \int_0^\pi (z - 1)(1 - \cos z)\, dz.$$

Integrate by parts with $u = z - 1$, $dv = (1 - \cos z)$, so that $du = dz$ and $v = z - \sin z$. Then,

$$\int_0^\pi (z - 1)(1 - \cos z)\, dz = \left[(z - 1)(z - \sin z) - \int (z - \sin z)\, dz \right] \Big|_0^\pi$$

$$= \left[\frac{z^2}{2} - z - z \sin z + \sin z - \cos z \right] \Big|_0^\pi = \frac{\pi^2}{2} - \pi + 2.$$

11. Sketch the solid whose volume is given by the triple integral

$$\int_0^2 \int_0^{\sqrt{4-x^2}} \int_{-\sqrt{4-x^2-y^2}}^{\sqrt{4-x^2-y^2}} dz\, dy\, dx \text{ and determine the volume.}$$

SOLUTION: The region of integration is

$$D = \left\{ (x, y, z) : 0 \leq x \leq 2; \text{for each } x, 0 \leq y \leq \sqrt{4 - x^2};\ \text{for each } x \text{ and } y, \right.$$

$$\left. -\sqrt{4 - x^2 - y^2} \leq z \leq \sqrt{4 - x^2 - y^2} \right\}.$$

The projection of this solid on the xy-plane is the region
$$R_{xy} = \left\{ (x, y) : 0 \leq x \leq 2;\ \text{for each } x,\ 0 \leq y \leq \sqrt{4 - x^2} \right\}, \text{ a quarter circle of radius 2.}$$

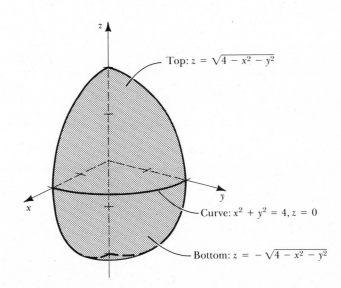

For each (x, y) in this projection, the solid contains a line whose z-values change from $z = -\sqrt{4 - (x^2 + y^2)}$ on the bottom to $z = \sqrt{4 - (x^2 + y^2)}$ on top. Rewrite these equations as $x^2 + y^2 + z^2 = 4$ to see that D is the portion of the sphere of radius two which projects onto the first quadrant in the xy- plane.

The volume is

$$V = \int_0^2 \int_0^{\sqrt{4-x^2}} \int_{-\sqrt{4-x^2-y^2}}^{\sqrt{4-x^2-y^2}} dz \, dy \, dx = \int_0^2 \int_0^{\sqrt{4-x^2}} 2\sqrt{(4-x^2) - y^2} \, dy \, dx.$$

Let $y = \sqrt{4 - x^2} \sin \theta$, $dy = \sqrt{4 - x^2} \cos \theta \, d\theta$; so $\sqrt{(4 - x^2) - y^2} = \sqrt{4 - x^2} \cos \theta$; when $y = 0$, $\theta = 0$, and when $y = \sqrt{4 - x^2}$, $\theta = \pi/2$, so

$$V = 2 \int_0^2 \int_0^{\pi/2} (\sqrt{4 - x^2} \cos \theta) \cdot \sqrt{4 - x^2} \cos \theta \, d\theta \, dx = 2 \int_0^2 (4 - x^2) \cdot \int_0^{\pi/2} \frac{1}{2}(1 + \cos 2\theta) \, d\theta \, dx$$

$$= \int_0^2 (4 - x^2) \left[\theta + \frac{1}{2} \sin 2\theta \right] \Big|_{\theta=0}^{\pi/2} dx = \frac{\pi}{2} \int_0^2 (4 - x^2) \, dx = \frac{\pi}{2} \left[4x - \frac{x^3}{3} \right] \Big|_0^2 = \frac{8\pi}{3}.$$

COMMENT: Notice that a surface may be top with respect to one projection, right with respect to a second projection and front with respect to a third; we'll label surfaces by all the roles it may play.

15. a) Rewrite the integral $\int_0^1 \int_0^{1-x} \int_0^{1-x-y} z \, dz \, dy \, dx$ in five alternative ways. **b)** Evaluate the triple integral.

SOLUTION: a) The region of integration is $D = \{(x, y, z) : 0 \le x \le 1;$ for each x, $0 \le y \le 1 - x;$ for each x and y, $0 \le z \le 1 - x - y\}$. The projection of this region onto the xy-plane is the triangle, $R_{xy} = \{(x, y) : 0 \le x \le 1;$ for each x, $0 \le y \le 1 - x\}$, bounded by the lines $x + y = 1$, $y = 0$, and $x = 0$. For each (x, y) in R the solid contains a line running from $z = 0$ on the bottom to $z = 1 - x - y$ on top. Thus the solid D is a tetrahedron bounded by the planes $x + y + z = 1$, $x = 0$, $y = 0$, and $z = 0$.

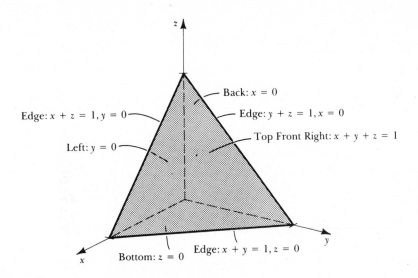

A second order of integration comes from describing the projection as
$R_{xy} = \{(x,y) : 0 \le y \le 1;$ for each y, $0 \le x \le 1-y\}$ with each line for fixed (x,y) still running
from $z = 0$ to $z = 1 - x - y$. The region of integration may thus be described as

$$D = \{(x,y,z) : 0 \le y \le 1; \text{ for each } y, \quad 0 \le x \le 1-y; \text{ for each } x \text{ and } y, \quad 0 \le z \le 1-x-y\}.$$

This gives the integral

$$\int_0^1 \int_0^{1-y} \int_0^{1-x-y} z \, dz \, dx \, dy.$$

The projection of the region D on the xz-plane is the triangle R_{xz} bounded by $x = 0$, $z = 0$, and
$x + z = 1$. For each (x,z) in R_{xz}, D contains a line running from $y = 0$ on the left to $y = 1 - x - z$
on the right. R_{xz} can be written in two ways:

$$R_{xz} = \{(x,z) : 0 \le x \le 1; \text{ for each } x, \quad 0 \le z \le 1-x\} \quad \text{and}$$
$$R_{xz} = \{(x,z) : 0 \le z \le 1; \text{ for each } z, \quad 0 \le x \le 1-z\}.$$

The first gives the description of D as

$$D = \{(x,y,z) : 0 \le x \le 1; \text{ for each } x, \quad 0 \le z \le 1-x; \text{ for each } x \text{ and } z, \quad 0 \le y \le 1-x-z\}$$

which results in the iterated integral

$$\int_0^1 \int_0^{1-x} \int_0^{1-x-z} z \, dy \, dz \, dx.$$

The second description of R_{xz} gives the description of D as

$$D = \{(x,y,z) : 0 \le z \le 1; \text{ for each } z, \quad 0 \le x \le 1-z; \text{ for each } x \text{ and } z, \quad 0 \le y \le 1-x-z\}$$

and results in the iterated integral

$$\int_0^1 \int_0^{1-z} \int_0^{1-x-z} z \, dy \, dx \, dz.$$

The projection of D onto the yz-plane is the triangle R_{yz} bounded by $z = 0$, $y = 0$, and $y + z = 1$. For each fixed (y, z) in R_{yz}, D contains a line running from $x = 0$ in the back to $x = 1 - y - z$ in the front. The description, $R_{yz} = \{(y, z) : 0 \le y \le 1; \text{ for each } y, \quad 0 \le z \le 1 - y\}$, leads to the description of D as $D = \{(x, y, z) : 0 \le y \le 1; \text{ for each } y, \quad 0 \le z \le 1 - y; \text{ for each } y \text{ and } z, 0 \le x \le 1 - z - y\}$. The corresponding iterated integral is

$$\int_0^1 \int_0^{1-y} \int_0^{1-z-y} z \, dx \, dz \, dy.$$

The alternate description $R_{yz} = \{(y, z) : 0 \le z \le 1; \text{ for each } z, \quad 0 \le y \le 1 - z\}$, leads to the description of D as

$$D = \{(x, y, z) : 0 \le z \le 1; \text{ for each } z, \quad 0 \le y \le 1 - z; \text{ for each } y \text{ and } z, \quad 0 \le x \le 1 - z - y\}.$$

The corresponding iterated integral is

$$\int_0^1 \int_0^{1-z} \int_0^{1-z-y} z \, dx \, dy \, dz.$$

The value of this last integral is

$$\int_0^1 \int_0^{1-z} \int_0^{1-z-y} z \, dx \, dy \, dz = \int_0^1 \int_0^{1-z} z[x] \Big|_{x=0}^{1-z-y} \, dy \, dz$$

$$= \int_0^1 \int_0^{1-z} z(1 - z - y) \, dy \, dz = \int_0^1 z \left[-\frac{(1 - z - y)^2}{2} \right] \Big|_{y=0}^{1-z} \, dz$$

$$= \int_0^1 z \left(-0 + \frac{(1 - z)^2}{2} \right) \, dz = \frac{1}{2} \int_0^1 (z^3 - 2z^2 + z) \, dz$$

$$= \frac{1}{2} \left[\frac{z^4}{4} - \frac{2z^3}{3} + \frac{z^2}{2} \right] \Big|_0^1 = \frac{1}{24}.$$

19. Rewrite the integral

$$\int_0^2 \int_0^{3\sqrt{4-z^2}/2} \int_0^{\sqrt{36-4y^2-9z^2}} z \, dx \, dy \, dz$$

in five alternative ways. Evaluate one of these.

SOLUTION: The region of integration, $D = \{(x, y, z) : 0 \le z \le 2; \text{ for each } z, 0 \le y \le \frac{3}{2}\sqrt{4 - z^2}; \text{ for each } y \text{ and } z, \quad 0 \le x \le \sqrt{36 - 4y^2 - 9z^2}\}$, has projection on the yz-plane, $R_{yz} = \{(y, z) : 0 \le z \le 2, \text{ for each } z, 0 \le y \le \frac{3}{2}\sqrt{4 - z^2}\}$. This projection is bounded on the left by $y = 0$ and on the right by $y = \frac{3}{2}\sqrt{4 - z^2}$ or $4y^2 + 9z^2 = 36$, an ellipse between z-values running from 0 to 2. For each fixed (y, z), D contains a line running from $x = 0$ in back to $x = \sqrt{36 - 4y^2 - 9z^2}$ or the ellipsoid $x^2 + 4y^2 + 9z^2 = 36$ in front. The region D is thus the part inside the ellipsoid lying in the first octant.

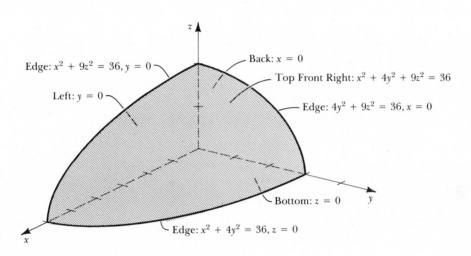

The alternate description, $R_{yz} = \{(y, z) : 0 \le y \le 3; \text{ for each } y, 0 \le z \le \frac{1}{3}\sqrt{36 - 4y^2}\}$, allows the description of D as

$$D = \{(x, y, z) : 0 \le y \le 3; \text{ for each } y, \quad 0 \le z \le \frac{1}{3}\sqrt{36 - 4y^2}; \text{ for each } y$$

$$\text{and } z, \quad 0 \le x \le \sqrt{36 - 4y^2 - 9z^2}\}.$$

This gives the integral

$$\int_0^3 \int_0^{\sqrt{36 - 4y^2}/3} \int_0^{\sqrt{36 - 4y^2 - 9z^2}} z \, dx \, dz \, dy.$$

The projection of D onto the xz-plane is the quarter ellipse R_{xz} bounded by $x = 0$, $z = 0$ and $x^2 + 9z^2 = 36$. For each (x, z) in R_{xz}, D contains a line running from $y = 0$ on the left to the ellipse $x^2 + 4y^2 + 9z^2 = 36$ or $y = \frac{1}{2}\sqrt{36 - x^2 - 9z^2}$ on the right. The description $R_{xz} = \{(x, z) : 0 \le x \le 6; \text{ for each } x, \quad 0 \le z \le \frac{1}{3}\sqrt{36 - x^2}\}$ leads to the description of D as $D = \{(x, y, z) : 0 \le x \le 6; \text{ for each } x, \quad 0 \le z \le \frac{1}{3}\sqrt{36 - x^2}; \text{ for each } x \text{ and } z,$ $0 \le y \le \frac{1}{2}\sqrt{36 - x^2 - 9z^2}\}$. The corresponding integral is

$$\int_0^6 \int_0^{\sqrt{36 - x^2}/3} \int_0^{\sqrt{36 - x^2 - 9z^2}/2} z \, dy \, dz \, dx.$$

The alternative representation, $R_{xz} = \{(x, z) : 0 \le z \le 2; \text{ for each } z, \quad 0 \le x \le \sqrt{36 - 9z^2}\}$

gives the description of D as

$$D = \{(x, y, z) : 0 \le z \le 2; \text{ for each } z, \quad 0 \le x \le \sqrt{36 - 9z^2};$$

$$\text{for each } x \text{ and } z, \quad 0 \le y \le \frac{1}{2}\sqrt{36 - x^2 - 9z^2}\}.$$

The corresponding integral is

$$\int_0^2 \int_0^{\sqrt{36-9z^2}} \int_0^{\sqrt{36-x^2-9z^2}/2} z \, dy \, dx \, dz.$$

The projection of D on the xy-plane is the quarter ellipse R_{xy} bounded by $x = 0$, $y = 0$, and $x^2 + 4y^2 = 36$. For each (x, y) in R_{xy}, D contains a line running from $z = 0$ on bottom to the ellipsoid or $z = \frac{1}{3}\sqrt{36 - x^2 - 4y^2}$ on top. The representation $R_{xy} = \{(x, y) : 0 \le x \le 6; \text{ for each } x, \quad 0 \le y \le \sqrt{36 - x^2}/2\}$ leads to the description $D = \{(x, y, z) : 0 \le x \le 6; \text{ for each } x, \quad 0 \le y \le \sqrt{36 - x^2}/2; \text{ for each } x \text{ and } y,$ $0 \le z \le \frac{1}{3}\sqrt{36 - x^2 - 4y^2}\}$. The corresponding integral is

$$\int_0^6 \int_0^{\sqrt{36-x^2}/2} \int_0^{\sqrt{36-x^2-4y^2}/3} z \, dz \, dy \, dx.$$

The alternate representation $R_{xy} = \{(x, y) : 0 \le y \le 3; \text{ for each } y, \quad 0 \le x \le \sqrt{36 - 4y^2}\}$ leads to the description

$$D = \{(x, y, z) : 0 \le y \le 3; \text{ for each } y, \quad 0 \le x \le \sqrt{36 - 4y^2};$$

$$\text{for each } x \text{ and } y, \quad 0 \le z \le \frac{1}{3}\sqrt{36 - x^2 - 4y^2}\}.$$

The corresponding integral, which is evaluated, is:

$$\int_0^3 \int_0^{\sqrt{36-4y^2}} \int_0^{\sqrt{36-x^2-4y^2}/3} z \, dz \, dx \, dy = \int_0^3 \int_0^{\sqrt{36-4y^2}} \left[\frac{z^2}{2}\right] \Big|_0^{\sqrt{36-x^2-4y^2}/3} dx \, dy$$

$$= \frac{1}{18} \int_0^3 \int_0^{\sqrt{36-4y^2}} (36 - 4y^2 - x^2) \, dx \, dy$$

$$= \frac{1}{18} \int_0^3 \left[(36 - 4y^2)x - \frac{x^3}{3}\right] \Big|_{x=0}^{\sqrt{36-4y^2}} dy$$

$$= \frac{8}{27} \int_0^3 (9 - y^2)^{3/2} \, dy.$$

Use the trigonometric substitution $y = 3\sin\theta$, $dy = 3\cos\theta \, d\theta$ and $(9 - y^2)^{3/2} = 27\cos^3\theta$ with $\theta = 0$ and $\pi/2$ when $y = 0$ and 3 respectively.

$$\frac{8}{27} \int_0^3 (9 - y^2)^{3/2} \, dy = 24 \int_0^{\pi/2} \cos^4\theta \, d\theta = 6 \int_0^{\pi/2} (1 + 2\cos 2\theta + \cos^2 2\theta) \, d\theta$$

$$= 6 \int_0^{\pi/2} \left(\frac{3}{2} + 2\cos 2\theta + \frac{1}{2}\cos 4\theta \right) d\theta = 6 \left[\frac{3}{2}\theta + \sin 2\theta + \frac{1}{8}\sin 4\theta \right] \Big|_0^{\pi/2}$$

$$= \frac{9\pi}{2}.$$

21. Use a triple integral to find the volume of the solid bounded by $x = 0$, $y = 0$, $x + y + z = 2$, and $x + y - z = 2$.

SOLUTION: The solid is the tetrahedron bounded laterally by $x = 0$ and $y = 0$, and above and below by $z = 2 - x - y$ and $z = x + y - 2$.

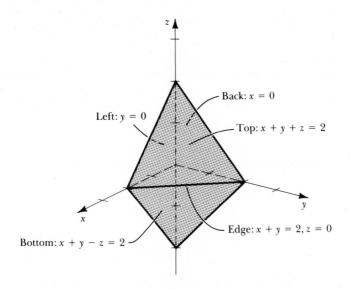

The projection of this solid on the xy-plane is $R_{xy} = \{(x, y) : 0 \le x \le 2;$ for each x, $0 \le y \le 2 - x\}$ and for each (x, y) in R_{xy}, the solid contains a line running from $z = x + y - 2$ on bottom to $z = 2 - x - y$ on top. A triple integral for the volume is

$$V = \int_0^2 \int_0^{2-x} \int_{x+y-2}^{2-(x+y)} dz\, dy\, dx = \int_0^2 \int_0^{2-x} (2(2-x) - 2y)\, dy\, dx$$

$$= 2 \int_0^2 \left[(2-x)y - \frac{y^2}{2} \right] \Big|_{y=0}^{2-x} dx = \int_0^2 (2-x)^2\, dx$$

$$= \left[-\frac{(2-x)^3}{3} \right] \Big|_0^2 = \frac{8}{3}.$$

Triple Integrals in Cylindrical and Spherical Coordinates

3. Evaluate $\displaystyle\int_0^\pi \int_0^{\pi/2} \int_0^{\sin\phi} \rho^2 \sin\phi \cos\phi \, d\rho \, d\phi \, d\theta$.

SOLUTION:

$$\int_0^\pi \int_0^{\pi/2} \int_0^{\sin\phi} \rho^2 \sin\phi \cos\phi \, d\rho \, d\phi \, d\theta$$

$$= \int_0^\pi \int_0^{\pi/2} \sin\phi \cos\phi \left[\frac{\rho^3}{3}\right]\Bigg|_{\rho=0}^{\sin\phi} d\phi \, d\theta$$

$$= \frac{1}{3}\int_0^\pi \int_0^{\pi/2} \sin^4\phi \cos\phi \, d\phi \, d\theta = \frac{1}{3}\int_0^\pi \left[\frac{(\sin\phi)^5}{5}\right]\Bigg|_{\phi=0}^{\pi/2} d\theta$$

$$= \frac{1}{15}\int_0^\pi d\theta = \frac{\pi}{15}.$$

7. Use either cylindrical or spherical coordinates to reexpress and evaluate

$$\int_0^2 \int_0^{\sqrt{4-x^2}} \int_0^{\sqrt{4-x^2-y^2}} \frac{z}{\sqrt{x^2+y^2}} \, dz \, dy \, dx.$$

SOLUTION: The domain of integration $D(x,y,z) = \{(x,y,z): 0 \le x \le 2$; for each x, $0 \le y \le \sqrt{4-x^2}$; for each x and y, $0 \le z \le \sqrt{4-x^2-y^2}\}$ has as its projection on the xy-plane the quarter circle of radius two lying in the first quadrant. For each (x,y) in this projection, z extends through D from $z = 0$ to the sphere of radius two, $x^2 + y^2 + z^2 = 4$.

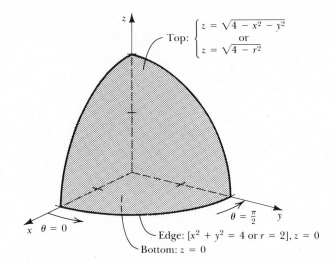

Use cylindrical coordinates because of the factor $z/\sqrt{x^2+y^2}$ in the integrand. The projection of D in the $r\theta$-plane can be described as $R_{r\theta} = \{(r,\theta) : 0 \le \theta \le \pi/2;$ for each $\theta,\ \ 0 \le r \le 2\}$ and since for each fixed (r,θ), z runs from $z = 0$ to the sphere $z = \sqrt{4-r^2}$, then D can be represented in terms of cylindrical coordinates as $D = \{(r,\theta,z) : 0 \le \theta \le \pi/2;$ for each θ, $0 \le r \le 2;$ for each r and $\theta,\ \ 0 \le z \le \sqrt{4-r^2}\}$. Replace $z/\sqrt{x^2+y^2}$ by z/r and the volume element $dz\,dy\,dx$ by $r\,dz\,dr\,d\theta$ to get

$$\int_0^2 \int_0^{\sqrt{4-x^2}} \int_0^{\sqrt{4-x^2-y^2}} \frac{z}{\sqrt{x^2+y^2}}\,dz\,dy\,dx = \int_0^{\pi/2} \int_0^2 \int_0^{\sqrt{4-r^2}} \frac{z}{r}\,r\,dz\,dr\,d\theta$$

$$= \int_0^{\pi/2} \int_0^2 \left[\frac{z^2}{2}\right]\Bigg|_{z=0}^{\sqrt{4-r^2}} dr\,d\theta = \frac{1}{2}\int_0^{\pi/2}\int_0^2 (4-r^2)\,dr\,d\theta = \frac{1}{2}\int_0^{\pi/2}\left[4r - \frac{r^3}{3}\right]\Bigg|_{r=0}^2 d\theta$$

$$= \frac{8}{3}\int_0^{\pi/2} d\theta = \frac{4\pi}{3}.$$

9. Use either cylindrical or spherical coordinates to reexpress and evaluate

$$\int_0^2 \int_{-\sqrt{4-y^2}}^{\sqrt{4-y^2}} \int_0^{\sqrt{4-x^2-y^2}} z\sqrt{x^2+y^2+z^2}\,dz\,dx\,dy.$$

SOLUTION: The domain of integration $D = \{(x,y,z) : 0 \le y \le 2;$ for each y, $-\sqrt{4-y^2} \le x \le \sqrt{4-y^2};$ for each x and $y,\ \ 0 \le z \le \sqrt{4-x^2-y^2}\}$ has as its projection on the xy-plane the semicircle of radius 2 bounded by $x = 0$ and $x^2 + y^2 = 4$ with $x \ge 0$. Each line with (x,y) fixed over this set runs from $z = 0$ on bottom to the sphere $x^2 + y^2 + z^2 = 4$ on top.

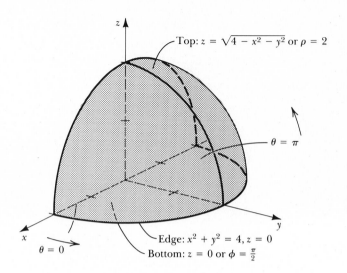

Top: $z = \sqrt{4 - x^2 - y^2}$ or $\rho = 2$

$\theta = \pi$

$\theta = 0$

Edge: $x^2 + y^2 = 4, z = 0$

Bottom: $z = 0$ or $\phi = \frac{\pi}{2}$

Use spherical coordinates because of the integrand, $z\sqrt{x^2 + y^2 + z^2}$. This quarter sphere is also very easy to describe in terms of spherical coordinates, $D = \{(\rho, \theta, \phi) : 0 \le \rho \le 2;$ for each ρ, $0 \le \phi \le \pi/2;$ for each ρ and ϕ, $0 \le \theta \le \pi\}$. Write the integrand as $z\sqrt{x^2 + y^2 + z^2} = \rho^2 \cos\phi$ and the volume element as $dz\, dx\, dy = \rho^2 \sin\phi\, d\rho\, d\phi\, d\theta$ to get

$$\int_0^2 \int_{-\sqrt{4-y^2}}^{\sqrt{4-y^2}} \int_0^{\sqrt{4-x^2-y^2}} z\sqrt{x^2 + y^2 + z^2}\, dz\, dx\, dy = \int_0^\pi \int_0^{\pi/2} \int_0^2 \rho^2 \cos\phi\, \rho^2 \sin\phi\, d\rho\, d\phi\, d\theta$$

$$= \int_0^\pi \int_0^{\pi/2} \cos\phi \sin\phi \left[\frac{\rho^5}{5}\right]\Bigg|_{\rho=0}^2 d\phi\, d\theta = \frac{32}{5} \int_0^\pi \left[\frac{(\sin\phi)^2}{2}\right]\Bigg|_{\phi=0}^{\pi/2} d\theta = \frac{16}{5}\pi.$$

17. Sketch the solid whose volume is given by $\displaystyle\int_0^{\pi/2} \int_0^2 \int_r^{\sqrt{8-r^2}} r\, dz\, dr\, d\theta$.

SOLUTION: The solid may be represented as $D = \{(r, \theta, z) : 0 \le \theta \le \pi/2;$ for each θ, $0 \le r \le 2;$ for each r and θ, $r \le z \le \sqrt{8 - r^2}\}$. The projection of this solid on the $r\theta$-plane is the part of the circle of radius 2 centered at the origin lying in the first quadrant. Over each (r, θ) in this quarter circle, the solid contains a line with z running from the cone $z = r$ to the sphere $r^2 + z^2 = 8$. The curve of intersection of the sphere and the cone is the circle $r = 2$ in the plane $z = 2$. The solid lies in the first octant, is bounded above by the sphere and is bounded below by the cone.

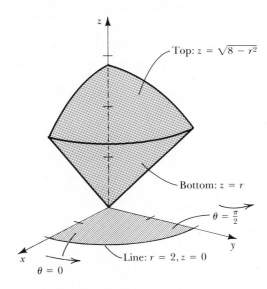

25. Use cylindrical or spherical coordinates to find the volume of the solid with boundaries $z = \sqrt{x^2 + y^2}$, $\sqrt{x^2 + y^2 + z^2} = 2$ and $\sqrt{x^2 + y^2 + z^2} = 3$.

SOLUTION: The solid lies between spheres of radius 2 and 3 and above the cone $z^2 = x^2 + y^2$. Use spherical coordinates to describe these surfaces as $\rho = 2$, $\rho = 3$, and $\phi = \pi/4$ respectively.

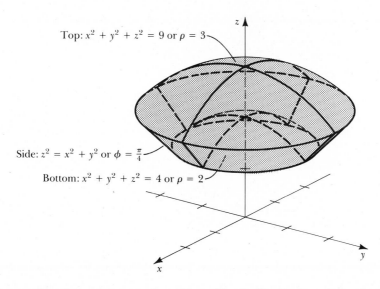

The solid can thus be represented as $D = \{(\rho, \theta, \phi) : 2 \leq \rho \leq 3; \ \ 0 \leq \phi \leq \pi/4; \ \ 0 \leq \theta \leq 2\pi\}$. The volume is thus

$$V = \int_0^{2\pi} \int_0^{\pi/4} \int_2^3 \rho^2 \sin \phi \, d\rho \, d\phi \, d\theta = \int_0^{2\pi} \int_0^{\pi/4} \sin \phi \left[\frac{\rho^3}{3} \right] \Big|_{\rho=2}^{3} d\phi \, d\theta$$

$$= \left(\frac{19}{3}\right) \int_0^{2\pi} \left[-\cos\phi\right]\Big|_{\phi=0}^{\pi/4} d\theta = \left(\frac{19}{3}\right)\left(1 - \frac{\sqrt{2}}{2}\right)(2\pi) = \frac{19(2-\sqrt{2})\pi}{3}.$$

31. A hole drilled through the center of a sphere of radius R removes half the volume of the sphere. What is the radius of the hole?

SOLUTION: If a hole of radius $\tilde{R}$ is drilled through a sphere of radius $R > \tilde{R}$, the solid that remains is bounded on the inside by the cylinder $r = \tilde{R}$ and on the outside by the sphere $z^2 + r^2 = R$.

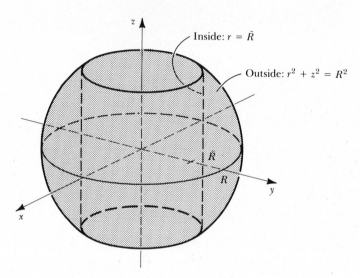

This solid may be represented in cylindrical coordinates as

$$D = \{(r,\theta,z): 0 \leq \theta \leq 2\pi;\ \text{for each } \theta, \quad \tilde{R} \leq r \leq R;\ \text{for each } r \text{ and } \theta,$$
$$-\sqrt{R^2 - r^2} \leq z \leq \sqrt{R^2 - r^2}\}.$$

Its volume is

$$V = \int_0^{2\pi} \int_{\tilde{R}}^R \int_{-\sqrt{R^2-r^2}}^{\sqrt{R^2-r^2}} r\,dz\,dr\,d\theta = \int_0^{2\pi} \int_{\tilde{R}}^R \sqrt{R^2 - r^2}\,(2r)\,dr\,d\theta$$

$$= \int_0^{2\pi} \left[-\frac{2}{3}(R^2 - r^2)^{3/2}\right]\Big|_{r=\tilde{R}}^R d\theta = \frac{2}{3}\left(\left(R^2 - \tilde{R}^2\right)^{3/2}\right) \cdot \int_0^{2\pi} d\theta$$

$$= \frac{4\pi(R^2 - \tilde{R}^2)^{3/2}}{3}.$$

Since V is half the volume of a sphere of radius R, $V = 2\pi R^3/3$, an equation for $\tilde{R}$ is $R^3 = 2\left((R^3 - \tilde{R}^3)^{3/2}\right)$ or $\tilde{R} = R\left(1 - (1/2)^{2/3}\right)^{1/2}$. The radius, $\tilde{R}$, of the hole is approximately $0.61\,R$.

Applications of Triple Integrals

5. Find the mass of the solid bounded by the planes $x = 0$, $y = 0$, $z = 0$, $x + y + z = 1$ and $3x + 3y + z = 3$. The density is described by $\sigma(x, y, z) = x$.

SOLUTION: The solid is sketched along with its projection on the xy-plane.

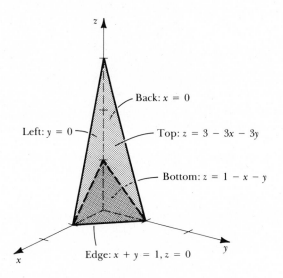

The projection is $R_{xy} = \{(x, y) : 0 \leq x \leq 1;$ for each x, $0 \leq y \leq 1 - x\}$. For each (x, y) in R_{xy} the solid contains a line running from $z = 1 - x - y$ on the bottom to $z = 3 - 3x - 3y$ on top. Thus, the solid is described as

$$D = \{(x, y, z) : 0 \leq x \leq 1; \text{ for each } x, \ 0 \leq y \leq 1 - x;$$
$$\text{for each } x \text{ and } y, \ 1 - x - y \leq z \leq 3 - 3x - 3y\}.$$

Since the density is $\sigma(x, y, z) = x$, then the mass is

$$M = \int_0^1 \int_0^{1-x} \int_{1-x-y}^{3-3x-3y} x \, dz \, dy \, dx = \int_0^1 \int_0^{1-x} x \left((3 - 3x - 3y) - (1 - x - y) \right) dy \, dx$$

$$= \int_0^1 \int_0^{1-x} x \left(2(1 - x) - 2y \right) dy \, dx = \int_0^1 x \left[2(1 - x)y - y^2 \right] \Big|_{y=0}^{(1-x)} dx$$

$$= \int_0^1 (x - 2x^2 + x^3) \, dx = \left[\frac{x^2}{2} - \frac{2x^3}{3} + \frac{x^4}{4} \right] \Big|_0^1 = \frac{1}{12}.$$

13. Find   a) the moments about the coordinate planes and   b) the center of mass of the solid bounded by the coordinate planes and the plane $x + y + z = 1$. The density of the solid is constant.

SOLUTION: a) The solid is a tetrahedron lying under the plane $z = 1 - x - y$ and above $z = 0$.

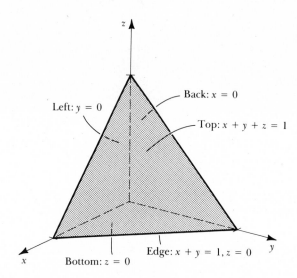

Its projection on the xy-plane is the region $R_{xy} = \{(x, y) : 0 \le x \le 1;$ for each $x, \ 0 \le y \le 1 - x\}$ so the solid may be represented as $D = \{(x, y, z) : 0 \le x \le 1;$ for each $x, \ 0 \le y \le 1 - x;$ for each x and $y, \ 0 \le z \le 1 - x - y\}$. With its density equal to a constant k, its mass (as found in EXERCISE 3) is $M = k/6$ and its moments are

$$M_{yz} = \iiint\limits_{D} x\sigma \, dV = \int_0^1 \int_0^{1-x} \int_0^{1-x-y} kx \, dz \, dy \, dx$$

$$= k \int_0^1 \int_0^{1-x} x\left((1 - x) - y\right) dy \, dx = k \int_0^1 x \left(\frac{(1 - x)^2}{2}\right) dx$$

$$= \frac{k}{2} \left[\frac{x^2}{2} - \frac{2x^3}{3} + \frac{x^4}{4}\right]\Bigg|_0^1 = \frac{k}{24},$$

$$M_{xz} = \iiint\limits_{D} y\sigma \, dV = \int_0^1 \int_0^{1-x} \int_0^{1-x-y} ky \, dz \, dy \, dx$$

$$= k \int_0^1 \int_0^{1-x} y\left((1 - x) - y\right) dy \, dx = k \int_0^1 \frac{(1 - x)^3}{6} dx = \frac{k}{6}\left[-\frac{(1 - x)^4}{4}\right]\Bigg|_0^1 = \frac{k}{24}, \quad \text{and}$$

$$M_{xy} = \iiint\limits_{D} z\sigma \, dV = \int_0^1 \int_0^{1-x} \int_0^{1-x-y} kz \, dz \, dy \, dx$$

$$= \frac{k}{2} \int_0^1 \int_0^{1-x} (1 - x - y)^2 \, dy \, dx = \frac{k}{2} \int_0^1 \left[-\frac{(1 - x - y)^3}{3} \right] \Big|_{y=0}^{1-x} dx = \frac{k}{6} \int_0^1 (1 - x)^3 \, dx$$

$$= \frac{k}{6} \left[\frac{(1 - x)^4}{4} \right] \Big|_0^1 = \frac{k}{24}.$$

b) The center of mass has coordinates

$$\bar{x} = \frac{M_{yz}}{M} = \frac{k/24}{k/6} = \frac{1}{4}, \qquad \bar{y} = \frac{M_{xz}}{M} = \frac{1}{4}, \quad \text{and} \quad \bar{z} = \frac{M_{xy}}{M} = \frac{1}{4}.$$

17. Find   a) the moments about the coordinate planes and   b) the center of mass of the solid bounded by the cylinder $x^2 + y^2 = 4$ and the planes $z = 1$ and $z = 5$. The density is $\sigma(x, y, z) = kz$.

SOLUTION: a) Since the solid is a right circular cylinder of radius 2, it is very easy to describe using cylindrical coordinates as $D = \{(r, \theta, z) : 0 \leq \theta \leq 2\pi; \ 0 \leq r \leq 2; \ 1 \leq z \leq 5\}$. Its mass was found in the SOLUTION to EXERCISE 7 to be $M = 48 k\pi$. Its moments are

$$M_{yz} = \iiint_D x\sigma \, dV = \int_0^{2\pi} \int_0^2 \int_1^5 (r \cos \theta)(kz)r \, dz \, dr \, d\theta$$

$$= k \int_0^{2\pi} \int_0^2 r^2 \cos \theta \left[\frac{z^2}{2} \right] \Big|_{z=1}^5 dr \, d\theta = 12k \int_0^{2\pi} \cos \theta \left[\frac{r^3}{3} \right] \Big|_{r=0}^2 d\theta = 32k \left[\sin \theta \right] \Big|_0^{2\pi} = 0,$$

$$M_{xz} = \iiint_D y\sigma \, dV = \int_0^{2\pi} \int_0^2 \int_1^5 (r \sin \theta)(kz)r \, dz \, dr \, d\theta = k \int_0^{2\pi} \int_0^2 r^2 \sin \theta \left[\frac{z^2}{2} \right] \Big|_{z=1}^5 dr \, d\theta$$

$$= 12k \int_0^{2\pi} \sin \theta \left[\frac{r^3}{3} \right] \Big| r = 0^2 \, d\theta = 32k \int_0^{2\pi} \sin \theta \, d\theta = 32k \left[-\cos \theta \right] \Big|_0^{2\pi} = 0, \quad \text{and}$$

$$M_{xy} = \iiint_D z\sigma \, dV = \int_0^{2\pi} \int_0^2 \int_1^5 (z)(kz)r \, dz \, dr \, d\theta$$

$$= k \int_0^{2\pi} \int_0^2 r \left[\frac{z^3}{3} \right] \Big|_{z=1}^5 dr \, d\theta = \frac{124k}{3} \int_0^{2\pi} \left[\frac{r^2}{2} \right] \Big|_{r=0}^2 d\theta = \frac{248k}{3} [\theta] \Big|_0^{2\pi}$$

$$= \frac{496k\pi}{3}.$$

b) The center of mass thus has cartesian coordinates

$$\bar{x} = \frac{M_{yz}}{M} = 0, \quad \bar{y} = \frac{M_{xz}}{M} = 0, \quad \text{and} \quad \bar{z} = \frac{M_{xy}}{M} = \frac{496k\pi/3}{48k\pi} = \frac{31}{9}.$$

29. Find   a) the moments of inertia about the coordinate axes and   b) the radii of gyration of the solid bounded by the hemisphere of radius 3 centered at $(0,0,0)$ and lying above the xy-plane. The density at a point is proportional to the square of its distance above the base.

SOLUTION: a) The solid is easily represented in spherical coordinates as $D = \{(\rho, \phi, \theta) : 0 \le \theta \le 2\pi; \; 0 \le \phi \le \pi/2; \; 0 \le \rho \le 3\}$. The density is $\sigma(\rho, \phi, \theta) = kz^2 = k(\rho \cos \phi)^2$ and its mass was found in the SOLUTION to EXERCISE 9 to be $M = 162k\pi/5$.

Its moments of inertia are

$$I_z = \iiint_D (x^2 + y^2)\sigma \, dV = \int_0^{2\pi} \int_0^{\pi/2} \int_0^3 (\rho^2 \sin^2 \phi)(k\rho^2 \cos^2 \phi)\rho^2 \sin \phi \, d\rho \, d\phi \, d\theta$$

$$= k \int_0^{2\pi} \int_0^{\pi/2} (\sin^3 \phi \cos^2 \phi) \left[\frac{\rho^7}{7}\right]\Big|_{\rho=0}^3 d\phi \, d\theta = \frac{3^7 k}{7} \int_0^{2\pi} \int_0^{\pi/2} \cos^2 \phi (1 - \cos^2 \phi) \sin \phi \, d\phi \, d\theta$$

$$= \frac{3^7 k}{7} \int_0^{2\pi} \left[-\frac{(\cos \phi)^3}{3} + \frac{(\cos \phi)^5}{5}\right]\Big|_{\phi=0}^{\pi/2} d\theta = \frac{2 \cdot 3^6 k}{35}(2\pi) = \frac{2916 k\pi}{35},$$

$$I_y = \iiint_D (x^2 + z^2)\sigma \, dV$$

$$= \int_0^{2\pi} \int_0^{\pi/2} \int_0^3 \left(\rho^2 \sin^2 \phi \cos^2 \theta + \rho^2 \cos^2 \phi\right) \left(k\rho^2 \cos^2 \phi\right) \left(\rho^2 \sin \phi\right) d\rho \, d\phi \, d\theta$$

$$= \frac{k3^7}{7} \int_0^{2\pi} \int_0^{\pi/2} \left(\cos^2 \theta(\sin^3 \phi \cos^2 \phi) + \cos^4 \phi \sin \phi\right) d\phi \, d\theta$$

$$= \frac{k3^7}{7} \int_0^{2\pi} \left(\frac{2}{15} \cos^2 \theta + \frac{1}{5}\right) d\theta = \frac{k3^7}{7} \int_0^{2\pi} \left(\frac{4}{15} + \frac{1}{15} \cos 2\theta\right) d\theta$$

$$= \frac{k3^7}{7} \left[\frac{4}{15}\theta + \frac{1}{30} \sin 2\theta\right]\Big|_0^{2\pi} = \frac{5832 k\pi}{35}, \quad \text{and}$$

$$I_x = \iiint_D (y^2 + z^2)\sigma \, dV$$

$$= \int_0^{2\pi} \int_0^{\pi/2} \int_0^3 \left(\rho^2 \sin^2 \phi \sin^2 \theta + \rho^2 \cos^2 \phi\right) \left(k\rho^2 \cos^2 \phi\right) \left(\rho^2 \sin \phi\right) d\rho \, d\phi \, d\theta$$

$$= \frac{k3^7}{7} \int_0^{2\pi} \int_0^{\pi/2} \left(\sin^2 \theta \left(\cos^2 \phi - \cos^4 \phi\right) \sin \phi + \cos^4 \phi \sin \phi\right) d\phi \, d\theta$$

$$= \frac{k3^7}{7} \int_0^{2\pi} \left(\frac{2}{15} \sin^2 \theta + \frac{1}{5}\right) d\theta = \frac{k3^7}{7} \int_0^{2\pi} \left(\frac{4}{15} - \frac{1}{15} \cos 2\theta\right) d\theta$$

$$= \frac{5832k\pi}{35}.$$

b) The radii of gyration have cartesian coordinates

$$\hat{x} = \sqrt{\frac{I_x}{M}} = \sqrt{\frac{5832k\pi/35}{162k\pi/5}} = \frac{6\sqrt{7}}{7} = \hat{y} \quad \text{and}$$

$$\hat{z} = \sqrt{\frac{I_z}{M}} = \sqrt{\frac{2916k\pi/35}{162k\pi/5}} = \frac{3\sqrt{14}}{7}.$$

31. Find the average height of that portion of the plane $3x + 2y + z = 6$ that lies in the first octant.

SOLUTION: The height at a point (x, y) is $h(x, y) = 6 - 3x - 2y$. The average of h is sought over the projection of the part of the plane $3x + 2y + z = 6$ in the first octant onto the xy-plane.

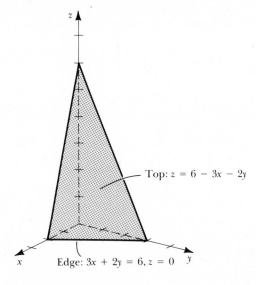

Top: $z = 6 - 3x - 2y$

Edge: $3x + 2y = 6, z = 0$

This projection is $R = \{(x, y) : 0 \leq x \leq 2; \text{ for each } x, \quad 0 \leq y \leq 3 - 3x/2\}$. Its area is

$$A = \iint_R dA = \int_0^2 \int_0^{3-3x/2} dy\, dx = \int_0^2 \left(3 - \frac{3}{2}x\right) dx = 3,$$

so the average of the height function $h(x, y)$ over R is

$$\bar{h} = \frac{1}{A} \iint_R h(x, y)\, dA = \frac{1}{3} \int_0^2 \int_0^{3-3x/2} (6 - 3x - 2y)\, dy\, dx$$

$$= \frac{1}{3} \int_0^2 \left[3(2-x)y - y^2 \right] \Big|_{y=0}^{3-3x/2} \, dx = \frac{1}{3} \int_0^2 \left(\frac{9}{4}(2-x)^2 \right) \, dx$$

$$= \left[-\frac{1}{4}(2-x)^3 \right] \Big|_0^2 = 2.$$

39. Paint in a one-gallon cylindrical can of height 6 inches and diameter 7 inches has a density that varies linearly from $55.3 \, \text{lb/ft}^3$ at the top of the can to $59.4 \, \text{lb/ft}^3$ at the bottom. How much does the paint weigh and where is the center of mass of the paint?

SOLUTION: A cylindrical coordinate system is introduced with origin at the center of the base of the can and with z axis along the center of the can. Then the density is $\sigma(r, \theta, z) = mz + b$, where $\sigma(r, \theta, 0) = 59.4 = m \cdot 0 + b$ and $\sigma(r, \theta, 1/2) = 55.3 = m \cdot (1/2) + b$. These equations imply that $b = 59.4$ and $m = -8.2$, so $\sigma(r, \theta, z) = 59.4 - 8.2(z)$ where z and r are measured in feet. The cylindrical can may be described as $D = \{(r, \theta, z) : 0 \leq \theta \leq 2\pi; \ 0 \leq r \leq 7/24; \ 0 \leq z \leq 1/2\}$ so the mass and moments are

$$M = \int_0^{2\pi} \int_0^{7/24} \int_0^{1/2} (59.4 - 8.2z) \, r \, dz \, dr \, d\theta$$

$$= \int_0^{2\pi} \int_0^{7/24} r \left[59.4z - 8.2 \frac{z^2}{2} \right] \Big|_{z=0}^{1/2} \, dr \, d\theta = 28.675 \int_0^{2\pi} \left[\frac{r^2}{2} \right] \Big|_{r=0}^{7/24} \, d\theta$$

$$= 28.675 \left(\frac{7^2}{2(24)^2} \right) (2\pi) = 7.663 \, \text{lb}.$$

The moments are

$$M_{yz} = \iiint_D x\rho \, dV = \int_0^{2\pi} \int_0^{7/24} \int_0^{1/2} (r \cos \theta)(59.4 - 8.2z) \, r \, dz \, dr \, d\theta$$

$$= 28.675 \int_0^{2\pi} \int_0^{7/24} \cos \theta \, r^2 \, dr \, d\theta = 28.675 \int_0^{2\pi} \left[\frac{r^3}{3} \right] \Big|_{r=0}^{7/24} \cos \theta \, d\theta$$

$$= 28.675 \left(\frac{(7/24)^3}{3} \right) \cdot [\sin \theta] \Big|_0^{2\pi} = 0,$$

$$M_{xz} = \iiint_D y\rho \, dV = \int_0^{2\pi} \int_0^{7/24} \int_0^{1/2} (r \sin \theta)(59.4 - 8.2z) \, r \, dz \, dr \, d\theta$$

$$= 28.675 \left(\frac{(7/24)^3}{3} \right) \int_0^{2\pi} \sin \theta \, d\theta = 0, \quad \text{and}$$

$$M_{xy} = \iiint\limits_{D} z\rho\, dV = \int_0^{2\pi} \int_0^{7/24} \int_0^{1/2} z\,(59.4 - 8.2z)\, r\, dz\, dr\, d\theta$$

$$= \int_0^{2\pi} \int_0^{7/24} r \left[59.4\frac{z^2}{2} - 8.2\frac{z^3}{3} \right] \Bigg|_{z=0}^{1/2} dr\, d\theta$$

$$= \frac{85}{12} \int_0^{2\pi} \left[\frac{r^2}{2} \right] \Bigg|_{r=0}^{7/24} d\theta = \frac{85}{12} \left(\frac{(7/24)^2}{2} \right) (2\pi) \approx 1.893.$$

The center of mass has cartesian coordinates

$$\bar{x} = \frac{M_{yz}}{M} = 0, \quad \bar{y} = \frac{M_{xz}}{M} = 0, \quad \text{and} \quad \bar{z} = \frac{M_{xy}}{M} \approx \frac{1.893}{7.663} \approx 0.247\,\text{ft}.$$

_____Chapter 15

Review Exercises

1. Suppose $f(x,y) = 4 - x - 2y$, R is the triangle in the xy-plane bounded by $x = 0$, $y = 0$, and $x = 4 - 2y$, and $\wp$ is the partition defined by the lines $x = 0$, $x = 1$, $x = 2$, $x = 3$, $x = 4$, $y = 0$, $y = 1/2$, $y = 1$, $y = 3/2$, and $y = 2$. Find the value of the Riemann sum if the R_i are the rectangles that lie entirely within R and (x_i, y_i) is chosen to be the upper left corner of R_i.

SOLUTION: The region R is sketched and the partition is indicated.

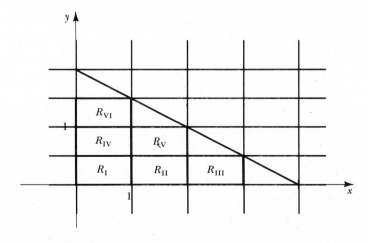

The value of ΔA_i is 1/2 for each of the rectangles $R_I, \ldots, R_{VI}$ so the Riemann sum with f evaluated at the upper left hand corners of the R_i is

$$f(0,1/2)\Delta A_I + f(1,1/2)\Delta A_{II} + f(2,1/2)\Delta A_{III} + f(0,1)\Delta A_{IV}$$
$$+ f(1,1)\Delta A_V + f(0,3/2)\Delta A_{VI}$$

$$= (4-0-1)\frac{1}{2} + (4-1-1)\frac{1}{2} + (4-2-1)\frac{1}{2}$$
$$+ (4-0-2)\frac{1}{2} + (4-1-2)\frac{1}{2} + (4-0-3)\frac{1}{2} = 5.$$

7. Evaluate $\displaystyle\int_1^4 \int_{\sqrt{y}}^y \ln\left(\frac{y}{x}\right) dx\, dy.$

SOLUTION: Integrate with respect to x by parts with $u = \ln(y/x)$, $dv = dx$, $du = -dx/x$, and $v = x$:

$$\int_1^4 \int_{\sqrt{y}}^y \ln\left(\frac{y}{x}\right) dx\, dy = \int_1^4 \left[x\ln\left(\frac{y}{x}\right) + \int dx \right]\Bigg|_{x=\sqrt{y}}^y dy$$

$$= \int_1^4 \left(y - \sqrt{y} - \sqrt{y}\ln(\sqrt{y}) \right) dy.$$

Integrate the last term by parts with $u = \ln\sqrt{y}$, $dv = \sqrt{y}$, $du = 1/(2y)$, and $v = (2/3)y^{3/2}$, so that

$$\int_1^4 \left(y - \sqrt{y} - \sqrt{y}\ln(\sqrt{y}) \right) dy = \left[\frac{1}{2}y^2 - \frac{2}{3}y^{3/2} - \left(\frac{2}{3}y^{3/2}\ln(\sqrt{y}) - \frac{1}{3}\int \sqrt{y}\, dy \right) \right]\Bigg|_1^4$$

$$= \left[\frac{1}{2}y^2 - \frac{4}{9}y^{3/2} - \frac{1}{3}y^{3/2}\ln y \right]\Bigg|_1^4 = \frac{79}{18} - \frac{8}{3}\ln 4.$$

15. a) Sketch the region of integration for $\displaystyle\int_0^4 \int_{-\sqrt{y}}^{\sqrt{y}} (4-y)\, dx\, dy.$ **b)** Reverse the order of integration and evaluate the resulting integral.

SOLUTION: **a)** The region of integration is represented as $R = \{(x,y) : 0 \le y \le 4;$ for each y, $-\sqrt{y} \le x \le \sqrt{y}\}$.

For each fixed y between 0 and 4, x varies along the horizontal line from one side of the parabola $y = x^2$ to the other side of this parabola.

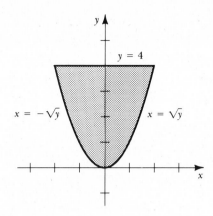

b) This region is also described as an x-simple region, $R = \{(x,y) : -2 \leq x \leq 2;$ for each x, $x^2 \leq y \leq 4\}$, so the double integral can be written as

$$\int_{-2}^{2} \int_{x^2}^{4} (4 - y)\, dy\, dx = \int_{-2}^{2} \left[4y - \frac{y^2}{2} \right] \Bigg|_{y=x^2}^{4} dx$$

$$= \int_{-2}^{2} \left(8 - 4x^2 + \frac{1}{2}x^4 \right) dx = \left[8x - \frac{4}{3}x^3 + \frac{1}{10}x^5 \right] \Bigg|_{-2}^{2} = \frac{256}{15}.$$

19. For the solid with base in the xy-plane and bounded by $x = y^2$, $x = 8 - y^2$ and $z = 4x$, find
   a) the area of the base, and b) the volume of the solid.

SOLUTION: The solid lies above the region in the xy-plane between the two parabolas $x = y^2$ and $x = 8 - y^2$.

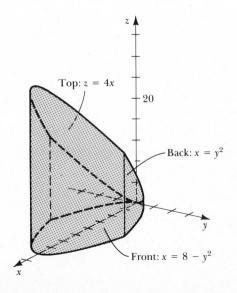

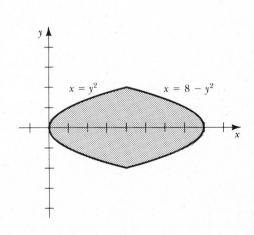

To find the y coordinates of the points of intersection, solve the equation $y^2 = 8 - y^2$ for $y = \pm 2$. This y-simple region can be described as $R = \{(x, y) : -2 \le y \le 2;$ for each $y,\ y^2 \le x \le 8 - y^2\}$.

a) The area of the base is

$$A = \iint_R dA = \int_{-2}^{2} \int_{y^2}^{8-y^2} dx\, dy = \int_{-2}^{2} (8 - 2y^2)\, dy = \left[8y - 2\frac{y^3}{3} \right] \Big|_{-2}^{2} = \frac{64}{3}.$$

b) The volume of the solid above the xy-plane and beneath the plane $z = 4x$ is

$$V = \iint_R 4x\, dA = \int_{-2}^{2} \int_{y^2}^{8-y^2} 4x\, dx\, dy = 2 \int_{-2}^{2} [x^2] \Big|_{x=y^2}^{8-y^2} dy$$

$$= 32 \int_{-2}^{2} (4 - y^2)\, dy = 32 \left[4y - \frac{y^3}{3} \right] \Big|_{-2}^{2} = \frac{1024}{3}.$$

25. Sketch the solid whose volume is represented by $\displaystyle\int_{0}^{\pi/2} \int_{0}^{2\sqrt{2}} \int_{r^2/8}^{\sqrt{9-r^2}} r\, dz\, dr\, d\theta$. Find the volume.

SOLUTION: The region of integration can be described by

$$D = \{(r, \theta, z) : 0 \le \theta \le \pi/2;\ \text{for each } \theta,\ 0 \le r \le 2\sqrt{2};\ \text{for each } r \text{ and } \theta,\ r^2/8 \le z \le \sqrt{9 - r^2}\}.$$

This region lies between the circular paraboloid $z = r^2/8$ and the sphere $z^2 + r^2 = 9$ over the part of the circle of radius $2\sqrt{2}$ centered at $(0,0)$ which lies in the first quadrant. The intersection of the paraboloid and sphere is determined by solving $z^2 + 8z - 9 = 0$ for $z = 1$ or -9, which implies that $r = 2\sqrt{2}$ so the surfaces intersect in the circle $r = 2\sqrt{2}$ in the plane $z = 1$.

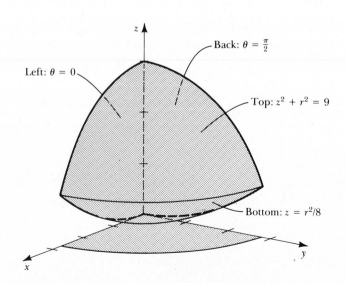

The volume is

$$V = \int_0^{\pi/2} \int_0^{2\sqrt{2}} \int_{r^2/8}^{\sqrt{9-r^2}} r\, dz\, dr\, d\theta = \int_0^{\pi/2} \int_0^{2\sqrt{2}} r(\sqrt{9-r^2} - (r^2/8))\, dr\, d\theta$$

$$= \int_0^{\pi/2} \left[-\frac{1}{3}(9-r^2)^{3/2} - \frac{1}{32}r^4 \right] \Bigg|_{r=0}^{2\sqrt{2}} d\theta = \frac{20}{3}[\theta] \Bigg|_0^{\pi/2} = \frac{10\pi}{3}.$$

29. Use either cylindrical or spherical coordinates to reexpress

$$\int_{-1}^1 \int_0^{\sqrt{1-x^2}} \int_0^{\sqrt{1-x^2-y^2}} z^2 \sqrt{x^2 + y^2 + z^2}\, dz\, dy\, dx$$

and evaluate the result.

SOLUTION: The domain of integration is $D = \{(x,y,z) : -1 \le x \le 1;$ for each x, $0 \le y \le \sqrt{1-x^2};$ for each x and y, $0 \le z \le \sqrt{1-x^2-y^2}\}$. This solid region lies under the sphere $x^2 + y^2 + z^2 = 1$ and above the xy-plane. Its projection on the xy-plane is the region between the x-axis and the semi-circle $x^2 + y^2 = 1$, $y \ge 0$. The solid is a quarter sphere.

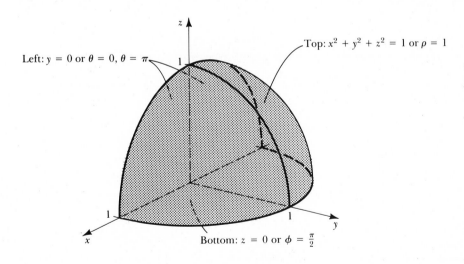

The form of the integrand and the shape of the region of integration suggest that spherical coordinates be used. Represent D as $D = \{(\rho, \theta, \phi) : 0 \le \theta \le \pi;\ 0 \le \phi \le \pi/2;\ 0 \le \rho \le 1\}$. Write the integrand as $z^2 \sqrt{x^2 + y^2 + z^2} = (\rho^2 \cos^2 \phi)\rho$ and the volume element as $dz\, dy\, dx = \rho^2 \sin \phi\, d\rho\, d\phi\, d\theta$. The integral is then

$$\int_0^{\pi} \int_0^{\pi/2} \int_0^1 (\rho^3 \cos^2 \phi)\rho^2 \sin \phi\, d\rho\, d\phi\, d\theta = \int_0^{\pi} \int_0^{\pi/2} \cos^2 \phi \sin \phi \left[\frac{\rho^6}{6} \right] \Bigg|_{\rho=0}^1 d\phi\, d\theta$$

$$= \frac{1}{6} \int_0^\pi \left[-\frac{(\cos\phi)^3}{3} \right] \Big|_{\phi=0}^{\pi/2} d\theta = \frac{1}{18} [\theta] \Big|_0^\pi = \frac{\pi}{18}.$$

39. Find the volume of the solid in the first octant bounded above by the planes $z = x/3$ and $x + 2y + 3z = 6$.

SOLUTION: The solid is bounded above by the two planes, below by $z = 0$, and laterally by $y = 0$.

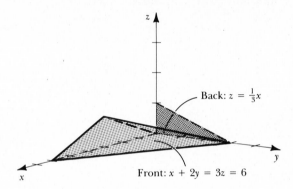

The only projection for which lines perpendicular to the projection plane run from between two surfaces without a change in formula is the projection onto the yz-plane. Eliminate x between the two equations $z = x/3$ and $x + 2y + 3z = 6$ to find the zy-equation of their line of intersection: $(3z) + 2y + 3z = 6$ or $y + 3z = 3$. The projection is $R_{yz} = \{(y,z) : 0 \leq y \leq 3;$ for each $y;$ $0 \leq z \leq 1 - y/3\}$. For each (y, z) in R_{yz}, there is a line in the solid running from $x = 3z$ in back to $x = 6 - 2y - 3z$ in front. The solid may be described as $D = \{(x, y, z) : 0 \leq y \leq 3;$ for each $y,$ $0 \leq z \leq 1 - y/3;$ for each y and $z,$ $3z \leq x \leq 6 - 2y - 3z\}$ so the volume is

$$V = \int_0^3 \int_0^{1-y/3} \int_{3z}^{6-3z-2y} dx\, dz\, dy = \int_0^3 \int_0^{1-y/3} (6 - 2y - 6z)\, dz\, dy$$

$$= \int_0^3 \left[6(1 - y/3)z - 3z^2 \right] \Big|_0^{1-y/3} dy = 3 \int_0^3 (1 - y/3)^2\, dy = 3 \left[-(1 - y/3)^3 \right] \Big|_0^3 = 3.$$

45. Find   a) the mass,   b) the moments about the axes, and   c) the center of mass for the lamina that has the shape of the region bounded by $x = 0$, $y = 0$, and $y = \sqrt{9 - x^2}$. The density is $\sigma(x, y) = x^2 + y^2$.

SOLUTION: The region is that part of the circle of radius 3 centered at $(0,0)$ which lies in the first quadrant.

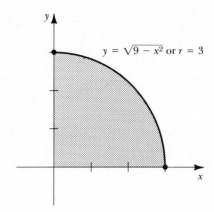

The form of the density function and the shape of the region suggest that polar coordinates be used. The region may be described as $R = \{(r,\theta) : 0 \leq \theta \leq \pi/2; \quad 0 \leq r \leq 3\}$, the density is $\sigma(r,\theta) = r^2$ and the element of area is $dA = r\,dr\,d\theta$. a) The mass is

$$M = \iint_R \sigma\,dA = \int_0^{\pi/2} \int_0^3 (r^2)r\,dr\,d\theta$$

$$= \int_0^{\pi/2} \left[\frac{r^4}{4}\right]\bigg|_{r=0}^3 d\theta = \frac{81}{4}[\theta]\bigg|_0^{\pi/2} = \frac{81\pi}{8}.$$

b) The moments are

$$M_y = \iint_R x\sigma\,dA = \int_0^{\pi/2} \int_0^3 (r\cos\theta)(r^2)r\,dr\,d\theta$$

$$= \int_0^{\pi/2} \cos\theta \left[\frac{r^5}{5}\right]\bigg|_{r=0}^3 d\theta = \frac{243}{5}[\sin\theta]\bigg|_0^{\pi/2} = \frac{243}{5}, \quad \text{and}$$

$$M_x = \iint_R y\sigma\,dA = \int_0^{\pi/2} \int_0^3 (r\sin\theta)(r^2)r\,dr\,d\theta$$

$$= \frac{243}{5}\int_0^{\pi/2} \sin\theta\,d\theta = \frac{243}{5}[-\cos\theta]\bigg|_0^{\pi/2} = \frac{243}{5}.$$

c) the center of mass has cartesian coordinates

$$\bar{x} = \frac{M_y}{M} = \frac{243/5}{81\pi/8} = \frac{24}{5\pi}, \qquad \bar{y} = \frac{M_x}{M} = \frac{24}{5\pi}.$$

49. Find the area of the portion of the saddle surface $z = 2 - x^2 + y^2$ that lies above $x^2 + y^2 \leq 2$.

SOLUTION: With the surface given by $z = f(x, y) = 2 - x^2 + y^2$ with $f_x = -2x$ and $f_y = 2y$, the surface area is

$$SA = \iint_R \sqrt{1 + (-2x)^2 + (2y)^2} \, dA$$

over the disk of radius $\sqrt{2}$. The forms of the region R and the integrand suggest that polar coordinates be used. Describe $R = \{(r, \theta) : 0 \leq \theta \leq 2\pi, 0 \leq r \leq \sqrt{2}\}$ and let $\sqrt{1 + 4x^2 + 4y^2} = \sqrt{1 + 4r^2}$ and $dA = r \, dr \, d\theta$ so that the surface area is

$$SA = \int_0^{2\pi} \int_0^{\sqrt{2}} \sqrt{1 + 4r^2} \, r \, dr \, d\theta = \int_0^{2\pi} \left[\frac{1}{12}(1 + 4r^2)^{3/2} \right] \Big|_{r=0}^{\sqrt{2}} d\theta$$

$$= \frac{13}{6} [\theta] \Big|_0^{2\pi} = \frac{13\pi}{3}.$$

16

Line and Surface Integrals

Sharpening your skills

You should review the material in CHAPTER 11 on dot and cross products of vectors; in CHAPTER 14 on partial derivatives, gradients, and normals to surfaces; in CHAPTERS 9 and 12 on curves in the plane or space; and in CHAPTER 15 on multiple integrals.

The practice problems below are followed by the numbers of the sections containing reference material.

Practice Problems

1. For $\mathbf{a} = \langle 1, 2, -3 \rangle$ and $\mathbf{b} = \langle -2, 0, 2 \rangle$, find   a) $\mathbf{a} \cdot \mathbf{b}$, and   b) $\mathbf{a} \times \mathbf{b}$.   (See SECTIONS 11.3 and 11.4)

2. For $f(x, y, z) = z \arctan(y/x)$, find   a) $\dfrac{\partial^2 f}{\partial x^2}$, $\dfrac{\partial^2 f}{\partial y^2}$ and $\dfrac{\partial^2 f}{\partial z^2}$,   b) the gradient of f, ∇f. (See SECTION 14.2)

3. Find the normal to the surface $z = x^3 + y^3$ at any point (x_0, y_0, z_0).   (See SECTION 14.6)

4. Find parametric equations for the ellipse $4x^2 + 9y^2 = 36$.   (See SECTION 9.4)

5. Evaluate $\displaystyle\int_0^1 (t\,\mathbf{i} + t^3\,\mathbf{j}) \cdot (e^t\,\mathbf{i} + \sin t\,\mathbf{j})\,dt$.   (See SECTION 12.2)

6. Evaluate   a) $\displaystyle\int_0^1 \int_x^1 xy\,dy\,dx$,   b) $\displaystyle\int_0^\pi \int_0^{\sin\theta} \sin\theta\, r\,dr\,d\theta$.   (See SECTIONS 15.2 and 15.3)

_____**16.1**

Vector Fields

7. Find   a) the divergence and   b) the curl of $\mathbf{F}(x, y, z) = xy \sin z\,\mathbf{i} + x^2 \cos y\,\mathbf{j} + z\sqrt{xy}\,\mathbf{k}$.

SOLUTION: a)

$$\text{div } \mathbf{F} = \nabla \cdot \mathbf{F} = \frac{\partial}{\partial x}(xy \sin z) + \frac{\partial}{\partial y}(x^2 \cos y) + \frac{\partial}{\partial z}(z\sqrt{xy})$$

$$= y \sin z - x^2 \sin y + \sqrt{xy}.$$

b) Expand the determinant below by cofactors of the first row,

$$\text{curl } \mathbf{F} = \nabla \cdot \mathbf{F} = \begin{vmatrix} \mathbf{i} & \mathbf{j} & \mathbf{k} \\ \dfrac{\partial}{\partial x} & \dfrac{\partial}{\partial y} & \dfrac{\partial}{\partial z} \\ (xy \sin z) & (x^2 \cos y) & (z\sqrt{xy}) \end{vmatrix}$$

$$= \left(\frac{\partial}{\partial y}(z\sqrt{xy}) - \frac{\partial}{\partial z}(x^2 \cos y) \right) \mathbf{i} - \left(\frac{\partial}{\partial x}(z\sqrt{xy}) - \frac{\partial}{\partial z}(xy \sin z) \right) \mathbf{j}$$

$$+ \left(\frac{\partial}{\partial x}(x^2 \cos y) - \frac{\partial}{\partial y}(xy \sin z) \right) \mathbf{k}$$

$$= \left(\frac{z}{2}\sqrt{\frac{x}{y}} - 0 \right) \mathbf{i} - \left(\frac{z}{2}\sqrt{\frac{y}{x}} - xy \cos z \right) \mathbf{j} + (2x \cos y - x \sin z) \mathbf{k}$$

$$= \frac{z}{2}\sqrt{\frac{x}{y}}\,\mathbf{i} + \left(xy \cos z - \frac{z}{2}\sqrt{\frac{y}{x}} \right) \mathbf{j} + (2x \cos y - x \sin z)\,\mathbf{k}.$$

13. Determine whether $f(x,y) = \sqrt{x^2 + y^2}$ is harmonic.

SOLUTION: The function f is harmonic only if $f_{xx} + f_{yy} = 0$. The first partials of f are $f_x = x/\sqrt{x^2 + y^2}$ and $f_y = y/\sqrt{x^2 + y^2}$. The second partials are

$$f_{xx} = \frac{\partial}{\partial x}\left[\frac{x}{\sqrt{x^2 + y^2}} \right] = \frac{\sqrt{x^2 + y^2} - x\dfrac{x}{\sqrt{x^2 + y^2}}}{(x^2 + y^2)} = \frac{y^2}{(x^2 + y^2)^{3/2}} \quad \text{and}$$

$$f_{yy} = \frac{\partial}{\partial y}\left[\frac{y}{\sqrt{x^2 + y^2}} \right] = \frac{x^2}{(x^2 + y^2)^{3/2}}, \quad \text{so}$$

$$f_{xx} + f_{yy} = \frac{y^2 + x^2}{(x^2 + y^2)^{3/2}} = \frac{1}{\sqrt{x^2 + y^2}} \neq 0 \quad \text{for any } (x, y).$$

Thus f is harmonic nowhere.

17. For $f(x,y,z) = x^2 + yz$ and $\mathbf{F}(x,y,z) = 2xy\,\mathbf{i} + (x^2 + z^2)\mathbf{j} + yz\,\mathbf{k}$, find $\nabla \cdot (f\mathbf{F})$ or state why the operation is not possible.

SOLUTION: The product $f\mathbf{F}$ of a scalar function defines the vector function

$$f\,\mathbf{F}(x,y,z) = \big((x^2 + yz)2xy\big)\,\mathbf{i} + \big((x^2 + yz)(x^2 + z^2)\big)\,\mathbf{j} + \big((x^2 + yz)yz\big)\,\mathbf{k}$$

$$= (2x^3y + 2xy^2z)\mathbf{i} + (x^4 + x^2yz + x^2z^2 + yz^3)\mathbf{j} + (x^2yz + y^2z^2)\mathbf{k}.$$

The divergence of this product is well defined as

$$\nabla \cdot (f\,\mathbf{F}) = \frac{\partial}{\partial x}(2x^3y + 2xy^2z) + \frac{\partial}{\partial y}(x^4 + x^2yz + x^2z^2 + yz^3) + \frac{\partial}{\partial z}(x^2yz + y^2z^2)$$

$$= (6x^2y + 2y^2z) + (x^2z + z^3) + (x^2y + 2y^2z)$$

$$= 7x^2y + x^2z + 4y^2z + z^3.$$

31. Verify the identity $\nabla \cdot (f\nabla g) = f\nabla^2 g + (\nabla f)d(\nabla g)$. Assume that f and g are scalar functions with continuous derivatives through the second order.

SOLUTION: Write $\nabla \cdot (f\nabla g)$ in terms of partial derivatives and expand by the product rule.

$$\nabla \cdot (f\nabla g) = \nabla \cdot \left(\left(f\frac{\partial g}{\partial x} \right)\mathbf{i} + \left(f\frac{\partial g}{\partial y} \right)\mathbf{j} + \left(f\frac{\partial g}{\partial z} \right)\mathbf{k} \right)$$

$$= \frac{\partial}{\partial x}\left(f\frac{\partial g}{\partial x} \right) + \frac{\partial}{\partial y}\left(f\frac{\partial g}{\partial y} \right) + \frac{\partial}{\partial z}\left(f\frac{\partial g}{\partial z} \right)$$

$$= \left(\frac{\partial f}{\partial x}\frac{\partial g}{\partial x} + f\frac{\partial^2 g}{\partial x^2} \right) + \left(\frac{\partial f}{\partial y}\frac{\partial g}{\partial y} + f\frac{\partial^2 g}{\partial y^2} \right) + \left(\frac{\partial f}{\partial z}\frac{\partial g}{\partial z} + f\frac{\partial^2 g}{\partial z^2} \right)$$

$$= \left(\frac{\partial f}{\partial x}\frac{\partial g}{\partial x} + \frac{\partial f}{\partial y}\frac{\partial g}{\partial y} + \frac{\partial f}{\partial z}\frac{\partial g}{\partial z} \right) + f\left(\frac{\partial}{\partial x}\left(\frac{\partial g}{\partial x} \right) + \frac{\partial}{\partial y}\left(\frac{\partial g}{\partial y} \right) + \frac{\partial}{\partial z}\left(\frac{\partial g}{\partial z} \right) \right)$$

$$= (\nabla f) \cdot (\nabla g) + f(\nabla \cdot (\nabla g)).$$

The notation ∇^2 is used for $\nabla \cdot \nabla$ or div(grad); thus the identity is verified.

———16.2

Line Integrals

3. Determine whether the curve $\mathbf{r}(t) = \sin \pi t\,\mathbf{i} + \cos 2\pi t\,\mathbf{j} + (t^2 - t + 2)\,\mathbf{k}$, $0 \le t \le 1$, is
a) smooth,   b) closed,   c) simple closed.

SOLUTION: a) $\mathbf{r}$ and its derivative $\mathbf{r}'(t) = \pi \cos(\pi t)\mathbf{i} - 2\pi \sin(2\pi t)\mathbf{j} + (2t-1)\mathbf{k}$ are continuous for $0 \le t \le 1$. However, $\mathbf{r}'(1/2) = \overrightarrow{0}$, so the curve is not smooth. b) Since $\mathbf{r}(0) = \mathbf{j} + 2\mathbf{k} = \mathbf{r}(1)$ the curve is closed.   c) The curve is not simple because for each $t : 0 \le t \le 1/2$, $\mathbf{r}(1-t) = \sin \pi(1-t)\mathbf{i} + \cos 2\pi(1-t)\mathbf{j} + ((1-t)^2 - (1-t) + 2)\,\mathbf{k} = \sin(\pi t)\mathbf{i} + \cos(2\pi t)\mathbf{j} + (t^2 - t + 2)\,\mathbf{k}$. Each point on the curve is hit twice.

7. Evaluate the line integral $\int_C xyz\,dx$, where C is described by $\mathbf{r}(t) = t\,\mathbf{i} + (t+2)\,\mathbf{j} + (2t-1)\,\mathbf{k}$, $0 \le t \le 1$.

SOLUTION: Since $x(t) = t$, $y(t) = (t+2)$, $z(t) = (2t-1)$, and $dx = x'(t)\,dt = dt$, then

$$\int_C xyz\,dx = \int_0^1 (t)(t+2)(2t-1)\,dt = \int_0^1 (2t^3 + 3t^2 - 2t)\,dt$$

$$= \left[\frac{1}{2}t^4 + t^3 - t^2\right]\Big|_0^1 = \frac{1}{2}.$$

15. Evaluate the line integral $\int_C (x^3 + y^3)\,ds$ where C is the circle $x^2 + y^2 = 4$ in the xy-plane, oriented clockwise, beginning and ending at $(2,0)$.

SOLUTION: Parameterize C by $x(t) = 2\cos t$, $y(t) = -2\sin t$, $z(t) = 0$ for $0 \le t \le 2\pi$. Then $x'(t) = -2\sin t$, $y'(t) = -2\cos t$, and $z'(t) = 0$ so $ds = \sqrt{(x')^2 + (y')^2 + (z')^2}\,dt = \sqrt{(-2\sin t)^2 + (-2\cos t)^2}\,dt = 2\,dt$. Thus

$$\int_C (x^3 + y^3)\,ds = \int_0^{2\pi} \left((2\cos t)^3 + (-2\sin t)^3\right) 2\,dt$$

$$= 16\int_0^{2\pi} \left((1 - \sin^2 t)\cos t - (1 - \cos^2 t)\sin t\right)\,dt$$

$$= 16\left[\sin t - \frac{\sin^3 t}{3} + \cos t - \frac{\cos^3 t}{3}\right]\Big|_0^{2\pi} = 0.$$

25. Evaluate $\int_C yx\,dx + x\,dy$ over each of the following simple closed curves:

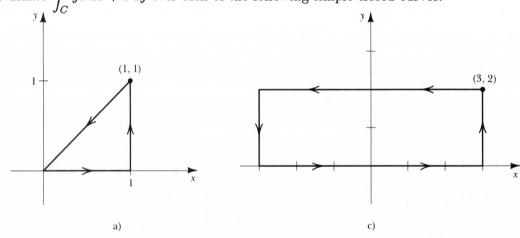

a)   c)

SOLUTION: For each simple closed curve, the line segments are denoted as C_1, C_2, C_3 (and C_4 in the cases of rectangles) where C_1 begins in the lower left hand corner, C_2 begins where C_1 ends, etc.

a) The parameterizations of the pieces are

$$C_1 : x(t) = t, \, y(t) = 0, \, 0 \le t \le 1 \text{ with } dx = dt \text{ and } dy = 0 \, dt.$$
$$C_2 : x(t) = 1, \, y(t) = t, \, 0 \le t \le 1 \text{ with } dx = 0 \, dt \text{ and } dy = dt.$$
$$C_3 : x(t) = 1 - t, \, y(t) = 1 - t, \, 0 \le t \le 1 \text{ with } dx = -dt \text{ and } dy = -dt.$$

Thus,

$$\int_C yx \, dx + x \, dy = \int_{C_1} + \int_{C_2} + \int_{C_3} yx \, dx + x \, dy$$

$$= \int_0^1 0t \, dt + t0 \, dt + \int_0^1 t1 \cdot 0 \, dt + 1 \, dt + \int_0^1 (1-t)(1-t)(-dt) + (1-t)(-dt)$$

$$= \int_0^1 \left(-(1-t)^2 + t \right) \, dt = \left[\frac{(1-t)^3}{3} + \frac{t^2}{2} \right] \Big|_0^1 = \frac{1}{6}.$$

c) Parameterization of the pieces are:

$$C_1 : x = -3 + t, \, y = 0, \, 0 \le t \le 6; \, dx = dt, \, dy = 0 \, dt.$$
$$C_2 : x = 3, \, y = t, \, 0 \le t \le 2; \, dx = 0 \, dt, \, dy = dt.$$
$$C_3 : x = 3 - t, \, y = 2, \, 0 \le t \le 6; \, dx = -dt, \, dy = 0 \, dt.$$
$$C_4 : x = -3, \, y = 2 - t, \, 0 \le t \le 2, \, dx = 0 \, dt, \, dy = -dt.$$

Thus,

$$\int_C yx \, dx + x \, dy = \int_{C_1} + \int_{C_2} + \int_{C_3} + \int_{C_4} yx \, dx + x \, dy$$

$$= \int_0^6 0(-3 + t) \, dt + (-3 + t)0 \, dt + \int_0^2 3t \cdot 0 \, dt + 3 \, dt$$

$$+ \int_0^6 2(3 - t)(-dt) + (3 - t)0 \, dt + \int_0^2 (2 - t)(-3)0 \, dt + (-3)(-dt)$$

$$= 0 + \int_0^2 3 \, dt - \int_0^6 (6 - 2t) \, dt + \int_0^2 3 \, dt = 0 + 6 + \left[(3 - t)^2 \right] \Big|_0^6 + 6 = 12.$$

29. Consider the integral $\int_C M \, dx + N \, dy + P \, dz$, where $M(x, y, z) = y^2 \sin z$, $N(x, y, z) = 2xy \sin z$, and $P(x, y, z) = xy^2 \cos z$.

a) Show that $\dfrac{\partial M}{\partial y} = \dfrac{\partial N}{\partial x}$, $\dfrac{\partial M}{\partial z} = \dfrac{\partial P}{\partial x}$, and $\dfrac{\partial N}{\partial z} = \dfrac{\partial P}{\partial y}$.

b) Evaluate the integral if C is the straight line joining $(0,0,0)$ and $(1,4,2)$.

c) Evaluate the integral if C is the curve from $(0,0,0)$ to $(1,4,2)$ described by

$$\mathbf{r}(t) = \frac{t}{2}\mathbf{i} + t^2\mathbf{j} + t\mathbf{k}, \quad 0 \le t \le 2.$$

d) Evaluate the integral if C is the circle $x^2 + y^2 = 4$ in the plane $z = 2$ with counterclockwise orientation.

SOLUTION: a) $\dfrac{\partial M}{\partial y} = 2y\sin z = \dfrac{\partial N}{\partial x}$, $\dfrac{\partial M}{\partial z} = y^2\cos z = \dfrac{\partial P}{\partial x}$, and $\dfrac{\partial N}{\partial z} = 2xy\cos z = \dfrac{\partial P}{\partial y}$.

b) Parametrize C by $x = t$, $y = 4t$, $z = 2t$, with $dx = dt$, $dy = 4\,dt$, $dz = 2\,dt$ for $0 \le t \le 1$.

$$\int_C y^2\sin z\,dx + 2xy\sin z\,dy + xy^2\cos z\,dz$$

$$= \int_0^4 (4t)^2\sin(2t)\,dt + 2t(4t)\sin(2t)(4\,dt) + t(4t)^2\cos(2t)(2\,dt)$$

$$= 48\int_0^1 t^2\sin(2t)\,dt + 32\int_0^1 t^3\cos(2t)\,dt$$

(integrate the second integral by parts with $u = t^3$ and $dv = \cos(2t)\,dt$)

$$= 48\int_0^1 t^2\sin(2t)\,dt + 32\left(\left[\frac{1}{2}t^3\sin(2t)\right]\Big|_0^1 - \frac{3}{2}\int_0^1 t^2\sin(2t)\,dt\right)$$

$$= \left[16t^3\sin(2t)\right]\Big|_0^1 = 16\sin 2.$$

c) Parametrize C by $x = t/2$, $y = t^2$, $z = t$ with $dx = \frac{1}{2}\,dt$, $dy = 2t\,dt$, $dz = dt$ for $0 \le t \le 2$.

$$\int_C y^2\sin z\,dx + 2xy\sin z\,dy + xy^2\cos z\,dz$$

$$= \int_0^2 (t^2)^2\sin t\left(\frac{1}{2}\,dt\right) + 2\left(\frac{1}{2}t\right)(t^2)\sin t(2t\,dt) + \left(\frac{1}{2}t\right)(t^2)^2\cos t\,dt$$

$$= \frac{5}{2}\int_0^2 t^4\sin t\,dt + \frac{1}{2}\int_0^2 t^5\cos t\,dt$$

(integrate the second integral by parts with $u = t^5$ and $dv = \cos t\,dt$)

$$= \frac{5}{2}\int_0^2 t^4\sin t\,dt + \frac{1}{2}\left([t^5\sin t]\Big|_0^2 - 5\int_0^2 t^4\sin t\,dt\right)$$

$$= \left[\frac{1}{2}t^5 \sin t\right]\Bigg|_0^2 = 16 \sin 2.$$

d) Parametrize C by $x = \cos t$, $y = \sin t$, $z = 2$ with $dx = -\sin t \, dt$, $dy = \cos t \, dt$ and $dz = 0 \, dt$ for $0 \le t \le 2\pi$.

$$\int_C y^2 \sin z \, dx + 2xy \sin z \, dy + xy^2 \cos z \, dz$$

$$= \int_0^{2\pi} (\sin t)^2 (\sin 2)(-\sin t \, dt) + 2(\cos t)(\sin t)(\sin 2)(\cos t \, dt) + (\cos t)(\sin t)^2 (\cos 2) 0 \, dt$$

$$= \sin(2) \int_0^{2\pi} \left(2 \cos^2 t - \sin^2 t\right) \sin t \, dt$$

$$= \sin(2) \int_0^{2\pi} (3 \cos^2 t - 1) \sin t \, dt = \sin(2) \left[-\cos^3 t + \cos t\right]\Bigg|_0^{2\pi} = 0.$$

16.3

Physical Applications of Line Integrals

---

7. Find the work done by the force $\mathbf{F} = (y^2 + xz)\mathbf{i} + xy\mathbf{j} + (x^2 - y)\mathbf{k}$ along the elliptical helix $\mathbf{r}(t) = 2\cos t \,\mathbf{i} + 3\sin t \,\mathbf{j} + t\,\mathbf{k}$ from $(2, 0, 0)$ to $(-2, 0, 3\pi)$.

SOLUTION: Along the path described by $\mathbf{r}(t)$, $d\mathbf{r} = (-2\sin t \,\mathbf{i} + 3\cos t \,\mathbf{j} + \mathbf{k})\, dt$ and $\mathbf{F}(x, y, z) = ((3\sin t)^2 + t(2\cos t))\,\mathbf{i} + (2\cos t)(3\sin t)\mathbf{j} + ((2\cos t)^2 - 3\sin t)\,\mathbf{k}$ as t varies from 0 to 3π, so the work is

$$W = \int_C \mathbf{F} \cdot d\mathbf{r} = \int_0^{3\pi} \left((9\sin^2 t + 2t\cos t)\mathbf{i} + 6\cos t \sin t \,\mathbf{j} + (4\cos^2 t - 3\sin t)\,\mathbf{k}\right)$$

$$\cdot (-2\sin t \,\mathbf{i} + 3\cos t \,\mathbf{j} + \mathbf{k})\, dt$$

$$= \int_0^{3\pi} \left(-18\sin^3 t - 4t\sin t \cos t + 18\cos^2 t \sin t + 4\cos^2 t - 3\sin t\right)\, dt$$

$$= \int_0^{3\pi} \left(-2t\sin 2t + 18(2\cos^2 t - 1)\sin t + 2(1 + \cos 2t) - 3\sin t\right)\, dt.$$

This first term is integrated by parts with $u = -2t$, $dv = \sin 2t$, so that $du = -2\, dt$ and $v = -(1/2)\cos 2t$;

$$\int (-2t\sin 2t)\, dt = t\cos 2t - \int \cos 2t \, dt = t\cos 2t - \frac{1}{2}\sin 2t.$$

Thus the integral for work is equal to

$$W = \left[(t\cos 2t - \frac{1}{2}\sin 2t) - 18\left(\frac{2}{3}(\cos t)^3 - \cos t \right) \right.$$

$$\left. + (2t + \sin 2t) + 3\cos t \right] \Big|_0^{3\pi} = 9\pi - 18.$$

17. Find a) the total mass and b) the center of mass of a wire whose shape is the triangle with vertices $(0,0,0)$, $(1,1,0)$, $(1,1,1)$ and whose density is $\rho(x,y,z) = \cos x + \cos y + \cos z$.

SOLUTION:

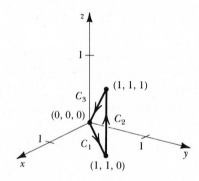

The three pieces of the curve C may be parameterized as

$C_1 : x = t,\ y = t,\ z = 0,\ 0 \le t \le 1$ with $ds = \sqrt{1^2 + 1^2 + 0^2}\, dt = \sqrt{2}\, dt$,

$C_2 : x = 1,\ y = 1,\ z = t,\ 0 \le t \le 1$ with $ds = \sqrt{0^2 + 0^2 + 1^2}\, dt = dt$, and

$C_3 : x = (1-t),\ y = (1-t),\ z = (1-t),\ 0 \le t \le 1$ with

$$ds = \sqrt{(-1)^2 + (-1)^2 + (-1)^2}\, dt = \sqrt{3}\, dt.$$

The integrals below will each be written as a sum of integrals over C_1, C_2, and C_3 with x, y, z, and ds on each curve as described above and with density $\rho(x,y,z) = \cos x + \cos y + \cos z$. a) The mass is

$$M = \int_C ds = \int_{C_1} + \int_{C_2} + \int_{C_3} ds$$

$$= \int_0^1 (\cos t + \cos t + \cos 0)\sqrt{2}\, dt + \int_0^1 (\cos 1 + \cos 1 + \cos t)\, dt$$

$$+ \int_0^1 (\cos(1-t) + \cos(1-t) + \cos(1-t))\sqrt{3}\, dt$$

$$= \int_0^1 \left(\sqrt{2}(1 + 2\cos t) + (2\cos 1 + \cos t) + 3\sqrt{3}\cos(1 - t) \right) dt$$

$$= \left[\sqrt{2}t + 2\sqrt{2}\sin t + (2\cos 1)t + \sin t - 3\sqrt{3}\sin(1 - t) \right] \Big|_0^1$$

$$= \sqrt{2} + (2\sqrt{2} + 1 + 3\sqrt{3})\sin 1 + 2\cos 1 \approx 10.089.$$

b) The coordinates of the center of mass are

$$\bar{x} = \frac{1}{M} \int_C x\rho\, ds = \frac{1}{M} \left(\int_0^1 t(2\cos t + 1)\sqrt{2}\, dt + \int_0^1 1(2\cos 1 + \cos t)\, dt \right.$$

$$\left. + \int_0^1 (1 - t)3\sqrt{3}\cos(1 - t)\, dt \right).$$

Substitute $\tau = (1 - t)$ in the last integral, then combine this integral with the similar term in the first integral and integrate by parts with $u = t$, $dv = \cos t$, $du = dt$ and $v = \sin t$.

$$\bar{x} = \frac{1}{M} \left[(2\sqrt{2} + 3\sqrt{3})(t\sin t + \cos t) + \frac{\sqrt{2}t^2}{2} + (2\cos 1)t + \sin t \right] \Big|_0^1$$

$$= \frac{1}{M} \left[\left(-\frac{3\sqrt{2}}{2} - 3\sqrt{3} \right) + (2\sqrt{2} + 3\sqrt{3} + 1)\sin 1 + (2\sqrt{2} + 3\sqrt{3} + 2)\cos 1 \right] \approx 0.56427,$$

$$\bar{y} = \frac{1}{M} \left(\int_0^1 t(2\cos t + 1)\sqrt{2}\, dt + \int_0^1 1(2\cos 1 + \cos t)\, dt \right.$$

$$\left. + \int_0^1 (1 - t)3\sqrt{3}\cos(1 - t)\, dt \right) = \bar{x}, \quad \text{and}$$

$$\bar{z} = \frac{1}{M} \left(\int_0^1 0(2\cos t + 1)\sqrt{2}\, dt + \int_0^1 t(2\cos 1 + \cos t)\, dt \right.$$

$$\left. + \int_0^1 (1 - t)3\sqrt{3}\cos(1 - t)\, dt \right).$$

Apply the same manipulations as above to the second and third integrals to write

$$\bar{z} = \frac{1}{M} \left[(1 + 3\sqrt{3})(t\sin t + \cos t) + (\cos 1)t^2 \right] \Big|_0^1$$

$$= \frac{1}{M} \left(-(1 + 3\sqrt{3}) + (1 + 3\sqrt{3})\sin 1 + (2 + 3\sqrt{3})\cos 1 \right) \approx 0.288.$$

Line Integrals
Independent of Path

1. Evaluate $\int_C yz\,dx + xz\,dy + xy\,dz$, where

   a) C is the straight line from $(0,0,0)$ to $(1,1,1)$.

   b) C is described by $\mathbf{r}(t) = t\,\mathbf{i} + t^2\,\mathbf{j} + t^3\,\mathbf{k}$, $0 \le t \le 1$.

SOLUTION: a) Parameterize the line by $x = t$, $y = t$, $z = t$ for $0 \le t \le 1$, with $dx = dt$, $dy = dt$, and $dz = dt$. The line integral is

$$\int_C yz\,dx + xz\,dy + xy\,dz = \int_0^1 t(t)\,dt + \int_0^1 t(t)\,dt + \int_0^1 t(t)\,dt$$

$$= 3\int_0^1 t^2\,dt = \left[t^3\right]\Big|_0^1 = 1.$$

b) Since $x = t$, $y = t^2$ and $z = t^3$, for $0 \le t \le 1$, then $dx = dt$, $dy = 2t\,dt$, and $dz = 3t^2\,dt$. The line integral is

$$\int_C yz\,dx + xz\,dy + xy\,dz = \int_0^1 t^2 t^3\,dt + \int_0^1 t(t^3)(2t)\,dt + \int_0^1 t(t^2)(3t^2)\,dt$$

$$= 6\int_0^1 t^5\,dt = \left[t^6\right]\Big|_0^1 = 1.$$

5. Determine if the differential form $(y + z)\,dx + (x + z)\,dy + (x + y)\,dz$ is exact.

SOLUTION: Definition 16.37 says that a differential form $\mathbf{F}\cdot d\mathbf{r}$ is exact if and only if the vector field $\mathbf{F} = M\mathbf{i} + N\mathbf{j} + P\mathbf{k}$ is conservative. THEOREM 16.43 says that $\mathbf{F}$ is conservative if and only if

$$\frac{\partial M}{\partial y} = \frac{\partial N}{\partial x}, \qquad \frac{\partial M}{\partial z} = \frac{\partial P}{\partial x}, \quad \text{and} \quad \frac{\partial N}{\partial z} = \frac{\partial P}{\partial y}.$$

For this differential form, $M = (y + z)$, $N = (x + z)$ and $P = (x + y)$, so $\dfrac{\partial M}{\partial y} = 1 = \dfrac{\partial N}{\partial x}$, $\dfrac{\partial M}{\partial z} = 1 = \dfrac{\partial P}{\partial x}$, and $\dfrac{\partial N}{\partial z} = 1 = \dfrac{\partial P}{\partial y}$. Thus, the form is exact.

13. Determine if $\mathbf{F}(x,y,z) = \cos(yz)\,\mathbf{i} - xy\sin(yz)\,\mathbf{j} - xy\sin(yz)\,\mathbf{k}$ is conservative.

SOLUTION: By THEOREM 16.43, $\mathbf{F} = M\,\mathbf{i} + N\,\mathbf{j} + P\,\mathbf{k}$ is conservative if and only if $\dfrac{\partial M}{\partial y} = \dfrac{\partial N}{\partial x}$, $\dfrac{\partial M}{\partial z} = \dfrac{\partial P}{\partial x}$, and $\dfrac{\partial N}{\partial z} = \dfrac{\partial P}{\partial y}$.

For this vector field, $M = \cos(yz)$, $N = -xy\sin(yz)$, and $P = -xy\sin(yz)$, so $\dfrac{\partial M}{\partial y} = -z\sin(yz)$, while $\dfrac{\partial N}{\partial x} = -y\sin(yz)$; so $\mathbf{F}$ is not conservative.

27. Find the potential function for the conservative function $\mathbf{F}(x,y,z) = (z\cos x - y\sin x)\,\mathbf{i} + (\cos x + z)\,\mathbf{j} + (\sin x + y - 2z)\,\mathbf{k}$.

SOLUTION: That this $\mathbf{F}$ is conservative everywhere follows from the SOLUTION to EXERCISE 17. Follow the solution to EXAMPLE 3 of the text to determine the potential f for $\mathbf{F}$.

Since   i) $\dfrac{\partial f}{\partial x} = M = (z\cos x - y\sin x)$,   ii) $\dfrac{\partial f}{\partial y} = N = \cos x + z$,   and   iii) $\dfrac{\partial f}{\partial z} = P = \sin x + y - 2z$, then $f(x,y) = \displaystyle\int (z\cos x - y\sin x)\,dx + k(y,z) = z\sin x + y\cos x + k(y,z)$ where $k(y,z)$ is determined by the conditions ii) and iii). By condition ii) $\dfrac{\partial f}{\partial y} = \cos x + \dfrac{\partial k(y,z)}{\partial y} = \cos x + z$ or $\dfrac{\partial k(y,z)}{\partial y} = z$, so $k(y,z) = \displaystyle\int z\,dy = zy + C(z)$. The function $C(z)$ in $f(x,y,z) = z\sin x + y\cos x + zy + C(z)$ is determined by condition iii), $\dfrac{\partial f}{\partial z} = \sin x + y + \dfrac{dC}{dz} = \sin x + y - 2z$, or $\dfrac{dC}{dz} = -2z$. Hence, $C(z) = -z^2$ ($+c$, where c is an arbitrary constant).

A potential function is $f(x,y,z) = z\sin x + y\cos x + zy - z^2$.

31. Sketch the region described by $\{(x,y) : |x| + |y| < 1\}$ in the xy-plane and determine whether it is   a) open b) closed and/or c) simple connected.

SOLUTION: Use the fact that $|a| = a$ if $a \geq 0$ and $|a| = -a$ if $a < 0$ to represent this set as the union of four sets (one for each possible combination of signs of x and y):
$\{(x,y) : |x| + |y| < 1\} = \{(x,y) : x + y < 1 \text{ and } x \geq 0, y \geq 0\}\cup$
$\{(x,y) : -x + y < 1 \text{ and } x < 0, y \geq 0\} \cup \{(x,y) : -x - y < 1 \text{ and } x < 0, y < 0\}\cup$
$\{(x,y) : x - y < 1 \text{ and } x \geq 0, y < 0\}$.

These sets lie in the first, second, third, and fourth quadrants respectively, and are bounded by lines which make $45°$ angles with the coordinate axes. The region does not include these lines.

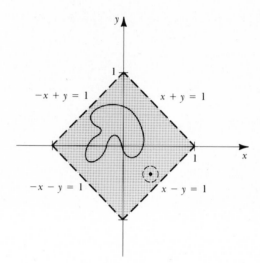

a) The region is open since each of its points lies in an open disk contained entirely in the region.

b) The region is not closed because it does not contain all its boundary points (the line segments).

c) The region is simply connected because each simple closed curve can be shrunk to a point without leaving the region.

37. a) Show that the line integral $\int_C y \ln z \, dx + x \ln z \, dy + \dfrac{xy}{z} \, dz$ is independent of path where C is the helix described by $\mathbf{r}(t) = \cos t \, \mathbf{i} + \sin t \, \mathbf{j} + t \, \mathbf{k}$ from $(1, 0, 2\pi)$ to $(1, 0, 4\pi)$.   b) Evaluate the integral.

SOLUTION: According to COROLLARY 16.44, the integral $\int_C \mathbf{F} \cdot d\mathbf{r}$ is independent of path if and only if D is a simply connected region containing C and the components of $\mathbf{F}$ satisfy $\dfrac{\partial M}{\partial y} = \dfrac{\partial N}{\partial x}, \dfrac{\partial M}{\partial z} = \dfrac{\partial P}{\partial x}, \dfrac{\partial N}{\partial z} = \dfrac{\partial P}{\partial y}$ in D.

Since $M = y \ln z$, $N = x \ln z$, and $P = \dfrac{xy}{z}$, then $\dfrac{\partial M}{\partial y} = \ln z = \dfrac{\partial N}{\partial x}, \dfrac{\partial M}{\partial z} = \dfrac{y}{z} = \dfrac{\partial P}{\partial x}$, and $\dfrac{\partial N}{\partial z} = \dfrac{x}{z} = \dfrac{\partial P}{\partial y}$ inside the simple connected region $D = \{(x, y, z) : z > 0\}$.

b) The conditions above on the components of $\mathbf{F}$ assure that $\mathbf{F}$ is conservative and thus that there is a scalar function $f : \nabla f = \mathbf{F}$ inside D. Determine f so that   i) $\dfrac{\partial f}{\partial x} = M = y \ln z$, ii) $\dfrac{\partial f}{\partial y} = N = x \ln z$ and iii) $\dfrac{\partial f}{\partial z} = P = \dfrac{xy}{z}$. By i), $f(x, y) = \displaystyle\int y \ln z \, dx + k(y, z) = xy \ln z + k(y, z)$.

By ii), $\dfrac{\partial f}{\partial y} = x \ln z + \dfrac{\partial k}{\partial y} = x \ln z$ so $k(x, y) = C(z)$ and by iii) the function $C(z)$ in $f(x, y, z) = xy \ln z + C(z)$ satisfies $\dfrac{\partial f}{\partial z} = \dfrac{xy}{z} + \dfrac{dC}{dz} = \dfrac{xy}{z}$, so $\dfrac{dC}{dz} = 0$; take $C(z) = 0$.

The potential of $\mathbf{F}$ is thus $f(x,y,z) = xy\ln z$. By THEOREM 16.40, $f = \nabla \mathbf{F}$ inside the simply connected region D; thus, since the curve C lies in D with endpoints at $(1,0,2\pi)$ and $(1,0,4\pi)$, the integral is

$$\int_C y\ln z\,dx + \int x\ln z\,dy + \int \frac{xy}{z}\,dz = f(1,0,4\pi) - f(1,0,2\pi)$$

$$= 1(0)\ln(4\pi) - 1(0)\ln(2\pi) = 0.$$

Green's Theorem

_____16.5

1. Verify Green's theorem for $\mathbf{F}(x,y) = x\,\mathbf{i} + xy\,\mathbf{j}$, where C is positively oriented and is the boundary of the square with vertices at $(0,0)$, $(1,0)$, $(1,1)$, and $(0,1)$.

SOLUTION: Parameterize the four sides of C as

$$C_1 : x(t) = t,\ y(t) = 0,\ 0 \le t \le 1 \text{ with } dx = dt,\ dy = 0$$
$$C_2 : x(t) = 1,\ y(t) = t,\ 0 \le t \le 1 \text{ with } dx = 0,\ dy = dt$$
$$C_3 : x(t) = 1 - t,\ y(t) = 1,\ 0 \le t \le 1 \text{ with } dx = -dt,\ dy = 0$$
$$C_4 : x(t) = 0,\ y(t) = 1 - t,\ 0 \le t \le 1 \text{ with } dx = 0,\ dy = -dt.$$

The line integral is thus

$$\int_C x\,dx + xy\,dy = \int_{C_1} + \int_{C_2} + \int_{C_3} + \int_{C_4} x\,dx + xy\,dy$$

$$= \int_0^1 t\,dt + t\cdot 0\,dt + \int_0^1 1\cdot 0 + 1t\,dt + \int_0^1 (1-t)(-dt) + (1-t)(1)(0)\,dt$$

$$+ \int_0^1 0\,dt + 0(1-t)(-dt)$$

$$= \int_0^1 (3t - 1)\,dt = \left[\frac{3}{2}t^2 - t\right]\Big|_0^1 = \frac{1}{2}.$$

Since $M = x$ and $N = xy$, then $\dfrac{\partial N}{\partial x} - \dfrac{\partial M}{\partial y} = y - 0 = y$, so the double integral in Green's theorem is computed over the square $R = \{(x,y) : 0 \le x \le 1; 0 \le y \le 1\}$:

$$\iint_R \left(\frac{\partial N}{\partial x} - \frac{\partial M}{\partial y}\right)dA = \int_0^1 \int_0^1 y\,dx\,dy = \int_0^1 [yx]\Big|_{x=0}^1 dy$$

$$= \int_0^1 y \, dy = \left[\frac{y^2}{2} \right] \Big|_0^1 = \frac{1}{2}.$$

The line integral and double integral are equal as predicted by Green's theorem.

3. Use Green's theorem to find $\int \mathbf{F} \cdot d\mathbf{r}$, where $\mathbf{F}(x,y) = 3y \sin^3 x \, \mathbf{i} + \cos^3 x \, \mathbf{j}$ and C is the positively oriented closed curve determined by $y = x^2$ and $y = x$.

SOLUTION: Since $M = 3y \sin^3 x$ and $N = \cos^3 x$, then $\dfrac{\partial M}{\partial y} = 3 \sin^3 x$ and

$\dfrac{\partial N}{\partial x} = -3 \sin x \cos^2 x$. Thus $\dfrac{\partial N}{\partial x} - \dfrac{\partial M}{\partial y} = -3 \sin x (\cos^2 x + \sin^2 x) = -3 \sin x$. The curve C encloses the region $R = \{(x,y) : 0 \leq x \leq 1; \text{ for each } x, x^2 \leq y \leq x\}$ so by Green's theorem the line integral is

$$\int_C (3y \sin^3 x) \, dx + \int (\cos^3 x) \, dy = \int_R \left(\frac{\partial N}{\partial x} - \frac{\partial M}{\partial y} \right) dA$$

$$= \int_0^1 \int_{x^2}^x (-3 \sin x) \, dy \, dx = -3 \int_0^1 (x - x^2) \sin x \, dx.$$

Integrate by parts twice, first with $u = x^2 - x$ and $dv = \sin x \, dx$, then with $u = 1 - 2x$ and $dv = \cos x \, dx$ to get

$$-3 \int_0^1 (x - x^2) \sin x \, dx = -3 \left[-(x - x^2) \cos x + \int (1 - 2x) \cos x \, dx \right] \Big|_0^1$$

$$= -3 \left[-(x - x^2) \cos x + (1 - 2x) \sin x - 2 \cos x \right] \Big|_0^1$$

$$= 3(\sin 1 + 2 \cos 1 - 2).$$

11. Use Green's theorem to evaluate $\int_C (x - y^3) \, dx + x^3 \, dy$, where C is the positively oriented unit circle with center at the origin.

SOLUTION: Since $M = x - y^3$ and $N = x^3$, then $\dfrac{\partial N}{\partial x} - \dfrac{\partial M}{\partial y} = (3x^2) - (-3y^2) = 3(x^2 + y^2)$. The inside of C is the disk, R, of radius one centered at the origin. Green's theorem then states that

$$\int_C (x - y^3) \, dx + (x^3) \, dy = \iint_R 3(x^2 + y^2) \, dA.$$

Since R is a disk and the integrand is $3(x^2 + y^2)$, use polar coordinates to write this double integral as

$$\iint\limits_{R} 3(x^2 + y^2)\, dA = \int_0^{2\pi} \int_0^1 (3r^2)r\, dr\, d\theta = \int_0^{2\pi} \left[\frac{3}{4}r^4\right]\Big|_{r=0}^1 d\theta = \frac{3}{4}\left[\theta\right]\Big|_0^{2\pi} = \frac{3\pi}{2}.$$

17. Use Green's theorem to find the area of the region inside the curve $x = \cos^3 t$, $y = \sin^3 t$, $0 \le t \le 2\pi$.

SOLUTION: Since $x = \cos^3 t$ and $y = \sin^3 t$ then $dx = -3\sin t \cos^2 t\, dt$ and $dy = 3\cos t \sin^2 t$ so $x\, dy = 3\cos^4 t \sin^2 t\, dt$ and $-y\, dx = 3\sin^4 t \cos^2 t\, dt$. Rather than use Formulas 16.46 or 16.47 to integrate either $x\, dy$ or $-y\, dx$, use 16.48 to calculate the area by the (simpler) integral

$$A = \frac{1}{2}\int_C x\, dy - y\, dx = \frac{1}{2}\left(\int_0^{2\pi} 3\cos^4 t \sin^2 t\, dt + 3\sin^4 t \cos^2 t\, dt\right)$$

$$= \frac{3}{8}\int_0^{2\pi} (4\sin^2 t \cos^2 t)(\cos^2 t + \sin^2 t)\, dt = \frac{3}{8}\int_0^{2\pi} (\sin^2 2t)\, dt$$

$$= \frac{3}{16}\int_0^{2\pi} (1 - \cos 4t)\, dt = \frac{3}{16}\left[t - \frac{1}{4}\sin 4t\right]\Big|_0^{2\pi} = \frac{3\pi}{8}.$$

COMMENT: When using line integrals to compute areas by Green's theorem, it is good practice to compute both $x\, dy$ and $y\, dx$ and then to determine which (if any) "average" of the form $\lambda x\, dx + (1 - \lambda)(y\, dx)$ is easiest to integrate. Notice that for any λ, the area, A, can be written as

$$A = \lambda A + (1 - \lambda)A = \lambda \int_C x\, dy + (1 - \lambda)\int_C (-y)\, dx$$

$$= \int_C \lambda x\, dy - (1 - \lambda)y\, dx.$$

_____**16.6**

Surface Integrals

3. Evaluate $\iint\limits_{S} xyz\, d\sigma$, where S is the portion of the plane $x + 2y + 3z = 6$ lying in the first octant.

SOLUTION: S is given by $z = f(x,y) = (6 - x - 2y)/3$ with $f_x = -1/3$ and $f_y = -2/3$.

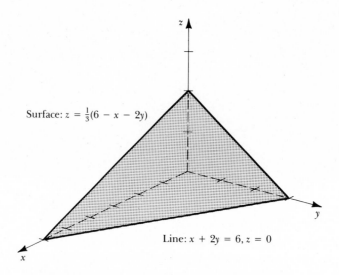

Surface: $z = \frac{1}{3}(6 - x - 2y)$

Line: $x + 2y = 6, z = 0$

The projection of the surface S onto the xy-plane is the region
$R = \{(x,y) : 0 \le x \le 6;$ for each $x, 0 \le y \le (6 - x)/2\}$. The surface integral is

$$\iint\limits_S xyz \, d\sigma = \iint\limits_R xy \left(\frac{6 - x - 2y}{3} \right) \sqrt{1 + \left(-\frac{1}{3} \right)^2 + \left(-\frac{2}{3} \right)^2} \, dA$$

$$= \frac{\sqrt{14}}{9} \int_0^6 \int_0^{(6-x)/2} x \left((6 - x)y - 2y^2 \right) \, dy \, dx$$

$$= \frac{\sqrt{14}}{9} \int_0^6 x \left[(6 - x)\frac{y^2}{2} - \frac{2}{3}y^3 \right] \Bigg|_{y=0}^{(6-x)/2} dx = \frac{\sqrt{14}}{9} \int_0^6 x \frac{1}{24}(6 - x)^3 \, dx.$$

Let $u = 6 - x$ to write this last integral as

$$\frac{\sqrt{14}}{(9)(24)} \int_0^6 (6 - u)u^3 \, du = \frac{\sqrt{14}}{(9)(24)} \left[\frac{3}{2}u^4 - \frac{1}{5}u^5 \right] \Bigg|_0^6 = \frac{9}{5}\sqrt{14}.$$

11. Evaluate $\iint\limits_S (x^2 + y^2 + z^2) \, d\sigma$, where S is the hemisphere $z = \sqrt{9 - x^2 - y^2}$.

SOLUTION: With $f(x,y) = \sqrt{9 - x^2 - y^2}$, the partials are $f_x = -x/\sqrt{9 - x^2 - y^2}$ and $f_y = -y/\sqrt{9 - x^2 - y^2}$ so the integrand is

$$(x^2 + y^2 + z^2) \, d\sigma = (x^2 + y^2 + 9 - x^2 - y^2)\sqrt{1 + \left(\frac{-x}{\sqrt{9 - x^2 - y^2}} \right)^2 + \left(\frac{-y}{\sqrt{9 - x^2 - y^2}} \right)^2} \, dA$$

$$= \frac{27}{\sqrt{9 - (x^2 + y^2)}} \, dA.$$

The hemisphere lies over the disk of radius 3 centered at the origin in the xy-plane. Both the integrand and the region of integration are conveniently described in polar coordinates;

$$(x^2 + y^2 + z^2) \, d\sigma = \frac{27}{\sqrt{9 - r^2}} \, r \, dr \, d\theta$$

and $R = \{(r, \theta) : 0 \le \theta \le 2\pi; 0 \le r \le 3\}$. The surface integral is

$$\iint_S (x^2 + y^2 + z^2) \, d\sigma = \iint_R \frac{27}{\sqrt{9 - r^2}} r \, dr \, d\theta = \int_0^{2\pi} \int_0^3 \frac{27r}{\sqrt{9 - r^2}} \, dr \, d\theta.$$

The inner integral is improper; its value is

$$\int_0^3 \frac{27r}{\sqrt{9 - r^2}} \, dr = \lim_{a \to 3^-} \int_0^a \frac{27r}{\sqrt{9 - r^2}} \, dr$$

$$= -27 \lim_{a \to 3^-} \left[\sqrt{9 - r^2} \right] \Big|_{r=0}^a = -27 \lim_{a \to 3^-} \left[\sqrt{9 - a^2} - 3 \right] = 81.$$

Thus the surface integral is

$$\iint_S (x^2 + y^2 + z^2) \, d\sigma = \int_0^{2\pi} 81 \, d\theta = 81 \, [\theta] \Big|_0^{2\pi} = 162\pi.$$

15. Determine $\iint_S \mathbf{F} \cdot \mathbf{n} \, d\sigma$, where $\mathbf{F}(x, y, z) = x^2 \, \mathbf{i} + y^2 \, \mathbf{j} + z \, \mathbf{k}$ and S is the portion of the plane $z = x + y + 1$ that lies above the triangle $0 \le x \le 1$, $0 \le y \le x$; $\mathbf{n}$ is directed downward.

SOLUTION: S is given by $z = f(x, y) = x + y + 1$ with $f_x = 1$ and $f_y = 1$ over $R = \{(x, y) : 0 \le x \le 1; \text{ for each } x, \ 0 \le y \le x\}$. The components of $\mathbf{F}$ are $M = x^2$, $N = y^2$ and $P = z = x + y + 1$. Since the normal is directed down, use Formula 16.56 to write

$$\iint_S \mathbf{F} \cdot \mathbf{n} \, d\sigma = \iint_R (M f_x + N f_y - P) \, dA$$

$$= \int_0^1 \int_0^x \left((x^2)(1) + (y^2)(1) - (x + y + 1) \right) \, dy \, dx$$

$$= \int_0^1 \left[(x^2 - x - 1)y - \frac{1}{2}y^2 + \frac{1}{3}y^3 \right] \Big|_{y=0}^x \, dy$$

$$= \int_0^1 \left(\frac{4}{3}x^3 - \frac{3}{2}x^2 - x\right) dx = \left[\frac{1}{3}x^4 - \frac{1}{2}x^3 - \frac{1}{2}x^2\right]\Big|_0^1 = -\frac{2}{3}.$$

17. Find the mass of the hemispherical shell described by $z = \sqrt{4 - x^2 - y^2}$ if its density at each point is given by $g(x, y, z) = 4 - z$.

SOLUTION: Since $z = f(x, y) = \sqrt{4 - x^2 - y^2}$, then $f_x = -x/\sqrt{4 - x^2 - y^2}$ and $f_y = -y/\sqrt{4 - x^2 - y^2}$, so the surface area element is

$$d\sigma = \sqrt{1 + \left(\frac{-x}{\sqrt{4 - x^2 - y^2}}\right)^2 + \left(\frac{-y}{\sqrt{4 - x^2 - y^2}}\right)^2} \, dA = \frac{2}{\sqrt{4 - (x^2 + y^2)}} \, dA.$$

The density is also $g(x, y, z) = 4 - z = 4 - \sqrt{4 - (x^2 + y^2)}$. The surface lies over the disk, R. of radius 2 centered at the origin in the xy-plane. Because of the forms of $d\sigma$, the density and the region in the xy-plane, polar coordinates are used to calculate the mass (the inner integral is improper):

$$M = \iint_S g(x, y, z) \, d\sigma = \iint_R \left(4 - \sqrt{4 - (x^2 + y^2)}\right) \frac{2}{\sqrt{4 - (x^2 + y^2)}} \, dA$$

$$= \int_0^{2\pi} \int_0^2 (4 - \sqrt{4 - r^2}) \frac{2}{\sqrt{4 - r^2}} r \, dr \, d\theta$$

$$= \int_0^{2\pi} \lim_{a \to 2^-} \left[-8\sqrt{4 - r^2} - r^2\right]\Big|_{r=0}^a d\theta$$

$$= \int_0^{2\pi} \lim_{a \to 2^-} \left(16 - 8\sqrt{4 - a^2} - a^2\right) d\theta = \int_0^{2\pi} 12 \, d\theta = 12 \, [\theta]\Big|_0^{2\pi} = 24\pi.$$

―――16.7

The Divergence Theorem

1. Use the divergence theorem to evaluate $\iint_S \mathbf{F} \cdot \mathbf{n} \, d\sigma$, where $\mathbf{F} = x\mathbf{i} + y\mathbf{j} + z\mathbf{k}$ and S is the the cylinder $x^2 + y^2 = 4$, $0 \le z \le 4$ with outward unit normal $\mathbf{n}$.

SOLUTION: The surface S bounds the right circular cylinder D which may be described in terms of cylindrical coordinates as $D = \{(r, \theta, z) : 0 \le \theta \le 2\pi; \ 0 \le r \le 2; \ 0 \le z \le 4\}$. The divergence of $\mathbf{F}$ is div $\mathbf{F} = \left(\dfrac{\partial}{\partial x}(x)\right) + \left(\dfrac{\partial}{\partial y}(y)\right) + \left(\dfrac{\partial}{\partial z}(z)\right) = 3$, so by the divergence theorem,

$$\iint_S \mathbf{F} \cdot \mathbf{n}\, d\sigma = \iiint_D \text{div } \mathbf{F}\, dV = \int_0^{2\pi} \int_0^2 \int_0^4 3r\, dz\, dr\, d\theta$$

$$= 3 \int_0^{2\pi} \int_0^2 r\,[z]\Big|_{z=0}^4 dr\, d\theta = 12 \int_0^{2\pi} \left[\frac{r^2}{2}\right]\Big|_{r=0}^2 d\theta = 24\,[\theta]\Big|_0^{2\pi} = 48\pi.$$

7. Use the divergence theorem to evaluate $\displaystyle\iint_S \mathbf{F} \cdot \mathbf{n}\, d\sigma$, where $\mathbf{F} = (x + e^y)\mathbf{i} + (xy + \sin z)\mathbf{j} -$

$(xz + \sqrt{xy})\,\mathbf{k}$, and S is the boundary of the tetrahedron bounded by the planes $x = 0$, $y = 0$, $z = 0$, and $2x + 3y + z = 6$.

SOLUTION: The surface S bounds the solid D.

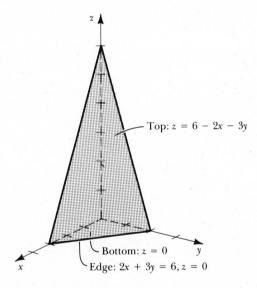

This solid may be described using cartesian coordinates as $D = \{(x, y, z) : 0 \le x \le 3$; for each x, $0 \le y \le (6 - 2x)/3$; for each x and y, $0 \le z \le 6 - 2x - 3y\}$. The divergence of $\mathbf{F}$ is

$$\text{div } \mathbf{F} = \frac{\partial}{\partial x}(x + e^y) + \frac{\partial}{\partial y}(xy + \sin z) - \frac{\partial}{\partial z}(xz + \sqrt{xy}) = 1 + x - x = 1.$$

Thus the surface integral is calculated by the divergence theorem as

$$\iint_S \mathbf{F} \cdot \mathbf{n}\, d\sigma = \iiint_D \text{div } \mathbf{F}\, dV = \int_0^3 \int_0^{(6-2x)/3} \int_0^{6-2x-3y} 1\, dz\, dy\, dx$$

$$= \int_0^3 \int_0^{(6-2x)/3} (6 - 2x - 3y) \, dy \, dz = \int_0^3 \left[(6 - 2x)y - \frac{3}{2}y^2 \right] \Big|_{y=0}^{(6-2x)/3} dx$$

$$= \frac{1}{6} \int_0^3 (6 - 2x)^2 \, dx = -\frac{1}{12} \left[\frac{(6-2x)^3}{3} \right] \Big|_0^3 = 6.$$

$$\underline{\hspace{6cm}}16.8$$

Stokes's Theorem

3. Verify Stokes's theorem for $\mathbf{F}(x, y, z) = 2z\,\mathbf{i} + x\,\mathbf{j} + 3y\,\mathbf{k}$ where S is the portion of the paraboloid $z = 9 - x^2 - y^2$ above the xy-plane. The normal $\mathbf{n}$ is directed upward.

SOLUTION: The surface S and its boundary C are graphed.

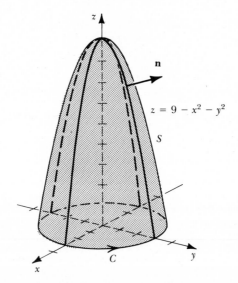

The surface is $S = \{(x, y, z) : z = 9 - x^2 - y^2; \ x^2 + y^2 \le 9\}$. The boundary is $C = \{(x, y, z) : x = 3 \cos t, y = 3 \sin t, z = 0, 0 \le t \le 2\pi\}$, and the projection of S on the xy-plane is $R = \{(x, y) : x^2 + y^2 \le 9\}$.

Along the curve C, $dx = -3 \sin t \, dt$, $dy = 3 \cos t$, and $dz = 0$, so the line integral is

$$\int_C \mathbf{F} \cdot d\mathbf{r} = \int_0^{2\pi} (2 \cdot 0)(-3 \sin t \, dt) + (3 \cos t)(3 \cos t) \, dt + 3(3 \sin t) 0 \, dt$$

$$= 9 \int_0^{2\pi} \cos^2 t \, dt = \frac{9}{2} \int_0^{2\pi} (1 + \cos 2t) \, dt$$

$$= \frac{9}{2}\left[t + \frac{1}{2}\sin 2t\right]\Big|_0^{2\pi} = 9\pi.$$

The curl of $\mathbf{F} = 2z\,\mathbf{i} + x\,\mathbf{j} + 3y\,\mathbf{k}$ is

$$\overrightarrow{\mathrm{curl}\,F} = \left(\frac{\partial}{\partial y}[3y] - \frac{\partial}{\partial z}[x]\right)\mathbf{i} + \left(\frac{\partial}{\partial z}[2z] - \frac{\partial}{\partial x}[3y]\right)\mathbf{j} + \left(\frac{\partial}{\partial x}[x] - \frac{\partial}{\partial y}[2z]\right)\mathbf{k}$$

$$= 3\,\mathbf{i} + 2\,\mathbf{j} + \mathbf{k}.$$

The surface is given by $z = f(x, y) = 9 - x^2 - y^2$ with $f_x = -2x$ and $f_y = -2y$. The projection of the surface onto the xy-plane can best be written in terms of polar coordinates as $R = \{(r, \theta) : 0 \le \theta \le 2\pi;\ \ 0 \le r \le 3\}$.

Formula 16.55 in SECTION 16.6 implies that the surface integral is

$$\iint\limits_S (\overrightarrow{\mathrm{curl}\,F}) \cdot \mathbf{n}\,d\sigma = \iint\limits_R (3\,\mathbf{i} + 2\,\mathbf{j} + \mathbf{k}) \cdot (-f_x\,\mathbf{i} - f_y\,\mathbf{j} + \mathbf{k})\,dA$$

$$= \iint\limits_R (3\,\mathbf{i} + 2\,\mathbf{j} + \mathbf{k}) \cdot (2x\,\mathbf{i} + 2y\,\mathbf{j} + \mathbf{k})\,dA$$

$$= \int_0^{2\pi}\!\!\int_0^3 (6r\cos\theta + 4r\sin\theta + 1)r\,dr\,d\theta$$

$$= \int_0^{2\pi} (6\cos\theta + 4\sin\theta)\left[\frac{r^3}{3}\right]\Big|_{r=0}^3 + \left[\frac{r^2}{2}\right]\Big|_{r=0}^3 d\theta$$

$$= \int_0^{2\pi} 9(6\cos\theta + 4\sin\theta) + \frac{9}{2}\,d\theta$$

$$= \left[54\sin\theta - 36\cos\theta + \frac{9}{2}\theta\right]\Big|_0^{2\pi} = 9\pi.$$

5. Use Stokes's theorem to evaluate $\int_C \mathbf{F} \cdot d\mathbf{r}$, where $\mathbf{F}(x, y, z) = 2y\,\mathbf{i} + z\,\mathbf{j} + 3y\,\mathbf{k}$, and where

C is the intersection of the sphere $x^2 + y^2 + z^2 = 1$ and the plane $z = 0$.

SOLUTION: The surface S and the curve C are graphed.

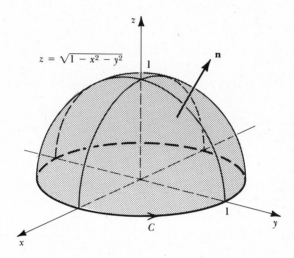

Let S be given by $z = f(x,y) = \sqrt{1 - x^2 - y^2}$ with $f_x = -x/\sqrt{1 - x^2 - y^2}$ and $f_y = -y/\sqrt{1 - x^2 - y^2}$. Then since

$$\overrightarrow{\operatorname{curl} F} = \left(\frac{\partial}{\partial y}(3y) - \frac{\partial}{\partial z}(z)\right)\mathbf{i} - \left(\frac{\partial}{\partial x}(3y) - \frac{\partial}{\partial z}(2y)\right)\mathbf{j} + \left(\frac{\partial}{\partial x}(z) - \frac{\partial}{\partial y}(2y)\right)\mathbf{k}$$

$$= 2\mathbf{i} - 2\mathbf{k},$$

the surface integral obtained from applying Stokes's theorem to $\displaystyle\int_C \mathbf{F} \cdot d\mathbf{r}$ is

$$\iint_S \overrightarrow{\operatorname{curl} F} \cdot \mathbf{n}\, d\sigma = \iint_R (2\mathbf{i} - 2\mathbf{k}) \cdot \left(\frac{x}{\sqrt{1 - x^2 - y^2}}\mathbf{i} + \frac{y}{\sqrt{1 - x^2 - y^2}}\mathbf{j} + \mathbf{k}\right) dA$$

where $R = \{(r,\theta) : 0 \le r \le 1;\ \ 0 \le \theta \le 2\pi\}$ is the projection of the surface S on the xy-plane. This integral is written in polar coordinates to give

$$\int_C \mathbf{F} \cdot d\mathbf{r} = \int_0^1 \int_0^{2\pi} \left(\frac{2r\cos\theta}{\sqrt{1 - r^2}} - 2\right) r\, d\theta\, dr$$

$$= \int_0^1 \frac{2r^2}{\sqrt{1 - r^2}} \left[\sin\theta\right]\Big|_{\theta=0}^{2\pi} - (2r)\,[\theta]\Big|_{\theta=0}^{2\pi}\, dr = \int_0^1 (-4\pi r)\, dr = \left[-2\pi r^2\right]\Big|_0^1 = -2\pi.$$

COMMENT: 1)   The order of integration in the double integral in polar coordinates was reversed from the customary order to avoid integrating the term $r^2/\sqrt{1 - r^2}$ with respect to r.

2) The curve C in EXERCISE 5 bounds many surfaces, the simplest of which is $S = \{(x, y, z) : z = 0; \ x^2 + y^2 \leq 1\}$. If this surface is used, then Stokes's theorem gives

$$\int_C \mathbf{F} \cdot d\mathbf{r} = \iint_S (\overrightarrow{\operatorname{curl} F}) \cdot (\mathbf{n}) \, d\sigma = \iint_R (2\mathbf{i} - 2\mathbf{k}) \cdot (0\mathbf{i} + 0\mathbf{j} + \mathbf{k}) \, dA$$

$$= -2 \iint_R dA = (-2)(\operatorname{area} R),$$

where R is the same unit circle used in the solution to EXERCISE 5. It is good practice to find the "simplest surface" of which C is the boundary.

_____16.9

Applications of the Divergence and Stokes's Theorem

3. Suppose the velocity of a fluid is described by $\mathbf{v}(x, y, z) = x^2 \mathbf{i} + y^2 \mathbf{j} + (z^2 - z) \mathbf{k}$. Determine at which points sources and sinks occur.

SOLUTION: Since div $\mathbf{v}(P)$ represents the rate of flow of fluid per unit volume at P, then P is a source if div $\mathbf{v}(P) > 0$ and a sink if div $\mathbf{v}(P) < 0$.

For the given flow, div $\mathbf{v} = \dfrac{\partial}{\partial x}(x^2) + \dfrac{\partial}{\partial y}(y^2) + \dfrac{\partial}{\partial z}(z^2 - z) = 2x + 2y + 2z - 1$. Sources are present at all points on the side of the plane $2x + 2y + 2z = 1$ whose coordinates satisfy $2x + 2y + 2z > 1$. The points where $2x + 2y + 2z < 1$ are all sinks.

9. Suppose that a cup of coffee is stirred with a velocity that can be approximated by

$$\mathbf{v}(x, y, z) = -\omega y \, \mathbf{i} + \omega x \, \mathbf{j},$$

where ω is the constant angular speed of the rotation. Show that $\mathbf{v}$ is not irrotational.

SOLUTION: By Formula 16.73, a vector field $\mathbf{v}$ is irrotational provided that curl $\mathbf{v} = \theta$. For the given flow,

$$\operatorname{curl} \mathbf{v} = \left(\frac{\partial}{\partial y}(0) - \frac{\partial}{\partial z}(\omega x) \right) \mathbf{i} - \left(\frac{\partial}{\partial x}(0) - \frac{\partial}{\partial z}(-\omega y) \right) \mathbf{j} + \left(\frac{\partial}{\partial x}(\omega x) - \frac{\partial}{\partial y}(-\omega y) \right) \mathbf{k}$$

$$= 2\omega \, \mathbf{k}.$$

Thus curl $\mathbf{v} \neq \overrightarrow{0}$ provided $\omega \neq 0$, so the flow is not irrotational.

_____Chapter 16
Review Exercises

1. Find a) the divergence and b) the curl of $\mathbf{F}(x, y, z) = y \sin z \, \mathbf{i} + x \sin z \, \mathbf{j} + xy \cos z \, \mathbf{k}$.

SOLUTION: a) The divergence is

$$\text{div } \mathbf{F} = \nabla \cdot \mathbf{F} = \frac{\partial}{\partial x}(y \sin z) + \frac{\partial}{\partial y}(x \sin z) + \frac{\partial}{\partial z}(xy \cos z)$$

$$= 0 + 0 + (-xy \sin z) = -xy \sin z.$$

b) The curl is

$$\text{curl } \mathbf{F} = \nabla \times \mathbf{F} = \begin{vmatrix} \mathbf{i} & \mathbf{j} & \mathbf{k} \\ \dfrac{\partial}{\partial x} & \dfrac{\partial}{\partial y} & \dfrac{\partial}{\partial z} \\ y \sin z & x \sin z & xy \cos z \end{vmatrix}$$

$$= \left(\frac{\partial}{\partial y}(xy \cos z) - \frac{\partial}{\partial z}(x \sin z) \right) \mathbf{i} - \left(\frac{\partial}{\partial x}(xy \cos z) - \frac{\partial}{\partial z}(y \sin z) \right) \mathbf{j}$$

$$+ \left(\frac{\partial}{\partial x}(x \sin z) - \frac{\partial}{\partial y}(y \sin z) \right) \mathbf{k}$$

$$= (x \cos z - x \cos z)\mathbf{i} - (y \cos z - y \cos z)\mathbf{j} + (\sin z - \sin z)\mathbf{k} = \overrightarrow{0}.$$

7. Show that $f(x, y) = xy - x^2 + y^2$ is harmonic.

SOLUTION: A function f is harmonic if and only if $\dfrac{\partial^2 f}{\partial x^2} + \dfrac{\partial^2 f}{\partial y^2} = 0$. The partials are $\dfrac{\partial f}{\partial x} = y - 2x$, $\dfrac{\partial^2 f}{\partial x^2} = -2$, $\dfrac{\partial f}{\partial y} = x + 2y$, and $\dfrac{\partial^2 f}{\partial y^2} = 2$, so $\dfrac{\partial^2 f}{\partial x^2} + \dfrac{\partial^2 f}{\partial y^2} = -2 + 2 = 0$ and f is harmonic.

17. Evaluate $\displaystyle\int_C e^x \, dx + xy \, dy + \ln xy \, dz$, where C is $\mathbf{r}(t) = t\mathbf{i} + e^t\mathbf{j} + t^2\mathbf{k}$, $1 \leq t \leq 3$.

SOLUTION: With $M = e^x$, $n = xy$, and $P = \ln xy$, note that $\dfrac{\partial N}{\partial z} = 0 \neq \dfrac{\partial P}{\partial y} = \dfrac{1}{y}$ so the integral is not independent of path. The line integral must be directly calculated; along C, $x(t) = t$, $y(t) = e^t$, and $z(t) = t^2$ for $1 \leq t \leq 3$ with $dx = dt$, $dy = e^t \, dt$, and $dz = 2t \, dt$. Thus,

$$\int_C e^x \, dx + xy \, dy + \ln(xy) \, dz$$

$$= \int_1^3 e^t \, dt + te^t(e^t \, dt) + \ln(te^t)(2t) \, dt$$

$$= \int_1^3 \left(e^t + te^{2t} + 2t^2 + 2t \ln t \right) \, dt$$

$$= \left[e^t + \left(\frac{1}{2}te^{2t} - \frac{1}{4}e^{2t} \right) + \frac{2}{3}t^3 + \left(t^2 \ln t - \frac{t^2}{2} \right) \right] \Big|_1^3$$

$$= \frac{5}{4}e^6 + e^3 - \frac{1}{4}e^2 - e + 9 \ln 3 + \frac{40}{3}.$$

21. Evaluate $\int_C \mathbf{F} \cdot d\mathbf{r}$, where $\mathbf{F} = y^2/(1+x^2)\mathbf{i} + 2y \arctan x \, \mathbf{j}$ and C is the ellipse $x^2 + 4y^2 = 1$.

SOLUTION: Use Green's theorem here, since the partial derivatives

$$\frac{\partial N}{\partial x} = \frac{\partial}{\partial x}(2y \arctan x) = \frac{2y}{1+x^2} \quad \text{and} \quad \frac{\partial M}{\partial y} = \frac{\partial}{\partial y}\left(\frac{y^2}{1+x^2} \right) = \frac{2y}{1+x^2}$$

are defined and continuous on the ellipse C and in its inside, R.

$$\int_C \mathbf{F} \cdot d\mathbf{r} = \iint_R \left(\frac{\partial N}{\partial x} - \frac{\partial M}{\partial y} \right) dA = \iint_R \left(\frac{2y}{(1+x^2)} - \frac{2y}{(1+x^2)} \right) dA = 0.$$

23. a) Show that the integral $\int_C yz \, dx + xz \, dy + xy \, dz$ is independent of path.

b) Evaluate the line integral over the helix $C : \mathbf{r}(t) = \cos t \, \mathbf{i} + \sin t \, \mathbf{j} + t \, \mathbf{k}$, $0 \leq t \leq 2\pi$.

SOLUTION: a) Since $M = yz$, $N = xz$, and $P = xy$ satisfy

$$\frac{\partial N}{\partial z} = x = \frac{\partial P}{\partial y}, \qquad \frac{\partial P}{\partial x} = y = \frac{\partial M}{\partial z}, \quad \text{and} \quad \frac{\partial N}{\partial x} = z = \frac{\partial M}{\partial y},$$

then by COROLLARY 16.44 the integral is independent of path.

b) There is a scalar function f : i) $\dfrac{\partial f}{\partial x} = M = yz$, ii) $\dfrac{\partial f}{\partial y} = N = xz$, and iii) $\dfrac{\partial f}{\partial z} = P = xy$.

By i) $f(x, y, z) = \int yz \, dx + k(y, z) = xyz + k(y, z)$. According to ii), $\dfrac{\partial}{\partial y}[xyz + k] = xz$, so $\dfrac{\partial k}{\partial y} = 0$ or $k(y, z) = C(z)$. By iii), $\dfrac{\partial}{\partial z}[xyz + C] = xy$ or $\dfrac{dC}{dz} = 0$. A potential for the vector field $\mathbf{F} = yz \, \mathbf{i} + xz \, \mathbf{j} + xy \, \mathbf{k}$ is $f(x, y, z) = xyz$, so the integral is

$$\int_C yz \, dx + xz \, dy + xy \, dz = f(1, 0, 2\pi) - f(1, 0, 0) = (1)(0)(2\pi) - (1)(0)(0) = 0,$$

where $(1, 0, 0)$ and $(1, 0, 2\pi)$ are the endpoints of C.

27. Find the work done by the force $\mathbf{F}(x, y, z) = (y + z)\mathbf{i} + (x + z)\mathbf{j} + (x + y)\mathbf{k}$ in moving an object along the curve described by $\mathbf{r}(t) = t\mathbf{i} + t^2\mathbf{j} + t^3\mathbf{k}$ from $(0, 0, 0)$ to $(1, 1, 1)$.

SOLUTION: The work is $W = \int_C \mathbf{F} \cdot d\mathbf{r}$.

This field is conservative since $\dfrac{\partial N}{\partial z} - \dfrac{\partial P}{\partial y} = 1 - 1 = 0$, $\dfrac{\partial P}{\partial x} - \dfrac{\partial M}{\partial z} = 1 - 1 = 0$, and $\dfrac{\partial N}{\partial y} - \dfrac{\partial M}{\partial x} = 1 - 1 = 0$. A potential function, $f(x, y, z)$, for which i) $\dfrac{\partial f}{\partial x} = (y + z)$, ii) $\dfrac{\partial f}{\partial y} = (x + z)$, and iii) $\dfrac{\partial f}{\partial z} = (x + y)$ is $f(x, y, z) = \int (y + z)\,dx + k(y, z) = xy + xz + k(y, z)$ where ii) $\dfrac{\partial}{\partial y}[xy + xz + k(y, z)] = x + \dfrac{\partial k(y, z)}{\partial y} = x + z$. Since $\dfrac{\partial k}{\partial y} = z$, then $k(y, z) = yz + C(z)$. Equation iii) implies that $\dfrac{\partial}{\partial z}[xy + xz + yz + C] = x + y + \dfrac{dC(z)}{dz} = x + z$ or $\dfrac{dC}{dz} = 0$. The potential is thus $f(x, y, z) = xy + yz + xz$.

Use the potential to evaluate the line integral for work

$$W = \int_C \mathbf{F} \cdot d\mathbf{r} = [xy + yz + xz]\Big|_{(0,0,0)}^{(1,1,1)} = (1 \cdot 1 + 1 \cdot 1 + 1 \cdot 1) - (0) = 3.$$

33. Evaluate $\iint_S y^2\,d\sigma$, where S is the portion of the cylinder $x^2 + y^2 = 1$ in the first octant bounded above by $z = 1$ and below by $z = 0$.

SOLUTION: S is described by $x = f(y, z) = \sqrt{1 - y^2}$ with $f_y = -y/\sqrt{1 - y^2}$ and $f_z = 0$ over the projection, R, of S on the yz-plane $R = \{(y, z) : 0 \le y \le 1, 0 \le z \le 1\}$.

$$\iint_S y^2\,d\sigma = \iint_R y^2 \sqrt{\left(\frac{-y}{\sqrt{1 - y^2}}\right)^2 + 0^2 + 1}\,dA = \int_0^1 \int_0^1 \frac{y^2}{\sqrt{1 - y^2}}\,dy\,dx.$$

Use the trigonometric substitution, $y = \sin\theta$, $dy = \cos\theta\,d\theta$ and $\sqrt{1 - y^2} = \cos\theta$ with $\theta = 0$ when $y = 0$ and $\theta = \pi/2$ when $y = 1$.

$$\int_0^1 \left(\int_0^1 \frac{y^2}{\sqrt{1 - y^2}}\,dy \right) dz = \int_0^1 \left(\int_0^{\pi/2} \frac{\sin^2\theta}{\cos\theta} \cos\theta\,d\theta \right) dz = \int_0^1 \left(\int_0^{\pi/2} \frac{1 - \cos 2\theta}{2}\,d\theta \right) dz$$

$$= \int_0^1 \left[\frac{1}{2}\theta - \frac{1}{4}\sin 2\theta \right]\Big|_{\theta=0}^{\pi/2} dz = \frac{\pi}{4}[z]\Big|_0^1 = \frac{\pi}{4}.$$

39. Determine $\displaystyle\iint_S (\sin x\, \mathbf{i} + (2 - \cos x)y\, \mathbf{j} + z\, \mathbf{k}) \cdot \mathbf{n}\, d\sigma$, where S is the parallelepiped which bounds $0 \le x \le \pi$, $0 \le y \le 2$, $0 \le z \le 1$; $\mathbf{n}$ is directed outward from S.

SOLUTION: The solid region inside S is $D = \{(x, y, z) : 0 \le x \le \pi; \ 0 \le y \le 2; \ 0 \le z \le 1\}$. By the divergence theorem,

$$\iint_S \mathbf{F} \cdot \mathbf{n}\, d\sigma = \iiint_D \operatorname{div} \mathbf{F}\, dV = \iiint_D \left(\frac{\partial}{\partial x}(\sin x) + \frac{\partial}{\partial y}\big((2 - \cos x)y\big) + \frac{\partial}{\partial z}(z) \right) dV$$

$$= \int_0^\pi \int_0^2 \int_0^1 3\, dz\, dy\, dx = 3 \int_0^\pi \int_0^2 [z]\Big|_{z=0}^1 dy\, dx$$

$$= 3 \int_0^\pi [y]\Big|_{y=0}^2 dx = 6\, [x]\Big|_0^\pi = 6\pi.$$

43. Evaluate $\displaystyle\int_C \big((y^2 - e^x)\mathbf{i} + (x^2 - \sin y)\mathbf{j} + (z^2 - \sin z)\mathbf{k}\big) \cdot d\mathbf{r}$, where C is the intersection of the paraboloid $z = x^2 + y^2$ and the plane $2x + 2y + z = 4$.

SOLUTION:

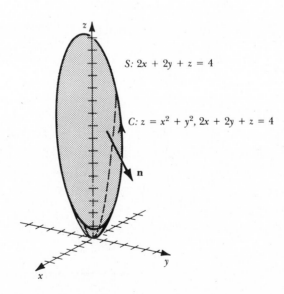

$S\colon 2x + 2y + z = 4$

$C\colon z = x^2 + y^2,\ 2x + 2y + z = 4$

$\mathbf{n}$

Let S be the part of the plane $z = f(x, y) = 4 - 2x - 2y$ whose projection onto the xy-plane lies inside the curve $x^2 + y^2 = 4 - 2x - 2y$. This curve describes the xy-coordinates of the curve of intersection of the paraboloid with the plane. The projection is obtained by completing squares; $R = \{(x, y) : (x + 1)^2 + (y + 1)^2 \le 6\}$, a disk of radius $\sqrt{6}$ centered at $(-1, 1)$.

The curl of **F** is

$$\operatorname{curl}(\mathbf{F}) = \begin{vmatrix} \mathbf{i} & \mathbf{j} & \mathbf{k} \\ \dfrac{\partial}{\partial x} & \dfrac{\partial}{\partial y} & \dfrac{\partial}{\partial z} \\ y^2 - e^x & x^2 - \sin y & z^2 - \sin z \end{vmatrix} = 0\,\mathbf{i} - 0\,\mathbf{j} + (2x - 2y)\,\mathbf{k}.$$

Apply Stokes's theorem with S as above to

$$\int_C \mathbf{F} \cdot d\mathbf{r} = \iint_S \overrightarrow{\operatorname{curl} F} \cdot \mathbf{n}\, d\sigma = \iint_R (\overrightarrow{\operatorname{curl} F}) \cdot (2\mathbf{i} + 2\mathbf{j} + \mathbf{k})\, dA$$

$$= \iint_R (0\,\mathbf{i} - 0\,\mathbf{j} + (2x - 2y)\,\mathbf{k}) \cdot (2\mathbf{i} + 2\mathbf{j} + \mathbf{k})\, dA = 2\iint_R (x - y)\, dA.$$

Since R is a disk centered at $(-1, -1)$, it is convenient to transform variables by the translation of coordinates $x = 1 + u$, $y = 1 + v$. R is mapped onto a disk in the uv-plane of radius $\sqrt{6}$ centered at $(0, 0)$. The Jacobean of the transformation is

$$J(u, v) = \left(\frac{\partial x}{\partial u}\right)\left(\frac{\partial y}{\partial v}\right) - \left(\frac{\partial y}{\partial u}\right)\left(\frac{\partial x}{\partial v}\right) = (1)(1) - (0)(0) = 1.$$

Thus, by Formula 16.49 of SECTION 16.5, the double integral above becomes

$$2\iint_R (x - y)\, dA = 2\iint_{\hat{R}} ((u - 1) - (v - 1))\,|J(u, v)|\, d\hat{A} = 2\iint_{\hat{R}} (u - v)\, d\hat{A},$$

where $d\hat{A} = du\,dv$ or $dv\,du$ depending on the order of integration.

Since $\hat{R}$ is a disk centered at the origin, it is convenient to change to polar coordinates. Then $\hat{R} = \{(r, \theta) : 0 \le \theta \le 2\pi;\ 0 \le r \le \sqrt{6}\}$ and $(\hat{u}, \hat{v})$ are replaced by $\hat{u} = r\cos\theta$, $\hat{v} = r\sin\theta$, with $d\hat{A} = r\,dr\,d\theta$. In its final form, the integral is equal to

$$\int_C \mathbf{F} \cdot d\mathbf{r} = 2\iint_{\hat{R}} (u - v)\, d\hat{A} = 2\int_0^{2\pi}\int_0^{\sqrt{6}} (r\cos\theta - r\sin\theta)r\,dr\,d\theta$$

$$= 2\int_0^{2\pi} (\cos\theta - \sin\theta)\left[\frac{r^3}{3}\right]\Bigg|_{r=0}^{\sqrt{6}} d\theta = 4\sqrt{6}\,[\sin\theta + \cos\theta]\Big|_0^{2\pi} = 0.$$

49. Use Green's theorem to find the area bounded above by one arch of the cycloid described by $x = t - \sin t$, $y = 1 - \cos t$, and below by the x-axis.

SOLUTION:

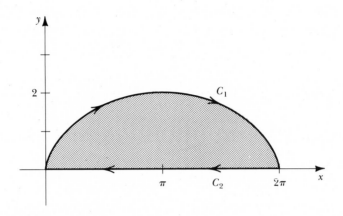

Parameterize the parts of the curve by

$C_1 : x = t - \sin t$, $y = 1 - \cos t$ for $0 \le t \le 2\pi$ with $dx = (1 - \cos t)\, dt$ and $dy = \sin t\, dt$

$C_2 : x = 4\pi - t$, $y = 0$ for $2\pi \le t \le 4\pi$ with $dx = -dt$ and $dy = 0$.

Since $C = C_1 \cup C_2$ is negatively oriented, then either of the forms $-x\, dy$ or $y\, dx$ can be used on $C_1 \cup C_2$. In general the second looks simpler, so calculate

$$A = \int_C y\, dx = \int_{C_1} y\, dx + \int_{C_2} y\, dx = \int_0^{2\pi} (1 - \cos t)(1 - \cos t)\, dt + \int_{2\pi}^{4\pi} 0(-dt)$$

$$= \int_0^{2\pi} (1 - \cos t)^2\, dt = \int_0^{2\pi} \left(\frac{3}{2} - 2\cos t + \frac{1}{2}\cos 2t \right) dt$$

$$= \left[\frac{3}{2}t - 2\sin t + \frac{1}{4}\sin 2t \right] \Big|_0^{2\pi} = 3\pi.$$

17.
Ordinary Differential Equations

Sharpening your skills

You should review the techniques of integration presented in CHAPTERS 4 and 7 and the separable differential equations presented in SECTION 6.7; these are called upon by the following practice problems.

Practice Problems

Evaluate the integrals in 1–5.

1. $\displaystyle\int \frac{1}{4 + x^2}\, dx$

2. $\displaystyle\int \frac{1 + 3u}{4 - u^2}\, du$

3. $\displaystyle\int (x^4 - x^2 y^3)\, dx$ (partial integration as in CHAPTER 15)

4. $\displaystyle\int \frac{3x^2 + 4x}{x^3 + 2x^2 + 1}\, dx$

5. $\displaystyle\int \frac{\sin^2 x}{\cos x}\, dx$

6. Find y if $\dfrac{dy}{dx} = 2x^{1/3}$.

7. Find y if $\dfrac{dy}{dx} = \dfrac{e^x + x}{\cos y}$, $y(0) = 0$.

17.1
Introduction
---

7. Verify that $y = \dfrac{Cx^2}{1 - Cx}$ is the general solution to $x^2 y' - y^2 - 2xy = 0$.

SOLUTION: Differentiate y with respect to x to obtain

$$y' = D_x \left[\frac{Cx^2}{1 - Cx} \right] = \frac{2Cx(1 - Cx) - (-C)Cx^2}{(1 - Cx)^2}$$

$$= \frac{2Cx - C^2 x^2}{(1 - Cx)^2}. \qquad \text{Thus,}$$

$$x^2 y' - y^2 - 2xy = \frac{x^2(2Cx - C^2 x^2)}{(1 - Cx)^2} - \frac{(Cx^2)^2}{(1 - Cx)^2} - \frac{2xCx^2(1 - Cx)}{(1 - Cx)^2}$$

$$= \frac{Cx^2(2x - Cx^2 - Cx^2 - 2x + 2Cx^2)}{(1 - Cx)^2} = 0.$$

Hence y is a solution for any choice of C.

13. Verify that $y = C_1 e^x + C_2 e^{-x} - x^2 - 2$ is the general solution to $y'' - y = x^2$.

SOLUTION: Differentiate y twice with respect to x to obtain $y' = D_x \left[C_1 e^x + C_2 e^{-x} - x^2 - 2 \right] = C_1 e^x - C_2 e^{-x} - 2x$ and $y'' = D_x [y'] = D_x [C_1 e^x - C_2 e^{-x} - 2x] = C_1 e^x + C_2 e^{-x} - 2$. Substitute these values for y'' and y into $y'' - y$ to obtain $y'' - y = (C_1 e^x + C_2 e^{-x} - 2) - (C_1 e^x + C_2 e^{-x} - x^2 - 2) = x^2$. Thus y and y'' solve the equation for any choices of C_1 and C_2.

17. a) Determine a first order differential equation whose solution is $y = Cx$.

   b) Find orthogonal trajectories to the curves $y = Cx$.

   c) Sketch representative graphs of the curves and of the orthogonal trajectories.

SOLUTION: **a)** Eliminate the constant C in the equation i) $y = Cx$ by differentiating once with respect to x to obtain ii) $y' = C$, then by eliminating C between i) and ii), $y' = y/x$. This is the first order differential equation whose solution is $y = Cx$.

b) The orthogonal trajectories have tangents at each point (x, y) whose slopes are negative reciprocals of the slopes of the tangents to the given curves. Since for these given curves, the slope of the tangent to the orthogonal trajectory satisfies $y' = -1/(y/x)$ or $y' = -x/y$.

This separable equation may be solved by the method of SECTION 6.7. The equivalent equation $yy' = -x$ may be integrated with respect to x to obtain $\int yy' \, dx = - \int x^2 \, dx$ or $y^2/2 = -(x^2/2) + K$.

An equivalent family of curves is $x^2 + y^2 = K$, since K is an arbitrary constant.

c) The given curves, $y = Cx$, are lines through $(0,0)$, each with slope C. The orthogonal trajectories, $x^2 + y^2 = K$, are circles centered at $(0,0)$ each with radius $\sqrt{K}$ (provided $K \geq 0$).

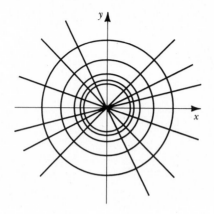

_____17.2

Homogeneous
Differential Equations

_____

3. Find the general solution to $y' = \dfrac{e^y}{y\sqrt{1 - x^2}}$.

SOLUTION: This equation is not homogeneous, but it is separable. It can be written as $ye^{-y}y' = 1/\sqrt{1 - x^2}$. Integrating this gives $\displaystyle\int ye^{-y}\,dy = \int \frac{1}{\sqrt{1 - x^2}}\,dx + C$ or $(-ye^{-y} - e^{-y}) = $ arcsin $x + C$. The general solution can be written as $y + 1 + e^y$ arcsin $x + Ce^y = 0$.

15. Find the general solution to $y' = \dfrac{y + \sqrt{x^2 + y^2}}{x}$.

SOLUTION: Care must be taken in factoring x^2 out of the term under the radical; recall that $\sqrt{x^2} = |x|$. This equation can be written as $y' = (y/x) + \frac{|x|}{x}\sqrt{1 + (y/x)^2}$, which is homogeneous in the sets where $x \neq 0$. Actually there are two equations to be solved here: $y' = (y/x) \pm \sqrt{1 + (y/x)^2}$ where the '+' sign holds for solutions where $x > 0$ and the '−' sign holds for solutions where $x < 0$.

Solve both equations by letting $v = y/x$, $y = vx$, and $y' = v + xv'$. Then the equations are $v + xv' = v \pm \sqrt{1 + v^2}$ or $v'/\sqrt{1 + v^2} = \pm 1/x$. These equations are integrated to give

$$\int \frac{dv}{\sqrt{1 + v^2}} = \pm \int \frac{1}{x}\,dx + C.$$

The integral on the left is integrated by the trigonometric substitution $v = \tan\theta$, with $dv = \sec^2\theta\,d\theta$ and $\sqrt{1 + v^2} = \sec\theta$.

$$\int \frac{dv}{\sqrt{1 + v^2}} = \int \frac{\sec^2\theta\,d\theta}{\sec\theta} = \int \sec\theta\,d\theta = \ln|\sec\theta + \tan\theta|$$

$$= \ln \left| \sqrt{1 + v^2} + v \right|.$$

Thus the solutions to these differential equations are $\ln \left| \sqrt{1 + v^2} + v \right| = \pm \ln x + C$. Resubstitute $v = y/x$ to obtain the general solution

$$\ln \left| \sqrt{1 + \frac{y^2}{x^2}} + \frac{y}{x} \right| = \pm \ln |x| + C.$$

Take the "+" sign with $x > 0$ to obtain $\sqrt{x^2 + y^2} + y = Cx^2$. Take the "−" sign with $x < 0$ to obtain $\sqrt{x^2 + y^2} - y = C$. Multiply both sides of this last equation by $\left(\sqrt{x^2 + y^2} + y \right)$ to obtain $x^2 = C \left(\sqrt{x^2 + y^2} + y \right)$, which is equivalent to the general solution in the first case.

19. Solve the initial value problem $y' = \dfrac{2x + y}{x + 2y}$, $y(1) = 1$.

SOLUTION: This differential equation is homogeneous since it can be written as $y' = \dfrac{2 + (y/x)}{1 + (2y/x)}$ for $x \ne 0$. Let $v = y/x$, with $y = vx$ and $y' = v + xv'$ to write the equation as $v + xv' = (2 + v)/(1 + 2v)$, which implies $xv' = (2 + v)/(1 + 2v) - v$ or $xv' = 2(1 - v^2)/(1 + 2v)$. This separable equation can be written as $(1 + 2v)v'/(1 - v)(1 + v) = 2/x$, which can be integrated to give

$$\int \frac{(1 + 2v)\, dv}{(1 - v)(1 + v)} = 2 \int \frac{dx}{x} + C.$$

The integrand on the left is expanded by using the partial fractions decomposition,

$$\frac{1 + 2v}{(1 - v)(1 + v)} = \frac{3/2}{(1 - v)} + \frac{-1/2}{(1 + v)}.$$

The integrals can be written as

$$\frac{3}{2} \int \frac{dv}{(1 - v)} - \frac{1}{2} \int \frac{dv}{(1 + v)} = 2 \int \frac{dx}{x} + C \quad \text{or}$$

$$-\frac{3}{2} \ln |1 - v| - \frac{1}{2} \ln |1 + v| = 2 \ln |x| + C.$$

The logarithms can be rearranged to yield $x^4(1 - v)^3(1 + v) = C$, where C is an arbitrary constant. Replace v with y/x and simplify to obtain $(x - y)^3(x + y) = C$.

Determine the particular solution which satisfies the initial condition $y(1) = 1$ by substituting $x = 1$ and $y = 1$ into the general solution and solving for C; $(1 - 1)^3(1 + 1) = C$ implies that $C = 0$. The particular (implicit) solution is $(x - y)^3(x + y) = 0$. Both $y = x$ and $y = -x$ satisfy this equation, but only $y = x$ solves the initial condition.

The solution to this initial value problem is $y = x$.

23. Find the general solution to the differential equation

$$y' = \frac{2x + y + 2}{x + 2y - 1}$$

by first making a substitution $x = u - a$ and $y = w - b$ where u and w are variables and a and b are appropriate constants. Then let $v = w/u$ and obtain a separable equation.

SOLUTION: When the suggested substitution is made with $\dfrac{dy}{dx} = \dfrac{dy}{dw} \cdot \dfrac{dw}{du} \cdot \dfrac{du}{dx} = (1)\dfrac{dw}{du}(1)$, the equation becomes

$$\frac{dw}{du} = \frac{2(u - a) + (w - b) + 2}{(u - a) + 2(w - b) - 1} = \frac{2u + w - (2a + b - 2)}{u + 2w - (a + 2b + 1)}.$$

This equation is homogeneous (in u and w) if a and b are chosen so that   i) $2a + b = 2$ and   ii) $a + 2b = -1$. This system of linear equations has the solution $a = 5/3$, $b = -4/3$ so with these values the equation becomes

$$\frac{dw}{du} = \frac{2u + w}{u + 2w}.$$

Notice that this is the same differential equation as was solved in EXERCISE 19 (with u and w in place of x and y), so its general solution is $(u - w)^3(u + w) = C$.

Resubstitute $u = x + (5/3)$ and $w = y - (4/3)$ to obtain the general solution

$$(x - y + 3)^3(x + y + 1/3) = C.$$

_____**17.3**

Exact Differential Equations

5. Determine whether the equation $y' = \dfrac{x^3 - xy^4}{2x^2y^3 + 5}$ is exact and, if so, solve it.

SOLUTION: Rewrite the equation as $(x^3 - xy^4)\, dx - (2x^2y^3 + 5)\, dy = 0$. Then $\dfrac{\partial}{\partial y}(x^3 - xy^4) = -4xy^3$ and $\dfrac{\partial}{\partial x}(-2x^2y^3 + 5) = -4xy^3$, so the equation is exact everywhere.

If the general solution has the form $u(x, y) = C$, then $\dfrac{\partial u}{\partial x} = (x^3 - xy^4)$ implies that $u(x, y) = \int(x^3 - xy^4)\, dx + C(y) = \dfrac{x^4}{4} - \dfrac{x^2y^4}{2} + C(y)$. The condition $\dfrac{\partial u}{\partial y} = -(2x^2y^3 + 5)$ implies that

$$\frac{\partial}{\partial y}\left[\frac{x^4}{4} - \frac{x^2 y^4}{2} + C(y)\right] = -(2x^2 y^3 + 5) \text{ or } \frac{dC}{dy} = -5 \text{ so } C(y) = -5y. \text{ Thus the general solution}$$

is $\dfrac{x^4}{4} - \dfrac{x^2 y^4}{2} - 5y = C$.

9. Determine whether the equation $y\,dx + dy = 0$ is exact and, if so, solve it.

SOLUTION: Since $\dfrac{\partial}{\partial y}(y) = 1$ and $\dfrac{\partial}{\partial x}(1) = 0$, this equation is not exact and cannot be solved as an exact equation.

17. Solve the initial value problem $\sin x \sin y\,dx - \cos x \cos y\,dy = 0$, $y(\pi/4) = \pi/2$.

SOLUTION: Since $\dfrac{\partial}{\partial y}(\sin x \sin y) = \sin x \cos y$ and $\dfrac{\partial}{\partial x}(-\cos x \cos y) = \sin x \cos y$, then the equation is exact.

If the general solution is written as $u(x,y) = C$, then   i) $\dfrac{\partial u}{\partial x} = \sin x \sin y$ and ii) $\dfrac{\partial u}{\partial y} = -\cos x \cos y$. Equation i) implies $u(x,y) = \int \sin x \sin y\,dx + C(y) = -\cos x \sin y + C(y)$. Equation ii) implies $\dfrac{\partial}{\partial y}[-\cos x \sin y + C(y)] = -\cos x \cos y$ or $\dfrac{dC}{dy} = 0$. Taking $C(y) = 0$, the general solution is $-\cos x \sin y = C$.

The initial condition, $y = \pi/2$ when $x = \pi/4$, implies that $-(\cos(\pi/4))(\sin(\pi/2)) = C$ or $C = -\sqrt{2}/2$. The particular solution for this initial value problem is $\cos x \sin y = \sqrt{2}/2$.

25. a) Change the equation $5x^2 y\,dx + (x^3 + y)\,dy = 0$ to an exact equation by multiplying by an integrating factor as described in EXERCISE 21 or 22 as appropriate. b) Solve the resulting equation and verify that the solution also satisfies the given equation.

SOLUTION: a) With $M(x,y) = 6x^2 y$ and $N(x,y) = x^3 + y$, then $N_x = 3x^2$ and $M_y = 6x^2$, so $N_x - M_y = -3x^2 = -\dfrac{1}{2y}M$ or, as in EXERCISE 21, $\dfrac{N_x - M_y}{M} = -\dfrac{1}{2y}$, a function of y alone. An integrating factor is thus

$$I(y) = \exp \int -\frac{1}{2y}\,dy = \exp\left(-\frac{1}{2}\ln|y|\right) = y^{-1/2} \quad \text{if } y > 0.$$

Multiplying through by $y^{-1/2}$, the equation

$$6x^2 y^{1/2}\,dx + (x^3 y^{-1/2} + y^{1/2})\,dy = 0 \quad \text{is exact,}$$

$$\text{since} \quad \frac{\partial}{\partial y}\left(6x^2 y^{1/2}\right) = 3x^2 y^{-1/2} \quad \text{and}$$

$$\frac{\partial}{\partial x}\left(x^3 y^{-1/2} + y^{1/2}\right) = 3x^2 y^{-1/2}.$$

b) The general solution, $u(x, y) = C$, satisfies i) $\dfrac{\partial u}{\partial x} = 6x^2 y^{1/2}$ and ii) $\dfrac{\partial u}{\partial y} = x^3 y^{-1/2} + y^{1/2}$. By

i), $u(x, y) = \int 6x^2 y^{1/2}\, dx + C(y) = 2x^3 y^{1/2} + C(y)$. By ii), $\dfrac{\partial}{\partial y}\left[2x^3 y^{1/2} + C(y)\right] = x^3 y^{-1/2} + y^{1/2}$

or $\dfrac{dC}{dy} = y^{1/2}$. Thus $C(y) = \frac{2}{3} y^{3/2}$ so the general solution is $u(x, y) = 2x^3 y^{1/2} + (2/3)y^{3/2} = C$.

This equation can be put into the form $y(3x^3 + y)^2 = C$. To verify this general solution, use implicit differentiation:

$$y'(3x^3 + y)^2 + 2y(3x^3 + y)(9x^2 + y') = 0,$$

or for $(3x^3 + y) \neq 0$, divide by $3(3x^3 + y)$ and rewrite the equation as $(x^3 + y)y' + 6x^2 y = 0$. Notice that $y = -3x^3$ is also a solution; thus the general solution is $y(3x^3 + 2)^2 = C$.

_____17.4

Linear First-Order Differential Equations

3. Find the general solution to $y' + 3y = xe^{-x}$.

SOLUTION: This first-order linear equation has coefficients of y' equal to 1, so with $P(x) = 3$, the integrating factor is $I(x) = \exp\left(\int P(x)\, dx\right) = \exp\left(\int 3\, dx\right) = e^{3x}$. After multiplying through by e^{3x}, the equation becomes $e^{3x}y' + 3e^{3x}y = xe^{3x}e^{-x}$. The left hand side is the derivative of a product, so this equation is $D_x\left[e^{3x}y\right] = xe^{2x}$ or on integrating, $e^{3x}y = \int xe^{2x}\, dx + C$. Integrate by parts with $u = x$, $dv = e^{2x}$, $du = dx$, and $v = \frac{1}{2}e^{2x}$ to obtain $e^{3x}y = (x/2)e^{2x} - (1/4)e^{2x} + C$. The general solution is thus $y = \dfrac{x}{2}e^{-x} - \dfrac{1}{4}e^{-x} + Ce^{-3x}$.

15. Find the general solution to $(x^2 + x)y' + (2x + 1)y = x^2 - 1$.

SOLUTION: This first-order linear equation must be divided by $(x^2 + x)$ to put it into the form where the integrating factor can be identified:

$$y' + \frac{2x + 1}{x^2 + x}y = \frac{x^2 - 1}{x^2 + x}.$$

In this form, $P(x) = \dfrac{2x + 1}{x^2 + x}$ so the integrating factor is

$$I(x) = \exp \int \frac{2x + 1}{x^2 + x}\, dx = \exp\left(\ln\left|x^2 + x\right|\right) = x^2 + x.$$

After multiplying by the factor the equation becomes $(x^2 + x)y' + (2x + 1)y = x^2 - 1$. The left hand side is the derivative of a product so the equation can be rewritten as $D_x\left[(x^2 + x)y\right] = x^2 - 1$, which can be integrated $(x^2 + x)y = \int (x^2 - 1)\,dx + C$ to obtain $(x^2 + x)y = x^3/3 - x + C$. The general solution is thus $y = \dfrac{x^3 - 3x + C}{3(x^2 + x)}$.

COMMENT: The differential equation in EXERCISE 15 is exact as it stands and could have been integrated directly.

19. Find a general solution to $y' + \dfrac{y}{x} = \dfrac{y^2}{x}$.

SOLUTION: This Bernoulli equation can be converted to a linear equation by first dividing through by the power of y on the right hand side to obtain $(y^{-2})y' + (1/x)y^{-1} = (1/x)$. Next let $w = y^{-1}$. Since $w' = -y^{-2}y'$, replace $y^{-2}y'$ by $-w'$ and y^{-1} by w to obtain the linear equation $-w' + (1/x)w = (1/x)$ or better $w' - (1/x)w = -1/x$.

Multiplication by the integrating factor $I(x) = \exp\left(\int -\frac{1}{x}\,dx\right) = \exp\left(-\ln x\right) = 1/x$ gives the equation $(1/x)w' - (1/x^2)w = -1/x^2$ or $D_x\left[(1/x)w\right] = -1/x^2$. Integrate both sides to obtain $(1/x)w = (1/x) + C$ or $w = 1 + Cx$. Substitute $w = 1/y$ to get the general solution to this problem.

$$\frac{1}{y} = 1 + Cx \qquad \text{or} \qquad y = \frac{1}{1 + Cx}.$$

23. An exhaust fan is turned on in a 16,000-ft^3 smoke-filled room with a carbon dioxide content of 0.25%. The fan brings in air with a carbon dioxide content of 0.05% at the rate of 300 ft^3/min and the uniformly mixed air leaves the room at the same rate. Assuming that no additional carbon dioxide is being produced in the room, how long does it take for the level of carbon dioxide to reach 0.15%?

SOLUTION:

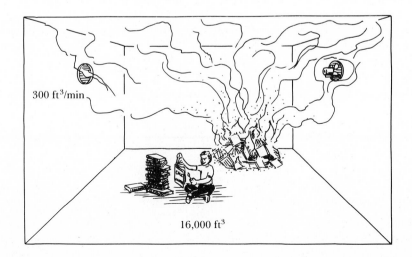

300 ft^3/min

16,000 ft^3

Let $A(t)$ be the amount of CO_2 at time t (in ft^3 carbon dioxide). As air is being vented by the fan this amount is changing at a rate equal to the difference in the rates of change of the amount of CO_2 in the incoming air and of the amount in the exhausted air. The incoming CO_2 is increasing at a rate of $(300\,ft^3\,air/min)$ times $(0.0005\,ft^3 CO_2/ft^3\,air)$ while the outgoing air is decreasing the amount of CO_2 at the rate of $(300\,ft^3\,air/min)$ times $(A\,ft^3 CO_2/16{,}000\,ft^3\,air)$. The differential equation describing $A(t)$ is thus $\dfrac{dA}{dt} = \dfrac{3}{20} - \dfrac{3}{160}A$ with the condition that $A(0) = (2.5 \times 10^{-3}) \times (1.6 \times 10^4) = 40\,ft^3$, the amount in the room when the fan was turned on.

The problem is to determine the time $\hat{t}$ when $A(\hat{t}) = (1.5 \times 10^{-3})(1.6 \times 10^4) = 24\,ft^3$, that is, when the concentration reaches 0.15%. To do this, solve the initial value problem

$$\frac{dA}{dt} + \frac{3}{160}A = \frac{3}{20}, \qquad A(0) = 40$$

for $A(t)$, then solve the equation $A(\hat{t}) = 24$ for $\hat{t}$.

The first-order linear differential equation above has the integrating factor $I(t) = \exp\left(\int (3/160)\,dt\right) = e^{3t/160}$. Multiplication by this factor gives

$$e^{3t/160}\frac{dA}{dt} + \frac{3}{160}e^{3t/160}A = \frac{3}{20}e^{3t/160},$$

or equivalently $D_t\left[e^{3t/160}A\right] = \frac{3}{20}e^{3t/160}$. This is integrated to give $e^{3t/160}A(t) = 8e^{3t/160} + C_0$, where C_0 is arbitrary. $A(t) = 8 + C_0 e^{-3t/160}$ is the general solution. The initial condition is applied, $40 = A(0) = 8 + C_0$, to imply that $C_0 = 32$. The amount of CO_2 in the room at time t is thus $A(t) = 8 + 32e^{-3t/160}$.

To determine when the concentration reaches 0.15% (that is, when $A = 24$) solve the equation $24 = A(\hat{t}) = 8 + 32e^{-3\hat{t}/160}$ for $\hat{t}$; $e^{-3\hat{t}/160} = \dfrac{24 - 8}{32}$ implies that $\hat{t} = -\dfrac{160}{3}\ln\left(\dfrac{1}{2}\right) = \dfrac{160}{3}\ln 2$. It will take $\hat{t} \approx 36\,min\,58\,sec$ to reduce the CO_2 to a concentration of 0.15%.

29. A particular solution to the Ricatti equation $y' = x^2 + y^2 - 2xy + 1$ is $y_1(x) = x$. Use the method described in EXERCISE 28 to find a solution satisfying $y(2) = 1$.

SOLUTION: Put the Ricatti equation into the form $y' = (1)y^2 + (-2x)y + (1 + x^2)$ to identify the data $P(x) = 1$, $Q(x) = -2x$, $R(x) = 1 + x^2$ and the given particular solution $y_1 = x$. The linear equation referred to in EXERCISE 28 to be solved for v is thus $v' + [(-2x) + 2(1)(x)]\,v = -1$ or $v' = -1$. This is integrated directly and has the general solution $v(x) = -x + C$. Thus the function of the form $y = y_1 + \dfrac{1}{v} = x + \dfrac{1}{C - x}$ also solves the Riccati equation. The constant C is determined by the initial condition; $1 = y(2) = 2 + \dfrac{1}{C - 2}$ implies that $C - 2 = -1$ or $C = 1$.

The solution to this problem is $y = x + \dfrac{1}{1 - x}$.

_____**17.5**

Second-Order Linear Equations: Homogeneous Type

3. Find the general solution to $y'' + 6y' + 9y = 0$.

SOLUTION: If $y = e^{mx}$ is a solution, then m solves the characteristic equation $m^2 + 6m + 9 = 0$. This factors as $(m+3)^2 = 0$ so $m = -3$ is a double root as in case II in the text. According to Formula 17.18, the general solution in this case is $y(x) = C_1 e^{-3x} + C_2 x e^{-3x}$.

7. Find the general solution to $y'' - 2y' + 5y = 0$.

SOLUTION: If $y = e^{mx}$ is a solution, then m satisfies $m^2 - 2m + 5 = 0$. By the quadratic formula, $m = (2 \pm \sqrt{4 - (4)5})/2 = 1 \pm 2i$, so this equation has complex roots with real part $r = 1$ and imaginary part $s = 2$. From Formula 17.19 the general solution is $y(x) = e^x [K_1 \cos(2x) + K_2 \sin(2x)]$.

9. Find the general solution to $y'' - 2y' = 0$.

SOLUTION: If $y = e^{mx}$ is a solution, then m satisfies $m^2 - 2m = 0$. This factors as $m(m-2) = 0$ and has real distinct roots $m = 0$, $m = 2$. According to Formula 17.17, Case I, the general solution is $y(x) = C_1 e^{0x} + C_2 e^{2x} = C_1 + C_2 e^{2x}$.

27. Find the general solution to $y''' - y'' + y' - y = 0$

SOLUTION: If $y = e^{mx}$ is a solution, then m satisfies $m^3 - m^2 + m - 1 = 0$ or $(m^2 + 1)(m - 1) = 0$. One root is the real root $m_1 = 1$ while the other two are the complex pairs with real part 0 and imaginary part 1. The general solution contains a term e^x corresponding to the root $m = 1$ and terms $e^{0x} \cos x$ and $e^{0x} \sin x$ corresponding to the complex roots. The general solution is

$$y(x) = C_1 e^x + [K_1 \cos x + K_2 \sin x].$$

31. Find the particular solution to the initial value problem $y'' + 6y' + 13y = 0$, $y(0) = 1$, $y'(0) = 0$.

SOLUTION: If $y = e^{mx}$ is a solution, then m satisfies $m^2 + 6m + 13 = 0$ or $m = (-6 \pm \sqrt{36 - 52})/2 = -3 \pm 2i$. According to Formula 17.19 the general solution is

$$y(x) = e^{-3x} [K_1 \cos(2x) + K_2 \sin(2x)] \quad \text{with}$$

$$y'(x) = e^{-3x}\left[(-3K_1 + 2K_2)\cos(2x) + (-2K_1 - 3K_2)\sin(2x)\right],$$

by the product rule.

The initial conditions imply that i) $(y(0) =)$ $e^0\left[K_1\cos(0) + K_2\sin(0)\right] = 1$ or $K_1 = 1$ and ii) $(y'(0) =)$ $e^0\left[(-3K_1 + 2K_2)\cos(0) + (-2K_1 - 3K_2)\sin(0)\right] = 0$ or $-3K_1 + 2K_2 = 0$. With $K_1 = 1$ and $K_2 = 3/2$, the particular solution is

$$y(x) = e^{-3x}\left[\cos(2x) + \frac{3}{2}\sin(2x)\right].$$

35. Find the particular solution to $y''' - 7y' + 6y = 0$, where $y(0) = 1$, $y'(0) = 0$, and $y''(0) = 0$.

SOLUTION: If $y = e^{mx}$ is a solution, then m satisfies $m^3 - 7m + 6 = 0$. Try $m = 2$ as a root; then, by long division this factors as $(m - 2)(m^2 + 2m - 3) = 0$ or $(m - 2)(m + 3)(m - 1) = 0$. Thus there are three distinct real roots $m = 1, 2, -3$, each corresponding to a solution to the differential equation $y = e^{mx}$. The general solution is thus $y(x) = C_1 e^x + C_2 e^{2x} + C_3 e^{-3x}$. The derivatives are $y'(x) = C_1 e^x + 2C_2 e^{2x} - 3C_3 e^{-3x}$ and $y''(x) = C_1 e^x + 4C_2 e^{2x} + 9C_3 e^{-3x}$, so the initial conditions are

$$
\begin{aligned}
(y(0) =) \quad & C_1 + C_2 + C_3 = 1 \\
(y'(0) =) \quad & C_1 + 2C_2 - 3C_3 = 0 \\
(y''(0) =) \quad & C_1 + 4C_2 + 9C_3 = 0.
\end{aligned}
$$

The solution to this system of linear equations is $C_1 = \frac{3}{2}$, $C_2 = -\frac{3}{5}$, and $C_3 = \frac{1}{10}$; thus the solution is

$$y(x) = \frac{3}{2}e^x - \frac{3}{5}e^{2x} + \frac{1}{10}e^{-3x}.$$

37. Find the particular solution to the boundary value problem $y'' + y = 0$, where $y(0) = 1$ and $y(\pi/2) = -1$.

SOLUTION: The characteristic equation $m^2 + 1 = 0$ has complex roots $m = \pm i$ with real part 0 and imaginary parts ± 1. The general solution is thus $y(x) = e^{0x}\left[K_1\cos(1x) + K_2\sin(1x)\right]$ or $y(x) = K_1\cos x + K_2\sin x$.

The boundary conditions imply that i) $(y(0) =)$ $K_1\cos(0) + K_2\sin(0) = 1$ or $K_1 = 1$ and ii) $(y(\pi/2) =)$ $K_1\cos(\pi/2) + K_2\sin(\pi/2) = -1$ or $K_2 = -1$.

The particular solution to this boundary value problem is $y(x) = \cos x - \sin x$.

51. Find an expression for the motion of the vibrating system described by the initial value problem $my''(t) + cy'(t) + ky(t) = 0$, $y(0) = y_0$, $y'(0) = y_0'$ where $m = 1$, $k = 16$, $c = 4$, $y_0 = 0$ and $y_0' = 1$.

SOLUTION: The initial value problem is $y'' + 4y' + 16y = 0$, $y(0) = 0$, $y'(0) = 1$. The characteristic equation, $m^2 + 4m + 16 = 0$, has roots $m = (-4 \pm \sqrt{16 - 64})/2 = -2 \pm (2\sqrt{3})i$.

The general solution is thus $y(t) = e^{-2t} \left[K_1 \cos(2\sqrt{3}t) + K_2 \sin(2\sqrt{3}t) \right]$ with
$y'(t) = e^{-2t} \left[(-2K_1 + 2\sqrt{3}K_2) \cos(2\sqrt{3}t) + (-2\sqrt{3}K_1 - 2K_2) \sin(2\sqrt{3}t) \right]$.
The initial conditions imply that

i) $(y(0) =) e^0 \left[K_1 \cos(0) + K_2 \sin(0) \right] = 0$ or $K_1 = 0$ and

ii) $(y'(0) =) e^0 \left[(-2K_1 + 2\sqrt{3}K_2) \cos(0) + (-2\sqrt{3}K_1 - 2K_2) \sin(0) \right] = 1$ or

$$-2K_1 + 2\sqrt{3}K_2 = 1.$$

Thus $K_1 = 0$ and $K_2 = \sqrt{3}/6$ are the values of the constants. The motion of the system is described by $y(t) = \dfrac{\sqrt{3}}{6} e^{-2t} \sin\left(2\sqrt{3}\,t\right)$.

_____**17.6**

Second-Order Linear Equations: Nonhomogeneous Type

COMMENT: A <u>strategy</u> for solving nonhomogeneous linear equations is to   i) Find the general solution to the homogeneous problem (with the right hand side set equal to zero). ii) Use either the method of variation of parameters or the method of undetermined coefficients to find a particular solution to the given nonhomogeneous equation.   iii) Write the general solution as the sum of the solutions to parts i) and ii).   iv) Use initial or boundary conditions, if any, to determine the coefficients in the general solution.

5. Solve $y'' + y = \tan x$ by using the method of variation of parameters.

SOLUTION: The homogeneous equation $y'' + y = 0$ has characteristic equation $m^2 + 1 = 0$ with complex roots $m = \pm i$. The general solution to this homogeneous problem is, by formula 17.19, $y(x) = K_1 \cos x + K_2 \sin x$.
In the method of variation of parameters, seek a particular solution to the nonhomogeneous equation of the form $y_p(x) = u_1(x) \cos x + u_2(x) \sin x$, where the functions u_1 and u_2 satisfy Formula 17.24,

$$u_1'(x) \cos x + u_2'(x) \sin x = 0,$$

and Formula 17.27,

$$u_1'(x) \left(D_x \left[\cos x \right] \right) + u_2'(x) \left(D_x \left[\sin x \right] \right) = \tan x \qquad \text{or}$$
$$u_1'(x)(-\sin x) + u_2'(x)(\cos x) = \tan x.$$

The solutions to this system of equations for u_1' and u_2' are given by Formulas 17.28 and 17.29 as

$$u_1' = \frac{\tan x (\sin x)}{(-\sin x)(\sin x) - (\cos x)(\cos x)} = -\frac{\sin^2 x}{\cos x} \quad \text{and}$$

$$u_2' = \frac{-\tan x (\cos x)}{(-\sin x)(\sin x) - (\cos x)(\cos x)} = \sin x.$$

The functions u_1 and u_2 are determined by integration;

$$u_1(x) = -\int \frac{\sin^2 x}{\cos x}\, dx = \int (\cos x - \sec x)\, dx$$

$$= \sin x - \ln|\sec x + \tan x| \quad \text{and}$$

$$u_2(x) = \int \sin x\, dx = -\cos x.$$

Thus a particular solution is $y_p(x) = (\sin x - \ln|\sec x + \tan x|)\cos x + (-\cos x)\sin x$ or $y_p(x) = -\cos x \ln|\sec x + \tan x|$.

The general solution is thus $y(x) = K_1 \cos x + K_2 \sin x - \cos x \ln|\sec x + \tan x|$.

COMMENT: 1) In applying the method of variation of parameters to the equation $Ay'' + By' + Cy = F(x)$, it is crucial to first divide by A and write the equation as $y'' + (B/A)y' + (C/A)y = F(x)/A$. The term $F(x)/A$ then becomes the $Q(x)$ used in the text.

2) It is good practice to use Equations 17.24 and 17.27 to determine u_1' and u_2': $u_1'(y_1) + u_2'(y_2) = 0$ and $u_1'(y_1') + u_2'(y_2') = Q(x)$. This system of equations is both easy to remember and easy to solve; whereas Formulas 17.28 and 17.29 to compute u_1' and u_2' directly may be complicated to remember and to use.

13. Solve the differential equation $y'' + 3y' - 4y = \sin x$ by using the method of undetermined coefficients.

SOLUTION: The homogeneous equation $y'' + 3y' - 4y = 0$ has characteristic equation $m^2 + 3m - 4 = 0$ with roots $m = -4$ and $m = 1$. The general solution to this homogeneous problem is $y(x) = C_1 e^{-4x} + C_2 e^x$.

The right-hand side term of the nonhomogeneous problem, $\sin x$, does not occur as part of the solution to the homogeneous problem, so a trial particular solution is $y_p(x) = A\sin x + B\cos x$ with $y_p'(x) = -B\sin x + A\cos x$ and $y_p''(x) = -A\sin x - B\cos x$. The coefficients A and B are determined so as to solve the equation $y_p'' + 3y_p' - 4y_p = \sin x$. Thus

$$(-A\sin x - B\cos x) + 3(-B\sin x + A\cos x) - 4(A\sin x + B\cos x) = \sin x$$

$$\text{or} \quad (-5A - 3B)\sin x + (-5B + 3A)\cos x = \sin x.$$

This implies that i) $(-5A - 3B) = 1$ and ii) $(3A - 5B) = 0$, so $A = -5/34$ and $B = -3/34$. The particular solution is $y_p(x) = -\frac{3}{34}\sin x - \frac{5}{34}\cos x$.

The general solution is thus

$$y(x) = C_1 e^{-4x} + C_2 e^x - \frac{5}{34}\sin x - \frac{3}{34}\cos x.$$

19. Solve the initial value problem $y'' + y' - 2y = 2x^2 - 3 \quad y(0) = 0, \, y'(0) = 0$.

SOLUTION: The homogeneous equation $y'' + y' - 2y = 0$ has characteristic equation $m^2 + m - 2 = 0$ with roots $m = -2$ and $m = 1$. Its general solution is $y(x) = C_1 e^{-2x} + C_2 e^x$.

No part of the right-hand side function, $2x^2 - 3$, appears in the solution to the homogeneous problem. Both terms in this function correspond to the repeated exponent 0, so the trial solution must contain all powers of x through the second; $y_p = Ax^2 + Bx + C$ with $y_p' = 2Ax + B$ and $y_p'' = 2A$. A, B, and C are determined by the equation $y_p'' + y_p' - 2y_p = 2x^2 - 3$. Thus

$$(2A) + (2Ax + B) - 2(Ax^2 + Bx + C) = 2x^2 - 3 \quad \text{or}$$
$$(-2A)x^2 + (2A - 2B)x + (2A + B - 2C) = (2)x^2 + (0)x + (-3).$$

This implies that i) $-2A = 2$, ii) $2A - 2B = 0$ and iii) $2A + B - 2C = -3$ from which it follows that $A = -1$, $B = -1$, and $C = 0$. A particular solution is $y_p(x) = -x^2 - x$.

The general solution is $y(x) = C_1 e^{-2x} + C_2 e^x - x^2 - x$ with $y'(x) = -2C_1 e^{2x} + C_2 e^{-x} - 2x - 1$. The initial conditions imply that i) $(y(0) =) \, C_1 e^0 + C_2 e^0 - 0 = 0$ or $C_1 + C_2 = 0$ and ii) $(y'(0) =) - 2C_1 e^0 + C_2 e^0 - 1 = 0$ or $-2C_1 + C_2 = 1$. The solution to this system of equations is $C_1 = -1/3$ and $C_2 = 1/3$, so the solution to the initial value problem is

$$y(x) = -\frac{1}{3}e^{-2x} + \frac{1}{3}e^x - x^2 - x.$$

25. Find an expression for the motion of the vibrating system described by the initial value problem $my''(t) + cy'(t) + ky(t) = F(t) \quad y(0) = y_0, \, y'(0) = y_0'$, where $m = 1$, $k = 16$, $c = 0$, $F(t) = \sin 4t$, $y_0 = 0$, $y_0' = 0$.

SOLUTION: The initial value problem to be solved is $y'' + 16y = \sin 4t$, $y(0) = 0$, $y'(0) = 0$. The homogeneous equation $y'' + 16y = 0$ has complex roots $m = \pm 4i$ to its characteristic equation $m^2 + 16 = 0$, so its general solution is $y(t) = C_1 \cos 4t + C_2 \sin 4t$.

Since the right-hand side term $\sin 4t$ appears in the solution to the homogeneous problem, then try $y_p(t) = At \cos 4t + Bt \sin 4t$ as a particular solution. Its derivatives $y_p'(t) = (A + 4Bt)\cos 4t + (B - 4At)\sin 4t$ and $y_p''(t) = (8B - 16At)\cos 4t + (-8A - 16Bt)\sin 4t$ satisfy the nonhomogeneous equation $y_p'' + 16y_p = \sin 4t$, so

$$[(8B - 16At)\cos 4t + (-8A - 16Bt)\sin 4t] + 16[At\cos 4t + Bt\sin 4t] = \sin 4t$$

or $(8B)\cos 4t + (-8A)\sin 4t = (0)\cos 4t + (1)\sin 4t.$

Thus $8B = 0$ and $-8A = 1$ or $A = -1/8$ and $B = 0$. The particular solution is $y_p(t) = -(1/8)t\cos 4t.$

The general solution is $y(t) = K_1\cos(4t) + K_2\sin(4t) - \frac{1}{8}t\cos(4t)$ with $y'(t) = -4K_1\sin(4t) + 4K_2\cos(4t) - \frac{1}{8}\cos(4t) + \frac{1}{2}t\sin(4t)$. The initial conditions are i) $(y(0) =) K_1\cos(0) + K_2\sin(0) - \frac{1}{8}(0) = 0$ or $K_1 = 0$ and ii) $(y'(0) =) (4K_2 - \frac{1}{8})\cos(0) - 4K_1\sin(0) - \frac{1}{2}(0) = 0$ or $4K_2 = \frac{1}{8}$. The constants are $K_1 = 0$ and $K_2 = \frac{1}{32}$. The motion of this vibrating system is given by $y(t) = \frac{1}{32}\sin(4t) - \frac{1}{8}t\cos(4t).$

17.7
Numerical Methods for First-Order Initial Value Problems

---

5. Approximate the solution to the initial value problem $y' = \left(\frac{y}{x}\right)^2 + \left(\frac{y}{x}\right)$, $y(1) = 1$ on the interval $[1,2]$ with $h = 0.1$

   a) using Euler's Method, b) using the Modified Euler's Method and c) using the Runge-Kutta Method.

SOLUTION: a) Apply Euler's Method with $f(x,y) = \left(\frac{y}{x}\right)^2 + \left(\frac{y}{x}\right)$, $x_i = 1 + i(0.1)$, $w_0 = 1.0$ and

$$w_i = w_{i-1} + h\,f(x_{i-1}, w_{i-1}) = w_{i-1} + h\left(\left(\frac{w_{i-1}}{x_{i-1}}\right)^2 + \left(\frac{w_{i-1}}{x_{i-1}}\right)\right)$$

$$= \left(1 + \frac{h}{x_{i-1}}\right)w_{i-1} + \frac{h}{(x_{i-1})^2}w_{i-1}^2.$$

Since $h = 0.1$ and $x_{i-1} = 1 + (i-1)(0.1)$, then

$$w_i = \frac{1 + 0.1i}{1 + 0.1(i-1)}w_{i-1} + \frac{0.1}{(1 + 0.1(i-1))^2}w_{i-1}^2.$$

The approximations generated by this formula are tabulated.

x_i	1.0	1.1	1.2	1.3	1.4	
w_i	1.00000	1.20000	1.42810	1.68874	1.987388	

x_i	1.5	1.6	1.7	1.8	1.9	2.0
w_i	2.33086	2.72771	3.18884	3.72827	4.36441	5.12177

b) Apply the Modified Euler's Method with x_i, f and h as before and with

$$w_0 = 1 \quad \text{and}$$

$$w_i = w_{i-1} + \frac{h}{2}\left(f\left(x_{i-1}, w_{i-1}\right) + f\left(x_i, w_{i-1} + hf\left(x_{i-1}, w_{i-1}\right)\right)\right)$$

$$= w_{i-1} + \frac{h}{2}\left[\left(\frac{w_{i-1}}{x_{i-1}}\right)^2 + \left(\frac{w_{i-1}}{x_{i-1}}\right) + \left(\frac{w_{i-1} + h\left[\left(\frac{w_{i-1}}{x_{i-1}}\right)^2 + \left(\frac{w_{i-1}}{x_{i-1}}\right)\right]}{x_{i-1}}\right)^2\right.$$

$$\left. + \left(\frac{w_{i-1} + h\left[\left(\frac{w_{i-1}}{x_{i-1}}\right)^2 + \left(\frac{w_{i-1}}{x_{i-1}}\right)\right]}{x_{i-1}}\right)\right].$$

The approximations generated by this formula are tabulated.

x_i	1.0	1.1	1.2	1.3	1.4
w_i	1.00000	1.21405	1.46302	1.75389	2.09572

x_i	1.5	1.6	1.7	1.9	2.0
w_i	2.50044	2.984155	3.56901	5.18200	6.32554

c) Apply the Runge-Kutta method with $w_0 = 1$ and for each i

$$k_1 = hf(x_{i-1}, w_{i-1}) = h\left[\left(\frac{w_{i-1}}{x_{i-1}}\right)^2 + \left(\frac{w_{i-1}}{x_{i-1}}\right)\right]$$

$$k_2 = hf\left(x_{i-1} + \frac{h}{2}, w_{i-1} + \frac{k_1}{2}\right) = h\left[\left(\frac{w_{i-1} + (k_1/2)}{x_{i-1} + (h/2)}\right)^2 + \left(\frac{w_{i-1} + (k_1/2)}{x_{i-1} + (h/2)}\right)\right]$$

$$k_3 = hf\left(x_{i-1} + \frac{h}{2}, w_{i-1} + \frac{k_2}{2}\right)$$

$$= h\left[\left(\frac{w_{i-1} + (k_2/2)}{x_{i-1} + (h/2)}\right)^2 + \left(\frac{w_{i-1} + (k_2/2)}{x_{i-1} + (h/2)}\right)\right]$$

$$k_4 = hf(x_i, w_{i-1} + k_3) = h\left[\left(\frac{w_{i-1} + k_3}{x_i}\right)^2 + \left(\frac{w_{i-1} + k_3}{x_i}\right)\right].$$

and

$$w_i = \frac{w_{i-1} + (k_1 + 2k_2 + 2k_3 + k_4)}{6}.$$

The approximations generated by this formula are tabulated.

x_i	1.0	1.1	1.2	1.3	1.4	1.5
w_i	1.00000	1.21588	1.46755	1.76236	2.10989	2.52291

x_i	1.6	1.7	1.8	1.9	2.0	
w_i	3.01877	3.62169	4.36640	5.30468	6.51711	

15. Determine the exact solution to $y' = \left(\frac{y}{x}\right)^2 + \left(\frac{y}{x}\right)$, $y(1) = 1$ on the interval $[1,2]$ with $h = 0.1$ and compare the exact values with those obtained using   a) Euler's Method,   b) the Modified Euler's Method and   c) the Runge-Kutta Method.

SOLUTION: The equation is homogeneous so the substitution $y = xu$ with $dy = x\,du + u\,dx$ is appropriate. The equation

$$dy = \left[\left(\frac{y}{x}\right)^2 + \left(\frac{y}{x}\right)\right]\,dx$$

becomes $x\,du + u\,dx = u^2\,dx + u\,dx$ or $\frac{du}{u^2} = \frac{dx}{x}$. This is integrated to obtain $-\frac{1}{u} = \ln x + C$ or $-\frac{x}{y} = \ln x + C$.

The initial condition implies that $-1 = C$, so the exact solution is

$$y = \frac{x}{1 - \ln x}, \qquad 1 \leq x \leq 2.$$

The values of $y_i = \frac{x_i}{1 - \ln x_i}$, $x_i = 1 + 0.1i$, $i = 1, \ldots, 10$ are tabulated below as are the errors $|w_i - y_i|$ for each of the three methods.

x_i	exact values $y_i = \dfrac{x_i}{1 - \ln x_i}$	errors $\|w_i - y_i\|$		
		Euler's Method w_i	Modified Euler's Method w_i	Runge-Kutta Method w_i
1.1	1.21589	1.59 10^{-2}	1.84 10^{-3}	6.56 10^{-6}
1.2	1.46757	3.95 10^{-2}	4.55 10^{-3}	1.61 10^{-5}
1.3	1.76239	7.37 10^{-2}	8.49 10^{-3}	2.90 10^{-5}
1.4	2.10993	1.23 10^{-1}	1.42 10^{-2}	4.79 10^{-5}
1.5	2.52298	1.92 10^{-1}	2.25 10^{-2}	7.56 10^{-5}
1.6	3.01889	2.91 10^{-1}	3.47 10^{-2}	1.16 10^{-4}
1.7	3.62186	4.33 10^{-1}	5.30 10^{-2}	1.76 10^{-4}
1.8	4.36667	6.38 10^{-1}	8.03 10^{-2}	2.69 10^{-4}
1.9	5.30510	9.41 10^{-1}	1.23 10^{-1}	4.21 10^{-4}
2.0	6.51778	1.40	1.92 10^{-1}	6.73 10^{-4}

_____Chapter 17

Review Exercises

5. Find the general solution to $e^x \sin y \, dx + e^x \cos y \, dy = 0$

SOLUTION: This first-order differential equation is both separable and exact. It is simplest to solve by separating variables, $dx + (\cos y / \sin y)\, dy = 0$, and integrating $\int dx + \int \dfrac{\cos y}{\sin y}\, dy = C$ to obtain $x + \ln|\sin y| = C$. Exponentiate both sides of this equation to obtain $e^x \sin y = C$.

9. Find the general solution to $y' = x^3 - 2xy$.

SOLUTION: This first-order linear equation should be written as $y' + 2xy = x^3$ in order to find the integrating factor $I(x) = \exp\left(\int 2x\, dx\right) = e^{x^2}$. Multiplying by this gives $e^{x^2} y' + 2x e^{x^2} y = x^3 e^{x^2}$ or $D_x\left[y e^{x^2}\right] = x^3 e^{x^2}$. This is integrated to obtain $y e^{x^2} = \int x^3 e^{x^2} + C$.

Use integration by parts with $u = x^2$ and $dv = x e^{x^2}\, dx$ to evaluate the integral.

$$\int x^3 e^{x^2}\, dx = \left[\frac{1}{2} x^2 e^{x^2} - \int x e^{x^2}\, dx\right] = \frac{x^2 - 1}{2} e^{x^2}.$$

The solution to the differential equation is thus $y e^{x^2} = \dfrac{(x^2 - 1)}{2} e^{x^2} + C$ or $y = \dfrac{x^2 - 1}{2} + C e^{-x^2}$.

11. Find the general solution to

$$\left(\frac{y}{x} \sin\left(\frac{y}{x}\right) + \cos\left(\frac{y}{x}\right)\right) dx - \sin\left(\frac{y}{x}\right) dy = 0.$$

SOLUTION: This first-order equation is homogeneous in the coefficients x and y and may be written as $y' = (y/x) + \cot(y/x)$. Let $v = y/x$, $y = xv$, and $y' = v + xv'$ to write this as $v + xv' = v + \cot v$ or $x(dv/dx) = \cot v$. Separate variables, $\tan v \, dv + (1/x) \, dx$, and integrate $\int \tan v \, dv = \int (1/x) \, dx + C$ to obtain $\ln|\sec v| = \ln|x| + C$ or $\sec(y/x) = Cx$. The general solution can be written as $y = x \operatorname{arcsec}(Cx)$.

15. Find the general solution to $xy' - 3y + x^4 y^2 = 0$.

SOLUTION: This first-order Bernoulli equation is first written as $xy^{-2}y' - 3y^{-1} = -x^4$. Let $w = y^{-1}$ with $w' = -y^{-2}y'$ to write this equation as $-xw' - 3w = -x^4$ or as a first-order linear equation for w, $w' + (3/x)w = x^3$. Multiply by the integrating factor $I(x) = \exp\left(\int \frac{3}{x} \, dx\right) = \exp(3\ln x) = x^3$ to obtain $x^3 w' + 3x^2 w = x^6$. This is equivalent to $D_x\left[x^3 w\right] = x^6$ which can be integrated, $x^3 w = \int x^6 \, dx + C$, to yield $x^3 w = (x^7/7) + C$ or $w = \dfrac{x^4}{7} + \dfrac{C}{x^3}$. Replace w by $1/y$ and rewrite the general solution as

$$y = \frac{1}{\dfrac{x^4}{7} + \dfrac{C}{x^3}} \qquad \text{or} \qquad y = \frac{7x^3}{x^7 + C}.$$

19. Find the general solution to $y'' + y = \sin x$.

SOLUTION: This is a second-order linear equation of nonhomogeneous type, so the first step is to solve the homogeneous problem, $y'' + y = 0$. The characteristic equation $m^2 + 1 = 0$ has complex roots $m = \pm i$ so the general solution to the homogeneous equation is $y(x) = K_1 \cos x + K_2 \sin x$. Since $\sin x$ already solves the homogeneous equation, try $y_p(x) = Ax\cos x + Bx\sin x$ as a particular solution. The derivatives are $y_p'(x) = (A + Bx)\cos x + (B - Ax)\sin x$ and $y_p''(x) = (2B - Ax)\cos x + (-2A - Bx)\sin x$. The coefficients are determined by the fact that $y_p'' + y_p = \sin x$ or

$$((2B - Ax)\cos x + (-2A - 2Bx)\sin x) + (Ax\cos x + Bx\sin x) = \sin x.$$

This becomes $(2B)\cos x + (-2A)\sin x = (0)\cos x + (1)\sin x$ which implies that $2B = 0$ and $-2A = 1$. The particular solution is thus $y_p(x) = -\frac{1}{2}x\cos x$.
The general solution is $y(x) = K_1 \cos x + K_2 \sin x - \frac{1}{2}x\cos x$.

29. Find the particular solution to the initial value problem $y'' + 5y' + 6y = 0$, $\quad y(0) = 1$, $y'(0) = 2$.

SOLUTION: This is a second-order linear equation of homogeneous type whose characteristic equation is $m^2 + 5m + 6 = 0$. The roots are $m = -3$ and $m = -2$, which implies that the general solution is $y(x) = C_1 e^{-3x} + C_2 e^{-2x}$ with $y'(x) = -3C_1 e^{-3x} - 2C_2 e^{-2x}$.
The initial conditions are i) $(y(0) =) \ C_1 + C_2 = 1$ and ii) $(y'(0) =) \ -3C_1 - 2C_2 = 2$. These imply that $C_1 = -4$ and $C_2 = 5$, so the particular solution to this initial value problem is $y(x) = -4e^{-3x} + 5e^{-2x}$.

A

Appendix A
Review Material

A.1

The Real Line

3. $-3x + 4 < 5 \implies -3x < (5-4)$. Multiplication of both sides of the inequality by a negative number changes the sense of the inequality, $(-1/3)(-3x) > (-1/3)(1)$, or $x > -1/3$.

9. Solve this quadratic inequality by rewriting it as a quadratic inequality with zero on the right-hand side; $x^2 + 2x - 3 \geq 0$. Factor the quadratic on the left, $(x+3)(x-1) \geq 0$. The product is nonnegative when both factors have the same sign; $(x+3) \geq 0$ and $(x-1) \geq 0$ or $(x+3) \leq 0$ and $(x-1) \leq 0$. The first pair of inequalities are simultaneously satisfied when $x \geq 1$ while the second pair is simultaneously satisfied when $x \leq -3$; thus, the solution set is $\{x : x \leq -3 \quad \text{or} \quad x \geq 1\}$.

13. By formula A.6, $|3x - 1| < 0.01$ if and only if $-0.01 < 3x - 1 < 0.01 \implies -0.01 + 1 < 3x < 0.01 + 1 \implies (1/3)(0.99) < x < (1/3)(1.01)$ or $0.33 < x < \dfrac{1.01}{3}$.

A.2

The Coordinate Plane

5. a) By formula A.8 the distance is

$$d\left((2,4),(-1,3)\right) = \sqrt{(2-(-1))^2 + (4-3)^2} = \sqrt{9+1} = \sqrt{10}.$$

b) By EXAMPLE 3 of SECTION A.2 the midpoint of the line segment joining $(x_1, y_1) = (2,4)$ and $(x_2, y_2) = (-1,3)$ is $\left(\frac{2+(-1)}{2}, \frac{4+3}{2}\right) = \left(\frac{1}{2}, \frac{7}{2}\right)$.

17. $4 \leq |x| \implies x \leq -4$ or $x \geq 4$; the y-coordinate may have any value while the x-coordinate is no closer to $x = 0$ (the y-axis) than 4.

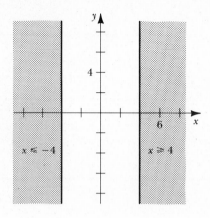

21. $|x - 1| < 3 \implies -3 < x - 1 < 3 \implies -2 < x < 4; \; |y + 1| < 2 \implies$
$-2 < y + 1 < 2 \implies -3 < y < 1.$

The set consists of those points with x-coordinates between -2 and 4 and with y-coordinate between -3 and 1.

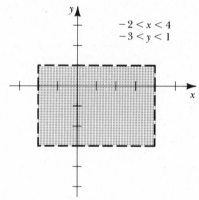

25. With $A(-1, 4)$, $B(-3, -4)$ and $C(2, -1)$ the distances are

$$d(A, B) = \sqrt{(-3 - (-1))^2 + (-4 - 4)^2} = \sqrt{68},$$
$$d(B, C) = \sqrt{(2 - (-3))^2 + (-1 - (-4))^2} = \sqrt{34}, \qquad \text{and}$$
$$d(A, C) = \sqrt{(2 - (-1))^2 + (-1 - 4)^2} = \sqrt{34}.$$

Since $(d(B, C))^2 + (d(A, C))^2 = 34 + 34 = 68 = (d(A, C))^2$, the triangle is a right triangle.

_____**A.3**

Trigonometric Functions

3. a) Refer to the graph of cosine in FIGURE A.13 to see that $\cos x = 1$ only when $x = 0$ and 2π.

c) Refer to the graph of sine in FIGURE A.13 to see that $\sin x = \frac{1}{2}$ for two values of $x \in [0, 2\pi]$. From Table A.1, one value is $x = \pi/6$; from the fact that $\sin(\pi - x) = \sin x$ it follows that the second value is $x = 5\pi/6$.

g) Refer to the graph of $\cot x$ in FIGURE A.14 to see that there are two values of x separated by π in the interval $[0, 2\pi]$. The smaller value $x \in [0, \pi]$ also satisfies $\tan x = \dfrac{1}{\cot x} = \dfrac{1}{-1} = -1$, so by Table A.1 this value is $x = 3\pi/4$. The second value is $x = 7\pi/4$.

i) Refer to the graph of $\csc x$ in FIGURE A.14 to see that $\csc x = 1$ only when $x = \pi/2$.

5. Since $\cos^2 t = 1 - \sin^2 t$ and $0 < t < \pi/2$, then

$$\cos t = \sqrt{1 - \sin^2 t} = \sqrt{1 - (4/5)^2} = 3/5 \text{ and } \tan t = \frac{\sin t}{\cos t} = \frac{4/5}{3/5} = \frac{4}{3}.$$

13. Reduce the values to those in Table A.1.

a)

$$\cot\left(\frac{13\pi}{6}\right) = \cot\left(\frac{\pi}{6} + 2\pi\right) = \cot\left(\frac{\pi}{6}\right)$$

since $\cot x$ has period π

$$= \frac{1}{\tan(\pi/6)} = \frac{1}{\sqrt{3}/3} = \sqrt{3}.$$

c)

$$\csc\left(-\frac{107\pi}{3}\right) = \csc\left(\frac{\pi}{3} - 36\pi\right)$$

since $\csc x$ has period 2π

$$= \csc\left(\frac{\pi}{3}\right) = \frac{1}{\sin(\pi/3)} = \frac{1}{\sqrt{3}/2} = \frac{2\sqrt{3}}{3}.$$

e)

$$\cos(-585°) = \cos(135° - 2 \cdot 360°)$$

since $\cos x$ has period $360°$

$$= \cos(135°) = \cos\left(\frac{3\pi}{4}\right) = -\frac{\sqrt{2}}{2}.$$

15.   a) The graph is similar to that of the sine function in FIGURE A.13 except that the replacement of x by $2x$ forces one period of the graph into the interval $[0, \pi]$ rather than $[0, 2\pi]$.

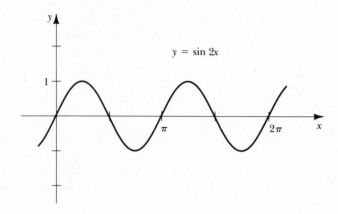

d) The graph is similar to that of the cosine in FIGURE A.13 except that the replacement of x by $\frac{1}{4}x$ forces one period of the graph into the interval $[0, 8\pi]$ rather than $[0, 2\pi]$.

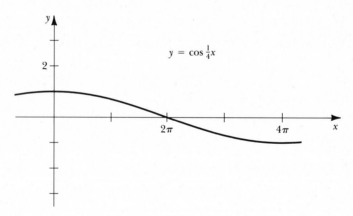

17. $\sin 2x = \cos x \iff 2\sin x \cos x = \cos x \iff \cos x(2\sin x - 1) = 0 \iff$ either $\cos x = 0$ or $\sin x = \frac{1}{2}$. The values of x which satisfy either of these are $x = \pi/2$, $x = 3\pi/2$, $x = \pi/6$, $x = 5\pi/6$.

Substitution of each of these into the original equation reveals that each is a solution.

29.

$$(\sin x + \cos x)^2 = \sin^2 x + 2\sin x \cos x + \cos^2 x = (\sin^2 x + \cos^2 x) + 2\sin x + \cos x$$

$$= 1 + \sin 2x$$

since $\sin^2 x + \cos^2 x = 1$ and $\sin 2x = 2\sin x \cos x$.

37.

$$\tan(t_1 + t_2) = \frac{\sin(t_1 + t_2)}{\cos(t_1 + t_2)} = \frac{\sin t_1 \cos t_2 + \cos t_1 \sin t_2}{\cos t_1 \cos t_2 - \sin t_1 \sin t_2}$$

Assume that $\cos t_1 \cos t_2 \neq 0$ and divide these factors out of both numerator and denominator. Then cancel the common factors.

$$= \frac{\dfrac{\sin t_1}{\cos t_1} \cdot \dfrac{\cos t_2}{\cos t_2} + \dfrac{\cos t_1}{\cos t_1} \cdot \dfrac{\sin t_2}{\cos t_2}}{1 - \dfrac{\sin t_1}{\cos t_1} \cdot \dfrac{\sin t_2}{\cos t_2}} = \frac{\tan t_1 + \tan t_2}{1 - \tan t_1 \tan t_2}.$$

Notice that if either $\cos t_1$ or $\cos t_2$ is zero then the corresponding tangent is undefined; so this assumption is implicit in the identity.

41.   The right triangle has base 35 and included angle $60°$ so the height of the cliff is

$$\text{height} = \text{side opposite} = 35 \tan 60° = 35\sqrt{3} \approx 61 \text{ ft.}$$

45.   Let θ_1 and θ_2 be the angles between the positive x-axis and lines l_1 and l_2 respectively; then $\tan \theta_i = m_i$.

Since $\theta = \theta_2 - \theta_1$, then

$$\tan \theta = \tan(\theta_2 - \theta_1) = \frac{\tan \theta_2 - \tan \theta_1}{1 + \tan \theta_2 \tan \theta_1}$$

by the identity established in EXERCISE 38 of SECTION A.3. Thus

$$\tan \theta = \frac{m_2 - m_1}{1 + m_1 m_2}.$$

———————————————————————————————A.4

Mathematical Induction

1.   Let S be the set of numbers for which this identity is true.

 i) $1 \in S$ since when $n = 1$, $1 = 1^2$.

ii) If $k \in S$ then $1 + 3 + 5 + \cdots + (2k - 1) = k^2$.

Add the next odd number to each side of the equation;

$$1 + 3 + 5 + \cdots + (2k - 1) + (2k + 1) = k^2 + (2k + 1) = (k + 1)^2$$
$$\text{or} \quad 1 + 3 + 5 + \cdots + (2(k + 1) - 1) = (k + 1)^2;$$

hence $(k + 1) \in S$.

By the axiom of mathematical induction, $S = N$, the set of natural numbers, so the identity is true for all natural numbers.

7.   Let S be the set of numbers for which this identity is true.

 i) $1 \in S$ since $1^3 = \dfrac{1^2(1 + 1)^2}{4}$.

ii) If $k \in S$ then $1 + 8 + 27 + \cdots + k^3 = \dfrac{k^2(k + 1)^2}{4}$.

Add the next integer cubed, $(k+1)^3$, to each side of this equation;

$$1 + 8 + 27 + \cdots + k^3 + (k+1)^3 = \frac{k^2(k+1)^2}{4} + (k+1)^3 = \frac{k^2(k+1)^2 + 4(k+1)^3}{4}$$

$$= \frac{(k+1)^2(k^2 + 4k + 4)}{4} = \frac{(k+1)^2(k+2)^2}{4},$$

so the equation is satisfied when $n = k+1$.

By the axiom of mathematical induction, $S = N$, so the identity is true for all natural numbers.

15.   Let S be the set of numbers for which the inequality is true.

i) $1 \in S$ since $1 + (1)a = 1 + a \le (1+a)^1$.

ii) If $k \in S$ the $(1 + ka) \le (1+a)^k$.

Add a to each side of the inequality:

$$(1 + ka) + a \le (1+a)^k + 1.$$

The right-hand side is

$$(1+a)^k + a + a - 1 = (1+a)^{k+1} - 1 \le (1+a)^{k+1},$$

thus the previous inequality can be written as $(1 + (k+1)a) \le (1+a)^k$; so $(k+1) \in S$.

By the axiom of mathematical induction, $S = N$, so the inequality is true for all natural numbers.

19.   Let S be the set of natural numbers for which $(x+y)$ is a factor of $x^{2n-1} + y^{2n-1}$.

i) $1 \in S$ since $x+y$ is a factor of $x^{2(1)-1} + y^{2(1)-1} = (x+y)$.

ii) If $k \in S$ then $x+y$ is a factor of $x^{2k-1} + y^{2k-1}$; that is,

$$\left(x^{2k-1} + y^{2k-1}\right) = (x+y)P(x,y),$$

where P is a polynomial in x and y.

For each (x,y),

$$x^{2(k+1)-1} + y^{2(k+1)-1} = x^{2k+1} + y^{2k+1}$$

Add and subtract the terms $x^{2k-1}y^2$

$$= x^2 x^{2k-1} - x^{2k-1}y^2 + x^{2k-1}y^2 + y^2 y^{2k-1}$$

$$= (x^2 - y^2)x^{2k-1} + y^2\left(x^{2k-1} + y^{2k-1}\right)$$

By the hypothesis above $x^{2k-1} + y^{2k-1} = P(x,y)(x-y)$

$$= (x-y)(x+y)x^{2k-1} + y^2 P(x,y)(x-y)$$

$$= \left((x+y)x^{2k-1} + y^2 P(x,y)\right)(x-y),$$

so $x-y$ is a factor of $x^{2(k+1)-1} + y^{2(k+1)-1}$ and $(k+1) \in S$.

By the axiom of mathematical induction, $S = N$, so the inequality is true for all natural numbers.

B

Appendix B
Practice Problem Answers

Chapter 1

1. a) $(-4, -8)$, $(4, 8)$, $(4, -8)$;
   b) $(0, 7)$, $(0, -7)$, $(0, 7)$;
   c) $(3/2, 0)$, $(-3/2, 0)$, $(-3/2, 0)$;
   d) $(0, e - \pi)$, $(0, \pi - e)$, $(0, e - \pi)$;
   e) $(\sqrt{3}, -\sqrt{3})$, $(-\sqrt{3}, \sqrt{3})$, $(-\sqrt{3}, -\sqrt{3})$.

2. a) $3x^2(x - 5)(x + 3)$;
   b) $(5 \sin x - 4)(\sin x - 1)$;
   c) $(3x - 4y^2)(9x^2 + 12xy^2 + 16y^4)$;
   d) $(2x - 1)(2x + 1)(4x^2 + 1)$.

3. a) $\dfrac{4(\sqrt{x} + 2)}{x - 2}$; b) $\dfrac{1}{7x^2(x + 2)}$; c) $\dfrac{\sqrt[3]{x^2} + \sqrt[3]{x} + 1}{x - 1}$; d) $\dfrac{-(2x - 3\sqrt{x})}{x - 1}$.

Chapter 2

1. a) $4x - 7$; b) $\dfrac{-4x}{(x^2 - 4)^2}$; c) $3x^2 + (1/x^2)$.

2. a) $3y = 4x + 1$; b) $4y = -3x + 18$.

3. a) $x = 0, 7, -2$; b) $x = \dfrac{5 \pm \sqrt{145}}{6}$; c) $x = 1$; d) $x = 5/2$.

Chapter 3

1. a) $4(4x^3 - 3x)^3(2x + 7)(28x^3 + 84x^2 - 9x - 21)$; b) $\dfrac{(x - 8)^2(4x + 31)}{(2x + 5)^2}$; c) $\dfrac{-y(2x + y^2)}{x(x + 3y^2)}$;

   d) $4 \cos 4x + 4 \tan(2x + 3) \sec^2(2x + 3)$; e) $\dfrac{\cos(x + y) - \cos(x - y)}{\sec^2 y - \cos(x + y) - \cos(x - y)}$;

   f) $-\frac{1}{2\sqrt{2}} x^{-3/2} - \frac{16}{3}(2x - 7)^{-5/3}$.

Chapter 4

1. a) $f(x) = x^2 + 7x - 8$; b) $f(x) = x + \sin 2x - (\pi/4)$;
   c) $f(x) = x^3 + 4x^2 + x - 2$; d) $f(x) = 2 - \sin x$.

2. a) $-4(3x^2 + 8x)(x^3 + 4x^2 - 8)^{-5}$; b) $6 \sin 3x \cos 3x = 3 \sin 6x$;
   c) $\frac{\sqrt{5}}{2} x^{-1/2} - \frac{3}{4} x^{-7/4}$; d) $9(2x - 7)(x^2 - 7x)^8$.

Chapter 5

1. a) $\frac{\pi}{6}\left((4\pi - 3)^3 + 27\right)$; b) $566\pi/15$; c) $7\pi/2$; d) $14197/14$.

Chapter 6

1. a) $-4/5$; b) $12/5$; c) $13/12$; d) $-33/65$; e) $16/65$; f) $-24/25$; g) $3\sqrt{13}/13$; h) $-63/65$.

2. a) does not exist; b) $\ln(\ln x) + C$.

3. a) $3/x$; b) $\dfrac{\sin^2 2x}{x} + 2\ln x \sin 4x$.

Chapter 7

1. a) $2\cosh 2x \cosh(\ln x) + (1/x)\sinh(2x)\sinh(\ln x)$; b) $\dfrac{\coth x \operatorname{sech}^2 x}{\ln 10}$;

c) $\arcsin 2x + \dfrac{2x}{\sqrt{1 - 4x^2}}$; d) $e^x \arctan x + \dfrac{e^x}{1 + x^2}$.

2. a) $\frac{1}{2}\arcsin(2x/3) + C$; b) $\frac{1}{4}(1 - e^{-16})$; c) $\pi/3$; d) $\frac{1}{2}\ln|\cosh 2x| + C$.

Chapter 8

1. a) $-4/5$; b) 0; c) ∞; d) 2.

2. a) 188; b) $1 + \sqrt{2}$; c) $-1 + e - e^2 + e^3$; d) $\dfrac{n(2n^2 - 9n + 1)}{6}$.

Chapter 9

2. a) $-1/2$; b) $-\sqrt{2}/2$; c) 0; d) $-1/2$.

3. a) $-(\pi/6) + 2k\pi, (7\pi/6) + 2k\pi$; b) $(2\pi/3) + 2k\pi, (4\pi/3) + 2k\pi$; c) $(2\pi/3) + k\pi$;
d) $(5\pi/6) + 2k\pi$.

4.

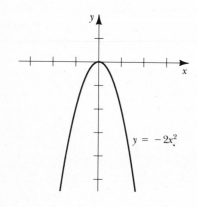

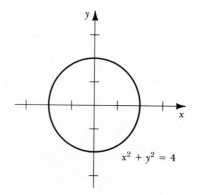

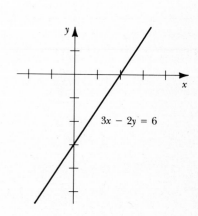

5. $y = -6x - 3$

6.   maxima: $x = \ldots, -2\pi, 0, 2\pi, \ldots$; minima: $\ldots, -\pi, \pi, 3\pi, \ldots$; increasing on $((2k-1)\pi, 2k\pi)$; decreasing on $(2k\pi, (2k+1)\pi)$.

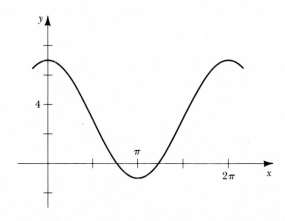

7.   a) $(85\pi/12) + 10\sqrt{3} - 12\sqrt{2} - 4.$ b) $(\tan\theta\sec\theta + \ln|\sec\theta + \tan\theta|)/2 + C.$

Chapter 10

1.   a) $(x+1)^2 + (y-2)^2 = 3^2$ b) $y + 18 = 2(x-3)^2$

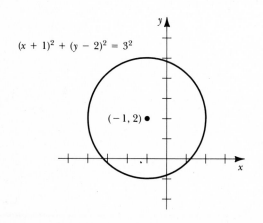

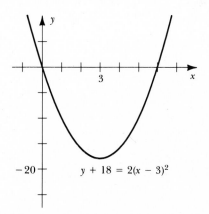

2. $\cos\theta = 1/\sqrt{5},\ \sin\theta = 2/\sqrt{5}$ or $\cos\theta = -1/\sqrt{5},\ \sin\theta = -2/\sqrt{5}.$

3. $3x^2 + 4y^2 + 6x - 9 = 0$

4.

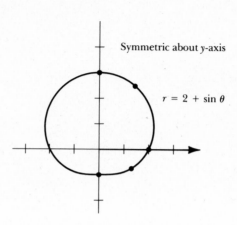

Symmetric about y-axis

$r = 2 + \sin\theta$

Chapter 11

1. b) 5; c) $(-1/-1/2)$.

2. a)

b)

c)

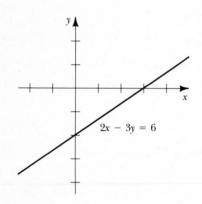

$2x - 3y = 6$

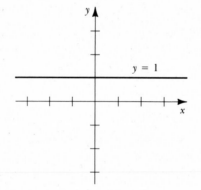

$y = 1$

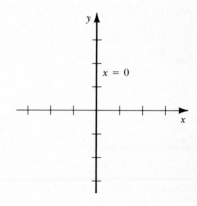

$x = 0$

3. a) $x = 11 - 10t$, $y = -7 + 7t$, $z = t$ for any t; b) $x = 1 + 2t$, $y = t - 2$, $z = 2 - 3t$ for any t;
c) $x = -1 + t$, $y = 1 + 2t$, $z = (1/4)t$ for any t.

Chapter 12

1. b) $y = 2x$; c) $4\sqrt{65} - \sqrt{5} + \dfrac{1}{4}\ln\left(\dfrac{8 + \sqrt{65}}{2 + \sqrt{5}}\right)$; a)

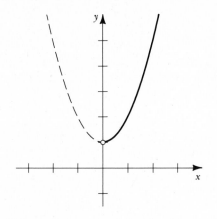

2. a)

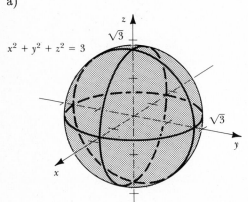

$x^2 + y^2 + z^2 = 3$

b)

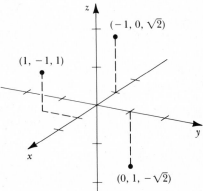

3. a) $\langle 3, -1, -2 \rangle$; b) $\langle 1, -1, 4 \rangle$; c) $\langle 4, -2, 2 \rangle$; d) -1; e) $\arccos(-\sqrt{15}/30)$; f) $3\mathbf{i} + 7\mathbf{j} + \mathbf{k}$; g) $\langle \sqrt{6}/3, -\sqrt{6}/6, \sqrt{6}/6 \rangle$.

4. a) $\mathbf{a} \cdot \mathbf{b} = 0$, $\mathbf{a} \neq \vec{\theta}$, $\mathbf{b} \neq \vec{\theta}$; b) $\mathbf{a} \times \mathbf{b} = \vec{\theta}$, $\mathbf{a} \neq \vec{\theta}$, $\mathbf{b} \neq \vec{\theta}$.

5. $20\sqrt{3}\,\mathbf{i} + 20\,\mathbf{j}$ 6. $x = 1 + t$, $y = -1 + 4t$, $z = 2 - t$, $0 \leq t \leq 1$.

7. a) $|t| > 1$; b) $\lim_{t \to 1} f(t)$ does not exist, $\lim_{t \to 1^+} f(t) = 0$, $\lim_{t \to \infty} f(t) = 1$.

8. a) $3(1 - 2t^4)/(1 + t^2 + 2t^4)^{3/2}$; b) te^t.

9. a) $((2t - 1)e^{2t}/4) + C$; b) $((t\sqrt{1 + t^2} + \ln(t + \sqrt{1 + t^2}))/2) + C$.

Chapter 13

1. a) parabola   b) ellipse   c) hyperbola

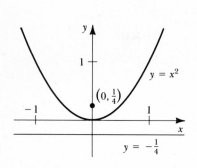

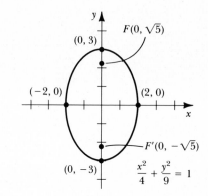

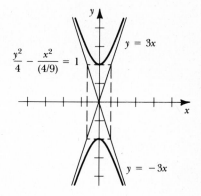

2. b) i) $(1/2, \sqrt{3}/2)$, ii) $(\sqrt{2}, \sqrt{2})$, iii) $(\sqrt{6}/2, \sqrt{2}/2)$.

3. a)   b)   c)

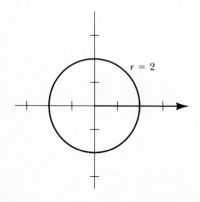

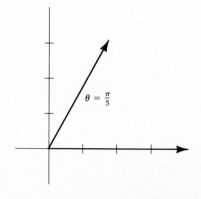

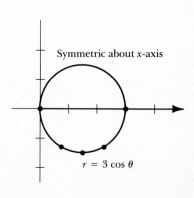

4.

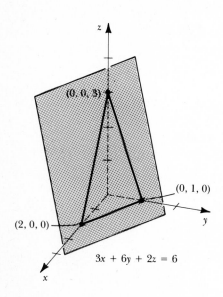

$(0, 0, 3)$

$(0, 1, 0)$

$(2, 0, 0)$

$3x + 6y + 2z = 6$

z

y

x

5.

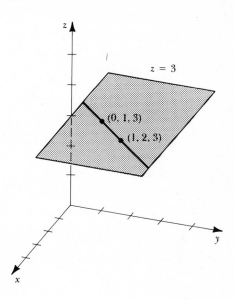

$z = 3$

$(0, 1, 3)$

$(1, 2, 3)$

z

y

x

Chapter 14

2.   a) 6;   b) does not exist;   c) 4.

3. $x \neq \pm\pi/2,\ \pm 3\pi/2,\ \ldots$ 4.   5

5.   a) $x/\sqrt{1 + x^2}$;   b) $3x^2 + 2x - 2$;   c) $(2x^2\cos(x^2) - \sin(x^2))/x^2$;   d) $4/(1 + 16x^2)$;
e) $e^{x^2}(2x\sin x + \cos x)$.

6.   1.995

7.   a) minimum at $x = 0$;   b) maximum at $x = 0$, minima at $x = e^{-1/2}$ and $x = -e^{-1/2}$.

8.   a) $\langle -2\sqrt{2}/5, \sqrt{2}/2, 3\sqrt{2}/10 \rangle$;   b) $-6\sqrt{2}/5$.   9. $2x + 4y - 5z + 5 = 0$

Chapter 15

1.   2

2.   a) $(e^2 - 1)/4$;   b) $-(6\sqrt{3} + 1)/15$;   c) 2/35;
d) $\dfrac{1}{3}\left(\ln\left(\dfrac{x - 1}{\sqrt{x^2 + x + 1}}\right) - \sqrt{3}\arctan\left(\dfrac{2x + 1}{\sqrt{3}}\right)\right) + C$;   e) $\ln(\sqrt{2} + 1) - (\sqrt{2}/2)$;   f) $\ln\sqrt{2}$.

3. a)

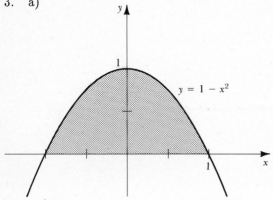

$y = 1 - x^2$

b)

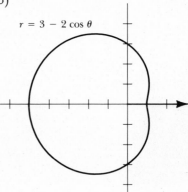

$r = 3 - 2 \cos \theta$

4.

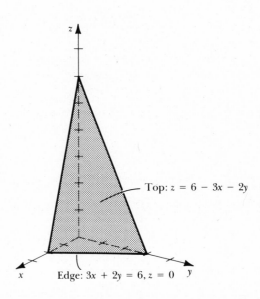

Top: $z = 6 - 3x - 2y$

Edge: $3x + 2y = 6, z = 0$

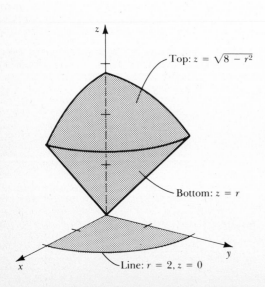

Top: $z = \sqrt{8 - r^2}$

Bottom: $z = r$

Line: $r = 2, z = 0$

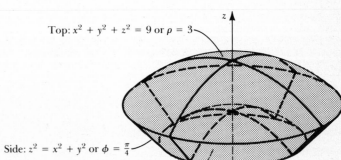

Top: $x^2 + y^2 + z^2 = 9$ or $\rho = 3$

Side: $z^2 = x^2 + y^2$ or $\phi = \dfrac{\pi}{4}$

Bottom: $x^2 + y^2 + z^2 = 4$ or $\rho = 2$

Chapter 16

1. a) -8;   b) $4\mathbf{i} + 4\mathbf{j} + 4\mathbf{k}$

2. a) $\dfrac{\partial^2 f}{\partial x^2} = \dfrac{2xyz}{(x^2+y^2)^2}$, $\dfrac{\partial^2 f}{\partial y^2} = \dfrac{-2xyz}{(x^2+y^2)^2}$, $\dfrac{\partial^2 f}{\partial z^2} = 0$.   b) $\nabla f = -\dfrac{yz}{x^2+y^2}\mathbf{i} + \dfrac{xz}{x^2+y^2}\mathbf{j} + \arctan(y/x)\mathbf{k}$.

3. $\mathbf{N} = -3x_0^2\,\mathbf{i} - 3y_0^2\,\mathbf{j} + \mathbf{k}$ 4. $x = 3\cos t$, $y = 4\sin t$, $0 \le t \le 2\pi$

5. $1 + 5\cos 1 - 3\sin 1$ 6.   a) $1/8$;   b) $2/3$

Chapter 17

1. $\frac{1}{2}\arctan\left(\frac{x}{2}\right)$ 2. $-\frac{7}{4}\ln(2-u) - \frac{5}{4}\ln(2+u) + C$ 3. $(x^5/5) - (x^3y^3/3) + C(y)$

4. $\ln(x^3 + 2x^2 + 1) + C$ 5. $\ln|\sec x + \tan x| - \sin x + C$ 6. $y = \frac{3}{4}x^{4/3} + C$

7. $y = \arcsin(e^x + (x^2/2) - 1)$